NUCLEAR
INSTRUMENTS
AND THEIR USES

NUCLEAR
INSTRUMENTS
AND THEIR USES

Arthur H. Snell, Editor

62- 20561

VOLUME I
Ionization detectors, Scintillators,
Cerenkov counters, Amplifiers:
assay, dosimetry, health physics

Wolfgang Franzen
L. W. Cochran
R. B. Murray
Burton J. Moyer
Edward Fairstein

Ellis P. Steinberg
G. S. Hurst
R. H. Ritchie
Karl Z. Morgan

JOHN WILEY & SONS, INC., NEW YORK · LONDON

FOREWORD

To discuss within the compass of one volume the widely ranging subject of the theory, design, and use of all kinds of nuclear detectors is impossible; let us therefore at the outset recognize that this book is incomplete. However, if the reader desires a rather thorough discussion of commonly used detectors in mature stage of development and an indication of how they may be used to give meaningful information, he may find assistance in these pages. Let us also recognize the pace of development of nuclear instruments and the pace of their obsolescence. New developments and improvements appear so continuously that one is hard put to assemble a book that is not out of date before it appears. Yet a compendium of accumulated experience can serve a useful purpose, and, to make a volume such as this both modern and even hopefully of somewhat lasting value, one perforce must choose to discuss instruments that have behind them a solid understanding in experience and theory but that are still in wide current use. Accordingly, the essays that follow have been chosen to fall in middle ground between, for example, the semiconductor counter, which is developing too rapidly for a firmly based review article, and the spintharoscope, which is, in my opinion, dead.

The collection that follows has been assembled by the Subcommittee on Instruments and Techniques of the Committee on Nuclear Science, National Academy of Sciences—National Research Council. Some of the authors of the individual articles and I are past or present members of the Subcommittee, and we have contributed our efforts to this book on a royalty-free basis. If the following essays are useful to the nuclear physicist, radiochemist, radiobiologist, health physicist, or instrumentalist, the Subcommittee members will feel that their mission in the National Academy will have been in some measure fulfilled.

Oak Ridge, Tennessee
July 1962

THE EDITOR

CONTENTS

1. Pulse Ionization Chambers and Proportional Counters   3
   Wolfgang Franzen and L. W. Cochran

2. Scintillation Counters   82
   R. B. Murray

3. A Survey of Cerenkov Counter Technique   166
   Burton J. Moyer

4. Electrometers and Amplifiers   194
   1. Electrometers, 194
   2. Pulse Amplifiers, 234
      Edward Fairstein

5. Counting Methods for the Assay of Radioactive Samples   306
   Ellis P. Steinberg

6. Applications to Radiation Dosimetry   367
   G. S. Hurst and R. H. Ritchie

7. Techniques of Personnel Monitoring and Radiation Surveying   391
   Karl Z. Morgan

Author Index   471

Subject Index   483

VOLUME I

Ionization detectors, Scintillators, Cerenkov counters, Amplifiers: assay, dosimetry, health physics

PULSE IONIZATION CHAMBERS AND PROPORTIONAL COUNTERS

WOLFGANG FRANZEN
Boston University
Boston, Massachusetts

and

L. W. COCHRAN
University of Kentucky
Lexington, Kentucky

A. The Creation of Ions
B. Life History of an Ion
C. The Nature of Observed Signals
D. Wall Effect
E. Ionization Chambers with Special Features
F. Techniques
G. Proportional Counters

A pulse-ionization chamber is an instrument designed to measure the amount of ionization produced in a gas or other medium by individual charged nuclear particles released in a nuclear disintegration or collision. For the purpose of performing a measurement of this kind, a static electric field is maintained between two electrodes; the space between the electrodes is filled with an insulating substance (usually a gas) in which the ionization is produced. When a charged nuclear projectile passes through the gas, positive and negative charges suddenly appear along the path of the particle. The charges move under the influence of the electric field, causing a transient current to flow through the gas and also through the electrical network connecting the two electrodes to each other. This current is amplified and recorded.

One can then interpret the profile, amplitude, and occurrence in time of the amplified signal in terms of certain characteristics of the original projectile, such as the orientation of its track in space, its energy, and its range. To accomplish such an interpretation, it is necessary to analyze the process of ionization as a function of the type and energy of the ionizing particle, as well as the dependence of this event on the composition of the gas. Furthermore, the electrical and geometrical conditions accompanying the flow of ionization current must be understood.

The original version of this chapter was written by Wolfgang Franzen at Princeton University in 1951 and was distributed as a technical report entitled "Theory and Use of Pulse Ionization Chambers" to a number of laboratories at that time.

3

A proportional counter is distinguished from a pulse-ionization chamber primarily by the fact that the charge released in the original ionization event is increased by electron multiplication in the high field region near one of the electrodes. The resulting amplification makes this device especially valuable as a spectrometer in the study of low-energy phenomena. We shall consider the operation of these two types of detector in some detail, but in order to keep the length of the discussion within bounds the operation of the associated electronic circuitry will be considered only very briefly.

A. The Creation of Ions

Energetic charged particles moving through a gas create ions by inelastic collisions with the outer electrons of gas atoms (in which case the ejected electrons may produce secondary ionization), by elastic collisions with gas atoms resulting in the production of energetic recoil particles, and finally by capture and loss of electrons on the part of the moving particle. The distinction between ionizing collisions is not always as clear-cut as implied by this description.

Molecular dissociation can give rise to ion-pair formation in polyatomic gases. Such molecular dissociation might be caused by an elastic collision between one of the atoms of a gas molecule and a moving particle. Furthermore, in gas mixtures metastable optical excitation levels of the atoms of one element may lie above the ionization potential of another element present in the mixture; in this case "delayed ionization" can be produced by collisions of the second kind between the two kinds of atoms. This process can occur in certain mixtures of inert and molecular gases.

In addition to expending its kinetic energy by ionization of gas atoms, the moving particle loses energy by excitation of optical levels and by transferring its kinetic energy to gas molecules in elastic collisions without producing ionization. In an actual situation the relative probability for the occurrence of different types of ionizing and nonionizing collisions would be expected to vary with the energy, charge, and mass of the moving particle. We would also expect a dependence on the composition of the stopping gas. The variation in the relative collision probability means that the fraction of the total energy of the stopped particle expended in ionization is a function of its initial energy; the fraction may differ for different particles and depends on the particular gas mixture used. Furthermore, particles of one kind and of one energy do not lose precisely the same amount of energy in passing through a given thickness of matter. The spread in energy loss is particularly large for a moving electron that may lose a large fraction of its energy in a single collision with another electron; this is not so for a heavy particle because of the large mass difference between the moving particle and stopping electrons. Since actual collisions occur at random, the total number of ions produced under given conditions is subject to statistical fluctuations. This question and the relationship between energy and ionization are discussed in the following sections.

I. Statistics of ion pair formation. The variation in the amount of energy lost by energetic charged particles in traversing a thin layer of matter cannot be calculated correctly by a statistical argument based on the assumption of random fluctuations in the number of impacts, primarily because of the large fluctuation in the energy loss per impact, including, for example, occasional collisions in which quite large energies are transmitted to secondary electrons (delta rays). Measured energy-loss distributions are broader than predicted by the simple statistical argument and, in general, are characterized by an asymmetric distribution with an excess of large energy losses.

As a rule, one may say that the statistical spread in the energy lost by a charged particle in passing through a given thickness of matter will be a Gaussian (symmetric) distribution only if the following conditions are fulfilled:

(a) The energy-loss distribution has a width on the energy scale large compared to the maximum possible energy transfer in a single collision.

(b) On the other hand, this width must be small compared to both the average total energy of the moving particle and its average energy loss.

These conditions are usually not met when a charged particle passes through a thin absorber.

A theory of the energy-loss distribution in thin absorbers has been developed by Landau[1] and Symon[2] and discussed by Moyal.[3] A further development of the theory was carried out by Blunck and Leisegang[4] and reviewed by Birkhoff.[5] In view of the complexity of the Landau-Symon theory, the reader is referred to Rossi's review[6] for a detailed exposition.

The fluctuation in the ionization produced in thin absorbers has been studied experimentally by several investigators. Rothwell[7] measured directly the energy loss of electrons of 1 to 2 Mev energy in passing through a thin proportional counter. An energy loss in the counter window of about 100 kev limited the investigation to electron energies above 1 Mev, where the specific ionization is nearly independent of energy. The observed distribution of energy losses, shown in Fig. 1, was in agreement with a Landau distribution in the high-energy region, but wider than Landau

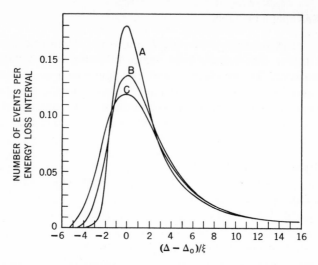

Fig. 1. Energy-loss distributions for minimum-ionizing electrons: curve A, theoretical distribution according to Landau; curve B, average experimental distribution in argon; curve C, average experimental distribution in krypton. Δ_0 is the most probable energy loss, Δ is the observed energy loss, and ξ is a parameter proportional to the number of electrons in the layer of matter. From Rothwell.[7]

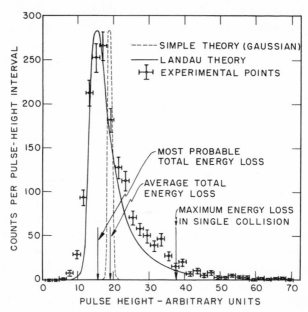

Fig. 2. Frequency distribution of energy losses of 31.5 Mev protons traversing proportional counter filled with 96% argon and 4% carbon dioxide. The histogram of experimental points shows standard deviations and channel widths. From Igo, Clark, and Eisberg.[9]

6

predicts on the low energy side, the discrepancy being greater in krypton than in argon. The experimental values of the most probable energy losses, however, are predicted correctly. Kageyama and Nishimura,[8] using a magnetic beta-ray spectrometer, obtained similar results for the distribution of electron energy losses in metal foils which seemed to be in agreement with the Blunck-Leisegang theory. Igo, Clark, and Eisberg,[9] employing a technique similar to Rothwell's, investigated the fluctuations in energy loss of 31.5 Mev protons with the results shown in Fig. 2. [It should be noted that the area under the theoretical curve (solid line) apparently has not been normalized to correspond to the total number of particles actually observed.]

The fluctuation in the total ionization produced by a charged particle that is stopped in the gas of an ionization detector also cannot be derived from a simple statistical agreement. Fano[10] has shown that in the case of hydrogen the value of the mean square deviation in the number of ion pairs is between one third and one half the mean square deviation to be expected if the process were governed by a Poisson distribution. This is a result of the fact that particles of energy E always lose exactly that much energy when they are brought to rest in the gas of an ionization detector. The requirement that the particle must have lost a definite energy in coming to rest restricts the number of impacts. Thus a particle that experiences an unusually large number of collisions in traveling a certain distance will also have lost an excessive amount of energy; it has less than the usual amount of energy left over in the remaining portion of the path, and the fluctuation in the total number of ionizing collisions is less than would be expected from a simple Poisson distribution.

There is comparatively little direct experimental information on statistical fluctuations in total ionization because such fluctuations are usually immeasurably small. For example, for the mean number of ion pairs produced by 5.298-Mev polonium alpha particles in hydrogen, namely $J_0 \cong 140,000$, the root mean square deviation of the actual number of ion pairs would be approximately $(0.4J_0)^{1/2} = 240$ (where we have used the factor 0.4 suggested by Fano), or 0.17% of the mean number of ion pairs liberated. Instrumental spreads (introduced, for example, by amplifier noise) are an order of magnitude larger than this value.

However, in the special case of proportional counters used for the detection of low-energy quanta (as in the experiments performed by Curran and his collaborators[11] and by Hanna and Pontecorvo[12]), the number of initial ion pairs may be so small that the fluctuation in this number makes a significant contribution to the spread of the experimental signal. (The actual spread is caused by the fluctuation just mentioned and by statistical variations in the multiplication process. Curran, Angus, and

Cockcroft[11] have succeeded in separating the contributions from these two effects, as described later in detail.) Curran concludes that the rms deviation in the number of ion pairs released by a photoelectron is slightly less than the square root of the mean number of ion pairs. However, when applying a small correction to his data (to account for the fact that the mean energy per ion pair in the mixture of 50% argon and 50% methane used by him is 28.5 ev[13] and not 32 ev as assumed), the rms deviation becomes very nearly equal to the square root of the mean number. The observations of Hanna, Kirkwood, and Pontecorvo[12] qualitatively agree with those of Curran, although no attempt was made by these authors to separate the fluctuations caused by multiplication from the fluctuation in the initial number of ion pairs. A further discussion of this question is presented in Sec. G of this chapter.

We might also mention the observation made by Stetter,[14] who has detected fluctuations in the amount of charge collected when alpha particles were stopped in various gases. However, the observed fluctuations appear to be mainly instrumental. Of interest is his rather surprising observation that the tracks of shortest range also contain the smallest number of ion pairs.

2. The relationship between energy and ionization. Because of the changing cross section for different types of collision during the process of stopping in the gas of an ionization chamber, the number of ion pairs per unit energy loss produced by a charged particle is, in general, a function of its energy. Early experiments, such as those of Gurney[15] and of Gibson and Gardiner,[16] showed, however, that ionization and energy are approximately proportional in most gases. Moreover, the average energy per ion pair is not very different for different particles, such as fast electrons and alpha particles. Consequently, many experimenters assumed as a working hypothesis that energy and ionization are in fact not only approximately but exactly proportional to each other and that there exists a unique constant W (the energy lost per ion pair produced) characteristic of each gas.

This question was reviewed by Gray[17] in 1944 on the basis of experimental evidence then available. Fano[18] in 1946 suggested an explanation for the approximate constancy of the energy per ion pair, and Bohr[19] in 1948 analyzed the production of ionization by electron impact, by nuclear collisions, and by capture and loss of extranuclear electrons.

The variation of the rate of ion production with particle energy can be discussed in the limit of high particle energy and small mass and charge, on the one hand, and in the limit of low particle energy and large mass and charge on the other. For light particles traveling with a velocity large compared to a velocity characteristic of the "velocity" of extranuclear electrons, namely $v_0 = e^2/\hbar$, energy loss occurs predominantly by direct impact between the moving particle and orbital electrons of the gas atom. In this case we may speak of a characteristic ratio of energy loss by excitation to energy loss by ionization. This ratio should change only slightly with particle energy, as long as the energy of the moving particle is sufficiently large, although a description of the process is complicated by the occurrence of delta rays (energetic secondary electrons).

Heavy particles, on the other hand, will lose an appreciable amount of energy by direct nuclear collisions, particularly at low energies. The "ionization efficiency" (proportion of energy expended in ion production) would certainly be greatly reduced for collisions of this type. This question has been discussed by Ling and Knipp[20] with particular emphasis on the ionization produced by fission fragments. Moreover, for all particles moving at a velocity small compared with the speed of the atomic electrons in the gas atoms, ionization by direct impact is no longer possible, and most of the energy loss must be attributed to nuclear collision and to capture and loss of electrons. The contribution of the mechanism of capture and loss to energy transfer and to the production of ionization for nuclear particles has never been satisfactorily computed, but theoretical estimates indicate that the mechanism is of considerable importance.[19,21] The older theoretical discussions of the capture-loss process[22-24] predict a cross section for electron loss that increases with particle energy and a cross section for electron capture that decreases extremely rapidly with increasing particle velocity. The two cross sections are approximately equal when $v = v_0$, and below this velocity one would expect the moving particle to spend an appreciable portion of time in an uncharged or partly charged state, a conclusion that is verified experimentally.[25]

In view of these observations, we would expect the relationship between energy and ionization to be particularly simple for fast electrons.[26,27] Energetic electrons rarely produce secondary electrons that have sufficient energy to cause further ionization, and nuclear collisions, although responsible for most of the small angle scattering experienced by the electrons, do not constitute an important source of energy transfer because of the disparity in masses. Furthermore, electrons cannot undergo any capture and loss processes, and the energy at which their velocity is equal to that of the atomic electrons is negligibly small, of the order of the ionization potential of the atom. Knowledge of the ionizing properties of electrons is also important for a discussion of the ionization produced by heavy particles because of the occurrence of delta rays.

Early experimental evidence on the relationship between energy and ionization for fast electrons was somewhat conflicting, with a preponderance of evidence indicating a probable increase in W for low-energy electrons. This is not in agreement with an experiment by Curran,[28] who bombarded a proportional counter filled with various gases with characteristic x rays from a number of elements. The x rays caused the liberation of monoenergetic photoelectrons, which in turn produced a definite

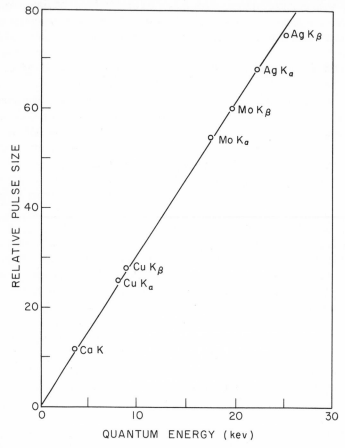

Fig. 3. Relationship between energy and ionization for electrons in nitrogen. This curve was obtained by Curran,[28] who bombarded a nitrogen-filled proportional counter with characteristic x rays of the elements indicated.

ionization pulse in a proportional counter. From the distribution in pulse sizes, the mean ionization produced by the photoelectrons can be inferred. For argon and nitrogen, the relation between energy and ionization is a simple proportionality. (See Fig. 3.)

Valentine,[29] using the beta rays from H^3 and the radiations following electron capture in Ar^{37}, measured the values of W between the energy limits of 0.2 and 46.7 kev in several gases. An upper limit of 10 % variation in W over this range was found, but the actual variation was believed to be much less. The ratios determined for W_{gas}/W_{argon} were compared with similar data for 340-Mev protons[30] and found to be the same within 2 or 3 %. No special precautions were taken to purify the gases used; in fact, methane to a pressure of 1 to 2 cm Hg was added to an atmosphere of the gas under observation for added stability in the measurements. This, of

TABLE I. W-VALUES IN ELECTRON VOLTS PER ION PAIR FOR ELECTRONS IN GASES

Authority	Valentine[29]	Jesse and Sadauskis[31,32]
Ionization Source	Ar^{37} and H^3	Ni^{63}, H^3, C^{14}
Method	Ionization Chamber and Proportional Counter	Ionization Chamber
Hydrogen	38.0	36.3
Helium	32.5*	42.3
Nitrogen	35.8	35.0
Oxygen	32.2	30.9
Neon		36.6
Argon	27.0	26.4
Krypton		24.2
Xenon		22.0
Air	35.0	34.0
Carbon Dioxide		32.9
Acetylene (C_2H_2)		25.9
Ethane (C_2H_6)		24.8
Ethylene (C_2H_4)		26.2
Methane (CH_4)	30.2	27.3

* Impure gas.

course, makes the resulting values of W, listed in Table 1, of questionable accuracy, particularly for the noble gases.

Jesse and Sadauskis,[31] using an ionization chamber, have determined the values of W for electrons and alpha particles, denoted by W_β and W_α, respectively, in a variety of carefully purified gases. All measurements were made relative to argon as a standard gas, the beta rays from Ni^{63}, H^3, and C^{14} serving as electron sources; Po^{210} and Am^{241} were used as alpha-particle sources. These measurements indicate no variation in W with electron energy and a constant ratio of W_α/W_β, probably equal to unity, for hydrogen and the noble gases. In the several other gases measured the ratio W_α/W_β was found to vary, but the variation seemed to come from a variation of W_α with the alpha-particle energy rather than a variation of W_β with beta-particle energy. In air, nitrogen, oxygen, and carbon dioxide W_α was 4 to 5% higher than the corresponding W_β, and in acetylene, ethane, ethylene, and methane W_α was 6 to 7% higher than W_β. Using S^{35} as an electron source, these authors[32] have made careful determinations of W in nitrogen, ethylene, and ethane with the results listed in Table 1. Although Jesse's values of W for electrons, given in Table 1, are all relative to argon as a standard, they are probably the most reliable data available because of the extreme care given to gas purification.

Using electrons of 1-to-34-Mev energy and an ionization chamber, Barber[33] has measured W at minimum ionization (1.7 Mev) in hydrogen, helium, and nitrogen and has investigated the variation of W with electron energy in this energy range. At 1.7 Mev he finds values of 37.8, 44.5, and 34.8 ev/ion pair for hydrogen, helium, and nitrogen, respectively, in good agreement with recent alpha-particle measurements. The relativistic increase in ionization as the energy is increased from the minimum ionization energy (1.7 Mev) to 34 Mev agrees with the expected increase in energy loss within 1% for nitrogen, indicating a constant value of W; in helium and hydrogen the increase in ionization is less than the predicted increase in energy loss. The effect is more certain in hydrogen, where an increase of about 3.3% in W is observed.

The discussion of the ionizing properties of heavy nuclear particles is necessarily more complicated than for fast electrons. Gray's analysis[17] of Gurney's data[15] (on the ionization produced by slow alpha particles in various gases) showed, however, that the relationship between energy and ionization is particularly simple for the noble gases and for hydrogen. Gray computed the ratio

$$(J_{gas}/J_{H_2})_{\text{range } x} \div (J_{gas}/J_{H_2})_{\text{range 20 mm}}$$

where J_{gas} = ionization produced in a particular gas by an alpha particle of the range specified and J_{H_2} = ionization produced in hydrogen by an alpha particle of the same energy. This ratio is constant within 1% for helium, argon, and neon but varies significantly (as much as 8%) in air. Gray compared all gases with hydrogen in the belief that the relationship between energy and ionization should be particularly simple in this case. This assumption has been criticized by Bethe.[34]

Gray's analysis suggests that energy and ionization are proportional for alpha particles in the noble gases and hydrogen (unless these quantities should accidentally vary with each other in exactly the same manner for each of the gases mentioned, and that is not likely). This conclusion has created a considerable amount of interest because of the widespread use of argon in ionization chambers operated with electron collection. To examine this question, Jesse[35] studied the total ionization produced by natural alpha particles in argon, with the conclusion that alpha-particle energy and ionization are proportional to each other within 0.5%, as shown in Fig. 4. These observations in argon were compared with Stetter's measurements in air.[14] However, more recent investigations[36] of the ionization produced in air by alpha particles have shown that much of the apparent variation of W with energy in air is probably caused by columnar recombination and lack of voltage saturation in the ionization chamber, so that the comparison is perhaps not very meaningful.

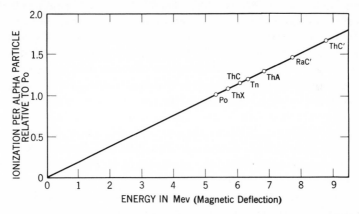

Fig. 4.   Ionization produced by natural alpha particles of various energies in argon. The experimental points were obtained by Jesse[35] by using a "slow" ionization chamber filled with argon.

Tunnicliffe and Ward[37] used monoenergetic neutrons to produce recoil protons, deuterons, and alpha particles in proportional counters containing mixtures of methane with deuterium and argon and of methane with helium and argon. On the assumption that the same specific ionization is produced by protons and deuterons of the same velocity, a comparison of the maximum recoil pulses from hydrogen and deuterium was interpreted as a comparison of W for protons of different energies; this led to the conclusion that ionization was proportional to energy in different percentage compositions of methane, deuterium, and argon for protons in the energy range of 200 to 500 kev. The value of W for alpha particles in argon was found to be about 8% greater than for protons of the same energy in the range of 200 to 400 kev. Because the experimental method required the use of gas mixtures, this result was obtained by extrapolating the observations made with mixtures of different composition to pure argon. More recently, Lowry and Miller[38] have measured the ionization yield of protons in argon in the energy range of 25 to 250 kev. Their results indicate a linear relationship between ionization and energy and a W-value of 26.5 $\pm$ 0.5 ev/ion pair, with an intercept of the energy axis at 1.4 $\pm$ 0.9 kev, indicating a slight ionization defect.

A number of other experiments[39–44] has provided somewhat contradictory information on the relationship between energy and ionization for heavy particles stopping in argon.

Qualitatively, one would expect a loss of efficiency of the ionizing process in stopping very slow, heavy particles. Madsen[45] measured the ionization by recoil particles from the alpha decay of Po, ThC, and ThC' by means of a proportional counter. With a filling of 95% argon and 5% air, he obtained a linear relation between energy and ionization, with a slope corresponding to 67 ev/ion pair and an intercept at about 40 kev. Jesse and Sadauskis,[46] using a hemispherical ionization chamber, observed that the W-values for recoils from the alpha decay of polonium are 4.5 and 4.1 times as large as the values obtained with alpha particles in argon and helium, respectively. A modification of the Madsen arrangement has been employed by Stone and Cochran,[47] who used a thin ThC-ThC' source to measure W for the recoils in several gases. Consistently higher W-values were obtained for the slow than for the fast recoils, and the ratios of these values to the W-values for alpha particles in the same gases varied from 1.8 to 3.8.

Madsen's observations have been discussed by Ling and Knipp[20] in their analysis of the ionization efficiency of fission fragments. It seems to be established that the distribution in the ratio of the ionizations produced by two associated fission fragments is broader than the distribution in the ratio of energies obtained from the masses. This observation is supported by evidence that the mean kinetic energy of fission fragments determined calorimetrically is appreciably higher than the value deduced from ionization yields. Fission fragments are more highly ionized in the initial parts of their paths through the gas of an ionization chamber (average initial charge 14 units[48]) than in the later parts of their paths; therefore, the proportion of the energy loss attributed to nuclear collisions increases toward the end of the track. Schmitt and Leachman[49] have suggested that one can write for the energy of a fission fragment $E = W_\alpha J_0 + E_0$, where W_α is the value of W for alpha particles in the stopping gas, J_0 is the total observed ionization, and E_0 is about 5.7 and 6.7 Mev for the light and heavy fragments, respectively.

In recent years numerous careful experiments[50–53] have been reported in which the W-values have been determined in a great variety of gases. These experiments utilized 5-Mev alpha particles and ionization chambers of such dimensions and at such pressures that the total energy of the alpha

TABLE 2. *W*-VALUES IN ELECTRON VOLTS PER ION PAIR
FOR ALPHA PARTICLES IN GASES

	Valentine and Curran[50]	Jesse and Sadauskis[51]	Bortner and Hurst[52]	Biber, Huber, and Müller[53]
Hydrogen	37.0	36.3	37.0	35.96
Helium	31.7*	42.7	46.0	
Nitrogen	36.0	36.6	36.3	36.50
Oxygen	32.2	32.5	32.2	
Neon		36.8		
Argon	25.9	26.4	26.4	
Krypton		24.1		
Xenon		21.9		
Air	35.2	35.5	35.0	34.95
Ammonia				30.5
Boron trifluoride			36.0	35.3
Carbon dioxide			34.3	34.3
Carbon tetrachloride				25.9
Hydrogen sulfide				23.4
Sulfur dioxide				32.5
Sulfur hexafluoride			35.7	
Freon-12			29.5	
Acetone			28.5	
Acetylene		27.5	27.7	
Benzene			27.5	
Butane			26.4	23.0
Ethane		26.6	26.7	
Ethylene		28.0	28.0	
Ethanol				32.6
Isobutane			26.1	
Methane	29.0	29.2	29.4	29.00
Methyl Iodide			24.8	
Propane			26.3	

* Impure helium.

particle was spent in the active volume of the chamber. Several of these results are summarized in Table 2, and it will be noted that, with the exception of helium, the results are in excellent agreement.

The importance of gas purification and the effect of trace amount of contaminant gases on the ionization produced have been shown best by measurements on helium, neon, and argon. In 1932 E. J. Williams[54] predicted theoretically an expected range of *W*-values for hydrogen that agreed with the experimentally measured value; however, by the same method of computation, Williams predicted a W-value for helium much higher than the experimental value of 30 ev/ion pair measured at that time. A possible explanation of this discrepancy suggested by Williams was that the experimentally measured ionization is excessively large because of ionization of impurity atoms by collisions with excited helium atoms. This explanation was confirmed in measurements by Jesse and Sadauskis[55] and by Bortner and Hurst,[56] who obtained experimental values of 42.7 and

TABLE 3.   CONSTANTS REQUIRED FOR THE
EVALUATION OF AN EFFECTIVE W_{ij} FOR
BINARY GAS MIXTURES

Mixture	W_i	W_j	a_{ij}
i j			
N_2—H_2	36.3	37.0	0.28
N_2—Ar	36.3	26.4	0.53
N_2—O_2	36.3	32.2	1.06
He—Ar	30.1	26.4	0.75
He—H_2	29.7	37.0	3.55
He—N_2	29.7	36.3	8.47
He—CH_4	30.3	29.4	0.68
H_2—Ar	37.0	26.4	1.78
H_2—CH_4	37.0	29.4	4.03
C_2H_2—N_2	27.8	36.3	0.26
C_2H_2—CO_2	27.8	34.3	0.93
C_2H_2—CH_4	27.8	29.4	0.39
CH_4—N_2	39.4	36.3	0.62
C_2H_2—He	27.8	30.3	0.058

46.0 ev/ion pair, respectively, for carefully purified helium gas and who demonstrated by deliberate addition of small amounts of contaminant gases that the earlier low values of W were caused by the ionization of impurities by collisions with the well-known metastable state of helium at 19.7 ev. Similar results have been obtained by Jesse and Sadauskis in neon. Another theoretical treatment of this problem has been presented by Erskine.[57]

Mixtures of various contaminant gases in argon have been investigated in detail by Melton, Hurst, and Bortner.[58] It was found that there is a particular concentration for each impurity gas that gives a minimum value of W for the mixture. Although contaminant gases with ionization potentials less than the metastable potential of 11.5 volts in argon resulted in a reduced value of W, it was found that several gases with ionization potentials greater than 11.5 volts also produce a decrease of W in argon.

For proper operation of ionization chambers and proportional counters, it is sometimes desirable to employ a mixture of two gases. The interpretation of data from such an instrument may require that an effective W for the gas mixture be known. In general investigations of gas mixtures, Bortner and Hurst,[59] Moe, Bortner, and Hurst,[60] and Strickler and Hurst[61] have found that an effective value W_{ij} for gas mixtures can be calculated by using the empirical equation

$$\frac{1}{W_{ij}} = \left(\frac{1}{W_i} - \frac{1}{W_j}\right)Z_{ij} + \frac{1}{W_j}$$

where $Z_{ij} = P_i/(P_i + a_{ij}P_j)$, P_i is the partial pressure of the gas having a value W_i, and P_j is the partial pressure of the gas having the value W_j. The constant a_{ij} is equal to the ratio of the stopping powers S_j/S_i for the component gases in some instances; however, it should be considered to be an empirical constant. Values of the constant a_{ij} for several gas combinations are listed in Table 3; other gas combinations are discussed in the references previously cited.

B. Life History of an Ion

At a time of the order of 10^{-7} sec after the passage of an ionizing particle through the gas of an ionization chamber the energy of the free ionization electrons has been reduced to a few electron volts. They will then begin to drift through the gas under the action of the applied electric field with a velocity that depends on the electric field, the gas pressure, and the constitution of the gas. The positive ions also produced in the ionization process will, of course, move through the gas much more slowly. In the course of their motion electrons may be captured by positive ions; this is termed recombination. In electronegative gases electrons may be captured by neutral atoms to form negative ions, a process called electron attachment. These negative ions may give up an electron to a positive ion; such an event also constitutes recombination.

Ionization chambers were originally used strictly as charge-measuring devices; that is, an amplifier was connected to one electrode of the chamber, and the current produced in the external network by the motion of the liberated ions was integrated over a comparatively long time (of the order of milliseconds). One would then observe a voltage pulse at the collector electrode that was directly proportional to the original number of ions released. This type of operation has several disadvantages. The difficulty of adequately accounting for recombination, the "pile-up" of pulses in experiments involving high counting rates, and the microphonics (response to mechanical oscillations at acoustic frequencies) of the slow amplifiers required, all contribute to the problems frequently encountered with such slow ionization chambers.

In recent years electron collection has therefore been used almost exclusively. In this mode of operation an amplifier is employed which has a frequency response such that the electrical signal resulting from the motion of the free ionization electrons is amplified, but the much slower motion of the positive ions does not give rise to a measurable output signal. In this way, nearly all of the difficulties previously mentioned are avoided. In their place a number of other problems arise, as discussed below.

1. Electron capture. In order to operate an ionization chamber with electron collection, it is necessary to eliminate impurities that might capture electrons to form negative ions. Since the amplifier responds only to fast signals and since negative ions have a much smaller mobility than free electrons, this kind of capture in effect makes the captured electrons unobservable. Although O_2 is the most common contaminant, other troublesome impurities are H_2O, NH_3, the halogens, HCl, and SiF_4. H_2O and O_2 occur as impurities in most laboratory gases; HCl is a constituent of some solder fluxes commonly used in the assembly of ionization chambers, and SiF_4 is formed when BF_3 comes in contact with water vapor in the presence of glass.

In each collision between an electron and a neutral electronegative gas atom, there is a probability h that the electron will attach itself to the atom to form a heavy negative ion. For most electronegative gases, h varies with the actual physical velocity (the so-called agitation velocity) of the electrons at the moment of impact. Values for the attachment probability as a function of electron agitation energy for several electronegative gases have been listed by Healey and Reed.[62].

The situation in oxygen has been investigated in detail; some of the experimental results[63-68] of the variation of the cross section for electron attachment with mean electron agitation energy are shown in Fig. 5. Bradbury[63] interpreted the mechanism of capture in the 2-ev region as a process in which electrons suffer inelastic collisions with oxygen molecules which reduces their energy sufficiently to allow the formation of O_2^-. Geballe and Harrison,[69] and Craggs et al.,[70] have suggested that the magnitude of the capture cross section at 2 ev may be accounted for by assuming dissociation; thus the 2-ev process leads to the formation of O^-, not O_2^-, as suggested by Bradbury. This argument is supported by Harrison and Geballe's[67] data, which, when corrected for ionization, do not exhibit the sharp peak in the attachment cross section at 2 ev observed by Bradbury.

Attachment in argon-oxygen mixtures has been investigated by Bortner and Hurst.[71] Although the attachment coefficient is independent of argon pressure (for a fixed x/p and fixed oxygen concentration, where x is the electric field intensity and p is the gas pressure), it is found to decrease with x/p and with oxygen concentration in qualitative agreement with the cross section variation shown in Fig. 5. Bortner and Hurst have also studied electron attachment in oxygen-nitrogen and oxygen-ethylene mixtures at

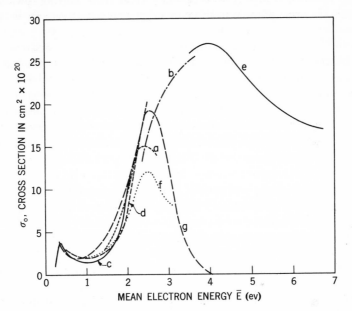

Fig. 5.   Cross section for electron capture by oxygen. Curve a, Bradbury;[63] curve b, Burch and Geballe;[64] curve c, Chanin and Biondi;[65] curve d, Doehring;[66] curve e, Harrison and Geballe;[67] curve f, Herreng;[68] curve g, Healey and Kirkpatrick.[62]

electron energies under 1 ev, where data had previously been very limited.[72] Attachment was found to depend on the partial pressures of both gases in the O_2—N_2 mixture, but only on the C_2H_4 pressure in the O_2—C_2H_4 mixture. These results have been interpreted in terms of a mechanism involving as a first step the formation of excited O_2^-; the excitation energy is then given up in a subsequent collision. Estimates have been made of the cross sections for de-excitation by collisions with various kinds of molecules.

McCutchen[73] found that the addition of 0.1 % O_2 to pure argon caused appreciable attachment losses to appear; however, the further addition of 2 % CO_2 to the mixture diminished the losses again, presumably because the presence of CO_2 reduces the electron agitation energy to a value near the minimum in the O_2 attachment curve at about 1 ev. This effect has been used to advantage by Facchini and Malvicini[74] by employing a filling consisting of 98 % A and 2 % N_2, which is insensitive to rather large oxygen contaminations over an extended range of operating voltage.

The effect of electron capture on the output signal from an ionization chamber has been discussed by Bistline[75] and by English[76], whose treatment is followed below. Let us consider an electron drifting toward the collector electrode of an ionization chamber with a drift velocity w. (The drift velocity w is distinguished from the agitation velocity u mentioned previously; u represents the actual physical velocity of the electrons. This distinction is discussed in greater detail later on.) If λ is the mean free path per unit pressure for collisions with electronegative gas molecules, then the number of collisions experienced every second by an electron with molecules of an electronegative gas present with a partial pressure p is up/λ. The number of collisions per unit distance of path moved in the direction of the field is $up/\lambda w$. Therefore, the probability of attachment while traveling distance dx in the direction of the field is given by $(hup/\lambda w)\,dx$. The decrease in the number N of electrons between x and $x + dx$ is then $dN = -(Nhup/\lambda w)\,dx$. In the case of a paralle plate chamber, in which the electric field is constant, λ, u, and w are independent of x, and we can integrate the expression for dN simply with the result

$$N = N_0 e^{-x/\lambda_c} \tag{2}$$

where N_0 = original number of electrons and λ_c = mean free path for capture = $\lambda w/hup$.

From this expression one can compute the reduction attributable to electron capture in the signal observed at the collector electrode. The current at the collector due to N charges moving with a drift velocity w, each having a charge $-e$ in an electric field X between the two electrodes that have a potential difference V_0 between them, is given by $i = -New(X/V_0)$, as we shall see later on. In a parallel plate chamber we can set $X = V_0/d$, where d = separation of the two electrodes. Also, since we are dealing with negative electrons moving in a direction opposite to the direction of the electric field, $w = -(dx/dt)$; x here is a coordinate measured along one of the lines of force of the field. The voltage signal S at the collector is then given by integrating the current over the collection time T and dividing by the electrostatic capacity C of the collector electrode relative to its surroundings:

$$S = \frac{1}{C}\int_0^T i(t)\,dt = -\frac{N_0 e}{Cd}\int_0^{x_0} e^{-x/\lambda_c}\,dx = -\frac{N_0 e}{Cd}\lambda_c(1 - e^{-x_0/\lambda_c}). \tag{3}$$

(Here x_0 is the distance from the point of origin of the electrons to the collector.)

The voltage signal in the absence of electron capture is evidently given by

$$S_0 = -\left(\frac{N_0 e}{Cd}\right) x_0$$

and the loss of negative signal due to capture is approximately equal to

$$S_0 - S \cong \tfrac{1}{2} S_0 x_0 / \lambda_c. \tag{4}$$

As an example, consider a chamber of average dimensions filled with pure argon (except for a small oxygen impurity) to a pressure of 1 atm. If we choose reasonable values for the electric field, and for u, w and λ, we find that oxygen should not be present to more than one part in 10^5 in order for the loss in signal due to electron capture to be less than 1%. At high pressures, the requirements on purity are more severe than given by this figure. The problems that are encountered in the treatment of gases to achieve such a degree of purity are discussed later on.

2. Recombination. The positive ions and electrons that are formed during the process of ionization can become unobservable by recombining with each other. The recombination may or may not be preceded by the formation of negative ions by electron attachment, depending on the presence or absence of electronegative gases. Two types of classifications of recombination events are useful: a classification based on the mechanism by which the excess energy available as a result of charge neutralization is carried off and a classification based on the "life-history" of the recombining ions.

The possible ways of carrying off excess energy have been identified by Massey and Burhop[77] as follows:

(a) Radiative recombination between an electron or negative ion on the one hand and a positive ion on the other in which the excess energy appears as an emitted photon; this effect is generally too weak to be important.

(b) Mutual neutralization by charge exchange between negative and positive ions in which the excess energy is carried away by the neutral atoms.

(c) Dielectronic recombination between an electron and a positive ion in which the surplus energy released by the recombination is taken up by a bound atomic electron, raising it to an excited state; the doubly excited atom may dissociate again or drop to a stable state by a radiative transition.

(d) Dissociative recombination between an electron and a polyatomic positive ion, leading to dissociation of the molecule.

(e) Three-body recombination between a negative ion, a positive ion, and a neutral atom in which the surplus energy is taken up as in (a) or (b) or taken away by the third body. A somewhat similar process may occur for electrons, positive ions, and neutral atoms. This process is of major importance. Historically, it has been discussed by J. J. Thomson[78] and Langevin[79] (for high gas pressures).

As far as the "life history" of the ions involved in recombination is concerned, one may distinguish between preferential recombination (which takes place between a negative ion, or electron, and the positive ion from which the electron was originally separated), columnar recombination (between ions distributed along the track of an ionizing particle), and volume recombination (between ions from the tracks of different particles). A very lucid discussion of these processes has been presented by Wilkinson,[80] who has shown that volume recombination is always negligible in a pulse-ionization chamber, although it may be a factor in a current chamber. For volume recombination to come into play, several tracks would have to appear simultaneously in the chamber; their ionization pulses could then not be resolved. Under these conditions, the chamber would no longer be usable as a pulse-ionization chamber.

Preferential recombination between heavy positive and negative ions is a process in which the electron ejected from a gas atom is captured very close to its point of liberation by another gas atom to form a negative ion. This negative ion then recombines with the positive ion which the electron left behind. If the gas is not electronegative, the ionization electron must undergo a collision very close to its point of liberation in order to be reflected to the neighborhood of its parent ion. Wilkinson has shown that, with the exception of preferential recombination at very high pressures in electronegative gases, these two types of event are very improbable.

Columnar recombination between heavy ions, on the other hand, is a common process that must be taken into account whenever electronegative gases are employed in an ionization chamber. Correction for the resulting loss of charge is usually made by employing the Jaffe theory of columnar recombination.[81] This theory assumes that electron capture of the ionization electrons leads to a radial distribution of positive and negative ions about the axis of the original particle track; the density of ions is assumed to have a Gaussian distribution about this axis. By considering that the clouds of positive and negative ions along the track pass over each other as they drift in opposite directions under the influence of the electric field, one can compute the fraction of them that will combine. Jaffe's theory assumes that the drift velocities and diffusion coefficients of positive and negative ions are the same. (The calculation of the loss of the charge becomes very complicated when this assumption is not made.) For this reason, the theory cannot be applied to columnar recombination between electrons and positive ions, since the electrons have much greater mobility and diffuse much more rapidly than positive ions. Furthermore, one would not expect Jaffe's model of the initial distribution of ions to be applicable when electron capture fails to take place immediately following the formation of the particle track. An adequate theory that accounts for the columnar recombination of positive ions and free electrons thus does not exist.

There is some experimental evidence that columnar recombination between electrons and positive ions is not negligible at high pressures, although opinion is divided on this question. Rossi[82] used a cylindrical ionization chamber filled with a mixture of 5 atm argon and $\frac{1}{4}$ atm carbon dioxide; he attributes his failure to achieve saturation with Po alpha particles (that is, to obtain a pulse height independent of applied voltage) to columnar recombination in the gas mixture. However, with a pure argon filling of 7 atm the effect disappeared; this is presumed to be consistent with an unusually large recombination coefficient in CO_2.

In general, in a gas in which there is no electron attachment, appreciable recombination due to any process should not be important; this again emphasizes the necessity for careful purification of the noble gases, particularly for work at high pressures. Experimentally, in an electron-pulse chamber, both recombination and electron capture result in a loss of pulse height; it is not possible to separate these two effects except by an analysis of the influence of the operating conditions of the chamber. For example, we have shown that the loss of signal due to capture in a parallel-plate chamber is proportional to the distance that the collected electrons must travel from their point of liberation to the collector electrode, whereas, in the case of columnar recombination, the maximum variation in pulse height under given operating conditions will be the result of different orientations of the ionizing particle tracks in the chamber; one would expect a greater loss of signal when the particle track is oriented along a line of force than when it is oriented at right angles to this direction, and there is no dependence on the distance of the track from the collector.

3. Mobility. Electrons and heavy ions behave very differently when they are liberated in a gas-filled ionization chamber or proportional counter to which an electric field has been applied. In moderate electric fields the mean kinetic energy of a heavy ion does not rise appreciably above the value $(3/2)kT$ (where k = Boltzmann's constant and T = absolute temperature) determined by thermal equilibrium with the neutral gas molecules in the absence of the electric field. Nevertheless, a drift velocity w is super-imposed on the thermal motion of the ion by the electric field; this velocity under the conditions stated is given by $w = \mu(X/p)$, where $X =$ electric field strength and $p =$ gas pressure. The mobility of the ion, μ, depends on the nature of the gas and the mass of the moving ion; it is largest for the lightest gases (helium and hydrogen) and decreases slightly as the mass of the ion is increased. Thus, for a mass 10 ion in xenon gas, $\mu = 2 \times 10^3$ cm/sec/(volt/cm)/mm Hg; the value for a mass 50 ion would be about half as great. The mobility for a mass 10 ion in helium is about ten times as large as in xenon but would not be much smaller for a heavier ion. Values of μ for many gases and ions of different masses have been listed by Loeb[83] and Tyndall[84] and are conveniently summarized by Wilkinson.[80] The mobility varies with the temperature, depends little on the charge of the ion, and is about the same for negative ions as for positive ions. The exact value of the mobility is seldom a matter of concern in ionization chambers and proportional counters, a rough value being adequate in instrument design. For very high X/p values, such as those encountered in a pro-portional counter, the variation of drift velocity with electric field intensity and gas pressure approaches a dependence of the form $w \propto (X/p)^{\frac{1}{2}}$ and the behavior of the mobility as a function of X/p may become quite complex.

For electrons, the application of an electric field causes an increase in their agitation energy, or "temperature"; the agitation energy is frequently expressed in terms of the ratio η of its value in the presence of the field to its value in the absence of the field, $(3/2)kT$. In general, η is a function of X/p and is much larger for inert than for molecular gases. This difference in behavior is due to the onset of inelastic collisions in the molecular gases at fairly low electron energies. Since the agitation energy depends on an equilibrium between the energy and momentum transferred to the electrons by the electric field and the energy and momentum that they lose in collisions with gas molecules, the occurrence of inelastic collisions at low electron energy prevents the equilibrium value of this energy from rising to a large value.

Superimposed on the large agitation velocity u of the electrons in the presence of the field, where $mu^2/2 = \eta(3/2)kT$, is a drift velocity w in the direction of the field. An approximate relationship between u and w can be derived by the following argument. Assume that at each collision the electron loses all memory of its motion before the collision; then consider that between collisions the electron experiences an acceleration Xe/m due to the electric field X (where $e =$ charge and $m =$ mass of an electron). A time λ/up elapses between collisions where λ is the mean free path of electrons at unit gas pressure. During this time the electron has an average velocity $\frac{1}{2}(Xe/m)(\lambda/up)$ in the direction of the field. This velocity we

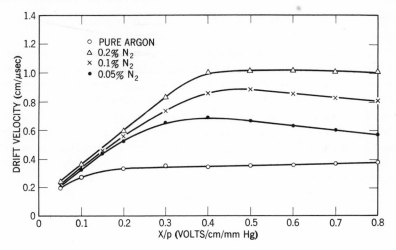

Fig. 6.   Electron drift velocity in argon-nitrogen mixtures.   From Bortner, Hurst, and Stone.[88]

identify with the drift velocity $w = Xe\lambda/2ump$.   It is interesting to observe that, for a fixed value of λ and X/p, the drift velocity w is inversely proportional to the agitation velocity u.

We can summarize experimental information on the drift velocity of electrons in pure gases as follows:

ARGON.   The early measurements of electron drift velocity by Nielsen[85] have been confirmed by recent careful experiments.[86–89]   Other measurements[90–92] are now known to have been affected by impurities.   It has been clearly demonstrated that the addition of even a few tenths of 1 % nitrogen will markedly increase the drift velocity of electrons in argon.   This observation is in agreement with the mechanism of reduction of agitation energy (and consequent increase in drift velocity) caused by inelastic collisions with impurity molecules, as discussed previously.

The drift velocity in pure argon and in argon-gas mixtures is a function of X/p alone and does not depend on the pressure separately;   this is believed to be true of all gases and gas mixtures.   The results of the drift velocity measurements of Bortner, Hurst, and Stone[88] on pure argon and argon-nitrogen mixtures are shown in Fig. 6;   Fig. 7 displays their observations on a 90 % argon-10 % methane mixture (commonly used as a filling for counters).   Extensive data on mixtures of argon-carbon dioxide, argon-methane, and argon-nitrogen have been presented by English and Hanna[90].

HELIUM.   Helium has been studied by Nielsen[85] and by Townsend and Bailey.[92]   For X/p between 0.5 and 2.5 volts/cm/mm Hg, their results are in rather good agreement; for higher values of X/p, Nielsen obtained significantly higher drift velocities than Townsend and Bailey.

NEON.   The observations of Nielsen[85] and Bailey[93] for neon containing 1% helium are in good agreement, the drift velocity increasing monotonically with X/p. At lower values of X/p, the drift velocities measured by English and Hanna[90] are somewhat larger and show a peaked structure that is usually characteristic of impurities in noble gases.

NITROGEN.   In the case of nitrogen, the drift velocities measured by several investigators are in fair agreement.[85,87,88,91,94] The results of

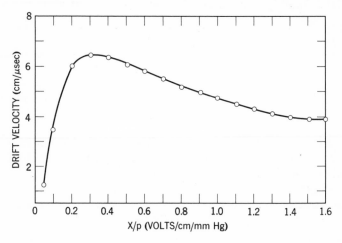

Fig. 7.   Electron drift velocity in a mixture of 90% argon and 10% methane. From Bortner, Hurst, and Stone.[88]

Bortner, Hurst, and Stone[88] can be represented by $w = [0.447\ (X/p) + 0.286]$ cm/μsec for X/p between 0.1 and 2.0 volts/cm/mm Hg; in this same range of X/p values the results of Crompton and Sutton[94] can be represented by $w = [0.513\ (X/p) + 0.273]$ cm/μsec. It appears that w rises more slowly with increasing X/p than would be expected from either of these equations. Thus at $X/p = 20$ volts/cm/mm Hg Crompton and Sutton find $w = 7.44$ cm/μsec, whereas the foregoing equations give 9.22 cm/μsec and 10.53 cm/μsec, respectively. However, electron pulse chambers are seldom operated at values of X/p larger than about 2 volts/cm/mm Hg.

CARBON DIOXIDE.   In this case the data of Rudd (quoted by Healey and Reed[62]), Skinker[95], and the Los Alamos observations (quoted by Rossi and Staub[96]) are all in fair agreement. The electron drift velocity can be represented quite well by $w = 0.41\ (X/p)^{1.5}$ cm/μsec for X/p between 0.5 and 7.0 volts/cm/mm Hg. Bortner, Hurst, and Stone[88] find a linear relationship between w and X/p for X/p between 0.2 and 2.0 volts/cm/mm Hg, which can be represented by $w = 0.50\ (X/p)$ cm/μsec.

HYDROGEN. Drift velocities in hydrogen have been measured by Crompton and Sutton[94] for values of X/p between 0.05 and 20 volts/cm/mm Hg. Their results can be represented approximately by $w = 1.0\ (X/p)^{0.5}$ cm/μsec for X/p less than 2 volts/cm/mm Hg. Above $X/p = 2$, the drift velocity varies roughly linearly with X/p and can be represented, to a fair degree of approximation, by $w = [0.3\ (X/p) + 0.8]$ cm/μsec.

BORON TRIFLUORIDE. Here, the Los Alamos observations (quoted by Rossi and Staub[96]) show a considerable spread, and they give a drift

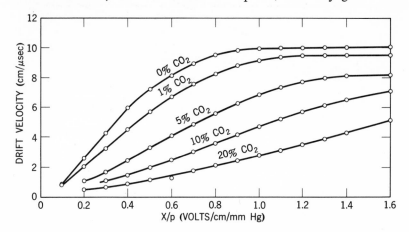

Fig. 8.   Electron drift velocity in methane-carbon dioxide mixtures. From Bortner, Hurst, and Stone.[88]

velocity (for given X/p) approximately twelve times larger than the velocity found by Bistline,[75] who made a detailed study of the mean free path for capture and other properties of BF_3. Bistline's results can be represented approximately by $w = 1.0\ (X/p)$ cm/μsec.

METHANE. The drift velocity of electrons in methane is very high, so that this gas is very useful when high counting speed is desired. Values obtained by Bortner, Hurst, and Stone[88] for methane and methane-carbon dioxide mixtures are shown in Figs. 8 and 9. These results may be of practical importance, since they show a large range of drift velocities, depending on the mixture and on the value of X/p. English and Hanna[90] obtained essentially the same variation of drift velocity with X/p; however, their measured velocities were, in general, slightly higher than those presented in Fig. 8.

ETHYLENE AND CYCLOPROPANE. Ethylene (C_2H_4) and cyclopropane (C_3H_6) have the same relative composition as polyethylene $(C_2H_4)_n$; thus

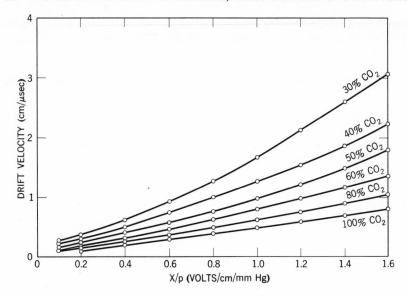

Fig. 9.   Electron drift velocity in methane-carbon dioxide mixtures.   From Bortner, Hurst, and Stone.[88]

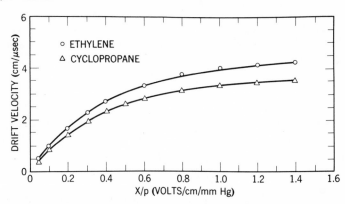

Fig. 10.   Electron drift velocity in ethylene and in cyclopropane.   From Bortner, Hurst, and Stone.[88]

either of these gases may be used with polyethylene to make Bragg-Gray type ionization cavities.   This arrangement has been used extensively for fast neutron dosimetry; hence it is important to know the electron-drift velocity for these gases.   The results of measurements on these gases by Bortner, Hurst, and Stone[88] are shown in Fig. 10.

AIR.   The results of Huxley and Zaazou,[97] Nielsen and Bradbury,[98] and Townsend and Tizard[99] are all in rather good agreement.   For X/p between

1 and 10 volts/cm/mm Hg, the drift velocity may be represented by $w = [0.42 \ (X/p) + 0.9]$ cm/μsec; for X/p above 10, the drift velocity is somewhat lower than predicted by this equation.

4. Diffusion of electrons. The electrons released as a result of the interaction of a moving charged particle with the gas of an ionization chamber will not drift exactly along the lines of force of the electric field of the chamber. Instead, they will tend to spread out by diffusion in the course of their motion toward the collector electrode. The particle current of electrons **j** can thus be expressed as the sum of two terms:

$$\mathbf{j} = -D \ \text{grad} \ n + n\mathbf{w}. \tag{5}$$

Here n is the electron density and D is the diffusion coefficient of the electrons in the gas. The first term of (5) describes the "diffusion current"; the second term accounts for the additional particle current arising from the motion of the electrons in the direction of the electric field with a drift velocity **w**.

The diffusion coefficient D is related to the mean free path λ, the agitation velocity u, and the gas pressure p by

$$D = \lambda u / 3p.$$

In a region of space in which no electrons are liberated and in which none disappears by attachment or recombination, the particle current **j** obeys the equation of continuity:

$$\partial n / \partial t = -\text{div} \ \mathbf{j}. \tag{6}$$

If we apply this relation to (5) and change to a set of Cartesian coordinates in which the variable z, chosen to be in the direction of the applied electric field, is replaced by a new variable $z' = z - wt$, application of (6) to (5) will lead to the usual form of the diffusion equation:

$$\partial n / \partial t = D \nabla'^2 n. \tag{7}$$

Here ∇'^2 represents the Laplacian operator with respect to the coordinates x, y, and z'.

If M electrons are initially concentrated at the origin, the proper solution to (7), which describes the spreading out of the electron cloud by diffusion, is then given by

$$n(x, y, z, t) = \frac{M}{(4\pi Dt)^{3/2}} \exp \left\{ -[x^2 + y^2 + (z - wt)^2]/4Dt \right\}. \tag{8}$$

Thus, while the electrons drift with a velocity w in the direction of the applied electric field, they diffuse outward at a rate specified by the root mean-square diffusion distance $\sqrt{2Dt}$.

Electron diffusion is of some importance in the operation of gridded ionization chambers, where loss of charge may occur by diffusion of the electrons to the grid wires even when the electric field configuration is such that no lines of force terminate on the grid wires, and in the analysis of wall effect; that is, the loss of charge to the walls of an ionization chamber. An extensive discussion of diffusion coefficients and agitation velocities of free electrons in gases may be found in Healey and Reed's book.[62]

C.   The Nature of Observed Signals

I. Effects of electron motion. The analysis of the voltage signal observed at the collector electrode of an electron-pulse chamber is in general more difficult than in the case of a conventional ionization chamber used to make a ballistic measurement of the total ionization. However, it is possible to extract a great deal of information from the electrostatic effects of the motion of the ionization electrons in an electron-pulse chamber; much of this information was unavailable with the older method of operation.

The order of events subsequent to the passage of a nuclear particle through the gas of an ionization chamber is the following. Electrons and positive ions are clustered initially along a pencil-shaped track; since they are in proximity to each other, the electric field created by their charges vanishes at appreciable distances from the track. The electric field of the chamber, on the other hand, imparts a drift velocity to the electrons, separating them from their parent ions which remain almost stationary during a time of the order of the electron collection time. As the two clouds of charge move away from each other, the electric field created by them can be described as arising from a line dipole with an average dipole moment per unit length of $J_0 x/R$, where $J_0 = $ total charge in either cloud, $x = $ separation of the two clouds, and $R = $ length of original particle track. Since x increases as a result of the motion of the electrons, there is a corresponding change in that portion of the electric field between the electrodes which is contributed by the ionization charges. When all free electrons have arrived at the positive (collector) electrode, their parent positive ions will have been displaced only slightly from their original location.

We are interested in determining the change in the potential of the collector electrode that results from this sequence of events. For this purpose, the general type of ionization chamber illustrated by Fig. 11 will be considered. The chamber consists of two electrodes between which a potential difference V_0 is maintained. The geometrical arrangement of the electrodes is usually such that the intensity of the electric field at any point can be specified by a single coordinate r measured along the lines of force, the surfaces $r = $ constant being equipotentials of the system. (This is possible in all cases in which the chamber possesses axial symmetry.)

We shall assume that the time constant of the RC network connecting the collector electrode to other conductors maintained at a constant potential (for example, ground potential) has been chosen to be very much longer than the electron collection time.* Thus, while the electrons travel to the collector, the electrodes are effectively insulated from each other.

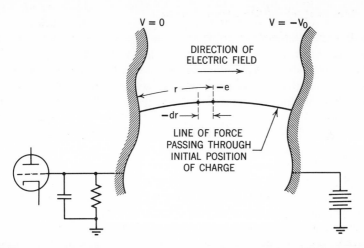

Fig. 11. Schematic picture of ionization chamber possessing axial symmetry. A charge $-e$ is liberated between the electrodes indicated by shading; initially the electrode at left is at ground potential and the one at right at a negative potential $-V_0$. The position of the charge in the electric field of the chamber is identified by the value of the coordinate r measured along the line of force passing through the location of the charge.

Energy conservation then requires that the work done by the electric field in displacing the charge $-e$ from r to $r - dr$ be equal to the change in the electrostatic energy stored in the chamber capacity:

$$(-e)X(-dr) = d(Q^2/2C) = (Q/C)\, dQ \cong V_0\, dQ \qquad (9)$$

where $Q = $ charge stored in the condenser ($Q \gg |e|$), $C = $ capacity of system, and $X = X(r) = $ electric field intensity. The current that will flow

---

* This is the usual mode of operation, the circuit element containing the low-frequency limiting time constant being placed at a later stage in the amplifier. For linear circuit elements, however, the location of the short time constant is not important, as far as the validity of the argument presented above is concerned.

in the external network as consequence of the displacement of the charge $-e$ through the distance $-dr$ is then given by

$$i = dQ/dt = e(X/V_0)\, dr/dt = -e(X/V_0)w \tag{10}$$

where $w = -dr/dt$ is the drift velocity of the charge $-e$. If the liberated charges are electrons and positive ions (of charge $-e$ and e, respectively), a current will flow which is the sum of the contributions of the motion of all the charges; that is, $i =$ output current $= i^+ + i^-$, where $i^+ = (e/V_0)\Sigma_\nu w_\nu^+ X_\nu^+$ and $i^- = -(e/V_0)\Sigma_\nu w_\nu^- X_\nu^-$, and we sum over all ions of both signs. (This argument follows closely the treatment of Bridge, Hazen, Rossi, and Williams.[82])

In a chamber filled with a purified gas in which no electron attachment takes place, the mobility of the free electrons is of the order of 1000 times as large as that of the positive ions, as we saw previously. As a consequence, the charge displaced through the chamber in time t namely, $Q(t) = \int_0^t i(t)\, dt$ increases very rapidly at first until all the electrons have been collected and then much more slowly until the positive ions have been collected. The voltage signal at the collector electrode as a function of time is

$$S(t) = Q(t)/C = (1/C)\int_0^t i(t)\, dt. \tag{11}$$

2. Electron collection time. Under certain conditions it is possible to derive simple expressions for the time T taken by an electron to drift from its point of liberation to the collector. We assume that the electron drifts along a line of force of the electric field in this process. Therefore, if we express the drift velocity as a function f of $X(r)/p$, it is possible to obtain T by direct integration of $w = -dr/dt = f(X/p)$:

$$T = -\int_{r_0}^{a} dr/f(X/p). \tag{12}$$

Here r_0 is the initial coordinate of the electron, as measured along a line of force, and a is the coordinate of the point at which the surface of the collector electrode intersects the line of force passing through the initial position of the ionization electron.

Almost all ionization chambers used in practice are parallel-plate chambers for which $X(r) = V_0/d = $ constant (where $d = $ separation of electrodes), cylindrical chambers consisting of two concentric cylindrical electrodes of radii a and b, respectively, for which $X(r) = [V_0/\log(b/a)]r^{-1}$, or spherical chambers having two concentric spherical electrodes of radii a and b, respectively, for which $X(r) = [V_0 ab/(b-a)]r^{-2}$. (Edge effects in the plane and cylindrical cases are not taken into account here; presumably these effects can be eliminated by use of suitable guard electrodes.) In general, then,

$$X(r) = kr^{-m} \tag{13}$$

where for the plane case $m = 0$ and $k = V_0/d$, for the cylindrical case $m = 1$ and $k = V_0/\log(b/a)$, and for the spherical case $m = 2$ and $k = V_0ab/(b - a)$.

In many gases the drift velocity can be expressed approximately in the following manner:

$$w = -dr/dt = \mu(X/p)^n = \mu(k/p)^n r^{-mn}. \tag{14}$$

Here μ is defined in such a way that w is expressed in cm/μsec when X/p is expressed in (volts/cm)/mm Hg. Thus in nitrogen $n = 1$ and $\mu = 0.45$ if X/p is reasonably large so that the constant term in the empirical equation for w can be neglected; in carbon dioxide $n = 1.5$ and $\mu = 0.41$. Integration then gives

$$t = \frac{1}{\mu}(p/k)^n \frac{1}{mn + 1}(r_0^{mn+1} - r^{mn+1}). \tag{15}$$

The collection time T defined by (12) is obtained by assigning to the coordinate r the value that it assumes at the surface of the collector electrode ($r = a$, where $a = 0$ for the plane parallel case):

$$T = \frac{1}{\mu}(p/k)^n \frac{1}{mn + 1}(r_0^{mn+1} - a^{mn+1}). \tag{16}$$

This is a general expression from which the collection time for various gases (differing in the constants μ and n, as described above) and for various geometrical conditions (defined by the values of m and k) can be computed. We can combine (15) and (16) to obtain

$$r(t) = r_0\{1 - [1 - (a/r_0)^{mn+1}]t/T\}^{1/(mn+1)}. \tag{17}$$

This equation describes the position of the electron as a function of time.

3. Pulse profiles in parallel-plate, spherical, and cylindrical ionization chambers. The shape of the voltage signal at the collector electrode generated by the motion of a single electron of charge e is given by (11), namely

$$S(t) = (1/C)\int_0^t i(t)\, dt$$

where $i(t) = (e/V_0)kr^{-m}(dr/dt)$ is the current that flows in the external network connecting the electrodes of the chamber. For the plane and spherical cases $i(t)$ can be written

$$i(t) = \frac{ek}{V_0}\left(\frac{1}{1-m}\right)\frac{d}{dt}(r^{1-m}).$$ (18)

whereas for the cylindrical case

$$i(t) = \frac{ek}{V_0}\frac{d}{dt}[\log r(t)].$$ (19)

Substitution of (18) in (11) then gives us for the parallel-plate chamber

$$S(t) = -(er_0/Cd)(t/T)$$ (20)

or the potential decreases linearly with time, reaching a minimum value of

$$S_0 = S(T) = -er_0/Cd$$ (21)

at $t = T$.

For a spherical chamber we have

$$S(t) = -\frac{e}{C}[ab/(b-a)]\frac{1}{r_0}\left\{\left[1 - \left(1 - \frac{a^{2n+1}}{r_0^{2n+1}}\right)t/T\right]^{-1/(2n+1)} - 1\right\}.$$ (22)

In this case the voltage signal decreases very slowly at first, but extremely rapidly later on, namely when $t \rightarrow T$. The minimum value of the potential is given by

$$S_0 = S(T) = -e/C[ab/(b-a)](1/a - 1/r_0).$$ (23)

For a cylindrical ionization chamber, the pulse profile is defined by

$$S(t) = \frac{e}{C\log(b/a)}[1/(n+1)]\log\{1 - [1 - (a/r_0)^{n+1}]t/T\}.$$ (24)

Here again the potential decreases slowly at first, but rapidly later, as the electron approaches the central wire (the collector electrode of radius a). The minimum value of the potential is reached when $t = T$ and is given by

$$S_0 = S(T) = -\frac{e\log(r_0/a)}{C\log(b/a)}.$$ (25)

The pulse profile in an actual case will not be caused by the motion of a single electron alone, but by the motion of a group of charges moving collectively under the influence of the electric field of the chamber. If the original particle track is short compared to the dimensions of the chamber, the free electrons will move together in a small cluster; the resulting profile will be similar to that observed for a single electron, except for the spreading out of the clusters by diffusion. If the track is quite long, however, the pulse profile will depend strongly on the orientation of the track in the chamber. We can derive its form in general by integrating over the charge distribution along the track.

4. Range-energy and specific ionization curves deduced from pulse profiles. As an illustration of the interpretation of the profile of a pulse due to electrons distributed initially along an extended particle track, we shall present the method of Sherr and Peterson.[100] Referring to Fig. 12,

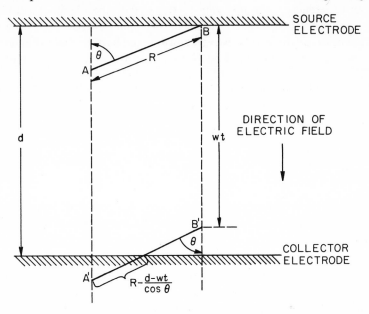

Fig. 12. Illustration of geometrical relations existing when a particle of range R is released from the surface layer of one electrode of a parallel-plate chamber. The liberated electrons drift toward the collector electrode with drift velocity w and are intercepted by this electrode.

consider that a fission fragment is ejected from a thin layer of uranium deposited on the "source electrode." In the process of stopping in the gas of the chamber, the fragment liberates positive ions and electrons along a track AB. Immediately, on formation of the track, these electrons begin to drift toward the collector electrode with drift velocity w. After a time $(d - R \cos \theta)/w$, where d = separation of electrodes, R = length of track, and θ = angle between direction of track and direction of electric field, the point of the track originally nearest the collector will be collected. From then on (and until the entire track has been collected), a constantly diminishing portion of the original track will contribute to the current flowing in the collector.

If we choose a system of rectangular coordinates with its origin at the tip of the track (point A) and its x-axis along the track, then the density of ionization along the track can be described by $\rho(x)$ so that the total charge along the track is given by

$$q = \int_0^R \rho(x)\, dx = \frac{e}{W} E(R) \tag{26}$$

where W = energy per ion pair in the gas of the chamber (assumed constant) and E = total energy of the particle that gave rise to the observed track. Prior to the arrival of any portion of the track at the collector electrode, the current induced by the motion of the charges is constant and has the value $i_0 = qw/d$, according to (10), where we set $X = V_0/d$.

At a time t later, a length $R - (d - wt)/\cos\theta$ (measured from tip) of the original track will have been collected. The current at that instant is given by

$$i(t) = \frac{w}{d} \int_{R-(d-wt)/\cos\theta}^R \rho(x)\, dx. \tag{27}$$

By setting $t' = t - (d - R\cos\theta)/w$, this can be written

$$i(t') = \frac{w}{d} \int_{wt'/\cos\theta}^R \rho(x)\, dx$$

so that

$$j(t') = i_0 - i(t') = \frac{w}{d} \int_0^{wt'/\cos\theta} \rho(x)\, dx = \frac{we}{Wd} E(wt'/\cos\theta). \tag{28}$$

Comparison with (26) now shows that if we plot the difference between the maximum current and the actual current against the time elapsed since the first instant of collection (which occurs when $t = (d - R\cos\theta)/w$), that is, if we plot $j(t')$ versus t', we obtain a curve that is identical with the range-energy curve for the ionizing particle (fission fragment), except for change of scale. These relationships are illustrated in Fig. 13. The derivative of $j(t')$ with respect to t' evidently will yield the specific ionization-energy relation in a similar manner.

5. Pulse spectrum due to an isotropic distribution of point charges. For an electron-pulse chamber, as we have seen, the signal amplitude depends on the location of the original disintegration track in the chamber as well as on the charge released. For a given spatial distribution of disintegration tracks, in general, a spectrum of pulse sizes results. This spectrum is particularly simple in the special case of disintegration tracks that are short compared to the dimensions of the chamber and that are distributed isotropically throughout its volume.

For the purpose of deriving expressions for this spectrum under various geometrical conditions, it is convenient to define the relative pulse height $\sigma = S_0 C/q$, where $S_0(r_0)$ is the absolute value of the actual voltage pulse arising from the collection of the charge $-q$, which was liberated at a distance $r_0 - a$ from the collector electrode (as measured along a line of force), and q/C is the maximum absolute value of the pulse which the charge $-q$ can possibly produce. Equations 21, 23, and 25 can then be summarized by the single equation

$$\sigma = V/V_0 \tag{29}$$

where $V = V(r_0)$ is the potential that corresponds to the equipotential surface $r = r_0$, and V_0 is the potential difference between the two electrodes.

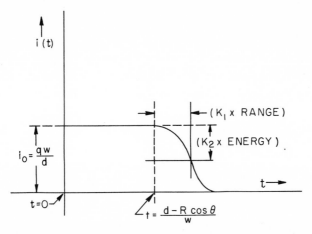

Fig. 13. Diagram illustrating the manner by which Sherr and Peterson[100] were able to deduce the range-energy curve for fission fragments from the profile of the current pulse produced when the electrons released in the ionization process drift toward the collector electrode, as shown in Fig. 12. Here $K_1 = (\cos \theta)/w$ and $K_2 = Wd/we$ are scaling factors.

Now for an isotropic distribution of point charges throughout the volume of the chamber, $dN = \beta \, dv$ charges originate from the volume element dv, where β = volume density of charges. The expression $dN/d\sigma$ can then be written

$$\frac{dN}{d\sigma} = \beta \left(\frac{dv/dr_0}{d\sigma/dr_0} \right). \tag{30}$$

But from (29) and (13), $d\sigma/dr_0 = V_0^{-1}(dV/dr_0) = V_0^{-1}kr_0^{-m}$, where k and m have the significance previously defined. Furthermore, we can set

$$dv/dr_0 = Kr_0^{m} \tag{31}$$

where K is a dimensional factor equal to the area of the plates for a parallel-plate chamber, equal to $2\pi \cdot$ (length of cylindrical electrodes) in the cylindrical case and to 4π in the spherical case. Substitution of these values in (30) then leads to

$$dN/d\sigma = \beta V_0 (K/k) r_0^{2m} \tag{32}$$

for the differential distribution of pulse heights corresponding to an isotropic distribution of short ionization tracks throughout the volume of an ionization chamber. From this result, an expression for $dN/d\sigma$ as a function of σ can be derived by eliminating r_0 with the help of (21), (23), and (25).

For the parallel-plate chamber we then obtain

$$dN/d\sigma = \beta Ad = N_0 \tag{33}$$

where $v = Ad =$ volume of chamber, $A =$ area of electrodes, and $N_0 = \beta v =$ total number of pulses. Thus the differential distribution is a uniform distribution, that is, pulses of all sizes up to the maximum pulse size q/C will occur in equal numbers. The integral distribution in this case is

$$N(\sigma) = \int_0^\sigma (dN/d\sigma)\, d\sigma = N_0 \sigma. \tag{34}$$

For a cylindrical chamber,

$$\frac{dN}{d\sigma} = \frac{2N_0 \log (b/a)}{(b/a)^2 - 1} (b/a)^{2\sigma} \tag{35}$$

where we set $v = \pi L(b^2 - a^2)$, $L =$ length of cylinders, and $N_0 = \beta v$. This distribution is sharply peaked at $\sigma = 1$ if $b \gg a$. Its width at half maximum is given by $\Delta\sigma_{1/2} = \log \sqrt{2}/\log (b/a)$, so that for $b/a = 400$, a common value, $\Delta\sigma_{1/2} = 0.059$. It is difficult to make $\Delta\sigma_{1/2}$ appreciably smaller than this value for a cylindrical chamber. The integral distribution is given by

$$N(\sigma) = N_0 \frac{(b/a)^{2\sigma} - 1}{(b/a)^2 - 1}. \tag{36}$$

In the spherical case, the differential distribution is

$$\frac{dN}{d\sigma} = 3N_0(a/b) \frac{(b/a) - 1}{(b/a)^3 - 1} [1 - \sigma(1 - a/b)]^{-4} \tag{37}$$

where $N_0 = \beta v = \beta(4/3)\pi(b^3 - a^3)$. This distribution has an exceedingly sharp maximum at $\sigma = 1$ if $b \gg a$, the width at half-maximum being $\Delta\sigma_{1/2} = (2^1 - 1)/(b/a)$, so that for $b/a = 10$, $\Delta\sigma_{1/2} = 0.019$. The corresponding integral distribution is

$$N(\sigma) = \frac{N_0}{(b/a)^3 - 1} \left\{ \frac{1}{[1 - \sigma(1 - a/b)]^3} - 1 \right\}. \tag{38}$$

In Fig. 14 the differential distributions obtained for the three geometries, with $b/a = 400$ for the cylindrical chamber and $b/a = 10$ for a spherical one, have been superimposed on a single graph. The distributions are normalized in such a way that all three curves represent the same total number of disintegrations. The superiority in resolution attained by use of a spherical arrangement is evident.

In Fig. 15 a comparison has been made between the predicted differential pulse spectrum for a cylindrical chamber with $b/a = 400$ and an experi-

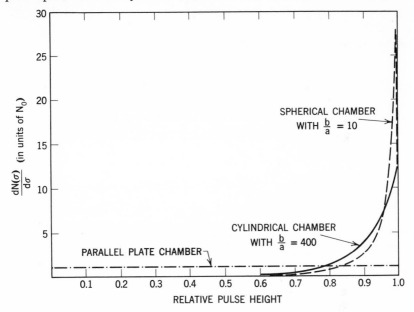

Fig. 14.   Predicted pulse spectra obtained from an isotropic distribution of point disintegration tracks for chamber operated with electron collection.

mentally observed spectrum obtained by bombarding a mixture of nitrogen and argon with slow neutrons. The electrical pulses in that case arise from the ionization produced by the disintegration products of the reaction $N^{14}(n, p)C^{14}$ in the gas of the chamber. The predicted curve (solid line) has been normalized to the actual total number of disintegrations and has been corrected for the finite "channel width" of the histogram into which the pulses were grouped. The experimental pulse spectrum was obtained by photographing the amplified electron pulses on an oscilloscope screen. Similar spectra have been recorded by Koontz and Hall.[101]

6. Pulse spectrum due to source on wall of chamber. In a commonly used arrangement, a source of particles is deposited as a thin

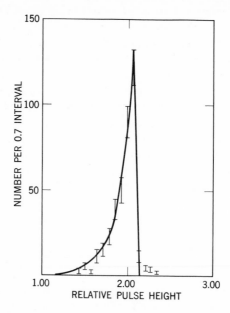

Fig. 15. Comparison between predicted pulse spectrum (solid line) and experimental spectrum (vertical bars) in a cylindrical ionization chamber operated with electron collection. The pulses are due to the reaction $N^{14}(n, p)C^{14}$; the gas mixture consisted of 1 atm argon + 1 atm N_2; $a = 5 \times 10^{-3}$ in., $b = 1$ in. From Franzen, Halpern, and Stephens.[43]

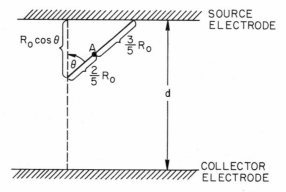

Fig. 16. Alpha-particle source located on one electrode of parallel-plate ionization chamber. The heavy line represents the track of an alpha particle, the point A being its center of charge.

film on one electrode of an ionization chamber. (The source could consist of a radioactive substance or of some substance in which disintegrations are produced by bombardment with neutrons or gamma-rays.) Let us assume that the chamber is of the parallel-plate type, as shown in Fig. 16. A homogeneous source of alpha particle of range R_0 (as measured in the gas of the chamber) is placed on one electrode, and we assume that $R_0 < d$. It is easy to show that the amplitude of the signal resulting from a particle track having a variable density of ionization along its length can be represented by the pulse from the center of charge of the track. If we assume a range-energy relation of the form $R = \alpha E^{3/2}$, the center of charge of a particle track is located at a distance $(2/5)R_0$ from the end of the track. Referring to Fig. 16, application of (21) leads to the conclusion that the pulse associated with a track making an angle θ with the field has an amplitude

$$S = (q/C)[1 - (3R_0/5d)\cos\theta] \tag{39}$$

where q = charge contained in track. For an isotropic angular distribution the probability that a given particle will be emitted at an angle between θ and $\theta + d\theta$ is $\sin\theta\, d\theta$, and the probability that a given track will have an amplitude between S and $S + dS$ is therefore $P(S)\, dS = \sin\theta\, d\theta = (d\cos\theta/dS)\, dS = C/q(5d/3R_0)\, dS$. Thus the probability for observing a given amplitude S is constant for values of S between $S = q/C$ (corresponding to $\theta = 90°$) and $S = (q/C)(1 - 3R_0/5d)$ and zero for all other values of S. This corresponds to a rectangular distribution of pulse heights.

In Fig. 17 a comparison has been made between the distribution just predicted and an experimental distribution obtained with alpha-particle sources deposited on one electrode of a parallel-plate chamber, as described by Rossi.[96] The predicted distributions, corrected for the finite channel width of the pulse-height analyser, are shown in solid outline. (In this case the finite channel width converts a rectangular distribution into a trapezoidal one.)

An analysis of the pulse-height distribution from a source located on the wall of a cylindrical ionization chamber has been presented by Rhodes, Franzen, and Stephens.[41]

7. Angular distribution of neutron recoils. The angular distribution of gas nuclei recoiling from collisions with fast neutrons can be inferred from the distribution in ionization pulses produced by the recoil nuclei. This is a method invented by Barschall and Kanner[102] and further applied by Coon and Barschall[103] and by Baldinger, Huber, and Proctor.[104]

Let us consider a collision between an incident neutron of mass m and initial kinetic energy E_0, and the nucleus of a gas atom of mass M. After the collision, the gas atom recoils at an angle θ to the direction of incidence of the neutron, where θ is measured in the center-of-mass system of the two colliding particles. We assume that the collision is an elastic one, and that the two colliding particles move with nonrelativistic velocities. In that case, the following relation holds between the cosine of the angle of recoil

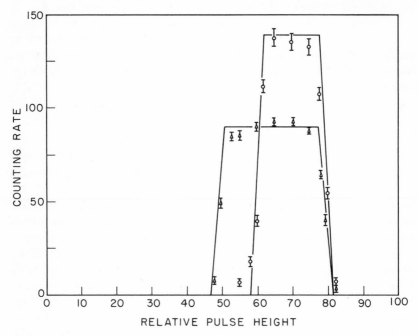

Fig. 17.   Pulse spectra obtained with source of alpha particles on one electrode of parallel-plate chamber, according to Rossi.[96]   The circles and triangles represent experimental points; solid lines are theoretical.

in the center-of-mass system and the kinetic energy E of the recoiling particle in the laboratory system:

$$E = E_{\max}\left(\frac{1 + \cos\theta}{2}\right). \tag{40}$$

Here $E_{\max}$ is the maximum energy that can be transferred in a head-on collision:

$$E_{\max} = \frac{4mM}{(m + M)^2}\, E_0. \tag{41}$$

Now let $P(E)\, dE$ be the probability that a given recoil particle will have a recoil energy between E and $E + dE$, while $\sigma(\theta)\, d\omega/4\pi$ is the probability that the struck particle will recoil into the element of solid angle $d\omega = 2\pi \sin\theta \, d\theta$, where $\sigma(\theta)$ is the differential scattering cross section in the center-of-mass system. Evidently

$$P(E) \, dE = \sigma(\theta)\tfrac{1}{2} \sin\theta \, d\theta. \tag{42}$$

But from (40) we infer that $dE = -E_{max}(\tfrac{1}{2} \sin\theta \, d\theta)$. Therefore,

$$\sigma(\theta) = -(1/E_{max})P(E), \tag{43}$$

which shows that the differential scattering cross section $\sigma(\theta)$ can be derived directly from the energy (and therefore the ionization pulse) distribution of the recoil nuclei.

8. The effect of amplifier response on pulse shape. The voltage pulses generated at the collector electrode of an ionization chamber are generally too small to be recorded or analyzed without further amplification. An amplifier of limited bandwidth will tend to distort the shape of the pulse profiles derived previously. It is necessary to employ a limited bandwidth in order to maintain a reasonable signal-to-noise ratio, to discriminate against low-frequency disturbances (hum, microphonics, flicker effect), and to prevent pile-up of two or more pulses that follow one another closely in time.

The subject of the effect of amplifier response on output-pulse shape is an extensive one and should properly be the subject of a separate chapter.* We shall therefore confine ourselves to a brief outline of the problem.

In the first place, it should be noted that a distortion of pulse shape by linear circuit elements will not affect the form of a pulse-height distribution if the input pulses differ from one another only in amplitude but have the same relative profile. In that case, the shape of the amplified output pulses may differ radically from the shape of the input pulses, but their amplitudes will nevertheless be proportional to the amplitudes of the corresponding input signals. Of principal importance, therefore, is not the alteration of the pulse shape itself, but a variation in the extent of this alteration from pulse to pulse caused by a changing pulse profile. For example, in the case of an ionization chamber with an isotropic distribution of disintegration tracks throughout its volume, the pulse profile is a function of the distance from the collector electrode at which the ionization track is formed, as can be seen by examination of (20), (22), and (24). A variation in pulse profile may also result from a varying spatial orientation of an extended track.

For a linear amplifier we can define a response function $\psi(t)$, where $\psi(t)$ is the output signal that results from placing unit charge instantaneously on the input grid of the amplifier at $t = 0$. The input grid is assumed to be

* See, for example, Chapter 4 of this book.

connected electrically to the collector electrode of the ionization chamber; $\psi(t - \tau)$ is therefore the output signal that corresponds to unit input at $t = \tau$, and $\psi(t - \tau)i(\tau) \, d\tau$ is the output that corresponds to an input charge $i(\tau) \, d\tau$ at $t = \tau$. The output signal generated by a current flow $i(\tau)$ in the input circuit is therefore given by the integral

$$S(t) = \int_{-\infty}^{t} i(\tau)\psi(t - \tau) \, d\tau. \tag{44}$$

The output signal $S(t)$ is thus a convolution of the input current pulse $i(\tau)$ and the response function of the amplifier $\psi(t)$.

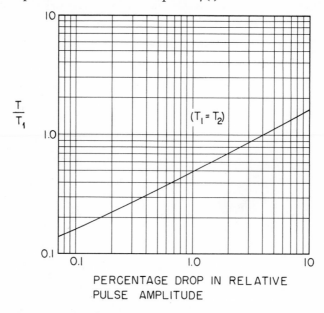

PERCENTAGE DROP IN RELATIVE
PULSE AMPLITUDE

Fig. 18.   Percentage drop in pulse amplitude for varying ratios of electron collection time T to amplifier time constant T_1. From Gillespie.[106]

A typical response function is represented by the *RC-RC* amplifier for which

$$\psi(t) = \frac{A}{C} \frac{T_1}{T_1 - T_2}(e^{-t/T_1} - e^{-t/T_2}) \tag{45}$$

where A is the gain of the amplifier and C is the input capacity of the system; T_1 and T_2 are the low- and high-frequency limiting time-constants of the amplifier, respectively. For maximum signal-to-noise ratio, it is frequently desirable to set $T_1 = T_2$, in which case

$$\psi(t) = (A/C)(t/T_1)e^{-t/T_1}. \tag{46}$$

Baldinger and Franzen[105] have made a general analysis of the effect of response functions on pulse amplitude. In particular, for a rectangular input current pulse of duration T and a response function of the type (46), they have shown that the output-pulse height will be proportional to $1 - (1/24)(T/T_1)^2$. If the variation in pulse height is to be restricted to less than 0.5% of the average pulse height, the common RC time constant of the amplifier T_1 should therefore be at least three times as long as the maximum electron collection time.

Gillespie[106] has analyzed the particular case of a triangular current pulse of duration T_1 (as observed, for example, in a parallel-plate ionization chamber) applied to the input of an amplifier with equal RC time constants. His predicted variation of the loss in relative pulse height with pulse duration is shown in Fig. 18.

D. Wall Effect

The term "wall effect" as used here refers to the effects of the loss of charge that occurs when particle tracks are intercepted by the walls or electrical boundaries of an ionization chamber. In general, ionization chambers are used either with a localized source of disintegration particles (usually deposited as a thin film on one of the electrodes) or with a gaseous source. Common examples of the first arrangement, in which particles are projected from a thin film into the interior of the gas volume, are alpha-particle sources located on one plate of a parallel-plate chamber (or on the outer electrode of a cylindrical chamber) and disintegration or recoil particles released by neutrons from a thin layer of a solid substance deposited on one electrode (as in fission chambers or in proton recoil neutron counters.) Under these circumstances, the wall effect, that is, the interception of tracks so that their whole charge is not collected, can be made negligible by the use of a parallel-plate chamber of appropriate dimensions. (However, in this case some particles of reduced energy that were back-scattered from the source holder will reach the sensitive volume of the chamber. This effect is far from negligible even for alpha particles, as pointed out by Crawford.[107] Moreover, for sufficiently small angles of emission relative to the surface of the source electrode, the energy loss due to passage through the solid material of the source always becomes appreciable. The magnitude of this effect depends on the thickness of the source.)

In the case of a gaseous source, ionization tracks are produced by the nuclei of the gas atoms or their disintegration products. Examples of such an arrangement are to be found in the photodisintegration experiments of Stetter and Jentschke,[108] and of Collie, Halban, and Wilson,[109] and the neutron recoil or disintegration experiments carried out by Barschall,[110] Koontz and Hall,[111] Franzen,[43] and Hanna.[40] Another example is found in the experiments of Curran et al.,[112] in which proportional counters were filled with a radioactive gas (tritium). In these cases the presence of wall effect has two consequences, namely distortion of the pulse-height distribution and alteration of the apparent total number of events, that is, change of the effective active volume of the ionization chamber.

In a parallel-plate chamber the electrodes are usually circular, and it is customary to surround the collector electrode by a "guard ring." This

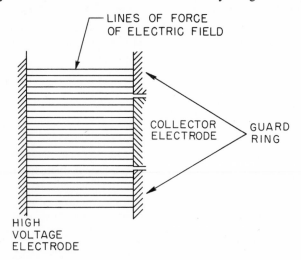

Fig. 19. Diagram illustrating the use of a guard ring with a parallel-plate chamber. The guard ring surrounds the circular electrode on all sides, and thus a uniform field is maintained within the sensitive volume of the chamber. (The horizontal lines indicate the direction of the lines of force.)

arrangement is illustrated by Fig. 19. The guard ring is insulated from the collector but is maintained at the same potential; it serves to define the sensitive volume of the chamber and to insure the uniformity of the electric field within this volume. Tracks originating within the gas of the chamber can then strike one of the electrodes, or they can spend part of their range within and part outside the sensitive volume. The boundaries of the sensitive volume are cylindrical if the electrodes are circular.

In a cylindrical chamber, tracks can be intercepted by the outer cylinder, or they can enter or leave sensitive region lengthwise. (The number of tracks intercepted by the central wire is ordinarily negligible.) Some attempt is usually made to define the sensitive volume of the chamber by means of cylindrical guard electrodes which surround the collector wire at its ends and which are maintained at the same potential as the wire. Complete avoidance of field distortion and accurate definition of the sensitive volume, however, can be achieved by use of Cockroft and Curran's double-guard electrode arrangement.[113] With this method (as illustrated in Fig. 20) it is possible to have plane boundaries for the ends of the sensitive volume. Thus in both parallel-plate and cylindrical chambers we deal with walls or boundaries that can be made plane and cylindrical.

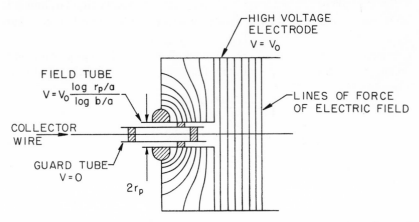

Fig. 20. Cockcroft and Curran's[113] arrangement for defining the sensitive volume of a cylindrical proportional counter. The diagram shows an axial section through the counter. The central cylindrical collector wire is surrounded by a guard cylinder which is at the same potential as the wire (in this case, zero or ground potential). Surrounding the guard tube is another cylindrical tube, the "field tube" of radius r_p, which is kept at a potential appropriate to its position in the cylindrical electric field as shown. (Here a = radius of wire, b = radius of high voltage electrode.)

In a spherical chamber, the outer electrode, which represents a spherical boundary, is usually the only important cause of wall effect.

I. Interception of particle track by plane boundary. An analysis of this case was first carried out by R. S. Wilson.[114] Consider a chamber having two infinite plane electrodes separated by a distance d, as shown in Fig. 21. A particle track originates at point A and is intercepted by one of the electrodes at point B. The probability that a given track will make an angle θ with the normal to the wall is given by $q(\theta)\,d\theta = 2\pi \sin\theta\,d\theta/4\pi = \sin\theta\,d\theta/2$. The probability that a track originating from a point at a distance x (where $x = R\cos\theta$) from the wall will travel a distance R before being intercepted is then $p_x(R)\,dR = q(\theta)\,d\theta$, so that $p_x(R)\,dR = (x/2R^2)\,dR$. Now, if R_0 represents the range of a particle in the gas of the chamber in the absence of wall effect, then

$$P(R)\,dR = \frac{dR}{2R^2}\int_0^R \frac{x\,dx}{R_0} = \frac{dR}{4R_0} \tag{47}$$

is the probability that a track originating at an arbitrary distance less than R_0 from the chamber wall will have a range R in the chamber. Thus the intercepted tracks are distributed uniformly in length, from zero length to the maximum range R_0. Of the tracks originating from the volume AR_0, where A is an area measured in a plane parallel to the wall of the chamber, a number equal to

$$nAR_0 \int_0^{R_0} P(R)\, dR = nAR_0/4 \qquad (48)$$

is intercepted by the wall (n = number of tracks originating from unit volume); this is one quarter of the total number nAR_0 of tracks capable of

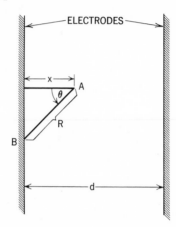

Fig. 21. Diagram illustrating the effect of the interception of a particle track by a plane boundary (in this case, the electrode of a parallel-plate ionization chamber). The particle originates at A and strikes the electrode at B, so that its range in the chamber is R.

being intercepted by virtue of the fact that they are formed at a distance less than the maximum particle range (R_0) from the wall.

From the range distribution it is possible to compute the distribution in energy spent within the chamber of particles that strike the walls. To do this analytically, we must assume an analytical range-energy relation, for example, an expression of the form $R_0 = \alpha E_0^{3/2}$, where E_0 = full particle energy. The distribution in energy of the intercepted particles is then given by $Q(E)\, dE = (3\alpha/8R_0)(E_0 - E)^{1/2}$. This distribution, in contrast to the track-length distribution, is not a uniform one.

2. Interception by spherical and cylindrical boundaries. The interception of a particle track formed near a spherical surface can be analyzed in an analogous manner. Figure 22 is intended to illustrate the geometrical relations existing in that case. The radius of the outer sphere is ρ, and r is the distance from the point of origin of the track (A) to the center of the spheres. Other distances and angles are as shown on the diagram. The probability that a track formed at r has an uninterrupted length R is again given by $p_r(R)\,dR = \sin\theta\,d\theta/2$. An elementary geometrical analysis for this case shows, however, that

$$\sin\theta\,d\theta = \frac{1}{2R^2}\left(\frac{\rho^2 + R^2 - r^2}{r}\right)dR. \tag{49}$$

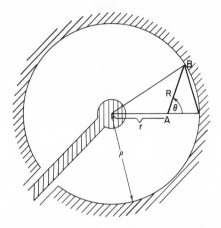

Fig. 22.   Effect of the interception of a particle track by a spherical surface (in this case, the outer electrode of a spherical ionization chamber).   The particle originates at A and strikes the wall at B.

The probability that an arbitrary track (among those which are capable, by virtue of their initial location, of reaching the outer sphere) has a length R independent of its starting point is then

$$P(R)\,dR = dR\int_{\rho - R}^{R} p_r(R)q(r)\,dr \tag{50}$$

where

$$q(r)\,dr = \frac{4\pi r^2\,dr}{(4/3)\pi[\rho^3 - (\rho - R_0)^3]}$$

is the probability that the track (whose origin must be at a distance less than R_0 from the outer sphere) will be formed at a distance r from the center of the concentric spheres.   On performing the integration, we obtain

$$P(R)\,dR = \left(\frac{3}{4}\right)\frac{\rho^2 - R^2/4}{3\rho^2 R_0 - 3\rho R_0^2 + R_0^3}\,dR. \tag{51}$$

If $R_0 \ll \rho$, this is again a uniform distribution $P(R)\,dR = dR/4R_0$, identical with the distribution obtained in the plane case, as we might expect. It is possible to generalize this observation by stating that the distribution in track lengths resulting from wall effect in a chamber of arbitrary geometry can be obtained very simply if the radius of curvature of all bounding surfaces is an order of magnitude larger than the maximum particle range. The distribution will then be a uniform one, the total number of intercepted tracks being one fourth the number of tracks that originate at a distance less than the maximum particle range from a boundary or wall.

By use of this principle, the wall-effect background due to interception by a cylindrical wall or boundary (where an exact calculation is very difficult) can be found very simply. It must be remembered, however, that in every case one must convert the track-length distribution into an energy distribution with the aid of a range-energy curve for the particle in question. An accurate analysis of the distortion of the pulse-height distribution by wall effect in a cylindrical geometry has been carried out by Skyrme, Tunnicliffe, and Ward.[115]

For monoenergetic electrons of low energy in proportional counters, wall effect does not usually have a serious effect on pulse-height resolution at the pressures commonly used. Electrons follow a tortuous path while stopping in the gas of the chamber; if any part of an electron track is intercepted by the wall, the probability that the ionization pulse associated with this track will fall outside the peak of the pulse-height distribution is rather high. West, Dawson, and Mandleberg[116] have observed no loss in resolution when as many as 50% of the monoenergetic electrons in the 40-to-85-kev range struck the wall of the counter.

At electron energies above 100 kev, electron ranges become quite large and wall effect becomes a more serious problem. Higher gas pressures may be used to diminish the electron range in the gas, but the necessary pressures rapidly become prohibitively large as the energy is increased. West and Rothwell[117] have eliminated the wall effect in a study of the gamma radiation from Br^{80} by locating a counter in a uniform magnetic field of 7000 gauss directed along the counter axis. Under these conditions, the gamma-ray peaks were clearly resolved, whereas they were not observable in the absence of the field. Newton, Rose, and Milsted[118] have used such an arrangement to measure gamma-ray energies up to 277 kev in a study of the radiations from Pu^{238}, Cm^{242}, and Cm^{243}; the resolution of the instrument was significantly better than that of a scintillation spectrometer.

It may be of interest to mention at this point that Stetter and Bothe[119] have succeeded in eliminating, to a large extent, the wall-effect background in a proportional counter by replacing the outer electrode of the counter by a grid wire structure. This is done in such a way that a particle track which ordinarily would be intercepted by a solid wall will now spend part of its range within the sensitive volume of the chamber and part of it outside this volume. The ionization produced outside the sensitive volume is collected on a separate electrode, thus giving rise to a signal in coincidence with the signal derived from the collector electrode within the chamber. The chamber signal is recorded only in the absence of a coincidence event of this kind. In this way only particles that spend their entire range within the chamber are recorded.

E. Ionization Chambers with Special Features

1. Grid ionization chambers. We have seen that in a chamber operated with electron collection the amplitude of the voltage pulse at the collector depends on the initial location of the disintegration track in the chamber. As a matter of fact, the pulse size is proportional to the fraction of the total potential difference (between the electrodes) that is traversed by the collected electrons, as can be seen by examining (21), (23), and (25). This can be understood on physical grounds by considering that the charge contributed by the electrons is diminished (during a time interval short compared to the collection time of the positive ions) by the image charge induced by the positive ions at the collector. In the case of cylindrical and particularly spherical chambers, this image charge is quite small if the positive ions are formed at an appreciable distance from the collector. In parallel-plate chambers, however, the image charge is directly proportional to the distance between collector and particle track. Thus the pulse spectra produced in such chambers with electron collection are wide rectangular distributions, as illustrated by Figs. 14 and 17.

One can eliminate the dependence of pulse height on location of track by introducing a grid between the two electrodes. This grid is kept at an intermediate potential and serves as an electrostatic shield between the collector electrode and the active volume of the chamber.

Grid chambers have been used extensively by Barschall,[103] Hanna,[40] and Gatti and Facchini.[44] A careful analysis of the operation of grid chambers has been carried out by Buneman, Cranshaw, and Harvey,[120] whose treatment is followed here.

Consider the parallel-plate chamber shown in Fig. 23. The grid (G) consists of parallel cylindrical wires of radius r; the centers of adjacent wires are separated by a distance g; the plane of the grid is at a distance b_0 from the collector electrode (B), and at a distance a_0 from the high-voltage electrode (A). A cloud of ions is formed at Q. In order to estimate the extent to which the collector electrode is shielded from the positive ions that remain at Q after the electrons have been collected, it is necessary to derive an expression for the configuration of the electric field. This can be done by using conformal representation of the electric field in terms of the complex function $W(z) = U(z) + iV(z)$, where $V = $ constant and $U = $ constant represent the equipotentials and lines of force of the electric field, respectively, $z = x + iy$, and x and y are rectangular coordinates defined

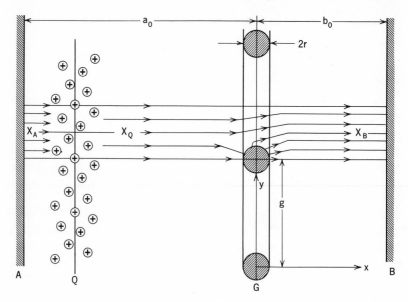

Fig. 23.   Diagram showing the geometrical arrangements of electrodes in a parallel-plate grid ionization chamber.   From Buneman, Cranshaw, and Harvey.[120]   The symbols are explained in the text.

by Fig. 23. (The origin of the coordinate system is at the center of one of the grid wires.) Buneman, Cranshaw, and Harvey[120] have derived the following expression for $W(z)$:

$$W(z) = iV_G + (\Delta X/2\pi) \, ig[\log \sinh (\pi z/g) - \log (\pi r/g)]$$

$$+ i\bar{X}z - i\bar{X}r^2(\pi/g) \coth (\pi z/g). \qquad (52)$$

Here V_G is the potential of the grid wires, $\Delta X = X_B - X_Q$ and $\bar{X} = (X_B + X_Q)/2$; X_B and X_Q are the electric fields between the grid wires and the collector, and between the ion cloud at Q and the grid wires, respectively, as indicated in Fig. 23. Similar functions describing the electric field about a wire grid between two plane electrodes have been derived by many authors, notably Maxwell,[121] Abraham,[122] and von Laue,[123] as well as a number of modern authors interested in the derivation of the amplification factor of triode vacuum tubes.[124,125]

The inefficiency of grid shielding, that is, the extent to which the grid wires fail to shield the collector electrode from the electric field in the ionization volume of the chamber, is defined by $\gamma = (dX_B/dX_Q)$ for constant potential difference $V_B - V_G$ between collector electrode and

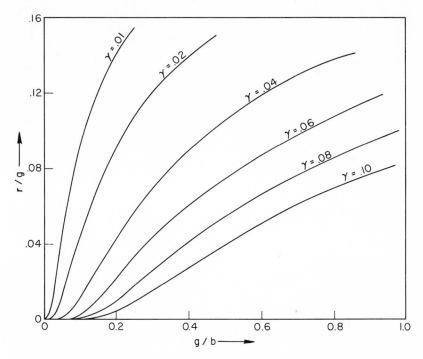

Fig. 24.   The relation between the ratio of grid radius to grid-wire separation (r/g) and the ratio of grid-wire separation to grid-collector spacing (g/b) for constant "inefficiency" γ. From Buneman, Cranshaw, and Harvey.[120]

grid; γ can be derived by differentiating $V_B - V_G = $ constant, with the result that

$$\gamma = (g/2\pi b) \log (g/2\pi r). \tag{53}$$

Here $b = b_0 - \pi(r^2/g)$. In Fig. 24 r/g is plotted as a function of g/b for constant γ. Evidently γ can be made as small as one wishes; that is, the shielding efficiency of the grid wires can be made arbitrarily large, by choosing an appropriate relation between the ratios g/b and r/g. However, the requirement for efficient shielding must be balanced against the condition that no lines of force terminate on the grid wires in order to minimize collection of electrons by the grid wires. This condition is approximately satisfied if

$$\frac{X_B}{X_A} = \frac{(V_B - V_G)/b_0}{(V_G - V_A)/a_0} \geq \frac{1 + 2\pi r/g}{1 - 2\pi r/g} \qquad (54)$$

where $V_B - V_G$ is the potential difference between grid and collector and $V_G - V_A$ is the potential difference between the grid and the high-voltage electrode. In Fig. 25 the proportion $1 - \omega$ of lines of force that end on the

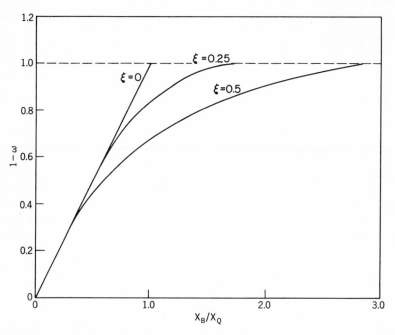

Fig. 25.   Relation between the proportion of the lines of force that end on the grid rather than on the collector $(1 - \omega)$ and the ratio of electric fields between grid and collector X_B and high voltage electrode and collector $(X_A = X_Q)$ for different values of $\xi = 2\pi r/g$. From Buneman, Cranshaw, and Harvey.[120]

collector electrodes rather than on the grid wires, where ω = fractional "grid loss," is plotted against the ratio X_B/X_Q for different values of the parameter $\xi = 2\pi r/g$. If, on this graph, X_B/X_Q (the ratio of the electric field between grid and collector to the field between high-voltage electrode and grid) is chosen so that $1 - \omega = 1$, that is, so that $\omega = 0$ for a given value of $\xi = 2\pi r/g$, (54) is satisfied, and no lines of force will end on the grid. Qualitatively, we can interpret (54) to mean that collection of electrons by the grid is avoided when the potential difference between the plane of the grid wires and the collector is much larger than this potential difference would be in the absence of the grid, a principle already known to Barschall.[103]

There is some question regarding the validity of the assumption that the collected electrons always follow the direction of the lines of force of the electric field as they drift toward the collector. One would expect that diffusion would cause a certain proportion of the electrons to deviate sufficiently from the lines of force to cause them to strike the grid wires, although condition (54) is strictly fulfilled. This effect would be most serious at high pressures and in pure rare gases (where the agitation energy and therefore the amount of electron diffusion is large).

Herwig, Miller, and Utterback[126] have made a detailed study in a variety of gases and gas mixtures of this and other effects encountered in the use of gridded parallel-plate chambers; among the effects not previously mentioned are gas multiplication about the grid structure and the variation of saturation characteristics.

2. High-pressure chambers. Ionization chambers can be operated successfully (that is, without excessive loss of pulse height) to pressures of the order of 100 atm if the gases used in the chamber are completely free of electronegative impurities. This has been demonstrated by Fulbright and Milton[127] and by Wilson, Collie, Halban, and their collaborators.[128] The requirements on purity in these cases are very severe; the consequent chemical problems are discussed later on; the influence of electron capture and columnar recombination was discussed earlier. Here we shall confine ourselves to a brief account of experimental work accomplished with high-pressure chambers.

Wilson, Collie, and Halban[128] have used cylindrical and spherical chambers made of a high tensile strength aluminum alloy, or of stainless steel, filled with deuterium to a pressure of the order of 35 atm. By this means, they made a new accurate determination[129] of the cross section for the photodisintegration of the deuteron by the gamma rays of Mg^{24} and ThC'', they studied the angular distribution of the neutron and proton emitted on photodisintegration of the deuteron by an analysis of the energy spectrum of the photoprotons,[130] and they discovered[131] a previously unknown gamma ray corresponding to an excited state of Mg^{24}, which is observed in the decay of Na^{24}.

Fulbright and Milton[127] used a chamber with an outer wall made of a mild steel forging. Inside this housing were two double chambers. Half of each chamber consisted of a central wire collector surrounded by a high-voltage electrode of rectangular cross section, one plane section of this electrode being common to both halves of the double chamber. A thin foil of aluminum on which radioactive sources could be deposited was mounted in the common plane. By operating the chamber with purified argon at very high pressures, the forbidden beta-ray spectra of Be^{10} and Cl^{36} were studied. By adding the pulses from the two halves of the chamber, backscattering of electrons from the source holder was eliminated as a source of energy spectrum distortion, and relatively thick sources could be used. The second double chamber, identical with the first, was used for calibration with a known spectrum.

F. Techniques

1. Gas purification. Frequent reference has been made to the fact that a high degree of purity is required for gases used in electron pulse chambers, particularly at high pressures. Of major importance in this connection is the removal of electronegative impurities such as O_2 and H_2O. It is also necessary, however, to consider the effect of non-electronegative impurities, such as N_2, H_2, and CO_2, on the operation of ionization chambers filled with one of the rare gases, as previously discussed.

ARGON. Klema and Allen[91] and Klema and Barschall[132] have purified argon by allowing it to circulate through heated calcium metal turnings.

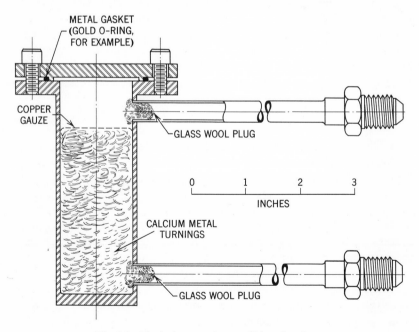

Fig. 26. Typical convection purifying chamber.

TABLE 4. TEMPERATURES AND FLOW RATES REQUIRED FOR THE REMOVAL OF OXYGEN AND THE REDUCTION OF NITROGEN CONCENTRATION TO LESS THAN 0.1% FROM ARGON, FOR VARIOUS HOT METAL PURIFIERS (AFTER GIBBS, SVEC, AND HARRINGTON[133]). WHERE HIGH FLOW RATES ARE INDICATED FOR OXYGEN, LOWER TEMPERATURES CAN BE USED AT LOWER FLOW RATES

	Oxygen		Nitrogen	
Metal	Temperature in ° C	Flow Rate in Liter/Min	Temperature in ° C	Flow Rate in Liter/Min
Barium	400	3.35	400	0.83
Calcium	650	3.75	650	0.83
90% Ca—10% Mg	475	0.83	500	0.83
Cerium	200	0.83	—	—
Brass (67% Cu—33% Zn)	600	4.20	—	—
Copper	600	5.10	—	—
Iron (94% Fe—3.5% C— 2.5% Si)	400*	0.83	—	—
Lanthanum	800	5.10	800	0.83
Magnesium	640	1.83	640	0.83
Thorium	800	5.10	800	1.83
Titanium	600	0.83	—	—
Uranium	200	1.83	900	0.83
Uranium	300	3.35	—	—
Zirconium	1000	3.35	1000	0.83

* CO_2 results from reaction.

The convection-current purifier used by these investigators consists of a metal chamber having a volume of the order of $\frac{1}{10}$ to $\frac{1}{20}$ of the ionization chamber to which it is attached with large diameter metal tubing. A typical purifier is shown in Fig. 26. The purifier is filled with calcium metal turnings that are outgassed in vacuum at a temperature higher than the final operating temperature. Typical outgassing and purification temperatures are 400 and 300° C, respectively, though it is now believed that this procedure does not remove nitrogen efficiently. Gibbs, Svec, and Harrington,[133] who have made a detailed study of many metallic getters, state that a temperature of 650° C is required for the reduction of nitrogen concentration below 0.1% by use of calcium turnings; nitrogen is less effectively removed at temperatures above 700° C. Recommended temperatures of operation for other metallic getters are listed in Table 4.

Argon can also be purified by fractional distillation at liquid nitrogen temperatures. In this case one makes use of the fact that the normal boiling point of argon ($-185.7°$ C) lies between the normal boiling points of oxygen ($-183.0°$ C) and nitrogen ($-195.8°$ C). The most volatile fraction will therefore contain an excess of nitrogen, whereas the least volatile fraction contains an excess of oxygen. In a multistage distillation process the middle fraction will concentrate argon at the expense of the other two gases. This procedure, incidentally, also automatically removes other impurities that have boiling points widely different from the boiling point of argon, such as hydrogen, neon, and helium, on the one hand, and carbon dioxide and water vapor, on the other hand.

TABLE 5. THE REACTION OF URANIUM METAL
WITH VARIOUS LABORATORY GASES

Gas	Temperature of Metal	Compound Formed
O_2	300° C	UO_2
N_2	600° C	U_2N_3
H_2O	600° C	$UO_2 + H_2$
Hydrocarbons	700° C	$UC + H_2$
CO_2	500° C	$CO + UO_2$
CO	750° C	$UC + UO_2$
H_2	250° C	UH_3 (Equilibrium dissociation pressure at this temperature is 5 mm Hg.)

After Newton.[135]

HELIUM. Helium may be handled in the same way as argon, but an even greater degree of purity is frequently required because of the pronounced effect of trace amounts of oxygen. The standard procedure for the production of very pure helium gas is passage through a liquid-nitrogen cooled charcoal trap.

HYDROGEN AND DEUTERIUM. These gases may be purified in a variety of ways. For many purposes, passage through liquid-nitrogen-cooled traps is adequate. Klema[134] purified mixtures of argon and hydrogen by circulating them through calcium hydride at 250° C. Newton[135] purified both inert gases and hydrogen (or deuterium) by circulation through heated uranium metal turnings. Uranium reacts with many gases and therefore is a very useful purification material, as can be seen by an inspection of Table 5. For the purification of the inert gases, Newton recommends passage through a quartz tube containing uranium turnings at 750 to 800° C. A particularly effective getter is spongy uranium, which is formed by thermal decomposition of uranium hydride (UH_3) under vacuum at 300 to 400° C. The spongy metal left behind is extremely reactive; it will react with all the gases listed in Table 5 at lower temperatures than those indicated, and it reacts with hydrogen (or deuterium) down to temperatures of the order of $-80°$ C.

For the purification of hydrogen, Newton recommends that uranium turnings be allowed to react with hydrogen gas at 250° C to form UH_3. In this process a large amount of heat is liberated, approximately 31,000 cal/mole. After the reaction is finished, the excess hydrogen is pumped off; in this process some UH_3 will decompose, since the dissociation pressure of UH_3 at this temperature is 5 mm Hg. The temperature is then raised to 400° C, and the flask containing the uranium compound is flushed several times (by pumping off the liberated gas). All further hydrogen removed by heating will be pure. Hydrogen can be removed at any desired pressure p_{mm} (in millimeters of Hg) by regulating the temperature in accordance with the relationship $\log p_{mm} = -(4500/T) + 0.28$. For deuterium, we have $\log p_{mm} = -(4500/T) + 9.43$. (Here T is the absolute temperature of the uranium metal turnings.)

A similar procedure has been used by English[76] for the purification of large quantities of hydrogen to be used with a high-pressure chamber. In his case the purifier through which the hydrogen was circulated by convection consisted of a stainless steel pipe, 2 in. in diameter, filled with 800 grams of clean uranium chips. The purifier was operated at 550 to 600° C for several weeks. During this time, the pulse height produced by Pu^{239} alpha particles in his ionization chamber, which had a total volume of 40 liters, gradually increased and finally reached a steady (saturation) value.

Stafford[136] filled a glass ionization chamber with extremely pure hydrogen by baking the chamber first in a vacuum and then sealing it off, its only remaining connection to the outside world being through a heatable palladium valve. The glass chamber was then placed in a pressure housing filled with hydrogen, which was admitted to the chamber through the palladium valve. Electron collection pulses were observed at 60 atm with this chamber. Nickel tubing can be substituted for the palladium valve.

Wilson, Halban, and collaborators[128] prepared pure deuterium by the following precedure. Dry sodium peroxide was dissolved in heavy water and put into an electrolytic cell. The oxygen produced by the electrolysis was evacuated through two liquid nitrogen traps to the open air. The liberated deuterium gas passed successively through a red-hot platinum spiral and a liquid nitrogen trap and was then adsorbed in activated charcoal at liquid nitrogen temperature until the pressure in the charcoal bottle rose to 1 atm. At that moment a second charcoal bottle was connected to the first and allowed to come to equilibrium with it. Pure deuterium gas can then be removed from the second bottle at will by raising its temperature. The only impurity that one might expect in the gas desorbed from the second bottle is CD_4.

METHANE. For most applications, methane, ethylene, and cyclopropane can be obtained in sufficient purity for use in ionization chambers by a fractional distillation procedure similar to that described for argon. The purification of ethylene is difficult and requires many distillation cycles. Beghian and Halban[137] have described a procedure for use in high-pressure chambers. A fractionating column consisting of 30 equivalent plates was employed; the column was immersed in liquid oxygen, and methane was distilled off at the temperature of liquid oxygen. Saturation pulses due to recoil protons from D-D neutrons were observed at a potential of 15,000 volts in a cylindrical chamber filled with methane purified in this manner to a pressure of 35 atm.

NITROGEN. Nitrogen can be freed of electronegative impurities very satisfactorily by convection circulation through a purifier containing calcium metal turnings, a procedure described by Klema and Allen[91] and Franzen.[43] At temperatures of 300° C and below, the reaction between nitrogen and calcium to form calcium nitride proceeds at a negligible rate, whereas water and oxygen will react vigorously. Uranium turnings are also quite effective at a temperature of 200° C, as are brass, copper, and cerium turnings at the temperatures indicated in Table 4.

CARBON DIOXIDE. Relatively pure carbon dioxide may be prepared by freezing the gas in a liquid nitrogen cooled trap containing gauze or copper turnings to prevent packing and then pumping on it. Allen and Rossi[138] have successfully purified CO_2 by circulating it through a calcium metal purifier at 140° C.

BORON TRIFLUORIDE. Commercial BF_3 probably contains O_2, SO_2, HF, and SiF_4 (from the reaction of HF with glass). In view of the fact that the purification procedures commonly used are not very refined, it has not been definitely established whether BF_3 itself has an appreciable electron attachment probability or whether the electron capture that is always observed in practice is due to residual electronegative impurities. The purification procedures described below are sufficiently good, however, to make it possible to obtain large electron pulses from alpha particles released in the $B^{10}(n, \alpha)Li^7$ reaction in ionization chambers and proportional counters filled with BF_3 to relatively low pressures (of the order of 1 atm).

Bistline's procedure[75] consists of allowing commercial BF_3 to react with dimethyl ether to form a liquid complex that removes SiF_4. The liquid complex is combined with calcium fluoride to form a calcium fluoroborate complex, which is then outgassed at 150° C in a small oven. The evolved gas is passed through fused outgassed sodium fluoride (to remove HF) and is frozen in a liquid air trap. A vacuum of the order of 10^{-5} mm Hg is then maintained over the frozen BF_3 for some time (to remove oxygen). The resulting material can be used to fill an ionization chamber to any desired pressure.

Fowler and Tunnicliffe's[139] method of purification is similar. These authors have discovered a number of surprising "aging" effects, as a result of which the amount of electron capture observed with a BF_3 chamber appears to diminish with time. The exact mechanism responsible for these effects is not understood.

2. Remark on construction techniques. Nearly all chambers described in the literature are of one of the following types:

(a) Parallel-plate chambers
(b) Parallel-plate chambers with grid
(c) Cylindrical chambers
(d) Spherical chambers

Parallel-plate chambers without grid are usually used with electron collection only when the source of particles to be detected is a thin film of a solid material deposited on one of the electrodes. Under these conditions, as we have seen, a rectangular distribution in pulse sizes is obtained, the width of which depends on the ratio of the range of the emitted particles to the depth of the chamber. The precise method of construction adopted for this type of chamber depends on the purpose for which it is intended to be used. Usually the electrodes are circular metal plates, the collector electrode being surrounded by a guard ring, as described previously. It is also customary to make the spacing between the electrodes much less than their diameter in order to minimize edge effects. A typical assembly consists of two parallel metal plates held in position by insulators that are surrounded by a cylindrical housing. Electrical leads are brought in through Kovar glass or Kovar porcelain lead-throughs. The addition of a support for the grid wires in grid chambers presents no special difficulty.

The construction of cylindrical electron pulse chambers presents special problems, in view of the requirement that the central electrode (wire) be tight, uniform in radius, concentric with the outer cylinder, and usually shielded by guard electrodes at each end. The central wire may be made of tungsten (as used by Wilson et al.[128]), platinum (Koontz and Hall[111]), or Kovar metal wire (Franzen et al.[43]). The advantage of a tungsten wire is that it can be heated to a high temperature in a vacuum in order to remove

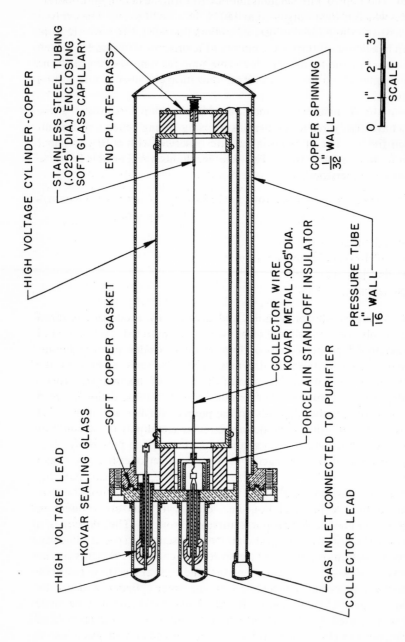

Fig. 27. Cylindrical ionization chamber constructed at the University of Pennsylvania in 1949 for the study of slow neutron disintegrations. Typical constructional features are pointed out.

spurious materials deposited on its surface and the fact that its alignment can be checked by x-ray examination of the assembly, as described by Wilson.[128] However, tungsten is not easy to handle, and kinks are very difficult to remove. A typical assembly of a cylindrical chamber is shown in Fig. 27. (This is a chamber constructed at the University of Pennsylvania in 1949.) Worthy of note are the use of porcelain stand-off insulators and the use of separate high-voltage and pressure-housing cylinders. It is customary to use lead, soft copper, or gold wire gaskets to seal removable flanges to the body of the chamber in order to avoid contamination of the chamber gases by the use of rubber gaskets. Hanna[40] recommends a gasket made of lead alloyed with 1% tin; this alloy is reputed to "creep" much less than pure lead. He also points out the desirability of using long, high-tensile-strength bolts to compress the gasket. For such bolts, the extension for a given force on the gasket is greater than for short thick bolts, so that creep of the gasket material will not lead to loss of gasket compression. Joints between metal parts of the chamber can be made with silver solder or with special alloy solders having somewhat lower melting points. Wilson[128] recommends a silver-tin alloy solder having a melting point of $300°$ C. The use of soft solder makes it difficult to heat the chamber to the temperature required for adequate outgassing.

Guard tubing may be made of hypodermic needle tubing, fine Kovar tubing, or platinized glass capillaries.

The design of a spherical ionization chamber is illustrated by Fig. 28. This is a chamber used by Manley, Agnew, Barschall, and collaborators,[140] and it illustrates the method of making electrical connection with, and of providing support for, the central collector electrode. Other types of spherical chambers have been described by Wilson.[128]

In neutron and gamma-ray experiments it is frequently desirable to use as little material for the housing of the chamber as possible. In this case, a high-tensile-strength aluminum alloy has advantages over other metals. However, copper, brass, and stainless steel housings are also frequently used, depending on the intended application.

Glass, porcelain, teflon, fluorothene, and polystyrene are satisfactory insulating materials. An excellent discussion of the relative merits of different insulating materials has been presented by Glass.[141] Teflon can be machined, but it has a tendency to "flow" under compression (as observed by Fulbright[127]). Fluorothene has better mechanical properties than teflon and is not so subject to this objection; it requires more compression when used as a gasket. If porcelain stand-offs are used, vents must be provided for dead-end screw holes. Careful cleaning of all surfaces before assembly is essential. This is usually accomplished by immersion in dilute acids (chromic, nitric, or hydrochloric), followed by thorough rinsing with distilled water and acetone or other pure organic solvents. (However, rinsing with carbon tetrachloride is bad because of the absorption of this material on the walls. Silver solder flux also must be removed very thoroughly.)

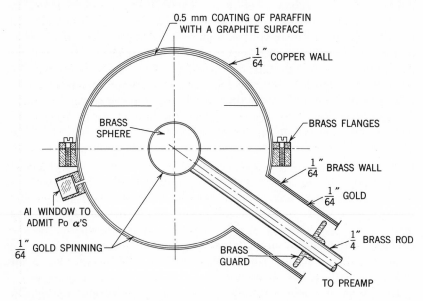

Fig. 28.   Spherical ionization chamber described by Manley, Agnew, et al.[140] This chamber was used as a neutron recoil chamber and illustrates constructional features.

G. Proportional Counters

A proportional counter differs from an ionization chamber in that the intensity of the electrical field in some part of the active volume of a proportional counter is large enough to cause the primary ionization electrons to produce secondary ionization. The most intense field is maintained in the vicinity of the collector electrode itself (the central wire of small diameter in the case of a cylindrical counter). It is here that each electron coming from the ionization track is able to acquire, between successive collisions with gas molecules, an energy equal to or larger than the ionization potential of the gas atoms. A small avalanche is generated as the secondary electrons in turn are accelerated toward the collector, producing further ionization.

The counter is strictly a "proportional" counter only over a limited range of applied potential. The multiplication process must be such that the interaction between avalanches produced by individual primary electrons is small; in that case, the charge finally collected is equal to the sum of the charges contained in the individual avalanches and is proportional to the primary ionization.

For a cylindrical or spherical proportional counter, the voltage pulse observed at the collector electrode is caused largely by the motion away from the collector of positive ions created in the avalanche, and only a minor contribution is made by the electrons released in the multiplication process. This state of affairs is a result of the fact that the electrons liberated near the central electrode traverse only a small fraction of the potential difference maintained between the electrodes of the chamber; the positive ions, on the other hand, travel through almost all of chamber potential. In this respect, the signal obtained from a proportional counter differs basically from an ionization chamber signal, which is primarily produced by electron motion.

I. Pulse profile in a proportional counter. We saw earlier that the drift velocity of a positive ion in an electric field $X(r)$ can be expressed as $w = dr/dt = \mu(X/p)$, where μ is the mobility of the ion, a quantity that is characteristic of the particular type of ion and the nature of the gas filling, and p is the gas pressure; r is a coordinate measured radially outward from the axis of the concentric cylindrical electrodes in a cylindrical counter and from the center of the concentric spherical electrodes in a spherical counter. Setting $X(r) = kr^{-m}$, where $k = V_0/\log(b/a)$ and $m = 1$ for a cylindrical counter and $k = abV_0/(b - a)$ and $m = 2$ for a spherical counter, as in (13), we obtain the following expression for the collection time of a positive ion which originates at $r = a$ (the surface of the collector electrode) and is collected by the negative high-voltage electrode ($r = b$):

$$T = \frac{p}{\mu k(m + 1)} (b^{m+1} - a^{m+1}). \tag{55}$$

For a cylindrical counter, we then have

$$T \cong \frac{p \log(b/a)}{2\mu V_0} b^2 \tag{56}$$

if $b \gg a$, which is true in all practical cases. This collection time is of the order of several hundred to a few thousand microseconds, depending on the dimensions and operating conditions of the counter and the nature of the gas filling. The equation corresponding to (17), which expresses the position of the positive ion as a function of time, is then, in general,

$$r(t) = a\left\{1 + \left[\left(\frac{b}{a}\right)^{m+1} - 1\right]\frac{t}{T}\right\}^{1/(m+1)} \tag{57}$$

The signal at the collector electrode of a cylindrical counter caused by the motion of a positive charge q away from the collector can then be expressed by analogy with (24):

$$S(t) = - \frac{q}{2C \log (b/a)} \log \left\{ 1 + \left[\left(\frac{b}{a} \right)^2 - 1 \right] \frac{t}{T} \right\}. \tag{58}$$

When $b \gg a$, this becomes

$$S(t) \simeq - \frac{q}{2C \log (b/a)} \log \left(1 + \frac{2V_0 \mu t}{pa^2 \log (b/a)} \right) \tag{59}$$

where we have made use of (56); C is the electrostatic capacity of the counter.

The absolute value of the negative signal represented by these equations rises very rapidly at first but much more slowly as t approaches T. The signal reaches approximately one half its final amplitude (q/C) at a time $t = (a/b)T$. For $a/b = 10^{-3}$, a common value, this would be one-thousandth of the collection time of the positive ion defined by (56). For this reason, despite the small mobility of positive ions, proportional counters can be used with fast amplifiers which reproduce the initial sharp rise of the (absolute value) of the voltage signal but which do not respond to the later slow change of potential that is caused by the motion of the positive ions through the weak electric field in the outer regions of the active volume of the counter. Similar remarks apply to spherical counters, for which the effect of the initial fast rise of the signal is even more marked than in the case just described.

The pulse profile given by (59) represents the effect of the motion of the charge cloud produced by a single primary ionization electron. For a practical case in which N_0 ion pairs are formed in the original ionizing event along an extended particle track in the counter, the time required for the ionization electrons to drift from their place of origin to the vicinity of the collector electrode, where the multiplication process will then take place, is different for electrons coming from different portions of the track. This variation in electron drift time depends, of course, on the orientation of the original ionization track with respect to the collector electrode. Thus, for a track that is formed in a direction perpendicular to the axis of a cylindrical collector electrode, ionization electrons from the farthest portion of the track will arrive in the multiplication region appreciably later than electrons released in the near portion of the track. The signal actually observed will then consist of a superposition of many positive ion avalanche signals which begin at various times, corresponding to the spread in electron arrival times. As a result, the total signal will, in general, tend to have a more gradual rise than that indicated by (59).

2. Statistics of proportional multiplication. The fluctuations in total ionization and in the number of ion pairs liberated in a short length of track have already been considered. In the case of a proportional counter an additional source of fluctuation in ionization is represented by statistical variations in the size of the avalanches produced by individual electrons near the collector electrode. A theory has been developed by Snyder[142] and others to predict the nature of this fluctuation. Let us assume that the probability of electron duplication per unit potential interval traversed by the electron is λ. If there is one particle at $x = 0$, then the probability of having one particle at x is $P_1(x)$, and the probability of having one particle at $x + dx$ is $P_1(x + dx) = P_1(x)(1 - \lambda\, dx)$. The probability of having two particles at $x + dx$ is $P_2(x + dx) = P_1(x)\lambda\, dx + P_2(x)(1 - 2\lambda\, dx)$. In general, we have $dP_R/dx = \lambda(R - 1)P_{R-1}(x) - \lambda R P_R(x)$. This is a differential-difference equation for $P_R(x)$, which can be solved by induction to give

$$P_N(x) = e^{-\lambda x}(1 - e^{-\lambda x})^{N-1} \tag{60}$$

for the probability of having N particles at x. The mean number of particles is $\bar{N} = e^{\lambda x}$, so that we can write

$$P_{N,\bar{N}} = \frac{1}{\bar{N}}\left[1 - \left(\frac{1}{\bar{N}}\right)\right]^{N-1} \tag{61}$$

for the probability distribution about the mean number $\bar{N}$. If $\bar{N} \gg 1$, this can be written

$$P_{N,\bar{N}} \cong (e^{-N/\bar{N}})/\bar{N}. \tag{62}$$

Now let us assume that there are M particles present at $x = 0$, instead of one, as assumed previously. The probability for having a total number $\nu = N + M$ particles at x is given by

$$P_\nu(x) = q_M\left[\frac{(\nu - 1)!}{(M - 1)!\ (\nu - M)!}\, e^{-\lambda M x}(1 - e^{-\lambda x})^{\nu - M}\right] \tag{63}$$

where q_M is the probability of having M particles initially. From this distribution, it follows that

$$\frac{\overline{\nu^2} - \bar{\nu}^2}{\bar{\nu}^2} = \frac{\overline{M^2} - \bar{M}^2}{\bar{M}^2} + \frac{1}{\bar{M}} - \frac{1}{\bar{\nu}} \tag{64}$$

is the relative mean square fluctuation (or the relative variance) in the total number of particles ν arriving at the collector wire. Usually $\bar{\nu}$ is such a large number, compared to the mean of the initial number of particles $\bar{M}$, that the last term in (64) can be neglected. This means that the relative spread in the final number of particles is independent of the multiplication factor v/M. The relative variance in the final number of particles is then the sum of the relative variance in the original number [namely $(\overline{M^2} - \bar{M}^2)/\bar{M}^2$] and a term $1/\bar{M}$, which is contributed by the multiplication process.

If the distribution in the original number of particles is characterized by a Poisson distribution, so that

$$\frac{\overline{M^2} - \bar{M}^2}{\bar{M}^2} = \frac{1}{\bar{M}}, \qquad \text{then} \qquad \frac{\overline{v^2} - \bar{v}^2}{\bar{v}^2} = \frac{2}{\bar{M}}, \qquad (65)$$

indicating that the multiplication process has the effect of doubling the relative variance of the original number of ions.

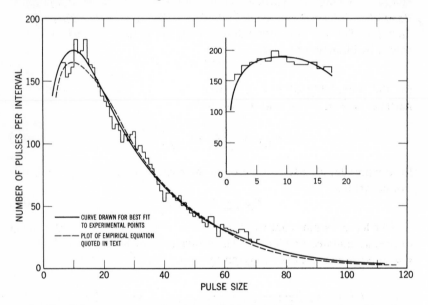

Fig. 29.   Pulse spectrum produced by individual photoelectrons released by ultra-violet light in a quartz-walled proportional counter filled with a mixture of argon and methane. The insert shows the same curve analyzed at higher gain. From Curran, Angus and Cockcroft.[11]

Ordinarily, it is not possible to separate experimentally the contributions to the relative variance of v caused by the fluctuation in the initial number of particles and the fluctuation brought about by the multiplication process when M is larger than unity. Curran[11] has succeeded in avoiding this difficulty by studying the distribution in pulse size resulting from the release of single photoelectrons by ultraviolet light. Figure 29 illustrates the spectrum of pulses observed under these conditions. The total gas gain for this experiment was about 1.4×10^5, and the counter was filled with a mixture of argon and methane. Surprisingly enough, the distribution seems to have a definite maximum, in contrast to the distribution predicted by (62), which decreases monotonically. Curran has fitted the pulse-height distribution of Fig. 29 by a distribution of the form $N^{1/2} e^{-N}$. A plot of this distribution, properly normalized, is superimposed as a dotted line on the graph of Fig. 29. From this equation, we would predict that $(\overline{N^2} - \bar{N}^2)/\bar{N}^2 = 0.68$, whereas (62) predicts that $(\overline{N^2} - \bar{N}^2)/\bar{N}^2 = 1.00$.

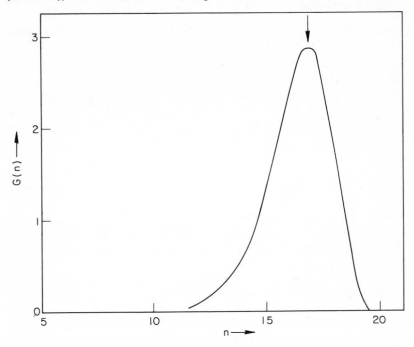

Fig. 30. Distribution in the number of ionizing collisions experienced by a single electron when traveling toward the central wire in a gas-filled proportional counter. From Curran, Angus, and Cockcroft.[11]

Curran also obtained a distribution in the number of ionizing collisions experienced by a single photoelectron on its way to the collector. This was done by using the empirical graph of Fig. 29 and assuming that the final number of particles is equal to 2^n, where n is the number of ionizing collisions. The resulting distribution in n (shown in Fig. 30) is narrowly centered about a maximum value at $n = 17$.

According to Fano,[10] for a particle that spends its entire energy in ionization, the fluctuation in the number of ion pairs is considerably smaller than would be expected from a Poisson distribution. In fact, he predicts that

$$\frac{1}{3\bar{M}} < \frac{\overline{M^2} - \bar{M}^2}{\bar{M}^2} < \frac{1}{2\bar{M}}. \tag{66}$$

If we now combine Curran's value of $(\overline{N^2} - \bar{N}^2)/\bar{N}^2 = 0.68$ with Fano's most optimistic estimate of $(\overline{M^2} - \bar{M}^2)/\bar{M}^2 = 1/3\bar{M}$ for M initial electrons, we obtain for the relative variance in the size of the final avalanche due to M original electrons

$$\frac{\overline{\nu^2} - \bar{\nu}^2}{\bar{\nu}^2} = \frac{1}{\bar{M}}, \tag{67}$$

which is just half as large as the value given by (65).

Bisi and Zappa[143] have investigated the statistical spread in pulse size in a proportional counter by using a variety of radioactive sources with energies between 2 and 70 kev. Except in the very low-energy region (0.25 kev), their data, with that of Hanna, Kirkwood, and Pontecorvo,[12] West,[144] and Newton and Rose (as quoted by West[145]), may be fitted nicely by the relation

$$\frac{\overline{\nu^2} - \bar{\nu}^2}{\bar{\nu}^2} = \frac{0.019}{E^{0.79}} \tag{68}$$

for the relative variance in terms of the energy E in kev dissipated by the stopped particle in the original track. If we use an average value of $W = E/\bar{M} \cong 27$ ev/ion pair for the gases used by these investigators, then (68) can be written

$$\frac{\overline{\nu^2} - \bar{\nu}^2}{\bar{\nu}^2} = \frac{0.34}{(\bar{M})^{0.8}}. \tag{69}$$

This experimentally measured relative variance should be compared with (67). Measurements at higher energies generally indicate a larger second moment of the statistical distribution than indicated by (69).

A general treatment of the statistics of multiplication processes based on the application of generating functions has been developed by O. R. Frisch (quoted by West[145]). On the basis of his treatment, which requires fewer specific assumptions than those used in the foregoing derivation, Frisch has derived an expression for the variance of the final number of multiplied particles identical with (64).

In addition to fluctuations in the number of ionization electrons and fluctuations due to the multiplication process, other factors contribute to the resolution of a proportional-counter spectrometer. Amplifier noise, track orientation, variation in diameter and positioning of the center wire, and attachment due to electronegative impurities may contribute to lack of resolution. With a properly designed proportional-counter spectrometer, however, a pulse-height resolution may be obtained for analysis of low-energy radiation, decidedly superior to the resolution obtainable with a scintillation spectrometer. This improvement in resolution is primarily a consequence of the·large number of primary ionization electrons in the proportional counter, as compared to the number of photoelectrons released from the photocathode of a photomultiplier, for an event of a specified energy.

3. Proportionality and calibration. Of considerable interest is the question of the operating range of proportional counters, that is, the range of applied potential over which the output pulse size is indeed proportional to the primary ionization. For practical reasons, it is usually desirable to operate a proportional counter with a multiplication factor not smaller than 10. When the multiplication factor is less than this value, the fluctuations in avalanche size previously discussed may have a significant effect on the signal-to-noise ratio, and there is no longer any particular advantage to be gained by operation in the proportional region.

As far as an upper limit on multiplication factor is concerned, Hanna, Kirkwood, and Pontecorvo[12] observed that the output pulse size ceases to be proportional to initial ionization when the absolute amplitude of the output voltage pulse exceeds a certain critical value S_c. In other words, the total amount of charge released in the multiplication process must not exceed $q_c = CS_c$, where C is the electrostatic capacity of the counter (including the input capacity of the amplifier). This condition is most conveniently expressed in terms of an energy E_c (expressed in electron volts) defined by $E_c = q_c W/e = CS_c W/e$, where W is the energy per ion pair in the counter gas and e is the electronic charge. E_c represents the energy that an energetic primary particle would have to dissipate in the gas of the counter operated without proportional multiplication (i.e., in the ionization chamber region) in order to liberate a total ionization charge equal to the critical value q_c. For the counter used by Hanna et al., $E_c = 10^8$ ev. From this criterion, one would then deduce an upper limit on the multiplication factor $A_c = E_c/E$ inversely proportional to the energy E dissipated in the primary ionizing event.

From a physical point of view, this explanation is very satisfactory. The upper bound on the total charge q_c released in the avalanche can be interpreted as representing a charge the size of which begins to approach the charge per unit length stored in the electrostatic capacity per unit length C_L of the counter. For a counter of the dimensions used by Hanna et al., $(b/a) = 500$, so that $C_L \sim 10^{-13}$ farad. (b and a are the radii of the outer and inner cylindrical electrodes, respectively.) With an applied potential of 1000 volts, the stored charge per unit length will then be of the order of 10^{-10} coulomb. On the other hand, for $E_c = 10^8$ ev, the limiting total number of ions released is E_c/W, corresponding to a total ionization charge of $eE_c/W \cong 5 \times 10^{-13}$ coulomb, or about $\frac{1}{200}$ of the stored charge, if we set $W = 30$ ev/ion pair. When the ionization begins to be a measurable fraction of the stored charge per unit length, the presence of the avalanche would be expected to produce a modification in the intensity of the local electric field, that is, space-charge saturation should set in, as actually observed.

Another important question in the operation of proportional counters relates to the problem of calibration. A proportional counter is not an absolute instrument in the sense that an ionization chamber may be, and calibration is therefore necessary. Of particular interest is a method of calibration applicable to the study of low-energy events. It is in the low-energy region, consisting of ionizing events in which an energy of less than about 100 kev is dissipated in the counter gas, that proportional counters have found the most characteristic and significant application in recent years. This is discussed in Sec. 4.

For events in this region of energy, photoelectrons released in the counter gas by characteristic x rays provide the most accurate and convenient method of calibration. The x rays may be fluorescent, emitted by thin metal foils and allowed to enter the active volume of the counter through a thin window, as in the experiments of Curran, Angus, and Cockcroft.[28] Hanna, Kirkwood, and Pontecorvo[12] used x rays from a crystal spectrometer. Insch[146] employed a source of In[114*], which emits gamma rays from an isomeric state at 24.1 kev, together with Zr and Cu fluorescent scattering foils, which in turn provided him with characteristic K x-ray lines at 15.7 and 8.05 kev.

A thin source of x rays consisting of an isotope undergoing K-capture provides a particularly convenient method of calibration. An assortment of isotopes with suitable half-lives and covering a range of energies is now available. Rothwell and West[147] and Beling, Newton, and Rose[148] have employed sources including such isotopes as Cr[51], Fe[55], Zn[65], Ge[71], Se[75], Pd[103], Cd[109], Sn[113], Gd[153], Yb[169], and Os[185], covering the energy range from 5 to 70 kev. Kirkwood, Pontecorvo, and Hanna[149] have used a gaseous source of Ar[37] mixed with the counter gas to obtain calibrations lines at 2.8 kev (due to the K x ray of Cl[37] emitted following K-capture by Ar[37]) and at 250 ev, which is attributed partly to L-capture (and subsequent emission of an L x ray), and partly to the escape of the K_α x ray from the active volume of the counter.

It is clear from this account that an abundance of possible sources of characteristic x rays is available. Another important problem connected

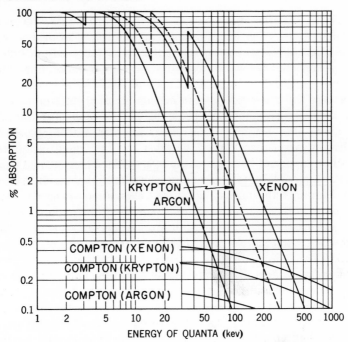

Fig. 31. Photoelectric and Compton absorption in a layer of argon, krypton, and xenon, 5 cm thick, at NTP. After West.[145]

with the use of calibrating characteristic x rays is related to the interpretation of the resulting pulse-height distribution. In the first place, it is evidently desirable to arrange matters in such a fashion that the predominant type of interaction of the x-ray photons with the counter gas consists of the photoelectric effect, in which electrons of discrete energies are ejected. This is not the case for Compton scattering in which a continuous distribution of electron energies is to be expected. It is instructive in this connection to examine Fig. 31, taken from West's article,[145] which displays the percentage absorption of electromagnetic radiation from 2 to 1000 kev in a 5-cm path length of argon, krypton, and xenon gas at normal temperature and pressure. The counter fillings most frequently employed consist of one of these monatomic gases mixed with a small proportion of a molecular gas. (The purpose of the molecular gas, whose interaction with the incident x rays we can neglect in a first approximation, is to reduce the electron agitation energy, as discussed earlier.)

It is evident from an examination of these curves that the Compton effect will provide an unimportant source of background for an argon filling and x rays of energy less than about 50 kev; for krypton and xenon, the photoelectric type of absorption will predominate below 100 and 200 kev, respectively. The discontinuities in absorption evident at certain x-ray energies in Fig. 31 correspond to the K-absorption edges of the three gases. At energies below the K-absorption edge, L absorption will take place.

Xenon as a counter gas possesses a number of significant advantages, particularly at energies above 50 kev. In the first place, its photoelectric-absorption cross section at energies above its K-absorption edge is significantly larger than that of the other two rare gases mentioned. In addition, by virtue of its high density at a specified pressure and temperature, it also has a larger stopping power than the other gases. As pointed out by Curran,[150] this means that ejected photoelectrons have a relatively short range in the counter gas, thus diminishing the importance of wall effect. For energies between the K-absorption edges of krypton and xenon, the photoelectric cross section of krypton exceeds that of xenon, as is evident in Fig. 31.

It might be thought from this discussion that the heavier rare gases are always preferable to argon as counter-gas fillings. However, so far we have not considered the events following the ejection of the photoelectron, usually (though not always) from the K-shell of a counter-gas atom. This question is related to the interpretation of the pulse-height distribution resulting from ionization. The ejected electron has an energy less than that of the incident x ray by the K-binding energy E_K and leaves behind it a vacancy in the K-shell of its parent atom. This vacancy may be filled by an electron with emission of a K x ray, or it may be filled without emission of an x ray, the excess energy being released in the form of kinetic energy of an Auger electron.[151] The probability for the emission of an x ray following the occurrence of a vacancy in one of the inner shells is characterized by a quantity denoted the *fluorescence yield*. If the fluorescence yield is large, a substantial proportion of photoelectric events in the counter gas will lead to the emission of x rays. If an emitted x ray succeeds in escaping from the active volume of the counter without releasing further electrons, the total ionization produced in the counter will correspond to an energy $E - E_K$, where E is the energy of the incident x ray, rather than to E itself. Thus there will be two peaks in the pulse-height distribution, one at the full energy of the incident x ray, and one at a lower energy, corresponding to the escape of the fluorescent counter-gas quantum. The second peak is termed the "escape peak" and constitutes a complicating feature in the interpretation of the pulse spectrum.

A typical escape peak in krypton, taken from the work of West and Rothwell,[152] is illustrated in Fig. 32. The illustration shows the pulse-height distribution observed in a krypton-filled counter bombarded with

24.2 kev x rays from Sn[113]. Evidently, two peaks separated by the K_α energy of krypton appear, as described earlier. (Escape peaks corresponding to the escape of K_α and K_β x rays are not resolved from each other in this case.)

The K-shell fluorescence yield increases steeply with atomic number; for argon, krypton, and xenon it has values of 0.11, 0.67, and 0.81,

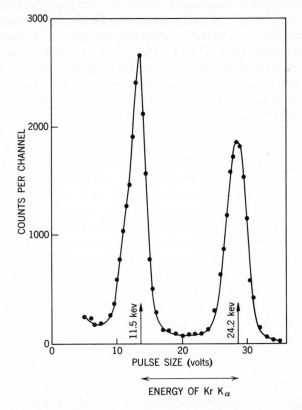

Fig. 32. Pulse size distribution resulting from bombardment of a krypton-filled counter with x-rays emitted by a Sn[113] source. The x-ray energy is 24.2 kev. Note the appearance of a fluorescent x-ray escape peak. From West and Rothwell.[152]

respectively.[150] In order to minimize the importance of the escape peak, it is desirable to have as small a fluorescence yield as possible. This consideration favors argon over the other rare gases, in contrast to the argument already advanced in favor of the heavier rare gases. It should be emphasized, however, that in a practical case the relative size of the escape peak is also influenced by the dimensions of the counter and the pressure of the filling gas. In order to escape, the fluorescent x ray must pass through the counter gas without interaction. The probability of escape, and therefore the relative size of the escape peak, is reduced by using a relatively large counter at a high pressure.

4. Applications. Proportional counters have been used for many years, but it is only recently that they have found extensive application in a region of energies for which they are ideally suited and in which, as far as energy resolution is concerned, their characteristics are unrivaled by any other radiation detector. The energy region in question extends from about 250 ev to 100 kev. It should be emphasized, of course, that proportional counters are frequently used to detect events in which an energy larger than 100 kev is dissipated in the counter gas. The natural advantage of proportional counters, however, lies in the low-energy region.

It may be of some interest to mention briefly a number of recent applications of proportional counters to the study of low-energy events. In the first place, the combination of a proportional counter with an amplifier and a pulse-height analyzer is rapidly replacing the Geiger counter as a detector in x-ray diffraction apparatus. Proportional counters have a much shorter resolving time, and can therefore be used at much higher counting rates, than Geiger counters. Moreover, the selection by a pulse-height analyzer of a relatively sharp line corresponding to a particular x-ray energy contributes to a very low background counting rate.

In applications to nuclear spectroscopy, proportional counters have been used to study the shape of the beta-ray spectra of H^3, C^{14}, and S^{35}. The analysis by Curran, Angus, and Cockcroft[112] and by Hanna and Pontecorvo[153] of the beta-ray spectrum of H^3, which has an end-point at 18.9 kev, is a particularly noteworthy example of a successful application of proportional counters to a problem that has found no other satisfactory solution. In all these cases the radioactive source was introduced into the counter in gaseous form.

Proportional counters have been used to study K- and L-capture of various radioactive isotopes. Wilson and Curran[154] demonstrated that Ni^{59} decayed with a half-life of 8×10^5 years by K-capture, whereas Ni^{63} decayed with the emission of soft beta particles. Brown, Hanna, and Yaffe[155] studied the long-lived K-capture decay of Ca^{41} by use of a proportional counter. The advantages of a proportional counter for studying K-capture of long half-life do not need to be emphasized. L-capture was observed by Pontecorvo and co-workers[149] for the first time in a proportional counter filled with Ar^{37}, as mentioned earlier. A number of interesting measurements of L-to-K-capture ratio have been performed by Dreven and Moljk[156] and by Langevin.[157] In Langevin's experiment the

L-to-K-capture ratio in Ge[71] was determined by adding the gaseous germanium compound GeH_4 to the counter-gas filling (propane). Among other interesting studies in which proportional counters have found application might be mentioned the investigation of L-shell internal conversion by Curran[28] and West,[158] the studies of inner bremstrahlung by Renard[159] and Langevin-Joliot,[160] and the analysis of mesic x rays emitted by light nuclei on capture of negative π-mesons by West and co-workers[161] and by De Benedetti.[162] For a more detailed description of these applications, the reader is referred to the excellent review articles by West,[145] Curran,[150] and Curran and Fulbright.[163]

REFERENCES

1. L. D. Landau, *J. Phys. U.S.S.R.*, **8**, 201 (1944).
2. K. R. Symon, thesis (Harvard University, 1948).
3. J. E. Moyal, *Phil. Mag.*, **46**, 263 (1955).
4. O. Blunck and S. Leisegang, *Z. Physik*, **128**, 500 (1950).
5. R. D. Birkhoff, *Handbuch der Physik*, Vol. 34 (Springer-Verlag, Berlin, 1958).
6. B. Rossi, *High Energy Particles* (Prentice-Hall, New York, 1952).
7. P. Rothwell, *Proc. Phys. Soc. (London)*, **B-64**, 911 (1951).
8. S. Kageyama and K. Nishimura, *J. Phys. Soc. Japan*, **7**, 292 (1952); **8**, 682 (1953).
9. G. J. Igo, D. D. Clark, and R. M. Eisberg, *Phys. Rev.*, **89**, 879 (1953).
10. U. Fano, *Phys. Rev.*, **72**, 26 (1947).
11. S. C. Curran, J. Angus, and A. L. Cockcroft, *Phil. Mag.*, **40**, 929 (1949).
12. G. C. Hanna, D. H. W. Kirkwood, and B. Pontecorvo, *Phys. Rev.*, **75**, 985 (1949).
13. S. C. Curran, A. L. Cockcroft, and G. M. Insch, *Phil. Mag.*, **41**, 517 (1950).
14. G. Stetter, *Z. Physik*, **120**, 639 (1943).
15. R. W. Gurney, *Proc. Roy. Soc. (London)*, **A-107**, 332 (1925).
16. G. E. Gibson and E. W. Gardiner, *Phys. Rev.*, **30**, 543 (1927).
17. L. H. Gray, *Proc. Cambridge Phil. Soc.*, **40**, 72 (1944).
18. U. Fano, *Phys. Rev.*, **70**, 44 (1946).
19. N. Bohr, *Kgl. Danske Videnskab. Selskab, Mat-fys. Medd.*, **18**, No. 8, 1 (1948).
20. R. C. Ling and J. K. Knipp, *Phys. Rev.*, **80**, 106 (1950); J. K. Knipp and R. C. Ling, *Phys. Rev.*, **82**, 30 (1951); J. K. Knipp, R. B. Leachman, and R. C. Ling, *Phys. Rev.*, **80**, 478 (1950); R. B. Leachman, *Phys. Rev.*, **83**, 17 (1951).
21. S. S. Schweber, unpublished monograph (University of Pennsylvania 1949).
22. L. H. Thomas, *Proc. Roy. Soc. (London)*, **A-114**, 561 (1927).
23. J. R. Oppenheimer, *Phys. Rev.*, **31**, 66 (1928); **31**, 349 (1928).
24. H. C. Brinkman and H. A. Kramers, *Proc. Amsterdam Akad.*, **33**, 973 (1930).
25. T. Hall, *Phys. Rev.*, **79**, 504 (1950); J. H. Montague, *Phys. Rev.*, **81**, 1026 (1951); F. L. Ribe, *Phys. Rev.*, **83**, 1217 (1951).
26. H. A. Bethe, *Ann. Physik*, **5**, 325 (1930).
27. E. Bagge, *Ann. Physik*, **30**, 72 (1937).
28. S. C. Curran, J. Angus, and A. L. Cockcroft, *Phil. Mag.*, **40**, 36 (1949).
29. J. M. Valentine, *Proc. Roy. Soc. (London)*, **A-211**, 75 (1952).
30. C. J. Bakker and E. Segre, *Phys. Rev.*, **81**, 489 (1951).

31. W. P. Jesse and J. Sadauskis, *Phys. Rev.*, **97**, 1668 (1955).
32. W. P. Jesse and J. Sadauskis, *Phys. Rev.*, **107**, 766 (1957).
33. W. C. Barber, *Phys. Rev.*, **97**, 1071 (1955).
34. H. A. Bethe, *Revs. Modern Phys.*, **22**, 216 (1950).
35. W. P. Jesse, H. Forstat, and J. Sadauskis, *Phys. Rev.*, **77**, 782 (1950).
36. K. Kimura, R. Ishawari, K. Yuasa, S. Yamashita, K. Miyake, and S. Kimura, *J. Phys. Soc. Japan*, **7**, 111 (1952); R. Ishawari, S. Yamashita, K. Yuasa, and K. Miyake, *J. Phys. Soc. Japan*, **11**, 337 (1956); C. Wingate, W. Gross, and G. Failla, *Phys. Rev.*, **105**, 929 (1957).
37. P. R. Tunnicliffe and A. G. Ward, *Proc. Phys. Soc.* (*London*), **A-65**, 233 (1952).
38. R. A. Lowry and G. H. Miller, *Phys. Rev.*, **109**, 826 (1958).
39. T. E. Cranshaw and J. A. Harvey, *Can. J. Research*, **A-26**, 243 (1948).
40. G. C. Hanna, *Phys. Rev.*, **80**, 530 (1950).
41. J. Rhodes, W. Franzen, and W. E. Stephens, *Phys. Rev.*, **87**, 141 (1952).
42. E. Stebler, P. Huber, and H. Bichsel, *Helv. Phys. Acta*, **22**, 362 (1949).
43. W. Franzen, J. Halpern, and W. E. Stephens, *Phys. Rev.*, **77**, 641 (1950).
44. U. Facchini and E. Gatti, *Nuovo cimento*, **7**, 589 (1950).
45. B. S. Madsen, *Kgl. Danske Videnskab. Selskab, Mat-fys. Medd.*, **13**, No. 8 (1945).
46. W. P. Jesse and J. Sadauskis, *Phys. Rev.*, **102**, 389 (1956).
47. W. G. Stone and L. W. Cochran, *Phys. Rev.*, **107**, 702 (1957).
48. N. O. Lassen, *Kgl. Danske Videnskab. Selskab, Mat-fys. Medd.*, **26**, No. 5 (1951).
49. H. W. Schmitt and R. B. Leachman, *Phys. Rev.*, **102**, 183 (1956).
50. J. M. Valentine and S. C. Curran, *Phil. Mag.*, **43**, 964 (1952).
51. W. P. Jesse and J. Sadauskis, *Phys. Rev.*, **90**, 1120 (1953).
52. T. E. Bortner and G. S. Hurst, *Phys. Rev.*, **93**, 1236 (1954).
53. C. Biber, P. Huber, and A. Müller, *Helv. Phys. Acta*, **28**, 503 (1955).
54. E. J. Williams, *Proc. Roy. Soc.* (*London*), **A-35**, 108 (1932).
55. W. P. Jesse and J. Sadauskis, *Phys. Rev.*, **88**, 417 (1952).
56. T. E. Bortner and G. S. Hurst, *Phys. Rev.*, **90**, 160 (1953).
57. G. A. Erskine, *Proc. Roy. Soc.* (*London*), **A-224**, 362 (1954); **A-67**, 640 (1954).
58. C. E. Melton, G. S. Hurst, and T. E. Bortner, *Phys. Rev.*, **96**, 643 (1954).
59. T. E. Bortner and G. S. Hurst, *Phys. Rev.*, **93**, 1236 (1954).
60. H. J. Moe, T. E. Bortner, and G. S. Hurst, *J. Phys. Chem.*, **61**, 422 (1957).
61. T. D. Strickler and G. S. Hurst, *Proc. Conf. Penetration Charged Particles in Matter*, 1959, to be published.
62. R. H. Healey and J. W. Reed, *The Behavior of Slow Electrons in Gases*, Amalgamated Wireless (Australia) 1941.
63. N. E. Bradbury, *Phys. Rev.*, **44**, 883 (1933).
64. D. S. Burch and R. Geballe, *Phys. Rev.*, **106**, 183 (1957).
65. L. M. Chanin and M. A. Biondi, *Westinghouse Research Laboratory Report 6-94439-7-R5* (1959).
66. A. Doehring, *Z. Naturforsch.*, **7a**, 253 (1952).
67. M. A. Harrison and R. Geballe, *Phys. Rev.*, **91**, 1 (1953).
68. P. Herreng, *Can. Phys.*, **38**, 6 (1952).
69. R. Geballe and M. A. Harrison, *Phys. Rev.*, **85**, 372 (1952).
70. J. D. Craggs, R. Thornburn, and B. A. Tozer, *Proc. Roy. Soc.* (*London*), **A-240**, 473 (1957).
71. T. E. Bortner and G. S. Hurst, *Health Physics*, **1**, 39 (1958).
72. G. S. Hurst and T. E. Bortner, *Radiation Research Supplement 1*, 547 (1959); *Phys. Rev.*, **114**, 116 (1959).

73. C. W. McCutchen, senior thesis (Princeton, 1950).
74. U. Facchini and A. Malvicini, *Nucleonics*, **13**, No. 4, 36 (1955).
75. J. A. Bistline, *Rev. Sci. Instr.*, **19**, 842 (1948).
76. W. N. English, *Rev. Sci. Instr.*, **22**, 598 (1951).
77. H. S. W. Massey and E. H. S. Burhop, *Electronic and Ionic Impact Phenomena* (Oxford at the Clarendon Press, 1952).
78. J. J. Thomson, *Phil. Mag.*, **47**, 337 (1924).
79. P. Langevin, *Ann. Chim. Phys.*, **28**, 289, 433 (1903).
80. D. H. Wilkinson, *Ionization Chambers and Counters* (Cambridge University Press, Cambridge, 1950).
81. G. Jaffe, *Ann. Physik*, **42**, 303 (1913).
82. H. S. Bridge, W. E. Hazen, B. Rossi, and R. W. Williams, *Phys. Rev.*, **74**, 1083 (1948).
83. L. B. Loeb, *Basic Processes of Gaseous Electronics* (University of California Press, Berkeley, 1955).
84. A. M. Tyndall, *The Mobility of Positive Ions in Gases* (Cambridge University Press, Cambridge, 1938).
85. R. A. Nielsen, *Phys. Rev.*, **50**, 950 (1936).
86. P. Herreng, *Compt. rend.*, **217**, 75 (1943).
87. L. Colli and U. Facchini, *Rev. Sci. Instr.*, **23**, 39 (1952).
88. T. E. Bortner, G. S. Hurst, and W. G. Stone, *Rev. Sci. Instr.*, **28**, 103 (1957).
89. J. M. Kirshner and D. S. Toffolo, *J. Appl. Phys.*, **23**, 594 (1952).
90. W. N. English and G. C. Hanna, *Can. J. Phys.*, **31**, 768 (1953).
91. E. D. Klema and J. S. Allen, *Phys. Rev.*, **77**, 661 (1950).
92. J. S. Townsend and V. A. Bailey, *Phil. Mag.*, **44**, 1033 (1922).
93. V. A. Bailey, *Phil. Mag.*, **47**, 379 (1924).
94. R. W. Crompton and D. J. Sutton, *Proc. Roy. Soc.* (*London*), **A-215**, 467 (1952).
95. M. F. Skinker, *Phil. Mag.*, **44**, 994 (1922).
96. B. Rossi and H. Staub, *Ionization Chambers and Counters* (McGraw Hill, New York, 1949).
97. L. H. G. Huxley and A. A. Zaazou, *Proc. Roy. Soc.* (*London*), **A-196**, 402 (1949).
98. R. A. Nielsen and N. E. Bradbury, *Phys. Rev.*, **51**, 69 (1937).
99. J. S. Townsend and H. T. Tizard, *Proc. Roy. Soc.* (*London*), **A-88**, 336 (1913).
100. R. Sherr and P. Peterson, *Rev. Sci. Instr.*, **18**, 567 (1947).
101. P. G. Koontz and T. A. Hall, *Rev. Sci. Instr.*, **18**, 643 (1947).
102. H. Barschall and M. Kanner, *Phys. Rev.*, **58**, 590 (1940).
103. J. H. Coon and H. H. Barschall, *Phys. Rev.*, **70**, 592 (1946).
104. E. Baldinger, P. Huber, and W. Proctor, *Helv. Phys. Acta*, **25**, 142 (1952).
105. E. Baldinger and W. Franzen, *Advances in Electronics and Electron Physics*, Vol. VIII (Academic Press, New York, 1956).
106. A. B. Gillespie, *Signal, Noise and Resolution in Nuclear Counter Amplifiers* (Pergamon Press, New York, 1953).
107. J. A. Crawford, *Atomic Energy Comm. Declassified Doc.*, *AECD-2034*.
108. G. Stetter and W. Jentschke, *Z. Phys.*, **110**, 214 (1938).
109. G. R. Bishop, C. H. Collie, H. H. Halban, A. Hedgram, K. Siegbahn, S. du Toit, and R. S. Wilson, *Phys. Rev.*, **80**, 211 (1950).
110. H. H. Barschall and M. E. Battat, *Phys. Rev.*, **70**, 245 (1946).
111. P. G. Koontz and T. A. Hall, *Phys. Rev.*, **72**, 196 (1947).
112. S. C. Curran, J. Angus, and A. L. Cockcroft, *Phys. Rev.*, **76**, 853 (1949).
113. A. L. Cockcroft and S. C. Curran, *Rev. Sci. Instr.*, **22**, 37 (1951).

114. R. S. Wilson, *Proc. Roy. Soc. (London)*, **A-177**, 382 (1940).
115. T. H. R. Skyrme, P. R. Tunnicliffe, and A. G. Ward, *Rev. Sci. Instr.*, **23**, 204 (1952).
116. D. West, J. K. Dawson, and C. J. Mandleberg, *Phil. Mag.*, **43**, 875 (1952).
117. D. West and P. Rothwell, *Phil. Mag.*, **41**, 873 (1950).
118. J. O. Newton, B. Rose, and J. Milstead, *Phil. Mag.*, **1**, 981 (1956).
119. W. Stetter and W. Bothe, *Z. Naturf.*, **64**, 61 (1951).
120. O. Buneman, T. E. Cranshaw, and J. A. Harvey, *Can. J. Research*, **A-27**, 191 (1949).
121. J. C. Maxwell, *Electricity and Magnetism*, Third Edition, Vol. I, Par. 203 (Oxford University Press, Oxford, 1904).
122. M. Abraham, *Arch. Elektrotech.*, **8**, 42 (1919).
123. M. von Laue, *Ann. Physik*, **59**, 465 (1919).
124. R. W. King, *Phys. Rev.*, **15**, 256 (1920).
125. F. B. Vogdes and F. R. Elder, *Phys. Rev.*, **24**, 683 (1924).
126. L. O. Herwig, G. H. Miller, and N. G. Utterback, *Rev. Sci. Instr.*, **26**, 929 (1955).
127. H. W. Fulbright and J. C. D. Milton, *Phys. Rev.*, **76**, 1271 (1949); **82**, 274 (1951).
128. R. S. Wilson, L. E. Beghian, C. H. Collie, H. H. Halban, and G. R. Bishop, *Rev. Sci. Instr.*, **21**, 699 (1950).
129. C. H. Collie, H. H. Halban, and R. S. Wilson, *Proc. Phys. Soc. (London)*, **A-63**, 994 (1950).
130. G. R. Bishop, L. E. Beghian, and H. H. Halban, *Phys. Rev.*, **83**, 1052 (1951).
131. L. E. Beghian, G. R. Bishop, and H. H. Halban, *Phys. Rev.*, **83**, 186 (1951).
132. E. D. Klema and H. H. Barschall, *Phys. Rev.*, **63**, 18 (1943).
133. D. S. Gibbs, H. J. Svec, and R. E. Harrington, *Ind. Eng. Chem.*, **48**, 289 (1956).
134. E. D. Klema, *Atomic Energy Comm. Declassified Doc.*, *AECD-2157*.
135. A. S. Newton, *Manhattan District Declassified Doc.*, *MDDC-724*.
136. G. H. Stafford, *Nature*, **162**, 771 (1948).
137. L. E. Beghian and H. H. Halban, *Proc. Phys. Soc. (London)*, **A-62**, 395 (1949).
138. J. S. Allen and B. Rossi, *Manhattan District Declassified Doc.*, *MDDC-448*.
139. I. I. Fowler and P. R. Tunnicliffe, *Rev. Sci. Instr.*, **21**, 734 (1950).
140. J. H. Manley, H. M. Agnew, H. H. Barschall, W. C. Bright, J. H. Coon, E. R. Graves, T. Jorgenson, and B. Waldman, *Phys. Rev.*, **70**, 602 (1946).
141. F. M. Glass, *Rev. Sci. Instr.*, **20**, 239 (1949).
142. H. S. Snyder, *Phys. Rev.*, **72**, 181 (1947).
143. A. Bisi and L. Zappa, *Nuovo cimento*, **II**, 988 (1955).
144. D. West, *Proc. Phys. Soc. (London)*, **A-66**, 306 (1953).
145. D. West, *Progress in Nuclear Physics*, Vol. 3 (Academic Press, New York, 1953).
146. G. M. Insch, *Phil. Mag.*, **41**, 857 (1950).
147. P. Rothwell and D. West, *Proc. Phys. Soc., (London)*, **A-63**, 541 (1950).
148. J. K. Beling, J. O. Newton, and B. Rose, *Phys. Rev.*, **86**, 797 (1952).
149. D. H. W. Kirkwood, B. Pontecorvo, and G. C. Hanna, *Phys. Rev.*, **74**, 497 (1948).
150. S. C. Curran, *Handbuch der Physik*, **45** (Springer-Verlag, Berlin, 1958).
151. E. H. S. Burhop, *The Auger Effect and Other Radiationless Transitions* (Cambridge University Press, Cambridge, 1952).
152. D. West and P. Rothwell, *Phil. Mag.*, **41**, 873 (1950).
153. G. C. Hanna and B. Pontecorvo, *Phys. Rev.*, **75**, 983 (1949).
154. H. W. Wilson, *Phys. Rev.*, **79**, 1932 (1950); **82**, 548 (1951).
155. F. Brown, G. C. Hanna, and L. Yaffe, *Phys. Rev.*, **84**, 1243 (1951).
156. R. W. P. Dreven and A. Moljk, *Phil. Mag.*, **1**, 1 (1956).

157. M. Langevin, *Compt. rend.*, **239**, 1625 (1954).
158. D. West and J. K. Dawson, *Proc. Phys. Soc.* (*London*), **A-64**, 586 (1951).
159. G. A. Renard, *J. Phys. radium*, **14**, 361 (1953); **16**, 575 (1955).
160. H. Langevin-Joliot, *Compt. rend.*, **241**, 286, 1390 (1955).
161. D. West, R. Batchelor, and E. F. Bradley, *Proc. Phys. Soc.* (*London*), **A-68**, 801 (1955).
162. M. Stearns, M. B. Stearns, S. De Benedetti, and L. Leipuner, *Phys. Rev.*, **97**, 240 (1955); **96**, 804 (1954); **93**, 1123 (1954).
163. S. C. Curran and H. W. Fulbright, *Beta- and Gamma-Ray Spectroscopy*, K. Siegbahn, Ed. (Interscience, New York, 1955).

2 SCINTILLATION COUNTERS

R. B. MURRAY
Oak Ridge National Laboratory
Oak Ridge, Tennessee

A. Inorganic Crystals
B. Organic Crystals and Plastics
C. Organic Liquids
D. Noble Gases
E. Photomultiplier Tubes and Counter Assembly
F. Applications of Scintillators

The first applications of the scintillation process to nuclear physics took place in the early part of this century, at which time it was rather widely used as a visual detector of alpha particles. Light flashes produced by alphas on a zinc sulfide screen were observed through a low-power microscope and individually recorded by the experimenter. By present standards, this represents an archaic and tedious counting method; it is nevertheless responsible for the accumulation of much of the significant nuclear data over a period of several decades. With the development of ionization chambers, proportional counters, and Geiger counters, the scintillation method fell into disuse until about 1947–1948. At that time the use of scintillating materials in conjunction with photomultiplier tubes, which permitted electronic detection and recording of individual counts, was demonstrated. The very rapid development of scintillation-counter techniques that has taken place since then represents possibly one of the most significant advances to date in the methods of experimental nuclear physics.

Briefly stated, a present-day scintillation counter consists of a scintillation detector (in the form of a solid, liquid, or gas) which produces flashes of light upon excitation by ionizing radiation; the scintillator is optically coupled to a photomultiplier tube which converts the incident photons into electrical pulses whose magnitude is proportional to the intensity of the initial light flash. This, in turn, is proportional to the total energy deposited by the charged particle in the detector. The photomultiplier pulses may be analyzed in terms of pulse height to provide information on the energy spectrum of the incident radiation, or they may simply be recorded to provide a measure of radiation intensity.

The use of the scintillation counter in its various forms has made possible the investigation of a large number of problems that would otherwise have

82

been extremely tedious if not impossible. As an example we may consider the field of gamma-ray spectroscopy, whose present state of development is due in large part to the use of scintillators. Prior to about 1949, gamma-ray energies were generally measured either by observing the beta spectrum of associated Compton recoils or photoelectrons or by interposing absorbers of various materials between the gamma source and detector (Geiger counter). As a result of the inherently low detection efficiency, or poor resolution, of these methods, the measurement of a complex gamma spectrum presented a significant experimental problem. The development of scintillation counters, however, has provided a convenient, high-efficiency spectrometer such that measurements of gamma-ray spectra from radioactive nuclei have become a fairly common laboratory operation. The impact of scintillation counting on the field of gamma-ray spectroscopy may be demonstrated by noting that about 93% of the reports on this subject in the 1957 *Physical Review* involve the use of a scintillation counter. The significant contributions of scintillators are by no means limited to this area, but include the detection and energy measurement of electrons, fast and slow neutrons, and light and heavy charged particles.

The reasons for the widespread application of scintillation counters to the detection and spectroscopy of nuclear radiations are severalfold. First, the fact that the light output is proportional to the energy deposited by a charged particle provides a tool for the direct measurement of a particle's energy. Indirectly, this permits energy measurements for nonionizing radiations, notably gammas and neutrons. In the case of gamma rays, interactions with electrons of the scintillator result in some events in which the total gamma energy is deposited in the counter. Neutron energies may be inferred through the complete absorption of recoil protons or the products of a nuclear reaction. In general, the relationship between light output and electron energy is nearly linear; departures from linearity are observed for heavier charged particles.

A second advantage is to be found in the fact that the density of solid scintillators is such that charged particles with energies in the Mev range are stopped in a scintillator only a few millimeters thick. For example, a crystal of CsI 1 mm thick will completely stop a 12-Mev proton; the range of such a proton in a proportional counter filled with 5 atm of argon would be 30 cm. The advantage of the crystal in this case is obvious. Further, the high density of inorganic solid scintillators ($3.1 < \rho < 4.5$ grams/cm^3 for the alkali iodides) permits the detection of gamma rays with a much higher efficiency than that possible with previous techniques. As an example, gamma rays incident normal to the plane face of a NaI(Tl) crystal 2 in. thick are detected with more than 90% efficiency for energies up to 0.3 Mev; the corresponding detection efficiency for a 5-Mev gamma is almost 50%.

A third feature of scintillation counters is to be found in their very fast response to ionizing radiation. The $1/e$ decay time for the light output of a scintillator ranges from $\sim 10^{-9}$ sec (organic liquids and noble gases) to $\sim 10^{-6}$ sec (inorganic crystals). The collection times of the fast scintillators are considerably shorter than those of ordinary proportional counters and ion chambers; this fact leads to the use of scintillation counters in experiments with high counting rates or when fast coincidences are to be recorded. Coincidence resolving times in the millimicrosecond region are currently obtained by the use of scintillators and fast pulse techniques.

A fourth feature of the scintillation method is the wide range of properties of scintillators which makes it possible for the experimenter to select a counter suited to a particular purpose. In terms of geometry, the availability of liquid scintillators makes possible the construction of a counter of virtually any shape and size. Indeed, liquid counters containing several hundred gallons of scintillator were used in the experiment to detect the free neutrino.[29] At the other end of the scale, thin slices of solid crystals a few thousandths of an inch thick are used to detect heavy charged particles. In general, the characteristics of a scintillator, such as density, chemical composition, decay time, and light output, determine its area of maximum usefulness.

The basic principles of scintillation counters have been rather thoroughly discussed in a number of excellent books and review articles.[3,4,21,30,94,109] In view of this fact, no attempt has been made here to consider all of the fundamentals; rather, the aim of this chapter is to provide a review of currently used techniques as well as interesting developments which have occurred within recent years. It is hoped that the references cited will provide the reader with a guide to the literature for more detailed information on any point. Secs. A through D cover the scintillation characteristics of inorganic crystals, organic crystals and plastics, organic liquids, and noble gases. The properties of currently available photomultiplier tubes are discussed briefly in Sec. E. Sec. F on applications reviews the use of previously described scintillators and photomultiplier tubes for specific purposes in nuclear physics experiments. No attempt has been made to discuss electronic circuitry which may be used in conjunction with scintillation counters. The subject of nuclear pulse amplifiers is treated in detail in Chapter 4. Circuits for regulated high-voltage supplies, coincidence measurements, pulse-height analysis, and special applications are in a continual state of development and would constitute the subject of a separate discussion. Information on electronic techniques is available in a large number of articles and books. (For a recent bibliography, see Ref. 109, p. 369.)

A. Inorganic Crystals

1. Methods of preparation. The inorganic scintillators that are most widely used at the present time are the alkali halides, in particular the alkali iodides. In order to achieve maximum density, optical transparency, and uniform activation, it is necessary to prepare the scintillator in the form of a single crystal. Single crystals of all the members of this series,

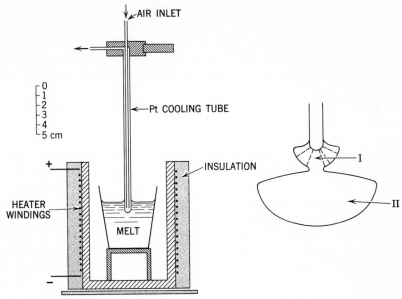

Fig. 1. Kyropoulos method for growing single crystals from the melt. From Kyropoulos.[76]

viz., LiI, NaI, KI, RbI, and CsI, have been prepared at various laboratories. Of these, LiI and NaI are hygroscopic and occur both in the hydrated and the anhydrous form. The hydrated material must, of course, be converted to the anhydrous state prior to the preparation of a crystal. Dehydration is accomplished by slow heating in a vacuum with an appropriate trap for condensing the water vapor. Crystal growth of the anhydrous material must be carried out in a vacuum or inert atmosphere. The growth of a crystal is generally accomplished by either of two well-known techniques, viz., the Kyropoulos method[76] or the Bridgman-Stockbarger method.[114]

Figure 1 is a schematic diagram taken from the original report of

Kyropoulos. The starting material is contained in a platinum crucible and is melted by raising the temperature of the surrounding furnace. A platinum tube with a hemispherical bottom is lowered into the melt. A stream of cooling air is then directed against the interior of the tube bottom, leading to the formation of crystals on the exterior surface. When this initial growth has reached a diameter several times that of the cooling tube, the tube is slowly withdrawn from the melt to such a point that only *one* crystal (labeled I in Fig. 1) remains in contact with the melt. The flow of cooling air is increased, and this single crystal is allowed to grow to a diameter slightly less than that of the crucible (II). It is then lifted from the melt and cooled slowly to room temperature. The Kyropoulos procedure requires a certain amount of experience and skill on the part of the operator in knowing just when and how far to extract the cooling tube from the melt in order to initiate the growth of crystal II. Using this technique, alkali-halide crystals have been grown with dimensions of the order of 6 in. or larger.[5]

In the Stockbarger method the starting material is contained in a crucible of platinum which is tapered to a conical point at the bottom. The crucible is allowed to fall slowly along the axis of a "double" furnace (Fig. 2) in which the temperature of the upper region is maintained above the melting point of the charge, while the lower half is held slightly below the melting point. The two halves of the furnace are separated by a platinum baffle so that a sharp temperature gradient occurs in passing through the region of the baffle. As the crucible of molten material drops, a seed crystal forms at the tip of the crucible; growth from this seed takes place as the melt is lowered past the baffle. A typical lowering speed is of the order of 1 in. per day. When the crystal has passed entirely into the lower half, the furnace is slowly brought to room temperature. (In the original Bridgman method the crucible simply falls into a cooler region without passing through a sharp temperature gradient.) The Bridgman-Stockbarger technique is rather widely used at the present time for the commercial preparation of alkali-halide crystals; single crystals of NaI(Tl) have been produced to about 9 in. in diameter and are commercially available.

Activation of alkali-halide crystals is usually carried out by mixing the activator impurity, in the form of a salt, with the starting material prior to growth. As an example, thallium, a frequently used activator, is added to the alkali iodides in the form of TlI. Activator concentrations are usually of the order of 10^{-1} mole %. A less frequently used technique for introducing the activator into the crystal lattice is that of diffusion of the impurity into a previously grown crystal. In this method both the crystal and activator are contained in an evacuated tube and are physically separated. Upon prolonged heating of the contents of the tube, the activator material diffuses into the crystal; the diffusion process may be effective only in a relatively thin surface layer.

A second group of inorganic crystals which has been found to scintillate is that of the tungstates, notably $CdWO_4$ and $CaWO_4$. The laboratory production of clear crystals of these materials has been reported by

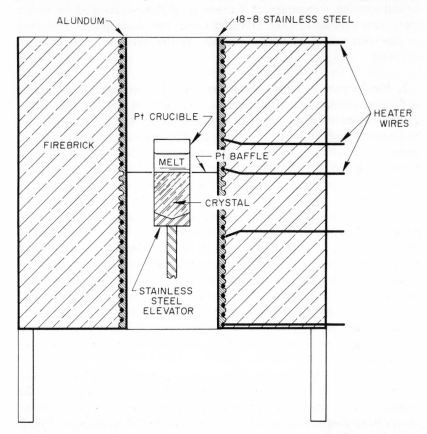

Fig. 2. Bridgman-Stockbarger method for growing single crystals from the melt. From Stockbarger.[114]

Gillette.[52] The melting points of both compounds are rather high ($>1300°$ C). Apparently it would be rather difficult to grow large transparent single crystals of the tungstates. A third group of interest is that of the sulfides, of which ZnS and CdS have been studied as alpha-particle counters. ZnS(Ag) and ZnS(Cu) are found to make very good alpha detectors. The preparation of ZnS in the form of a clear single crystal requires specialized techniques; for scintillation counting purposes ZnS is used as a fine powder whose particle size is only a small fraction of a millimeter. The activated ZnS powder is prepared by thoroughly mixing pure ZnS with a salt of the activator (e.g., Ag NO_3) in the presence of a low-melting flux such as NaCl. The ingredients are heated to more than 1000° C for a period varying from a few minutes to over an hour. The crystal-growing techniques of Greene et al.[43] have resulted in rather large clear crystals of pure ZnS and CdS; this development may lead to the future use of single crystals of the sulfides in scintillation counting.

2. Mechanism of scintillation process. The physical events responsible for the luminescence of inorganic solids are not understood in detail at the present time so that it is not possible to give an accurate and quantitative description of this process. The general features, however, appear to be sufficiently well known to permit a qualitative discussion. It is not feasible to consider here the scintillation mechanism in all inorganic crystals, since considerably different processes may occur in the various types of crystals. We take as an illustrative example, however, the case of an activated alkali halide, whose luminescence is caused primarily by the presence of the activator in small concentration. The interaction of a charged particle with such a crystal may be considered to occur in three essentially distinct steps: (a) the charged particle in slowing down loses its energy primarily to electrons of the crystal, resulting in ionization and excitation of the constituents of the crystal lattice; (b) the energy deposited by the charged particle migrates to an activator center or to a trapping center and is stored there; and (c) the energy is emitted in the form of a photon or in a nonradiative transition resulting in thermal excitation of the lattice.

Turning first to the passage of the charged particle through the crystal, we wish to examine the state of the crystal in the immediate vicinity of the particle's path. This can best be understood by referring to the electronic energy band diagram characteristic of an ionic crystal, as shown in Fig. 3. This figure demonstrates the concept that the possible energy levels available to an electron in a crystal are divided into allowed bands which are separated by forbidden bands. In the ground state of the crystal the filled bands are completely occupied. Upon passage of a charged particle, electrons may receive sufficient energy to be divorced from a particular lattice site and raised to the conduction band; this process is referred to as *ionization*. The electron vacancy remaining in the valence band is known as a hole and, in the case of ionization, is no longer bound to the electron. Both electron and hole are thus free to wander independently

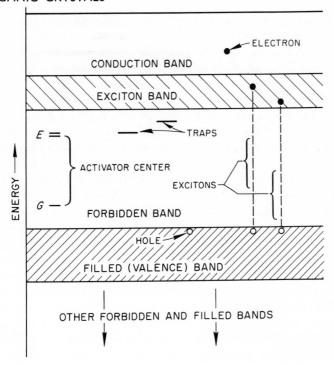

Fig. 3.   Electronic energy band diagram of an ionic crystal.

through the lattice, and each may contribute to electrical conductivity in the crystal.

An alternative event is one in which the energy imparted to the electron is not sufficient to raise it to the conduction band so that it remains bound electrostatically to the hole in the valence band. This process is referred to as *excitation*, and the resulting electron-hole pair is known as an *exciton*.[77] An exciton, presumably, can wander through the crystal lattice but does not contribute to electrical conductivity as it has no net charge. The exciton can be thought of as a hydrogenlike "atom" consisting of two particles of equal and opposite charge. On this basis the exciton is expected to exist in bound, hydrogenlike states whose highest excited state is adjacent to the ionization continuum and therefore coincides with the bottom of the conduction band. We are thus led to the concept of an exciton band whose upper limit is the bottom of the conduction band and whose lower limit is the exciton ground state. The otherwise "discrete" exciton levels are smeared into a continuum within the exciton band as a result of translational motion. In an alkali halide the width of the upper forbidden band (Fig. 3) may be 6–8 ev, whereas that of the exciton band is of the order of 1 ev. Numerous experimental investigations lend support to this concept of the exciton.[77] The role of the exciton in the scintillation process in both unactivated NaI and NaI(Tl) has been discussed in detail by Van Sciver,[134] who attributes the luminescence in pure NaI at 3030 A to exciton annihilation.

The presence of the thallium activator provides a number of impurity centers distributed through the lattice; Tl^+ ions are thought to occupy, at random, sites of the alkali metal ions. The existence of these impurity centers gives rise to localized electronic energy levels in the forbidden band below the conduction band. The activator ion can exist in both the ground state and excited states (denoted G and E in Fig. 3). The energy levels characteristic of the impurity can be represented as discrete levels as a result of the very dilute concentration of the activator. In addition to the activator ions, we may expect other impurity centers throughout the crystal, viz., F-centers, V-centers, or vacant lattice sites, to serve as electron or hole traps or as exciton traps.

A more explicit representation of the energy levels associated with an activator center is given in Fig. 4, in which the ground state and only one excited state are shown. The impurity center may be raised to an excited state either by absorption of photons from, say, an external source (transition AB), by capture of an exciton, or by the successive capture of an electron and a hole (in either order).

The sequence of events leading to a scintillation may now be pictured. The passage of a charged particle through the crystal results in the formation of excitons, electrons in the conduction band, and holes in the valence band, each of which is considered free to wander through the lattice. The energy lost by the incident particle thus migrates from the immediate vicinity of the particle's path and is deposited at various activator sites, or trapping centers, by the process of exciton capture or by electron-hole capture. In the case of an activator center, it will be raised to one of several possible excited states. If an allowed transition is permitted between this excited state and the ground state, it is then possible for a photon to be emitted as in transition CD. The lifetime of such an excited state prior to the emission of dipole radiation is the order of 10^{-8} sec. It will be noted that the energy of the emitted photon CD is less than that absorbed in transition AB. (This is a consequence of the fact that the equilibrium configuration of the system is different in the excited state and ground state, so that the minima in the potential energy curves at A and C do not occur at the same values of the configuration coordinate r. The absorption and emission events AB and CD take place along vertical lines as indicated, however, according to the Franck-Condon principle.) It is well that this difference in energy exists; otherwise, the absorption

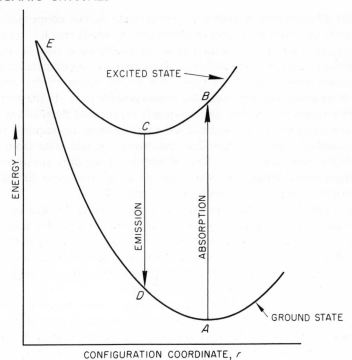

Fig. 4. Schematic diagram of electronic energy levels of an activator center. Only one of many possible excited states is shown. Configuration coordinate r may be considered as an internuclear spacing.

band of the activator would completely overlap the emission spectrum. After emission of the photon, the potential energy of the center is that characterized by point D; the system then returns to the equilibrium configuration at A, giving up an amount of energy DA to thermal excitation of the lattice (phonon emission). The wavelength of light emitted from a thallium-activated alkali halide occurs in the visible or near ultraviolet region. As a result of thermal fluctuations about the potential energy minimum C, the emission spectrum is broadened into a band rather than a single sharp line.

Another possibility exists for de-excitation of the excited state: if the potential energy is raised along the path CE by thermal excitation, it is possible to undergo the nonradiative transition EA, the energy difference EA being returned to the lattice. This process competes with the radiative transition, and its rate of occurrence is temperature-dependent, since the probability of reaching point E by thermal fluctuations is proportional to $e^{-E'/kT}$, where E' is the energy difference characteristic of the well depth EC.

Another possibility is that the excited state is not connected to the ground state through an allowed transition, in which case it is referred to as a metastable state. The lifetime of metastable states may be orders of magnitude longer than 10^{-8} sec. They may be depopulated by non-radiative transitions of the type CEA or by means of the electron's receiving enough energy to reach a nonmetastable state. In the latter case, the transition probability again depends on thermal fluctuations and is expected to go as $e^{-E/kT}$, where E is the activation energy required to raise an electron from its metastable state to an excited state from which radiation can occur. The effect of additional impurity sites serving as electron traps or hole traps is expected to be analogous to that of a metastable state in that de-excitation is delayed.

A distinction may be drawn between de-excitation through an allowed transition (occurring within $\sim 10^{-8}$ sec after excitation) and that through a metastable state with a much longer decay time. According to Garlick,[53] radiation of the first type is generally referred to as *fluorescence*, whereas that of the second type is known as *phosphorescence* or *afterglow*. The term *luminescence* may be applied to either.

The presence of metastable states or traps is demonstrated by thermo-luminescence experiments,[111] in which a crystal is cooled to a low temperature, irradiated briefly with charged particles or light, and then allowed to warm slowly, during which time its emission spectrum is recorded. The presence of strong emission at certain characteristic temperatures T_i corresponds to the de-excitation of metastable states, or traps, with a corresponding well depth E_i.

In conclusion, it may be noted that surprisingly few studies of a fundamental nature have been carried out on the alkali halides in an attempt to understand the basic mechanisms responsible for their response to charged particles. A particularly significant and intriguing question is that of why all alkali iodides serve as efficient scintillators whereas the other alkali halides in general scintillate very weakly or not at all. The present understanding of inorganic scintillators is hampered by a lack of adequate experimental information and would be greatly improved by further detailed studies on the absorption spectra and emission spectra of very pure crystals and activated crystals, temperature-dependent effects in the luminescence intensity and decay times, and the response of crystals to various charged particles. In addition, detailed calculations of activator energy levels in various alkali halides, such as that given by Williams[138] for KCl(Tl), would be of great value.

3. Decay of light following excitation. The light emitted by an alkali-halide crystal following excitation by a charged particle is generally found to decay in time with an exponential (or nearly exponential) dependence,

$$I = I_0 e^{-\lambda t}. \tag{1}$$

The transition probability λ is a characteristic of a particular type of crystal, its activator, and crystal temperature. The quantity $1/\lambda$ is referred to as the *decay time*. Examination of the luminescence from alkali halides[6] shows that frequently several modes of decay, each characterized by a particular λ, are superimposed. We will generally be concerned, however, only with the fastest decay time. In a scintillation counter in which the crystal is optically coupled to a photomultiplier tube the exponential decay of light following the passage of a charged particle gives rise to a corresponding exponential current decay at the photomultiplier anode. This current is integrated on a condenser network whose time constant is RC. Denoting the anode current by $i = i_m e^{-\lambda t}$, the voltage developed across the condenser is given by

$$V = \frac{i_m R}{\lambda RC - 1} (e^{-t/RC} - e^{-\lambda t}). \tag{2}$$

In the usual application RC is chosen to be large ($\sim$ hundreds of microseconds) and the above equation can be written for small t as

$$V \approx \frac{i_m}{\lambda C} (1 - e^{-\lambda t}). \tag{3}$$

This situation is illustrated in Fig. 5. The decay time of a given crystal can be determined by observing the amplified voltage pulse, as in Fig. 5; it is, of course, necessary that the rise-time of the pulse amplifier be much faster than $1/\lambda$. As an illustration, oscilloscope traces of such pulses from two inorganic scintillators are shown in Fig. 6. In general, the decay time of a particular crystal type, such as NaI(Tl), may be expected to vary somewhat from one individual crystal to another, so that listed values of $(1/\lambda)$ should be taken as typical rather than exact numbers. Such a variation can arise, for example, as a result of different activator content in various crystals.[36,115] The decay time may also be a function of the nature of the incident particle; this effect has been reported for CsI(Tl)[115] and unactivated CsI.[55] Widely different decay times result from alpha and gamma excitation of pure CsF.[135]

4. Temperature-dependent effects. The competition between radiative and nonradiative transitions leads to a temperature-dependence of both the luminescence intensity and decay time. Following the model of Bonanomi and Rossel,[6] we denote by λ and λ' the probabilities per unit

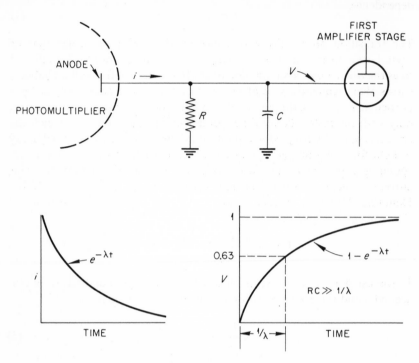

Fig. 5. Illustration of current and voltage pulses from a photomultiplier following excitation of a scintillator by nuclear radiation at time zero.

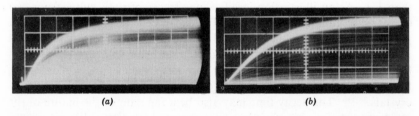

(a)   *(b)*

Fig. 6. Voltage pulses from two inorganic crystals on 6342 photomultipliers. Signal was amplified by Tektronix 53/54L preamplifier (rise time 10^{-2} μsec) and displayed on Tektronix 545 oscilloscope (amplifier rise time 10^{-2} μsec). (a) NaI(Tl), gamma-ray excitation. Full scale = 2 μsec, $(1/\lambda) \approx 0.3$ μsec. (b) LiI(Eu), slow-neutron excitation. Full scale = 5 μsec, $(1/\lambda) \approx 1.3$ μsec. Quoted values of $(1/\lambda)$ are only approximate values derived from above traces.

time for a radiative and a nonradiative transition. As previously indicated, λ and λ' are taken to be temperature-dependent and are written as

$$\lambda = Se^{-E/kT}$$
$$\lambda' = S'e^{-E'/kT} \tag{4}$$

where S and S' are amplitude factors. The luminescence intensity I, as a function of temperature, is given by

$$\frac{I}{I_0} = \frac{\lambda}{\lambda + \lambda'} = \frac{1}{1 + (S'/S)e^{-\epsilon/kT}} \tag{5}$$

where $\epsilon = (E' - E)$. It should be noted that (5) is a consequence of the assumption that luminescence centers *of some sort* exist in the crystal and that de-excitation may occur either by a radiative or nonradiative transition; it is not necessarily assumed that the luminescence centers are associated with a deliberately added activator, such as thallium. Indeed, the experimental results of Bonanomi and Rossel indicate that (5) describes well the temperature-dependence of luminescence in the unactivated alkali iodides in the region between room temperature and the liquid nitrogen point. Figure 7, taken from their work, shows the measured luminescence intensity of "pure" (in the sense that they were not deliberately activated) crystals as a function of temperature. An experiment by Van Sciver and Bogart[136] has indicated, however, that a maximum occurs in the intensity versus temperature curve for pure NaI, just at the liquid nitrogen point, and that the intensity decreases by approximately $\frac{1}{4}$ in going from 77 to 4° K. Similarly, the pulse height from nonactivated CsI reaches a maximum near 40° K.[74] Such behavior is clearly inconsistent with (5). The conclusion seems to be that the simple picture of temperature-dependence previously given is at least partly correct as applied to unactivated alkali iodides but must be modified to account for the decrease in pulse height at very low temperatures. In the case of the thallium-activated crystals studied by Bonanomi and Rossel, the intensity as a function of temperature did not exhibit the behavior of Fig. 7 in every case. Some of the crystals showed temperature-independent modes of decay as well as components increasing in intensity with decreasing temperature. The principal component of CsI(Tl) was actually found to *decrease* in intensity as the temperature was lowered. Similar results on CsI(Tl) are reported by Knoepfel et al.[85]

The luminescence decay time $(1/\lambda)$ is seen in (4) to be temperature-dependent such that $(1/\lambda)$ increases exponentially with decreasing temperature. This predicted behavior was observed over a wide range of values of $(1/\lambda)$ for some of the decay modes of the alkali iodides. In other decay modes $(1/\lambda)$ was found to be temperature-independent; according to (4), this would correspond to $E \approx 0$.

In addition to basic studies of the scintillation process, it appears that the use of certain inorganic crystals at low temperatures may have practical applications. In the case of pure NaI, the luminescence emission

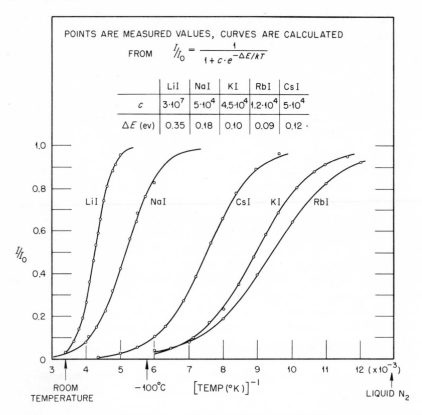

Fig. 7. Temperature dependence of light intensity from unactivated alkali iodides. From Bonanomi and Rossel.[6]

at the liquid nitrogen point is about twice that of a Tl-activated crystal at room temperature, whereas the decay time of the cooled pure crystal is only 0.06 μsec compared with about 0.3 μsec for room temperature NaI(Tl).[136] Beghian and co-workers[19] have used pure NaI at liquid nitrogen temperature for time-of-flight measurements in the millimicro-second range. In the case of LiI(Eu), cooling to the liquid nitrogen point results in a considerable improvement in the scintillation response to fast neutrons.[95] The luminescence intensity increases at lower temperatures, whereas the decay time stays almost constant at about 1.2 μsec. Pure CsI at liquid nitrogen temperature is reported to have a very high light output and might prove useful for the detection of low-energy particles.[55,57]

5. Response to charged particles. The scintillation response of various inorganic crystals to charged particles has been the subject of study at a number of laboratories (see Refs. 7 and 149 for recent bibliographies). Considering the alkali iodides, it is generally found that a plot

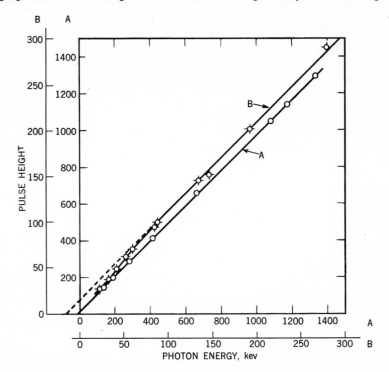

Fig. 8a. Pulse height versus energy for gamma rays on NaI(Tl). From Engelkemeir.[39]

of light output versus particle energy is nearly linear over a rather wide energy range for light charged particles such as electrons, protons, and deuterons. For alpha particles and heavier nuclei departures from linearity are observed. Illustrative examples of these effects are given in Figs. 8a, b, and c. Figure 8a, taken from the work of Engelkemeir,[39] demonstrates the pulse height as a function of energy for a NaI(Tl) crystal excited by gamma rays. The scintillation response is, of course, due to electrons produced by gamma-ray interactions within the crystal itself. It should be noted in Fig. 8a that for most practical purposes the response to gamma rays can be considered as a linear function of energy; however, in the low-energy region (below several hundred kev) a distinct nonlinearity is observed. The question of nonlinearity in the scintillation response of NaI(Tl) to low-energy electrons has been the subject of some discussion in the literature and has been summarized elsewhere.[21,94] The most recent experiments[21,39] represent a thorough and detailed study of this question and have yielded results, with various crystals and different electronic techniques, in good agreement with Fig. 8a. It is therefore not permissible

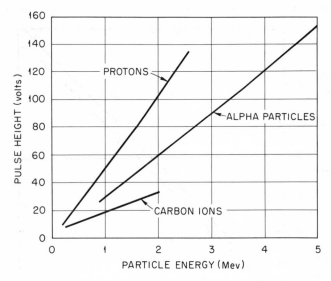

Fig. 8b.   Pulse height versus energy from protons, alphas, and C[12] ions on CsI(Tl). From Bashkin et al.[7]

to depend on a strictly linear output from gamma rays on NaI(Tl) for purposes of establishing the linearity or zero of a multichannel analyzer. In doing precise gamma-ray spectroscopy, especially in the low-energy region, it is advisable to establish a calibration curve for the counter and electronic system in use, using gamma-ray sources of known energy as calibration points.

   Typical response of an inorganic scintillator to heavier particles is shown in Fig. 8b, taken from Bashkin et al.[7] This figure shows pulse height as a function of energy for protons, alphas, and C[12] ions on CsI(Tl) and illustrates clearly the decreasing pulse height per Mev in going from protons to heavier particles. The response of NaI(Tl) to charged particles varying from electrons to fission fragments is summarized in Fig. 8c, in which scintillation efficiency is plotted as a function of differential energy loss of the charged particle in the crystal. *Scintillation efficiency* is here defined as dL/dE, the slope of a pulse height versus energy curve, and is a differential quantity representing the number of photons emitted per unit energy loss of the charged particle. The experimental data in Fig. 8c are summarized from a number of experiments; very similar behavior is observed for CsI(Tl) and KI(Tl).[86] It is seen that the scintillation efficiency actually passes through a maximum for protons in the Mev region and is

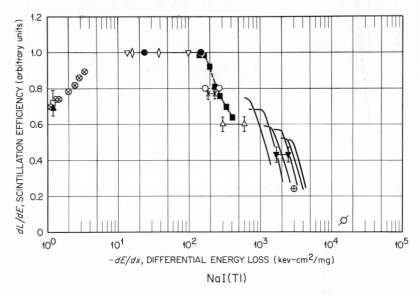

Na I(Tl)

Fig. 8c. Scintillation efficiency as a function of differential energy loss for various charged particles on NaI(Tl). Experimental data have been taken from a number of papers. ▲, □, ⊗ electrons; ▽, ◇, ○ protons; ×, ● deuterons; ■, △ alphas; ⊕ Na²³ ions; ▼ Ne²⁰ ions; ⊘ fission fragments; smooth curves represent heavy ions, B¹⁰ through Ne²⁰.

smaller both for electrons and heavier particles. A phenomenological interpretation of this behavior has been given elsewhere.[86] Briefly stated, the increasing scintillation efficiency at low values of dE/dx is attributed to the formation of energy carriers, whereas the decreasing scintillation efficiency for heavy particles results from the depletion of available activator sites as a consequence of the high ionization density in the wake of the incident particle.

The scintillation response of an alkali-iodide crystal is dependent on the activator concentration. Figures 9a, b, taken from the work of Eby and Jentschke,[36] demonstrate the dependence of pulse height and decay time of NaI(Tl) on the thallium content. The scintillation efficiency of LiI(Eu)

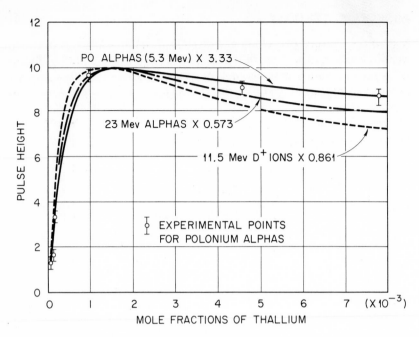

Fig. 9a. Pulse height versus thallium content for NaI(Tl). From Eby and Jentschke.[36]

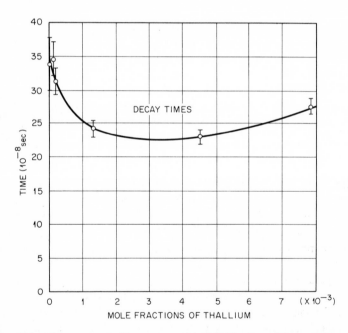

Fig. 9b. Decay time versus thallium content for NaI(Tl). From Eby and Jentschke.[36]

100

to various charged particles is a function of europium content, as shown in Fig. 10. The ordinate of Fig. 10 represents the gamma-ray equivalent energy at which the slow-neutron peak occurs. It is seen that the properties of both NaI(Tl) and LiI(Eu) are relatively insensitive to activator content

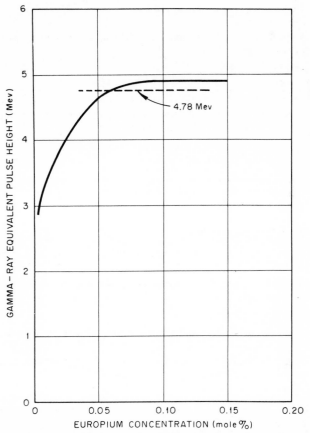

Fig. 10. Gamma-ray equivalent pulse height of slow-neutron peak in LiI(Eu) as a function of europium content. Li$^6(n, \alpha)T$ reaction Q-value = 4.78 Mev. Taken from work of J. Schenck at Oak Ridge National Laboratory.

for concentrations of more than 0.1 mole % but may vary sharply below this concentration.

Finally, we note the significant variation in decay time for various particles in the case of CsI(Tl). Storey et al.[115] observed a decay time of 0.43 μsec for 4.8-Mev alpha particles and 0.7 μsec for 662-kev electrons. Aside from its intrinsic interest, this property provides a means of particle discrimination, to be discussed in Section F.

6. Characteristics of some inorganic scintillators. The properties of some inorganic crystals which have been studied and used as scintillators are listed in this section. The conversion efficiency, where listed, represents the ratio of emitted photon energy to incident particle energy.

1. NaI(Tl)

    Decay time: 0.3 μsec

    Emission spectrum: Band centered at 4200 A, about 800 A wide at half-maximum

    Density (gram/cm³): 3.67

    Conversion efficiency: 13%

    Principal uses: Gamma-ray and charged-particle detection and spectroscopy

    Other properties: Available as large clear crystals which are hygroscopic and must be sealed in an airtight environment.

    Refs.: 4, 36, 132, 134, 136

2. NaI (pure) at the liquid nitrogen point

    Decay time: 0.06 μsec

    Emission spectrum: See Figs. 11a and 11b.

    Density (gram/cm³): 3.67

    Conversion efficiency: 25%

    Principal uses: Detection and spectroscopy of low-energy gammas and charged particles; short decay time permits high counting rates or fast coincidences.

    Other properties: Emission spectrum very sensitive to traces of thallium

    Refs.: 19, 134, 136

3. CsI(Tl)

    Decay time: Reported from 0.43 μsec (alpha particles) to 1.1 μsec (gamma rays)

    Emission spectrum: Broad spectrum extending from blue to red, maximum in red

    Density (gram/cm³): 4.51

    Light output: Somewhat less than that of NaI(Tl) as determined with blue-sensitive photomultiplier

    Principal uses: Gamma-ray and charged-particle detection and spectroscopy. Especially convenient to use as it is nonhygroscopic. Variation in decay time for various particles permits particle discrimination.

    Other properties: Available as large, clear, nonhygroscopic crystals. Has higher detection efficiency for gammas than NaI(Tl). The matching of CsI(Tl) with a red-sensitive photomultiplier offers an interesting possibility. A long-lived phosphorescence following exposure to room light has been reported.

    Refs.: 7, 51, 56, 78, 93, 115

4. CsI (pure) at the liquid nitrogen point

    Decay time: 0.6 μsec

Emission spectrum: Complex spectrum extending from near ultraviolet through visible; peak intensity around 4000 A.

Density (gram/cm³): 4.51

Conversion efficiency: 35 to 40% for alpha excitation

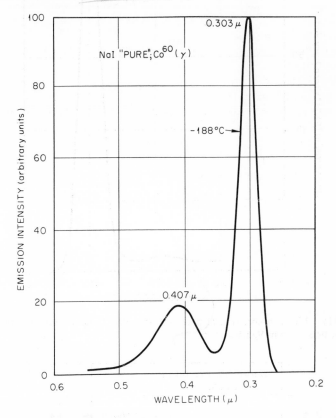

Fig. 11a. Emission spectrum of pure NaI at −188° C upon excitation by Co⁶⁰ gamma rays, from Van Sciver.[134]

Principal uses: Possibly as gamma-ray detector and spectrometer with greater density and higher effective atomic number than NaI. High conversion efficiency might be useful in detection of low-energy gammas or charged particles.

Other properties: Nonhygroscopic

Refs.: 42, 55, 57, 78

5. LiI(Eu)

Decay time: 1.1 to 1.3 μsec

Emission spectrum: See Fig. 11c.

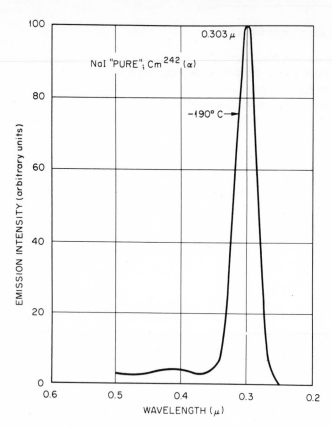

Fig. 11*b*. Emission spectrum of pure NaI at −190° C upon excitation by Cm[242] alpha particles. From Van Sciver.[134]

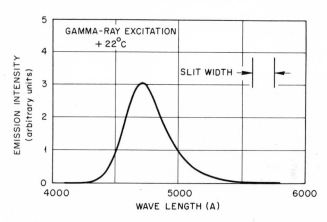

Fig. 11*c*. Emission spectrum of Li⁶I(Eu) at 22° C upon excitation by gamma rays. No correction has been applied to account for spectral sensitivity of detector (RCA 6903, S-13 spectral response). From Hanson et al.[69]

Density (gram/cm³): 4.06

Light output: About one third that of NaI(Tl)

Principal uses: High-efficiency detector for slow neutrons. Detection and energy measurement of fast neutrons.

Other properties: Very hygroscopic, subject to radiation damage from excessive exposure to slow-neutron beam or ultraviolet light. Large clear crystals available commercially; also available as enriched Li⁶I(Eu).

Refs.: 95, 101, 116

6. KI(Tl)

Decay time: 1 μsec or longer

Emission spectrum: Band centered at 4100 A, about 900 A wide at half-maximum

Density (gram/cm³): 3.13

Light output: About one fourth to one fifth that of NaI(Tl).

Principal uses: As nonhygroscopic crystal for detection and spectroscopy of charged particles

Other properties: Exhibits long phosphorescence, has a weak radioactive background due to presence of K⁴⁰. Nonhygroscopic. Can be grown as large, clear crystals.

Refs.: 44, 56

7. CsF (unactivated)

Decay time: 0.005 μsec for gamma excitation, 0.2 μsec for alpha-particle excitation

Emission spectrum: Band at 3900 A for gamma excitation, band at 4250 A for alpha excitation

Density (gram/cm³): 3.59

Light output: About 5% of the light output of NaI(Tl) for gammas, very weak pulses from alphas

Principal uses: Possibly as a very fast detector for gamma rays

Other properties: Can be easily grown as a clear crystal; hygroscopic.

Refs.: 134, 135

8. ZnS(Ag)

Decay time: Originally reported to be ∼10 μsec. Recent measurements with fast electronics indicate 0.04–0.1 μsec with additional component of ∼5 μsec.

Emission spectrum: Band centered near 4500 A

Density (gram/cm³): 4.10

Conversion efficiency: 28% for alpha particles

Principal uses: Detection of alpha particles, fission fragments. Also may be suspended in a plastic for fast-neutron detection.

Other properties: Currently available only in multicrystalline powder form, not transparent to its emitted light. Good discrimination against gamma rays, electrons.

Refs.: 64, 79, 88

9. $CdWO_4$

Decay time: About $\frac{1}{2}$ μsec

Emission spectrum: Maximum at $\sim$5300 A upon x-ray excitation

Density (gram/cm³): 7.9

Light output: Somewhat less than that of NaI(Tl)

Principal uses: Possibly as a detector and spectrometer for gamma rays, seldom used at present time

Other properties: High melting point (1325° C). High density and high atomic number result in a very large gamma-ray absorption coefficient providing a high gamma-ray detection efficiency. Apparently difficult to grow as large single crystal. Relatively inert chemically. Very high refractive index, $n_D = 2.2$–2.3.

Refs.: 52

A number of other inorganic crystals have been found to scintillate, but they seem to offer relatively little improvement over those already listed, except in certain restricted applications. LiF is an example of an alkali halide that might provide an extremely useful scintillator for neutron detection and energy measurement. Its low effective atomic number would make it relatively insensitive to gamma rays, and it is readily available as large, clear, nonhygroscopic crystals. An early report on this material[45] indicated luminescent response of unactivated LiF to nuclear particles at the dry-ice point. Recent studies of both activated and unactivated LiF at several laboratories, however, have not yielded an observable scintillation response. Numerous attempts to activate LiF at Armour Research Foundation and Harshaw Chemical Company have not yet been successful.[1,117]

Inorganic scintillation crystals are now available commercially from a number of sources. Some of the suppliers are Harshaw Chemical Company, Cleveland, Ohio; Levinthal Electronic Products, Palo Alto, California; Isomet Corporation, Palisades Park, New Jersey; National Radiac, Inc., Newark, New Jersey; and Isotopes, Inc., Westwood, New Jersey.

B. Organic Crystals and Plastics

1. Preparation. The organic materials that are found to be efficient scintillators generally fall in the class of aromatic hydrocarbons, both pure and substituted. The presence of slight traces of impurities in organic scintillators can result in a substantial quenching of the light output. For this reason it is necessary to purify the starting material rather carefully before crystal growth. In contrast to the alkali halides, no activator is added to organic crystals. Various techniques are available for purification of organic materials, such as passing through an absorption column (containing, say, activated alumina), successive recrystallizations from solution, extraction, and fractional distillation. These processes may be applied singly or in sequence to a given material; the particular purification method depends entirely on the chemical composition of the scintillator and the expected impurities. Repeated recrystallization from various solutions will frequently yield a sufficiently pure product. More detailed discussions of chemical methods are given in the book by Curran[30] and the report by Sangster and Irvine.[118] Crystal growth is usually accomplished by the Bridgman method with the starting material sealed in a glass ampoule. The ampoule containing the melt is lowered slowly through the furnace at a rate of the order of inches per day. The melting points of solid organic scintillators are generally much lower than those of inorganic crystals, for example, anthracene (217° C), trans-stilbene (124° C), compared with sodium iodide (651° C). The organic crystals most frequently used are readily available commercially; anthracene and stilbene crystals are advertised in sizes up to about $3\frac{1}{2}$ in. in diameter by 4 in. long.

Plastic scintillators usually consist of an organic scintillator dissolved in either polystyrene or polyvinyltoluene. The optimum concentration of the solute is of the order of a few percent or less. A detailed description of the preparation of a number of plastic scintillators has been given by Buck and Swank.[9] Their method consists of polymerization of the liquid monomer-fluor solution. It was found that the scintillation characteristics of the product depended sensitively on the purity and freshness of the monomer used; accordingly, the monomers (styrene and vinyltoluene) were purified immediately before use by vacuum distillation. The fluorescent solutes were obtained commercially as a specially purified grade. No additional plasticizers or catalysts were added to the solution. The monomer-fluor solution was placed in a glass vessel and evacuated to remove dissolved air. The vessel was then sealed off under vacuum and placed in a constant-temperature oil bath for a period of seven days to permit polymerization. At the end of this period, the polymer was cooled to room temperature; slow cooling was necessary to prevent formation of bubbles or cracking of the plastic.

Wouters[144] has recently described a technique for "fast" polymerization of plastic scintillators, with attention to the problem of producing large scintillators. This process is an autocatalytic one in which the reaction temperature is maintained by the exothermic nature of the process; the excess heat of reaction must be removed by carefully designed heat exchangers.

Plastic scintillators are now available commercially from a number of suppliers and can be obtained in the form of disks, cylinders, thin films, or long rods. One of the chief advantages of plastic scintillators is the wide variety of shapes and sizes in which they can be obtained. In particular, quite large scintillators, whose dimensions are of the order of many inches, are available. An interesting case is that of a scintillator, 42 in. in diameter by $3\frac{1}{2}$ in. thick, fabricated for cosmic ray studies.[31]

2. Mechanism of scintillation process. The scintillation process in organic compounds, both solid and liquid, is primarily a molecular phenomenon and as such may be distinguished from the case of inorganic solids whose luminescence is intimately associated with the energy-band structure of ionic crystals. Organic solids are classified as molecular crystals; the intermolecular bonding is quite weak, compared with the bonding in an ionic crystal, and arises primarily from Van der Waals forces. On the basis of a number of studies of photoluminescence in organic crystals, it is concluded that luminescence arises from the de-excitation of a molecule from its first excited electronic state. The dependence of molecular potential energy on a configuration coordinate is analogous to the energy level diagram of Fig. 4. In addition to various electronic states, the molecule will possess states of different vibrational energy. The energy difference between vibration states is small, however, compared to the separation of electronic states. The absorption spectrum of an organic solid shows several absorption peaks, corresponding to transitions from various vibrational levels of the ground state to the first electronic state. The luminescence emission spectrum exhibits a similar structure, but it is found at a somewhat longer wavelength. This wavelength shift occurs for the same reason as that discussed in the case of inorganic crystals. An example of the luminescence emission spectrum from an organic crystal (stilbene) is shown in Fig. 12 to illustrate the several closely spaced emission bands. The stilbene crystal was excited by ultraviolet light. In general, the absorption and emission spectra of organic compounds overlap some-what, so that the short wavelength end of the emission spectrum is sharply attenuated. Photoluminescence experiments with organic crystals demonstrate quite high quantum efficiencies (photons emitted per photon absorbed) upon excitation to the first excited state, approaching 90 to 100% in the case of anthracene. When the crystal is excited to the second electronic excited state, or higher, the quantum efficiency remains essentially the same, and the emission spectrum is again that from the first excited state. These facts indicate a very efficient process operating to permit de-excitation from the higher states to the first excited state from which a radiative transition takes place. This process has frequently been described as a nonradiative transition analogous to *CEA* of Fig. 4, whereas Birks[3] has presented arguments in favor of very fast fluorescence from the higher states to the ground state, followed by reabsorption of the emitted radiation by neighboring molecules. The majority of organic compounds do not exhibit luminescence, in spite of the fact that they absorb light in the visible or ultraviolet; this property demonstrates the existence of non-radiative processes permitting de-excitation of the molecule to the ground state.

A very important mechanism in the scintillation response of organic crystals is that of energy transfer from one molecule to another, especially, in the case of dilute solutions, energy transfer from the solvent to the solute molecules. A study of mixed organic crystals of the benzene series

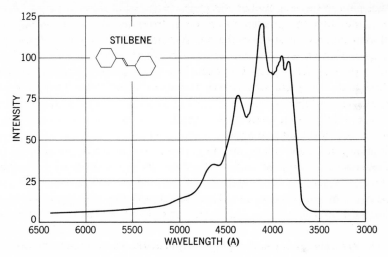

Fig. 12. Emission spectrum of stilbene at room temperature. From Sangster and Irvine.[118]

by Bowen et al.[10] showed that a small admixture of one compound in solid solution with another could have a profound effect on the emission spectrum. In general, if a higher member of the series were added to a lower member (anthracene in naphthalene or naphthacene in anthracene), the emission spectrum would shift from that of the solvent to that of the solute at very low solute concentrations, of the order of 10^{-4} to 10^{-3}. The problem of identifying the energy transport mechanism has been the subject of a number of investigations and theories. Bowen and co-workers suggested exciton migration. Franck and Livingston[46] proposed that energy transfer occurs not by excitons but by a quantum-mechanical resonance process, that of sensitized fluorescence. Birks[3,11] presents a series of arguments opposed to either of these mechanisms, favoring that of photon emission and reabsorption; primary photon emission is assumed to arise from highly excited states. The subject of energy transfer in organic scintillators is actually very complex; the energy transport mechanism is apparently not just one of the above processes but a combination of them. The detailed nature of the energy transport process depends on the particular properties of the scintillator itself, i.e., its solute concentration, whether there is more than one solute, electronic energy levels of the solvent and solute, etc. Discussions and summaries of this subject have been given by Brooks,[12] Kallman and Furst,[123] and Birks.[140]

The energy-transfer process from polymer to solute in plastic solid solutions has been discussed in detail by Swank and Buck,[119] who conclude that photon transfer contributes to the process but that the major effect is a nonradiative energy exchange resulting from the interaction of molecular electric dipoles. A study of the polystyrene-anthracene system by Krenz[80] showed that at very low concentrations of anthracene (below about 5×10^{-4}) the transfer of excitation occurs by photon emission and absorption. At higher concentrations energy transport takes place through a nonradiative molecular process.

The scintillation process in organic compounds exhibits a further difference from that in inorganic crystals in that the luminescence emission from organic materials occurs much faster, by a factor of the order of 100. Decay times of organic solids and plastics are of the order of 10^{-8} sec and thus correspond to the predicted lifetime of an excited electronic state before an allowed transition. This fact requires that energy transfer in the case of a solid solution or plastic take place in a time shorter than 10^{-8} sec.

3. Properties depending on temperature and concentration. It is found that the light output of organic crystals in general increases with decreasing temperature. This is in the same direction as that for most of the alkali iodides, both activated and unactivated, as previously noted. The pulse height from gamma activation of all crystals studied by Sangster and Irvine[118] increased in cooling from room temperature to $-70°$ C. The pulse-height increase in this temperature interval ranged from a few percent (e.g., diphenylbutadiene) to a factor of 4 (tetraphenylethylene). The temperature dependence of light output from anthracene, naphthalene, and mixtures of the two, was the subject of a study by Liebson,[91] who found an increase of a factor of 3 in naphthalene and less than a factor of 2 in anthracene upon cooling from room temperature to $100°$ K. Measurements on stilbene indicated little variation in light output over the same temperature range. The decay time of an organic crystal may also be temperature dependent; Elliot et al.[37] report a *decrease* in the decay time of anthracene in cooling to $4°$ K amounting to a factor of 2, whereas the decay time of stilbene was almost temperature independent, decreasing only slightly from room temperature to 78° K. Birks[13] has pointed out a correlation between light output S and decay time τ of the form

$$\log S = \text{constant} + B\tau. \qquad (6)$$

The experimental data on anthracene can be well fitted with this equation when B is a negative constant. Equation 6 is derived by Birks on the basis

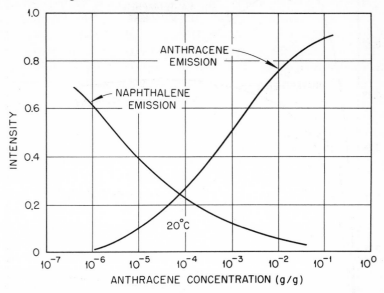

Fig. 13. Emission intensity from mixed naphthalene-anthracene crystals as a function of anthracene concentration. From Bowen et al.[10]

of a scintillation process involving repeated photon emission and reabsorption within the crystal.

The scintillation properties of mixed crystals and plastics are rather strongly dependent on solute concentration. As an example, Fig. 13 shows the naphthalene and anthracene emission intensities in a series of mixed anthracene-naphthalene crystals as a function of anthracene content. It is seen that the light output is predominantly that of anthracene at a concentration as low as $\sim 10^{-3}$. The dependence of emission intensity versus solute concentration for a number of plastic scintillators is shown in Fig. 14a. The decay time as a function of solute concentration for the case of tetraphenylbutadiene in polystyrene is shown in Fig. 14b. It may be noted in Fig. 14b that a 0.5% solution of tetraphenylbutadiene in polystyrene has a decay time of about 7×10^{-9} sec (compared with $\sim 30 \times 10^{-9}$ sec for anthracene) and yields more than one third the light output of pure anthracene, which is the most efficient organic crystal

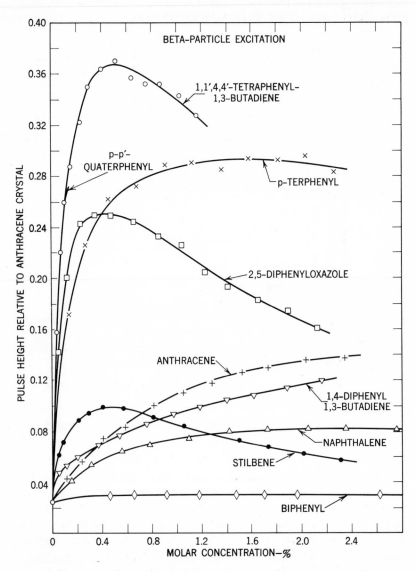

Fig. 14a. Pulse height versus concentration for several polystyrene solid solution scintillators, using beta-particle excitation. Pulse heights are given relative to an anthracene crystal "standard" using a 5819 photomultiplier. No correction is made for the spectral response of the photosurface. From Swank and Buck.[119]

scintillator known at this time. The curves in Fig. 14a were calculated to fit the data points[119] from an equation of the form

$$\text{pulse height} = \text{const} \times \left(\frac{q_0 + \sigma c}{1 + \sigma c}\right)\left(\frac{1}{1 + mc}\right) \tag{7}$$

where q_0 is the quantum efficiency of the solvent, c is the molar concentration of the solute, σ is a parameter related to the probability of energy transfer to the solute, and m is a parameter associated with "self-quenching" in

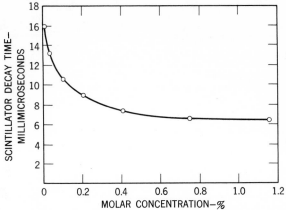

Fig. 14b. Scintillation decay time versus concentration of tetraphenylbutadiene in polystyrene, under pulsed x-ray excitation. From Swank and Buck.[119]

the solute. Equation 7 is based on a nonradiative energy transfer process and is seen to provide a good fit to the data. Further, the value of q_0 determined from these measurements was found to be a property of the solvent, in agreement with theory; for polystyrene $q_0 = 0.16$; for polyvinyltoluene $q_0 = 0.21$.

4. Response to charged particles. The scintillation response of organic materials differs in several respects from that of inorganic crystals, as previously noted. The principal differences are (1) a much faster decay time for the organics; (2) the conversion efficiency of organics is generally less than that of inorganic crystals; (3) the difference in light output per Mev from various charged particles is significantly greater for organic scintillators; and (4) organic crystals have a nonlinear relationship between pulse height and energy for heavy charged particles over a rather wide range of energy. Items 2, 3, and 4 are demonstrated in Figs. 15a, b taken from Taylor et al.[132]

The scintillation response of anthracene to gamma rays (electrons) has been the subject of several investigations; the results generally indicate a

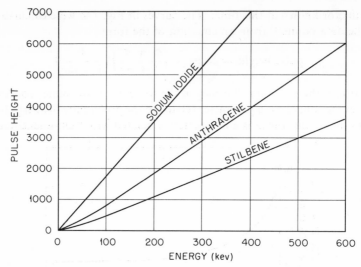

Fig. 15a. Pulse heights from electron excitation of sodium iodide, anthracene, and stilbene as a function of electron energy. Ordinate scale is arbitrary. From Taylor et al.[132]

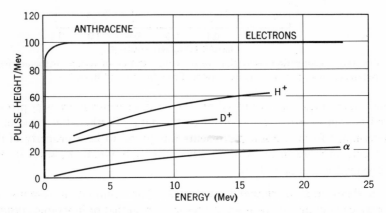

Fig. 15b. Pulse height per Mev for various particles on anthracene, as a function of particle energy. The arbitrary ordinate scale has been chosen so that the maximum value for electrons is 100 units per Mev. From Taylor et al.[132]

linear response above 100 or 125 kev. (See, for example, Ref. 71.) A recent report by Johnston and co-workers[72] on a thin bare crystal indicates a linear relationship, upon excitation by an external electron beam, in the region of 10 to 120 kev. The response of anthracene to photoelectrons in the 6-to-30-kev region, resulting from x-ray bombardment, was found to be essentially linear.[14] A plot of pulse height versus energy for the low-energy data[14,72] does not pass through the origin but intercepts the energy axis at a value of about 3 or 4 kev. The nonlinear response of organic crystals to heavier charged particles, as well as the variation of scintillation efficiency with ionization density, has been studied by various authors. Birks[8] has proposed a function to describe the response of organic scintillators to charged particles which has the form

$$\frac{dL}{dx} = \frac{A\left(\dfrac{dE}{dx}\right)}{1 + B\left(\dfrac{dE}{dx}\right)} \tag{8}$$

where dL/dx is the light output per unit path length for a particle whose differential energy loss is dE/dx; A and B are constants. The pulse height L as a function of energy is obtained by integrating (8),

$$L(E) = A \int_0^E \frac{dE}{1 + B\left(\dfrac{dE}{dx}\right)}. \tag{9}$$

Equation 8 was proposed by Birks on the basis of a theoretical model in which he assumed that the local concentration of "damaged" molecules, along the path of the incident particle, is proportional to dE/dx. The probability of quenching the fluorescence radiation by an affected molecule is proportional to their concentration, thus leading to the denominator $[1 + B (dE/dx)]$ in (8). Equation 9 predicts the nonlinear response to heavy charged particles as well as the difference in scintillation efficiency for various charged particles and is in quite good agreement with the experimental data on anthracene. Models suggested by other authors do not seem to be in significantly better agreement with experiment, although the fit may be just as good as that given by (9). As an example, Fig. 16 shows the response of anthracene to various charged particles as measured and calculated from a function suggested by Wright.[139] A detailed comparison of the various models may be found elsewhere.[12] It appears that the response of anthracene to various charged particles is typical of organic scintillators. In general, the pulse height per Mev for alpha particles is much less than that for electrons, the ratio being about 0.1 for anthracene, stilbene, and a number of plastic scintillators. This is referred to as the α/β ratio.

Both organic crystals and plastics are subject to radiation damage upon prolonged bombardment by electrons or heavier particles; the damage is manifest as a decrease in pulse height with increasing radiation exposure.

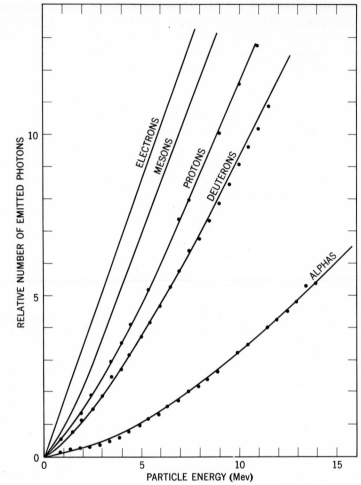

Fig. 16.   Scintillation response of anthracene to ionizing particles. Points are experimental, curves are calculated. From Wright.[139]

Birks[3] reports that for Po[210] alpha particles on anthracene, the light intensity I decreases as

$$\frac{I}{I_0} = \frac{1}{1 + 10^{-11}N} \qquad (10)$$

where N is the total number of alphas/cm^2 that have struck the crystal. This effect imposes a limit on the useful lifetime of a crystal; for most applications, of course, 10^{11} counts amounts to a generous lifetime. Radiation damage effects in plastics resulting from electron bombardment have been reported by Hinrichs.[58]

5. Characteristics of some organic crystals. The scintillation properties of some organic crystals are listed in this section. It should be understood that rather wide variations in the parameters listed can be expected from one crystal to another. This is particularly true of the conversion efficiency and the decay time; numbers differing by a factor of 2 or more may be found in the literature. The principal applications of organic scintillators are the detection and spectroscopy of betas and the fast detection of gammas, especially in fast coincidence work. The density of organic crystals is generally about 1.2 grams/cm³. Because of their low density and low atomic number, organic crystals are much less efficient gamma detectors than NaI(Tl) or CsI(Tl) and are generally less suitable for gamma-ray spectroscopy. As a result of their high hydrogen content, organic crystals are used for fast-neutron detection.

1. Anthracene, $C_{14}H_{10}$: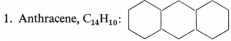

Decay time: About 30×10^{-9} sec for electron excitation; may be different for alphas. Conflicting reports in literature.

Emission spectrum: Maximum near 4400 A

Conversion efficiency: About 5%

Other properties: Can be obtained in a variety of shapes and sizes, with dimensions up to several inches. Anthracene is the most widely studied organic crystal and is probably the most frequently used.

Refs.: 12, 81, 118

2. *Trans*-stilbene, $C_{14}H_{12}$:

Decay time: About 4 to 8×10^{-9} sec for electron excitation; reported to be different for alphas.

Emission spectrum: Maximum near 4100 A

Light output: About one half that of anthracene

Other properties: Available commercially as clear, colorless, single crystals with dimensions up to several inches; crystals are sensitive to thermal and mechanical shock. Especially useful as very fast detector.

Refs.: 12, 81, 118

3. Quaterphenyl, $C_{24}H_{18}$:

Decay time: About 4×10^{-9} sec

Emission spectrum: Maximum near 4400 A

Light output: About 90% that of anthracene

Other properties: Combines fast decay time with high light output. Microcrystalline material is available commercially. Crystals are reported to be clear and tough and to have good thermal and chemical stability.

Ref.: 118

Other organic crystals have been the subject of study but appear to have no particular advantage over the foregoing and are rather little used. Properties of a number of organic crystals are discussed by Sangster and Irvine.[118]

6. Characteristics of some plastic scintillators.

Plastic solution scintillators generally have quite short decay times, of the order of a few millimicroseconds, and are thus useful for high counting rate experiments and fast coincidence work. Since plastic scintillators can be made quite large, they may serve as high-efficiency detectors for fast neutrons. Their response to charged particles shows the same general features as anthracene. (See Fig. 16.) The light output of useful organic plastics is typically one quarter to one half that of anthracene. A rather large number of organic plastics has been studied; their properties are compared in several tabulations.[94,120] We restrict attention to a few with optimum light output. The secondary solute, where listed, serves as a wavelength shifter to convert the fluorescence spectrum to a region of greater photocathode sensitivity. The density of plastic scintillators is somewhat greater than 1 gram/cm^3.

1. Solvent: Polystyrene
   Primary solute: Tetraphenylbutadiene, 16 grams/liter of monomer
   Secondary solute: None
   Decay time: 4.6×10^{-9} sec
   Emission spectrum: Maximum near 4500 A
   Light output: 36% of anthracene
   Ref.: 120

2. Solvent: Polyvinyltoluene
   Primary solute: p-terphenyl, 36 grams/liter of monomer
   Secondary solute: p,p'-diphenylstilbene, 0.9 gram/liter of monomer
   Decay time: About 3×10^{-9} sec or less
   Emission spectrum: Maximum near 3800 A
   Light output: 48% of anthracene
   Ref.: 120

3. Solvent: Polyvinyltoluene
   Primary solute: p-terphenyl, 36 grams/liter of monomer
   Secondary solute: tetraphenylbutadiene, 0.2 gram/liter of monomer
   Decay time: 4×10^{-9} sec
   Emission spectrum: Maximum near 4450 A
   Light output: 45% of anthracene
   Ref.: 120

A recent comparison of plastic scintillators containing aromatic substituted oxazoles has been reported by Basile.[15]

Plastic scintillators, under various trade names, are available from a number of commercial suppliers. These plastics are advertised as having a typically fast decay time of the order of a few millimicroseconds, with light output about one half that of anthracene. Several of the manufacturers are Crystals, Inc., Westwood, New Jersey; Nuclear Enterprises, Ltd., Winnipeg, Canada; Pilot Chemicals, Inc., Watertown, Massachusetts; Cadillac Plastic and Chemical Company, Detroit, Michigan; and National Radiac, Inc., Newark, New Jersey.

C. Organic Liquids

Numerous problems in high-energy physics, cosmic ray studies, or low-level counting experiments require the use of large-volume scintillators. Organic liquid scintillators are well suited for these purposes, since they can be obtained in large quantities (gallons) and poured into a container of any shape and size. The scintillation properties of organic liquids are quite similar to those of organic solids; in particular, plastic solutions and liquid solutions are both made up of a solvent, primary solute, and, perhaps a secondary solute. The purpose of these ingredients is the same in both cases: the solvent acts as the principal stopping medium; energy deposited in the solvent is transferred to the primary solute which emits its characteristic fluorescence radiation; the secondary solute serves as a wavelength shifter to convert the emission spectrum of the primary solute to a longer wavelength to provide increased photocathode efficiency. Longer wavelength radiation also means a longer photon mean free path, resulting in more efficient light collection in large-volume scintillators. (See Fig. 18.) In addition, liquid scintillators may contain a *secondary solvent* whose function is to provide a more efficient transfer of excitation energy to the solutes.[47] The secondary solvent may be added to the solution in a concentration of the order of hundreds of grams per liter, compared with solute concentrations of a few grams per liter.

I. Preparation. Organic liquid scintillators may suffer a significant loss of light from the presence of small amounts of impurities, just as organic crystals. For this reason it may be necessary to subject the starting materials to purification steps such as repeated fractional distillation. This may be especially true of the bulk material (solvent), typically xylene or toluene. Solutes, which are required in considerably smaller quantities, are now available in "scintillation-grade" purity from several firms (e.g., Pilot Chemicals, Inc., Nuclear Enterprises, Ltd., and Arapahoe Chemicals,

Inc., Boulder, Colorado) and generally do not require further purification. Organic liquids are especially susceptible to quenching by dissolved oxygen. To achieve maximum light output it is necessary to remove the oxygen by bubbling an inert gas, such as nitrogen or argon, through the solution. An example of the improvement in light output upon removal of dissolved

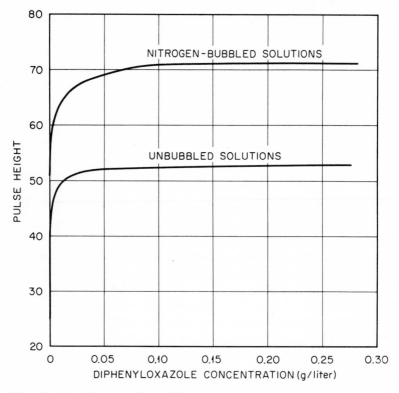

Fig. 17. Scintillation pulse height (relative to anthracene as 100) versus diphenyloxazole concentration for a 3 gram/liter terphenyl-xylene solution, illustrating effect of nitrogen bubbling. From Pringle et al.[110]

oxygen by nitrogen bubbling is shown in Fig. 17, taken from the report by Pringle et al.[110] Similar results were reported by Ott and co-workers,[108] who observed a 23 % increase in pulse height upon passing argon through several solutions. An alternative method of oxygen removal is that of vacuum distillation of the solution. Chleck and Ziegler[32] have reported an effective ultrasonic method of degassing in an atmosphere of argon which results in a minimum amount of evaporation and loss of solution. The role of oxygen in the quenching process has been studied experimentally by Seliger et al.,[121] who found evidence that the principal effect was one of *solute* quenching. A detailed theoretical treatment of oxygen quenching apparently has not yet been given.

Finally, it is important to note that the scintillator must be used in a cell whose walls (possibly plastic) or reflecting coating are not soluble in the solution itself.

2. General properties of organic liquids. The scintillation characteristics of organic liquids are generally quite similar to those of organic solids, particularly plastic solutions. The mechanism of the scintillation process is basically the same molecular phenomenon previously discussed; the roles of the ingredients of a liquid solution are given above. A plot of light output versus solute concentration exhibits a maximum, as in the case of plastic solutions. An experimental study by Furst and Kallman[48] indicates that for a large number of solutions studied the intensity I as a function of solute concentration C is given by

$$I = \frac{PC}{(Q + C))R + C)} \tag{11}$$

where P, Q, and R are parameters characteristic of a particular solvent-solute combination. The parameters were found to be significantly different for electrons and alpha particles. Optimum solute concentrations are in the range of a few grams per liter. Other authors[73] have proposed somewhat different expressions for I versus C, which are also in accord with experiment.

The light output of several organic solutions studied by Seliger and Ziegler[122] has been found to increase with decreasing temperature in the interval between room temperature and $-36°$ C. They examined solutions of DPO, PBD, αNPO, and anthracene at concentrations of 4 grams/liter, 8 grams/liter, 3.2 grams/liter, and 1 gram/liter, respectively, in vacuum-distilled *m*-xylene.* The slopes of the lines obtained by plotting pulse height versus temperature ranged from 0.4 to 1 % per ° C. On the basis of these results, Seliger and Ziegler were led to suggest that a solution of gas-free DPO + POPOP in xylene at temperatures below $-35°$ C might be more efficient than crystal anthracene.†

The response of liquid scintillators to charged particles is presumably quite similar to that of organic solids, although detailed studies of this point seem to be lacking. The α/β ratio of organic liquids is small, of order 0.1. The pulse height versus energy relationship for electrons is found to

---

  *   DPO = PPO = 2,5-diphenyloxazole.
     PBD = 2-phenyl-5-(4-biphenyl)-1,3,4-oxadiazole.
     αNPO = 2-(1-naphthyl)-5-phenyloxazole.
  † POPOP = 1,4-di-[2-(5-phenyloxazolyl)]-benzene.

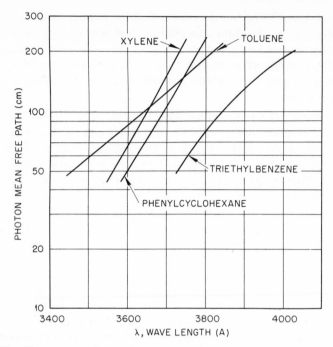

Fig. 18. Photon mean free path versus wavelength for several organic solvents,
Plotted from data given by Hayes et al.[60]

be linear above at least 0.5 Mev in the case of a solution containing
p-diphenylbenzene and POPOP.[59] The light output from usable organic
solutions may typically be 40–60% that of anthracene. It is to be emphasized, however, that the pulse size from a given liquid may depend
sensitively on its purity, the sample size and reflector, and especially on the
spectral response characteristics of the particular photomultiplier in use.
This point has been the subject of a paper by Swank et al.,[124] who point
out that a difference of a factor of 2 can be obtained in the pulse-height
ratio of two liquid scintillators when the spectral-response characteristics
of the detection system are varied.

The decay times of liquid scintillators are of the order of a few millimicroseconds, comparable with those of plastic solutions. For this reason,
liquid scintillators are applicable to very fast coincidence studies.

The primary solvents that have proved most satisfactory and that have
been used most frequently are toluene, xylene, and phenylcyclohexane. For
use in large volumes, the mean free path of a photon in the solvent is an
important parameter. Figure 18, taken from the work of Hayes et al.,[60]
illustrates the photon mean free path as a function of wavelength for

various solvents. The use of isopropylbiphenyl as a solvent has been recently reported by Buck and Swank.[16] It appears to offer several advantages over previously used solvents: it has low flammability and volatility, a somewhat greater efficiency for gamma-ray detection, and is less subject to quenching by dissolved oxygen and heavy metals.

A rather large number of primary and secondary solutes has been tried out. One of the most successful primary solutes has been p-terphenyl in a concentration of about 5 grams/liter. Solutes of the "phenyloxazole" and "oxadiazole" types have recently been adopted, following their introduction by Hayes and co-workers.[61] Some general conclusions concerning the choice of an efficient liquid scintillator were given by Hayes et al. and are reproduced here:

1. A double-solute liquid scintillator is capable of yielding a better combination of wavelength and pulse height than a single-solute system. This makes it slightly preferable in small-volume counters and immensely superior in large-volume detectors.

2. The best secondary solutes are 1,4-di-[2-(5-phenyloxazolyl)]-benzene (POPOP) and 2,5-di-(4-biphenyl)-oxazole (BBO).

3. p-Terphenyl is an excellent primary solute in conjunction with POPOP or BBO.

4. The concentration range 0.05–0.5 gram/liter seems to be preferable for POPOP and BBO; the commonly required compromise between economy and response suggests the choice of 0.1 gram/liter. Similar reasoning suggests 4 grams/liter as a good primary-solute concentration.

Detailed tables describing the characteristics of a vast number of organic solutions may be found in various research reports and reviews (e.g., Refs. 61, 94, 120). Rather than duplicate this information, we quote a table from Hayes et al.[61] in which four of the "most notable organic scintillators" are listed.

TABLE I. SOME USEFUL ORGANIC SOLUTION
SCINTILLATORS

Solvent	Primary Solute (conc. in grams/liter)	Secondary Solute (conc. in grams/liter)	Relative Pulse Height*
Toluene	PPO(3)		1.00
Toluene	p-Terphenyl(4)	POPOP(0.1)	1.22
Toluene	PBD(10)		1.28
p-xylene	PBD(10)		1.40

* Compared to an anthracene crystal of pulse height 1.99. Liquid scintillator pulse heights measured with sample volume of 1 ml, aluminum reflector, and DuMont 6292 photomultiplier tube.

3. Loaded liquid scintillators. For certain purposes it is desirable to add a particular element, or elements, to the contents of a liquid scintillator. For example, a high-efficiency neutron detector is made possible by loading a liquid with a substance having a high cross section for neutron capture resulting in the emission of energetic charged particles (or gamma rays). Boron is a popular candidate for this role, neutron capture taking place through the $B^{10}(n, \alpha)$ reaction with a relatively high cross section. Cadmium has also been used; the solution responds to capture gamma rays immediately following neutron capture in the cadmium. Boron can be successfully added to scintillating solutions as methyl borate. Muehlhause and Thomas[96] describe a solution of equal volumes of methyl borate and phenylcyclohexane, with 4 grams/liter PPO and 16 mg/liter diphenylhexatriene. Bollinger and Thomas[17] examined a number of solutions containing methyl borate and found maximum pulse height in a combination of methyl borate plus toluene (equal parts) containing 4 grams/liter PBD and 20 mg/liter POPOP. One difficulty encountered with the methyl borate solutions used by both groups is a very low pulse height from $B^{10}(n, \alpha)$ reaction products; the scintillation efficiency was about $\frac{1}{40}$ that of electrons of the same energy.[96] The use of borazole $(B_3N_3H_6)$ solutions has been described by Kirkbride[82] and by Hoover and Dohne.[62] The large-volume liquid scintillators used in the free-neutrino detection experiments incorporated cadmium salts for the detection of neutrons after they had been thermalized by proton collisions. Cadmium propionate, $Cd(C_3H_5O_2)_2$, was initially used; better results were later obtained with a solution of cadmium octoate, $Cd(C_8H_{15}O_2)_2$, in triethylbenzene with terphenyl as the primary solute and POPOP wavelength shifter.[112]

The gamma-ray detection efficiency of liquid scintillators can be improved in principle by the addition of heavy elements (high atomic number). Considerable difficulty has been encountered with this scheme, however, as a result of strong quenching effects upon addition of heavy-element materials or as a result of their low solubility in usable solvents. Some recent results by Kallman et al. are encouraging and indicate that useful solutions may be obtained with the right combination of ingredients.[83] Liquid scintillators loaded with B, Gd, Cd, Pb, or Sm are advertised by Nuclear Enterprises, Ltd.

In conclusion, we may note recent reviews[65,100] of the applications of liquid scintillators to various counting problems.

D. Noble Gases

The use of noble gases as scintillation detectors for charged particles has taken place only in the last few years. Gas scintillation counters have been developed and used in several laboratories. Rather little work, however, dealing with the basic physical processes responsible for the observed properties of gas scintillators has been reported, and only a few general statements will be made concerning the scintillation mechanism.

When a charged particle passes through a gas, it loses energy primarily by inelastic collisions, leaving in its path excited atoms and ions. The de-excitation and recombination processes following give rise to the emission of photons. The various modes of photon emission are discussed briefly by Northrop and Gursky.[106] They point out that a direct radiative transition to the ground state of an atom will give rise to radiation that will be resonance-trapped and will lead to a delay in escape of the energy from the gas. The primary energy deposited in metastable states can be transferred by thermal collisions to nearby resonance levels and thus be emitted as resonance radiation. Photons from the de-excitation of excited ions escape directly, since they are not resonance-trapped. The remaining process is that of photon emission resulting from the recombination of an ion and electron. This process is invoked to explain the effects observed in binary gas mixtures. (See Fig. 22.)

The emission spectra from noble gases lie in the ultraviolet, generally beyond the range of sensitivity of ordinary photomultiplier tubes. The emission spectra resulting from the stopping of alpha particles in argon, xenon, and helium have been examined by Bennett et al.[18] Their results indicated a complex band structure in the case of helium and argon and a broad, unresolved band from xenon centered near 3300 A. The most intense lines observed from the helium and argon samples were found to arise from traces of nitrogen, even in concentrations as low as 10^{-5}. The lines due to normal atomic helium or argon transitions were very weak compared with those of nitrogen. The nitrogen lines were attributed to nonradiative excitation of nitrogen by collisions with helium and argon in metastable states. Koch and Lesueur[84] report the mean wavelength of emission from the rare gases in an experiment utilizing absorption filters; values ranged from 2500 A for argon to 3900 A for helium.

I. Purity. Gas scintillators are quite sensitive to impurities in small concentration. In the first experiments with gas scintillation counters it was observed that a continual decrease in light output occurred, starting immediately after the initial filling of the gas cell. These effects have been attributed to poisoning of the noble gas by vapors emitted from gasket materials, counter walls, etc. Northrop and Nobles[102] have examined the light output from a xenon scintillator as a function of impurity content. (See Fig. 19.) It is seen that a few percent of oxygen and methane reduce the light output by a factor of more than 5. They point out, however, that the quenching effects illustrated in Fig. 19 are small compared to the natural contamination occurring in a counter, where impurity concentrations too small to be registered as pressure changes may completely destroy the light output. The natural contaminants are probably chiefly hydrocarbons.[105]

There are several techniques available to combat the poisoning problem. Nobles[103] found that a substantial improvement was realized in a counter utilizing a quaterphenyl wavelength shifter when the system was operated

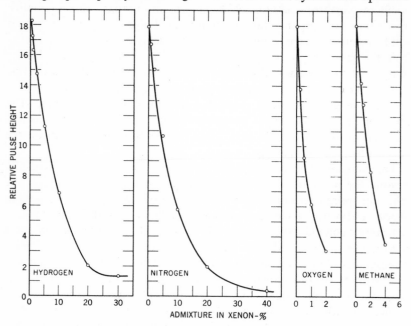

Fig. 19.   Pulse height from xenon gas scintillator as a function of concentration of added gas.   From Northrop and Nobles.[102]

at 0° C rather than at room temperature. Several workers have employed continual gas purification systems. A hot uranium metal purifier was successfully used by Northrop and Nobles;[102] the purifier contained finely powdered uranium at 800° C and a second section of cold uranium for hydrogen absorption. Sayres and Wu[125] have described a system that utilizes a hot calcium purifier (400° C) and a gas circulating pump. Their gas cell was designed so that it was not necessary to use rubber O-rings as a seal around the photomultiplier. A glass circulating pump applied in conjunction with commercial barium getters was used by Bennett[24] to obtain noble gases with very low nitrogen content (less than 5 parts in 10^9 in helium). Impurities such as H_2, O_2, CO, and CO_2 are also efficiently removed by barium. An alternative method for achieving gas purity which would appear to be quite simple is that of continuously flowing fresh gas through the counter. This technique has been used by Villaire and Wouters,[137] and by Boicourt and Brolley.[23]

2. Wavelength shifters. The short wavelength emission spectrum of gas scintillators in general imposes the requirement of a wavelength shifter in order to obtain maximum signal from the photomultiplier. In order to take advantage of the fast decay time of a gas scintillator, it is necessary that the wavelength shifter be as fast as the gas. In addition, it is important that the wavelength shifter have a high quantum efficiency to yield maximum light output. Various materials have frequently been used in this capacity to date, especially quaterphenyl and tetraphenylbutadiene.

TABLE 2. RELATIVE SCINTILLATION EFFICIENCIES
FOR VARIOUS COMBINATIONS OF GAS AND
WAVESHIFTER

Waveshifter	Argon	Krypton	Xenon
p-quaterphenyl	—	0.247	0.438
Diphenylstilbene	0.202	0.567	1.000
1,1,4,4-tetraphenylbutadiene	0.144	0.356	0.699
POPOP	0.071	0.172	0.366
POPOP-diphenylstilbene*	0.066	0.170	0.337
αNPO	0.037	0.090	0.176

* First the POPOP and then the diphenylstilbene were evaporated on the phototube face.

Northrop[104] has recently compared the relative scintillation efficiencies of several combinations of gas and waveshifter combinations upon excitation by alpha particles. The wavelength shifters were organic solids which were deposited by vacuum evaporation onto the face of a DuMont 6292 photomultiplier; optimum thickness for the layer was found to be about 20–30 $\mu g/cm^2$. The results of Northrop's work are reproduced in Table 2. The data presented there were normalized to the xenon-diphenylstilbene combination whose light output was found to be about the same as alpha particles on NaI(Tl). It is of particular interest to note that diphenylstilbene produced significantly better results than any other material.

The importance of using a wavelength shifter is clearly demonstrated in the work of Sayres and Wu[125] who report relative pulse heights with and without quaterphenyl for both a glass photomultiplier (6292) and a quartz photomultiplier (Kl306). For the case of xenon at a pressure of 6 psi, the results are indicated in Table 3.

TABLE 3.   RELATIVE SCINTILLATION EFFICIENCIES FROM
Po[210] ALPHAS IN XENON AT 6 psi, ILLUSTRATING
EFFECT OF QUATERPHENYL WAVESHIFTER
AND QUARTZ-WINDOW PHOTOMULTIPLIER

Photomultiplier and Waveshifter	Relative Pulse Height
6292 with quaterphenyl	105
6292 without quaterphenyl	6
K1306 with quaterphenyl	145
K1306 without quaterphenyl	88

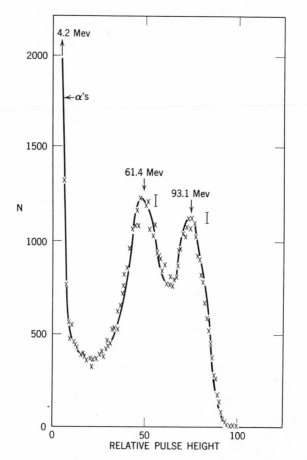

Fig. 20.   Spectrum of fission fragments from U[235] in 29 psi of xenon, using a K1306 photomultiplier and quaterphenyl wavelength shifter.   From Sayres and Wu.[125]

The use of a small admixture of nitrogen gas in argon and helium was found by Eggler and Huddleston[38] to increase the light output; a plot of pulse height versus nitrogen content yields a curve with a maximum at about 10% nitrogen in argon and of order 0.1% nitrogen in helium. Northrop and Nobles[102] looked for such an effect but did not observe a light increase upon adding nitrogen to helium; admixtures of 1 ppm to 10% were used. They suggested that nitrogen may act as a waveshifter only in those systems that otherwise have no efficient waveshifter-reflector arrangement.

3. Scintillation response. Gas scintillators have two outstanding characteristics that make them particularly useful in certain experiments: (a) a fast decay time, of the order of millimicroseconds[103] and (b) the light output per Mev is quite insensitive to the charge and mass of the particle being stopped in the gas. The second feature has led to the use of gas scintillators as fission detectors; the pulse size from a fission fragment, in contrast to other scintillators, is much greater than the background of pulses from natural alpha activity. As an illustration, Fig. 20 shows the observed fission spectrum of U^{235} in a xenon scintillation counter using a quartz-window photomultiplier and quaterphenyl wavelength shifter. Peaks from the light and heavy fission fragments are clearly resolved.

The pulse height versus energy relationship for protons, deuterons, and helium ions stopped in pure xenon was found to be linear between 2 and 5 Mev; points for all three types of particles fell on the same straight line.[103] The line did not extend through the origin but intercepted the energy axis at about $\frac{1}{2}$ Mev. It is not clear that this is a property of the gas scintillator but may have arisen from an unknown systematic error. Further work is needed to clarify this point.

Another advantage of a gas scintillator is its strong discrimination against gamma-ray background. Sayres and Wu compared the pulse-height response of a gas scintillator, anthracene, and CsI(Tl) to Po^{210} alpha particles and radium gamma rays. The results are reproduced in Table 4. The advantages of the gas counter in this respect are quite striking.

TABLE 4. A COMPARISON OF THE RELATIVE PULSE HEIGHTS OF Po^{210} ALPHA PARTICLES AND THE PEAK EFFECT OF 5-mg RADIUM GAMMA SOURCE IN THE GAS SCINTILLATOR AND IN SOLID SCINTILLATORS

Scintillator	Pulse Height of Alpha Source	Maximum Pulse Height of Gamma Source
CsI (1 mm thick)	160	75
Anthracene (3 mm thick)	22	77
He + 10% Xe (60 psi total) (6292 tube with quaterphenyl)	105	5

The relative pulse heights from various gas scintillators, as determined by Northrop and Nobles, were 32:16:5:1:10 for Xe:Kr:A:Ne:He. A quaterphenyl waveshifter was employed in this determination. The results of Sayres and Wu on Xe, Kr, and A are in essential agreement with these

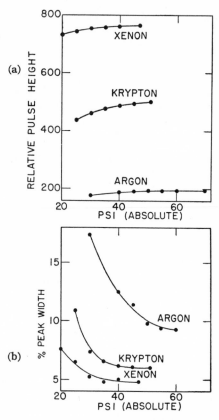

Fig. 21. For the noble gases: argon, krypton, and xenon. Excitation by alpha particles. (*a*) Relative pulse height as a function of absolute pressure; (*b*) Per cent peak width as a function of absolute pressure. In each case the pressure is as high or higher than that necessary to stop the alpha particles in the gas volume. The 6292 photomultiplier and source holder were both coated with quaterphenyl. From Sayres and Wu.[125]

ratios and are illustrated in Fig. 21*a*. It is observed that the light output increases slowly with increasing pressure, even though the alpha particles are completely stopped in the gas in every case. The resolution that they obtained for Po[210] alpha particles is shown in Fig. 21*b*. They report an energy spread of about 4% under optimum conditions.

The light output from binary mixtures of noble gases has been the subject of an investigation by Northrop and Gursky.[106] They found that the light intensity from a gas falls rapidly to a minimum with the addition of a small concentration of a *heavier* gas and rises with the further addition of the heavy gas. This effect is illustrated in Fig. 22 for A-Kr, A-Xe, He-Kr,

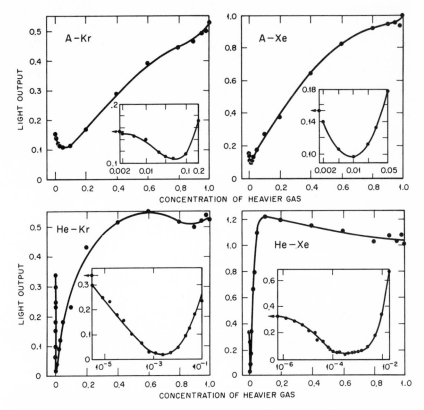

Fig. 22. Scintillation light output of binary noble gas mixtures for U[234] alpha particles detected by a 6292 photomultiplier and amplified by an electronic system having $RC = 0.5$ μsec clipping. The ordinates have been normalized to the light obtained from pure xenon. The abscissas are the fraction by pressure of the heavier gas in the mixture. The semilog inserts show the detail of the left part of each curve. Data shown were obtained with diphenylstilbene as a waveshifter. From Northrop and Gursky.[106]

and He-Xe mixtures. These results are qualitatively interpreted by the authors in terms of the formation of noble-gas molecular ions.

In addition to their use as fission detectors, gas scintillators have been studied as possible detectors of slow neutrons. If a thin film containing, say, a boron compound is deposited on a surface in contact with the scintillating gas, the $B^{10}(n, \alpha)$ reaction products ($He^4 + Li^7$) will cause the gas to scintillate immediately after neutron capture. This scheme has been explored by Sayres and Wu, who resolved clearly the He^4 and Li^7 peaks in the pulse-height spectrum. It is also obvious that slow neutrons can be detected through fission events in a substance such as U^{235} or U^{233}. Another possible use of gas scintillators is that of a fast-neutron spectrometer: the idea is to incorporate in the scintillator some He^3 gas that will undergo the $He^3(n, p)T$ reaction. The total energy released in the reaction products is just the sum of the original neutron energy plus the reaction Q-value (0.77 Mev), so that a pulse-height analysis of neutron-induced pulses should provide information on the spectrum of incident neutrons. This scheme appears to be quite feasible, although it has apparently not yet been put into practice. Figure 22 illustrates that a mixture of 90% He—10% Xe gives as much, or slightly more, light than pure xenon, so there should be no major problem in getting a reasonable signal.

Finally, it is of interest to note some preliminary work reported by Northrop and co-workers[105] on scintillations from liquified noble gases. They found that liquid and solid xenon emit significantly more light than gaseous xenon. The light output from solid xenon, upon alpha excitation, is comparable to that from alphas on NaI(Tl). Liquid xenon, used in conjunction with a K1306 photomultiplier, exhibited similar results. Liquid and solid argon and krypton were also observed to scintillate but with somewhat weaker intensity than xenon. It was further observed that a quartz-window photomultiplier had essentially the same efficiency as a glass tube with waveshifter. The decay time of the liquids and solids was about 10^{-8} sec.[102] Solid xenon would appear to be an interesting candidate for gamma-ray detection and spectroscopy by virtue of its density, atomic number, and fast decay time. Scintillations in liquid helium upon excitation by alpha particles have been reported from two laboratories.[146,147] Pulses were observed from both liquid and gaseous helium with nearly the same pulse amplitude. Wavelength shifters are necessary as the emission spectrum is in the ultraviolet. Liquid helium scintillators are of particular interest as polarization analyzers for fast neutrons.

E. Photomultiplier Tubes and Counter Assembly

1. General properties of photomultipliers. In a scintillation counter the photomultiplier tube performs the all-important function of converting the light flashes from the scintillator into current pulses. In order to achieve optimum results with such a counter, it is desirable that the photomultiplier serve as a fast ($\sim 10^{-9}$ sec) linear amplifier of high gain ($\sim 10^6$) and low noise, with a minimum spread in size of the output pulse per incident photon and a minimum spread in transit time of the photo-electrons. The successful application of the scintillation method to nuclear spectroscopy is due in large part to the fact that present-day photomultipliers fulfill the foregoing requirements. The basic elements of a photomultiplier are the photocathode, which serves to convert a fraction of the incident photons into electrons, and a series of dynodes, which amplify the initial photoelectron pulse by secondary emission. The photocathode material used in most commercial photomultipliers is an intermetallic compound of cesium and antimony. In the first models of photomultipliers the Cs-Sb layer was deposited on a metallic backing located in the interior of the tube. Examples of this scheme are the RCA 1P21 and 1P28, which were widely used in the early days of scintillation counting. The end-window photomultipliers, more recently developed, are generally much more suitable for coupling to a scintillator. In this type the photocathode is deposited as a semitransparent layer on the interior surface of a glass (or quartz) window located at the end of the tube. In most photomultipliers the external surface of the end-window is flat for easy coupling to a flat-surfaced crystal unit; the RCA 5819, however, has a convex window that requires a shaped optical light pipe.

An important parameter in the choice of a photomultiplier is its spectral response characteristics. The spectral response curve may depend, for example, on the preparation of the particular photocathode material, whether it is deposited as a semitransparent layer or on an opaque backing, and the transmission of the glass or quartz envelope. Most of the photomultipliers currently used for scintillation counting have an S-11 response whose maximum is near 4400 A. This matches rather well the peak emission intensity of a number of scintillators (see preceding sections). Several spectral response curves are shown in Figs. 23a, b, c. The peak quantum efficiency (photoelectrons per incident photon) of a photocathode is of the order of 10%. *It is to be emphasized* that rather broad limits are attached to the wavelength of the maximum in the response function of a given type, viz., ± 500 A. For this reason, one can expect considerable variation of response between tubes, even tubes of the same type, number, and manufacturer. For best results in scintillation spectrometry, it is necessary to select carefully the photomultiplier that is best suited to a given crystal. Another important property of the photocathode is the thermionic emission of electrons, which may be of the order of 5000 electrons/cm²/sec at room temperature. It is, of course, desirable to minimize the resulting photomultiplier "dark current." Lowering the photocathode temperature is an effective means of doing so; the thermionic emission is reduced by about a factor of 2 for every $10°$ C near room temperature. The need for minimizing dark current generally arises

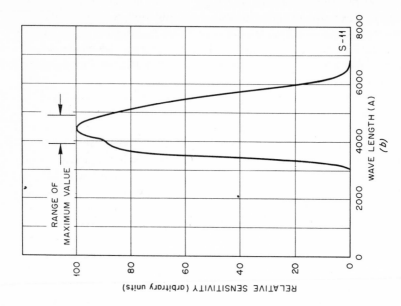

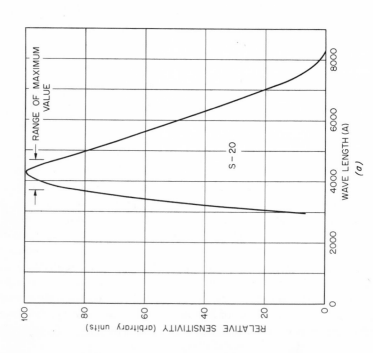

Fig. 23. Spectral sensitivity curves of (a) S-20 response, (b) S-11 response. From RCA Tube Handbook.

only in those cases in which the signal pulse is quite small, since the individual dark-current pulses are themselves very small.

The dynode material used in commercial photomultipliers may be either Cs—Sb or Ag—Mg. The secondary emission ratio σ is, of course, a function of the accelerating voltage applied from one dynode to the next. If a

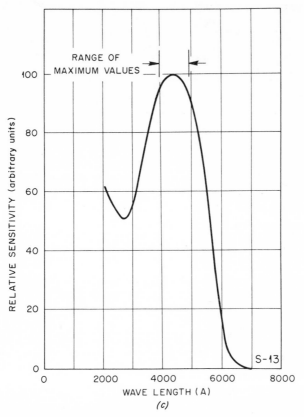

Fig. 23c. Spectral sensitivity curve, S-13 response.

tube has k dynodes, the over-all current gain is σ^k. Since σ is roughly proportional to the voltage between dynodes, it is clear that the over-all gain is a very sensitive function of the applied voltage; for this reason, it is necessary to use a well-stabilized high-voltage supply for quantitative scintillation spectrometry. It has also been observed that for many photomultipliers the gain is a function of count rate. This effect is demonstrated for a group of four DuMont 6292's in Fig. 24, taken from Bell et al.[20] They found that the gain shifts were worst in the DuMont 6292 (2 in.), 6363 (3 in.), and 6364 (5 in.). Some RCA 6342 tubes showed only a few percent effect, others none. The RCA 5819 generally showed no shift. The

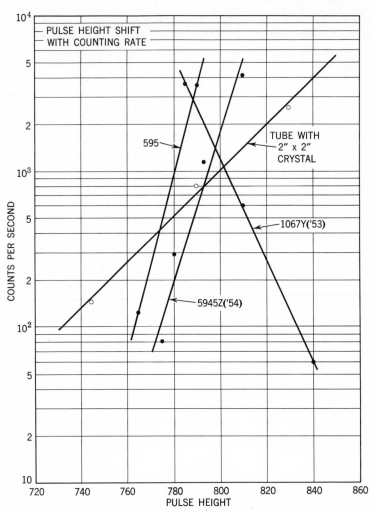

Fig. 24. Shift in pulse height with counting rate obtained for several 6292 photo-multipliers. A Cs[137] source was used; the counting rates were varied by changing the source position. Labels denote particular tubes. From Bell et al.[20]

results obtained seemed to indicate that the gain shift is primarily a dynode effect. This conclusion is reinforced by a study of dynode fatigue effects by Cathey,[148] who found significant shifts in photomultiplier gain for anode currents of the order of 1 μa and greater. Dynode fatigue effects are attributed to changes in cesium content of the dynode surface. Even in tubes that have Ag—Mg dynodes, the photocathodes are formed from cesium vapor and cesium will always be present on the dynode surfaces.

The performance of photomultipliers may be profoundly affected by the presence of quite small magnetic fields, even the earth's field. The effect is one of reduced gain in the presence of the field and arises from the deflection of electrons in transit. The magnitude of the effect in an RCA 5819, taken from the report by Engstrom et al.,[40] is shown in Fig. 25. The influence of magnetic fields can be minimized by surrounding the photo-multiplier with a cylindrical mu-metal shield of about $\frac{1}{16}$-in. thickness. These shields are available commercially (e.g., James Millen Manufacturing

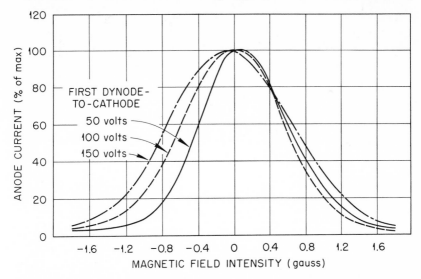

Fig. 25. Sensitivity of 5819 photomultiplier to magnetic fields, showing variation with cathode-first dynode voltage. Magnetic field is parallel to dynode-cage axis. From Engstrom et al.[40]

Company, Inc., Malden, Massachusetts) in a variety of shapes and sizes to accommodate present-day photomultipliers. For best results the shield should extend beyond the photocathode surface.

For some applications it is important that the spread in electron transit time from photocathode to anode be a minimum. This property is significant in fast coincidence work or in time-of-flight measurements in which time intervals in the millimicrosecond range are of interest. The transit-time spread (full width at half-maximum) in the RCA 6810 is about 9 mμsec whereas in DuMont tubes such as the 6292 the spread is more nearly 20 mμsec. The difference between the two types of tube lies in the dynode structure: RCA tubes have a circular array of dynodes which provides fairly strong electric fields to draw the secondary electrons away from the dynode surface, whereas DuMont tubes have a more extended

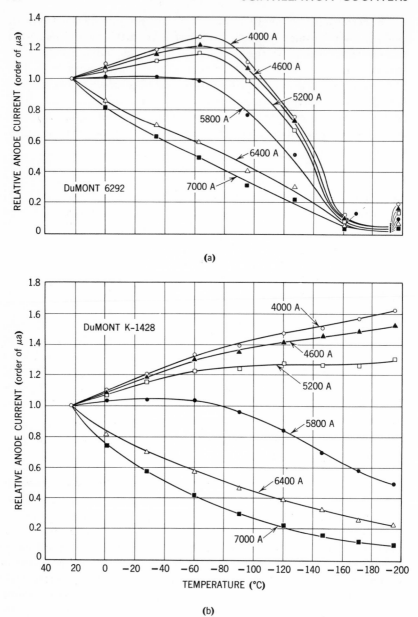

Fig. 26.   Relative photomultiplier gain as a function of temperature for various wave lengths of monochromatic light on (*a*) DuMont 6292 and (*b*) DuMont K-1428. The K-1428 differs from the 6292 in that a thin metallic backing has been evaporated over the photocathode during tube manufacture.

"box" structure. The new RCA 6810 A, with a shaped photocathode, has a transit-time spread of 1–3 mμsec. The EMI 6097, with a "venetian blind" dynode structure, is reported to have a transit-time spread of 18 mμsec.[128]

The appearance of satellite pulses, or "after-pulses," has been observed in many photomultipliers following the main pulses. The after-pulses are generally small compared to the main pulse and occur within a period ranging from millimicroseconds to microseconds after the initial signal. This topic is reviewed by Mott and Sutton.[94]

The gain of a photomultiplier tube is a function of its temperature. Furthermore, the magnitude and sign of the gain shift as a function of temperature depend on the wavelength of light incident on the photocathode. These effects have been studied in various photomultipliers from room temperature to the liquid nitrogen point by Murray and Manning.[149] An illustration of the gain change with temperature for a typical commercial tube (DuMont 6292) is shown in Fig. 26a. The sharp drop in response for all wavelengths at the lowest temperatures is a consequence of the increasing resistivity of the photocathode. It is seen that the tube response falls virtually to zero at the liquid nitrogen point. This effect is eliminated by depositing a thin metallic layer over the photocathode during the manufacture of the tube; the DuMont K-1428 is such a tube. Figure 26b illustrates the fact that the gain of the K-1428 holds up quite well down to liquid nitrogen temperature for light in the short wavelength region, and is thus suitable for scintillation-counting purposes at low temperatures. The wavelength dependence of gain shift, as observed in Figs. 26a and 26b, is a result of the changing spectral sensitivity characteristic of the cathode with decreasing temperature.[126]

2. Characteristics of various photomultipliers. In this section the characteristics of some currently used photomultipliers are listed (Table 5). A more comprehensive table may be found in the review of Mott and Sutton.[94] Detailed data sheets for particular photomultipliers are available from the manufacturers.

The development of photomultipliers is in a continual state of evolution. At the present time considerable effort is being devoted to (a) improvement of photocathodes to provide greater sensitivity and lower dark current, (b) the manufacture of large-area photocathodes for use with large scintillators, and (c) improvement of the transit-time spread to make possible more accurate time measurements. Of particular interest is the recent development of new multialkali photocathodes reported by Sommer.[127] These cathodes have the composition Sb-K-Na-Cs; they are reported to have the highest red-sensitivity of any photocathode and a blue-sensitivity

TABLE 5. CHARACTERISTICS OF A FEW USEFUL PHOTOMULTIPLIER TUBES

Tube Number	Photocathode Size (in.)	Window	Spectral Response	Dynode Material	Number of Stages	Average Multiplier Gain
RCA 1P28	$\frac{15}{16} \times \frac{5}{16}$ (internal)	Corning 9741	S-5	Cs—Sb	9	1.25×10^6 at 1000 volts
RCA 5819	$1\frac{1}{16}$ dia	lime glass	S-11	Cs—Sb	10	5×10^5 at 1000 volts
RCA 6199	$1\frac{1}{4}$ dia	lime glass	S-11	Cs—Sb	10	6×10^5 at 1000 volts
RCA 6342	$1\frac{11}{16}$ dia	lime glass	S-11	Ag—Mg	10	6×10^5 at 1500 volts
RCA 6372	$4\frac{1}{8} \times 3$ (side of bulb)	Corning 7052	S-11	Cs—Sb	10	6×10^5 at 1000 volts
RCA 6655	$1\frac{11}{16}$ dia	lime glass	S-11	Cs—Sb	10	5×10^5 at 1000 volts
RCA 6810A	$1\frac{11}{16}$ dia	lime glass	S-11	Ag—Mg	14	12.5×10^6 at 2000 volts
RCA 6903	$1\frac{5}{8}$ dia	fused silica	S-13	Ag—Mg	10	4×10^5 at 1000 volts
RCA 7326	$1\frac{11}{16}$ dia	lime glass	S-20	Ag—Mg	10	1.5×10^5 at 1800 volts
RCA 7265	$1\frac{11}{16}$ dia	lime glass	S-20	Ag—Mg	14	9.4×10^6 at 2400 volts
DuMont 6291	$1\frac{1}{4}$ dia	lime glass	S-11	Ag—Mg	10	2×10^6 at 145 volts/stage
DuMont 6292	$1\frac{1}{2}$ dia	lime glass	S-11	Ag—Mg	10	2×10^6 at 145 volts/stage
DuMont 6363	$2\frac{1}{2}$ dia	lime glass	S-11	Ag—Mg	10	2×10^6 at 145 volts/stage
DuMont 6364	$4\frac{3}{16}$ dia	lime glass	S-11	Ag—Mg	10	2×10^6 at 145 volts/stage
DuMont K1306	$1\frac{1}{2}$ dia	fused silica	S-13	Ag—Mg	10	2×10^5 at 105 volts/stage
DuMont K1328	14 dia	lime glass	S-11	Ag—Mg	12	5×10^5 at 105 volts/stage
EMI 6255B	$1\frac{3}{4}$ dia	quartz	S-13	Cs—Sb	13	4×10^7 at 110 volts/stage
EMI 6099B	$4\frac{3}{8}$ dia	pyrex	S-11	Cs—Sb	11	2.5×10^6 at 125 volts/stage
EMI 9536B	$1\frac{3}{4}$ dia	pyrex	S-11	Cs—Sb	10	4×10^5 at 100 volts/stage
EMI 9545B	10 dia	sodaglass	S-11	Cs—Sb	11	4×10^6 at 2200 volts
CBS CL 1012	1.35 dia	lime glass	S-11	Ag—Mg	10	2×10^6 at 1750 volts
CBS 7817	1.75 dia	lime glass	S-11	Ag—Mg	10	2×10^6 at 1750 volts
CBS 7818	2.70 dia	lime glass	S-11	Ag—Mg	10	2×10^6 at 1750 volts

that is even greater than the S-11 response cathode which is customarily used in scintillation counting.[41]   The dark emission of the multialkali photocathode is reported to be significantly lower than that of Cs—Sb, in spite of its much greater red-sensitivity.   Further, the conductivity of the multialkali photocathode at low temperatures is larger than that of a Cs—Sb surface, so that some multialkali photocathode tubes are operable at liquid nitrogen temperature.[149]

3. Scintillation counter assembly.   Proper optical coupling of the scintillator to the photomultiplier is an important feature in the assembly

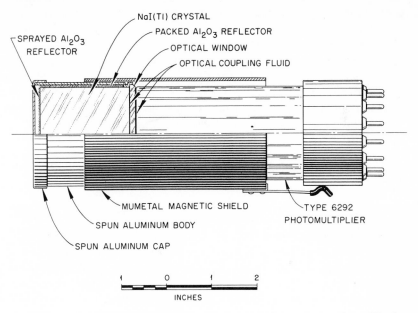

Fig. 27.   Schematic diagram of assembled scintillation counter, using a Harshaw-packaged 2 × 2 in. NaI(Tl) crystal on a 6292 photomultiplier.

of a counter. It is, of course, desirable that as much light as possible be directed to the photocathode. In the case of single crystals, the crystal unit [e.g., NaI(Tl)] can be obtained commercially as a single package with the crystal hermetically sealed and optically coupled to a transparent window. A schematic diagram of such a unit, mounted on a photomultiplier with a 2-in. diameter is shown in Fig. 27. The crystal may be optically coupled to the window with a transparent viscous medium such as Dow-Corning 200 silicone fluid (10^6 centistokes); the same material may be used to couple the entire unit to the photomultiplier window. The use of an optical coupling fluid in these places is needed to minimize the change in refractive index as light passes from the face of the crystal toward the photocathode. (A sharp change in refractive index corresponds to a small critical angle resulting in total reflection of much of the light at the interface. If the refractive index discontinuity is minimized, more light will be transmitted.) The sides and rear face of the crystal may be surrounded by a reflecting material, such as alpha-alumina (Al_2O_3) or magnesium oxide (MgO). Bell[4] has pointed out that magnesium oxide has a better reflecting power than any available specular surface; it appears, however, that it may react slightly with NaI, whereas alpha-alumina does not.

In some cases it may be desirable to separate the crystal from the photocathode; for example, if the crystal must be located in a restricted volume or in the presence of a magnetic field. In such a case it is necessary to interpose a transparent light pipe between crystal and photomultiplier. The use of a light pipe may also be advisable with a thin crystal where better resolution is obtained if the light is distributed uniformly over the photocathode. Lucite, quartz, or glass may be used as light pipes in various applications; it is, of course, necessary that the light pipe be transparent to the emission spectrum of the crystal. The transmission characteristics of various light pipes have been studied by Harris and Bell.[63] They concluded that best results are obtained if the cylindrical walls of the light pipe have a high polish and are loosely surrounded by aluminum foil. Optical coupling of the foil to the light pipe, as with DC-200 fluid, is to be avoided, since it can decrease the transmission significantly.

Very often the requirements of an experiment cannot be met with a commercially available crystal unit, so that the experimenter must do his own mounting. The general techniques are the same as those previously discussed with respect to reflectors, light pipes, etc. A description of a crystal unit using thin crystals, NaI(Tl), about 0.040 in. thick, has been given by Whetstone et al.[141] They report line widths of the order of 3% for protons in the Mev range.

Mounting a very large scintillation crystal poses a somewhat more challenging problem. Several laboratories have been using NaI(Tl) crystals of about 9-in. diameter for "total-absorption" spectrometry of gamma rays. The mounting technique reported by Davis and co-workers[35] involves coupling the crystal to three DuMont 6364 photomultipliers ($4\frac{3}{16}$-in. photocathode). The crystal was covered with a 0.005-in. aluminum foil which had been sprayed on the interior with a highly reflective coating of alpha-alumina and sodium silicate. An airtight seal was provided by Apiezon-Q. Figure 28 illustrates a commercially prepared housing for a NaI(Tl) crystal of $9\frac{3}{8}$-in. diameter; the crystal was grown and packaged by Harshaw Chemical Company.

In the case of liquid scintillators, the assembly of the counter is determined to a large extent by the conditions and geometry of the experiment. Very often the photocathode is placed in direct contact with the liquid; an alternative is to contain the liquid in a cell which is then optically coupled to the photocathode. In the first technique it is important that the liquid be uncontaminated by the gasket used to form the liquid-tight seal around

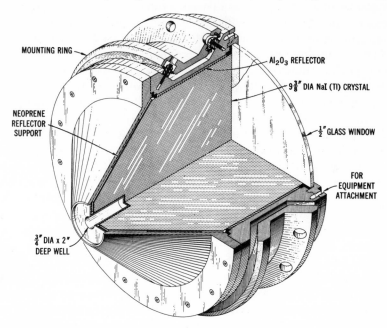

MOUNTING RING

Al₂O₃ REFLECTOR

9⅜″ DIA NaI (Tl) CRYSTAL

NEOPRENE
REFLECTOR
SUPPORT

½″ GLASS WINDOW

FOR
EQUIPMENT
ATTACHMENT

¾″ DIA x 2″
DEEP WELL

Fig. 28.   Sketch of 9¼-in. diameter NaI(Tl) gamma-ray spectrometer crystal showing ¾-in. diameter × 2-in.-deep well in truncated end. Crystal and assembly prepared by Harshaw Chemical Company.

the photomultiplier. Thomas[133] has discussed an assembly technique that is designed to combat this problem. The reflective coating surrounding the liquid should be chosen to give optimum light output; the merits of several materials used for this purpose are compared by Bollinger and Thomas.[17]

The performance of gas scintillation counters depends upon the choice of photomultiplier, waveshifter, reflector, and upon the precautions taken to maintain the gas free of impurities. Details may be found in various discussed in papers Section D.

4. Resolution of scintillation counters. One of the most important parameters characterizing a scintillation spectrometer is the line width associated with the peak arising from the absorption of monoenergetic radiation. This property is frequently described in terms of the quantity $\Delta E/E$, where ΔE is the full width at half-maximum of a peak occurring at pulse height E. There are several effects which contribute to line broadening in a scintillation counter, both in the scintillator and in the photomultiplier. The statistical spread arises from the following sources: (a) number of photons emitted per scintillation event in the crystal, (b) number of emitted photons that are incident on the photocathode, (c) number of photoelectrons emitted by the cathode per incident photon, (d) number of photoelectrons that are collected by the first dynode, and (e) the secondary emission ratio at each succeeding dynode. The first two items are properties of the crystal and the optical coupling, whereas the remaining items are properties of the tube. In connection with item (d), the resolution can be optimized by the choice of the proper voltage on the focus grid in a tube such as the 6292. Whetstone et al.[141] observed a broadening of peak width by a factor of 2 as the focus grid voltage was raised from 50 to 200 volts. A detailed treatment of the shape and width of a line arising from monoenergetic particles is actually a rather complicated subject. This problem has been discussed in some detail by both Wright[142] and Breitenberger.[22] With certain simplifying assumptions the square of the fractional line width is expected to be of the form

$$(\Delta E/E)^2 = \alpha + \beta/E, \qquad\qquad (12)$$

where α and β are constants. The first term, α, arises from properties of the crystal and light guide and represents the variance in transfer of optical photons from the crystal to the photocathode. The second term is associated with statistical fluctuations in processes occurring in the photomultiplier. On the basis of (12) a plot of $(\Delta E/E)^2$ versus $1/E$ should result in a straight line with a positive intercept at $(1/E) = 0$.

An experimental investigation by Kelley et al.[87] separates the contributions to the line width of a NaI(Tl) spectrometer arising from the crystal and from the photomultiplier. They observed that with Cs^{137} gamma rays (662 kev) on a NaI(Tl) crystal the over-all line width was 7.3 to 7.4%. When the crystal was replaced by a cathode-ray tube light flasher producing constant amplitude light pulses of the same size as the 662-kev NaI(Tl) pulses, the photomultiplier line width was 4.0 to 4.4%. These results indicate an intrinsic crystal energy spread of about 6%. Further, experimental values of $(\Delta E/E)^2$ versus $1/E$ do not fall on a straight line but exhibit a distinct curvature in the region of several hundred kev. This behavior has also been observed experimentally by Bisi and Zappa[154] (see Fig. 29), who attribute the departure from a straight line to the fact that the parameter α of (12) is expected to depend on the energy of incident gammas. A further contribution to the "anomalous" behavior

of Fig. 29 is indicated by Zerby and coworkers,[150] who take into account
the effect of the nonlinear response of NaI(Tl) to electrons. (See Fig. 8a.)
This nonlinear response gives rise to an intrinsic line width in the scintillation response to those gammas which interact with the crystal through a
Compton or pair-production event. This intrinsic line width is a function
of both the crystal size and the energy of the incoming gamma. For a
$2\frac{1}{2}$-in.-dia by 2-in.-high crystal the intrinsic line width is negligible up to

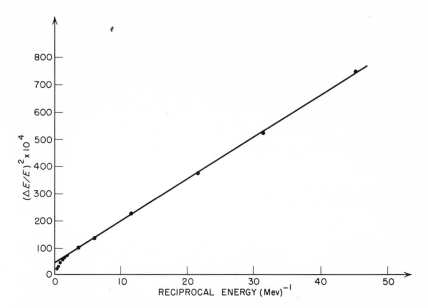

Fig. 29. Plot of $(\Delta E/E)^2$ as a function of reciprocal energy, for gamma rays on a
3 × 3 in. NaI(Tl) crystal. Data from Ref. 154.

about 100 kev, reaches a maximum value of 5 % at 400 kev, and amounts to
1.5 % at 2.5 Mev. These values remain substantially the same for larger
crystals but become smaller with decreasing crystal size. The contribution
of the intrinsic line width is thus most significant in the region of several
hundred kev to several Mev.

The energy spread of a NaI(Tl) spectrometer is frequently quoted as that
obtained with Cs^{137} gamma rays. Under the best conditions, and with a
selected tube, line widths of 7 % have been obtained.

F. Applications of Scintillators

1. Detection and spectroscopy of charged particles. The response
of various scintillators to charged particles, such as protons, deuterons, or

alpha particles, has been discussed in preceding sections. The detection and energy measurement of protons and deuterons, especially in experiments with charged-particle accelerators, is frequently accomplished with thin crystals of NaI(Tl) or CsI(Tl). These crystals combine several properties that make them especially suitable for this purpose, viz., a high

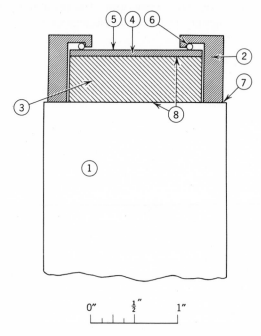

0"   ½"   1"

Fig. 30. Scintillation counter assembly for NaI(Tl) crystal 0.040 in. thick: (1) DuMont 6292 photomultiplier; (2) aluminum frame; (3) glass light pipe ½-in. thick with 1½-in. diameter; (4) NaI(Tl) crystal 0.040 in. thick with 1½-in. diameter; (5) Mylar 0.25 mils thick plus Al foil 0.1 mg/cm² thick; (6) "O" ring; (7) R313 cement; and (8) 10⁶ centistokes silicone oil at each interface. From Whetstone et al.[141]

stopping power, large light output, nearly linear response with particle energy, reasonably fast decay times, and the requirement of a relatively small volume. Inorganic crystals may also be used for the detection of alphas and heavier particles. A ZnS(Ag) screen is frequently used for this purpose, although it is not useful as a spectrometer, since the ZnS particles are not transparent to the luminescence radiation and there is no unique relationship between output pulse height and particle energy.

For use as a charged-particle detector, it is generally necessary that the particles be incident directly on the face of the crystal or that they penetrate only a thin layer of foil. For this reason, the experimenter must often prepare his own crystal rather than obtain a commercial unit. The crystal-mounting scheme used by Whetstone et al.[141] for the detection of protons in the Mev range is shown in Fig. 30. The NaI(Tl) crystal of 0.040-in. thickness is mounted on a glass light pipe $\frac{1}{2}$ in. thick, which serves to distribute the light over the photocathode surface. The use of lucite as a light pipe was not satisfactory because the scintillator-light pipe interface became cloudy after some use. The rear face of the crystal was covered with a thin (0.00025-in.) film of Mylar plus an aluminum foil reflector of thickness 0.1 mg/cm². The purpose of the top cover was to provide a moisture barrier to permit the crystal to be handled in ordinary air. The detector was used in an evacuated housing; at the end of nine months there was no detectable change in pulse heights or resolution.

CsI(Tl) may be somewhat easier to use in some applications, since it is nonhygroscopic. A convenient alpha counter may be constructed quite simply with the use of a commercial unit, consisting of a CsI(Tl) crystal of thickness 0.010 in., which is permanently cemented to a glass plate $\frac{1}{8}$ in. thick. For applications in which sharp resolution is unnecessary, this unit can be coupled directly to a photomultiplier without the use of an additional light pipe or reflecting foils.

There are, of course, many examples of the use of scintillation crystals for charged-particle detection and spectroscopy. In the interest of brevity, we mention only a few illustrative cases. NaI(Tl) and CsI(Tl) have been used as proton detectors in several versions of "recoil-proton telescopes" that are employed in fast-neutron spectroscopy and fast-neutron flux measurements. In such an instrument a thin plastic foil (perhaps polyethylene) is separated from the scintillation crystal unit by one or more proportional counters. The instrument is placed in the neutron flux such that the neutrons are incident on the plastic foil parallel to the foil-scintillation crystal axis. Protons are emitted from the foil in the forward hemisphere by $n\text{-}p$ scattering events; those protons emitted in a small cone about a scattering angle of 0 degrees pass through the proportional counters and strike the crystal. The energy E_p of such a proton is very nearly the same as that of the incident neutron E_n, since $E_p = E_n \cos^2 \theta$ where θ, the scattering angle, is small. A multiple coincidence between the scintillator and the proportional counters identifies the event as one caused by a proton and not a spurious count. The pulse height of the signal from the scintillation counter provides a measure of the energy of the incoming neutron. One must, of course, consider the energy loss of the proton in escaping from the foil, in passing through the proportional counters, and through any reflecting foil that may cover the exposed face of the crystal. The neutron-energy resolution is affected by these processes as well as by the inherent resolution of the scintillation counter. The full width at half-maximum of the peak resulting from 13.7-Mev neutrons on a spectrometer of this type, constructed by Johnson and Trail,[75] was 5.3 %.

As a second case, we may note the use of a thin KI(Tl) crystal as an alpha counter monitoring the number of $T(d, n)He^4$ reactions occurring in the target of a Van de Graaff accelerator. This reaction is widely used as a source of monoenergetic neutrons in the 13-to-20-Mev region. Figure 31a,

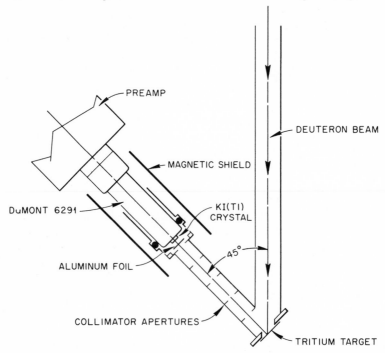

Fig. 31a.   Geometrical arrangement for detecting alpha particles from $T(d, n)He^4$ reaction.   From Kern and Kreger.[89]

taken from a report by Kern and Kreger,[89] illustrates the geometrical arrangement. A small fraction of the alphas produced in the $T(d, n)He^4$ events passed through the collimator apertures, through an aluminum foil, and struck the 2-mm-thick KI(Tl) crystal which was mounted on a DuMont 6291 photomultiplier. The aluminum foil was inserted to absorb low-energy deuterons (several hundred kev) scattered from the zirconium tritide target. The peak energy of the $T(d, n)He^4$ alpha particles, after passing through the aluminum foil, was 1.1 Mev. The resulting pulse-height spectrum is shown in Fig. 31b. Pu²³⁹ alpha particles were used to calibrate the energy scale; their energy, after penetrating the foil, was 4.5 Mev. The low-energy background in Fig. 31b is attributed to scattered deuterons; the absolute number of alpha counts was determined by reflecting the high-energy side of the $T(d, n)$He^4 peak about its center. Knowing the angular distribution of the products of the $T(d, n)$He^4 reaction, the solid angle of acceptance at the KI(Tl) crystal, and the number of alpha counts, it is then possible to calculate the number of neutrons per cm^2 incident on other counters in the laboratory.

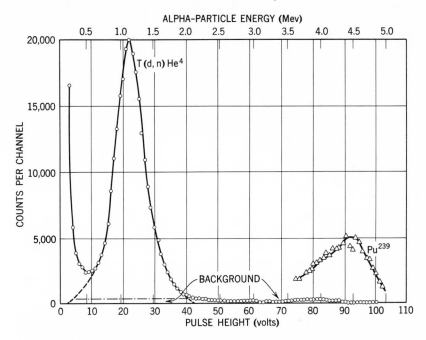

Fig. 31b. Pulse height spectra from $T(d, n)$He^4 alphas and Pu^{239} alphas on KI(Tl) counter. Both groups of alphas have been degraded in energy by passing through the 1.10 mg/cm^2 aluminum foil, which is provided to stop the scattered deuterons. The energy scale is based on 4.5 Mev for the degraded Pu^{239} alphas. From Kern and Kreger.[89]

Both inorganic and organic scintillators have been used for the detection of very heavy charged particles, such as fission fragments. As discussed previously, they are not particularly well suited for this purpose, as the pulse height per Mev is *much* smaller for a fission fragment than for a proton or alpha particle. Indeed, the pulse height from fission fragments on CsI(Tl) is only a factor of 2 greater than that from Po^{210} alphas.[49] The low value of pulse height per Mev need not be a particular disadvantage in every case. For example, Fraser and Milton[50] have used plastic scintillators 0.015 in. thick (Nuclear Enterprises 101 plastic) to detect the arrival of fission fragments from Cf^{252} in a time-of-flight experiment. For many experiments in fission physics, gas scintillators are more satisfactory detectors and are apparently coming into wider use at many laboratories.

Discrimination between various charged particles is made possible by electronic inspection of the shape of the scintillation pulse in certain inorganic crystals, notably CsI(Tl). As indicated in Sec. A, the decay time of CsI(Tl) is found to be a function of the specific energy loss of the incident particle and varies from 0.43 μsec for 5-Mev alpha particles to 0.70 μsec for 0.66-Mev electrons. This technique of particle discrimination has recently been employed by Becker[153] to distinguish protons from alphas in a study of the $B^{10}(d, \alpha)Be^8$ reaction. In this experiment the particle discrimination circuit essentially measured the time required for a pulse to reach half its maximum amplitude. This information was then used to select those pulses whose decay time corresponded to that of an alpha particle. Particle discrimination with CsI(Tl) promises to be a very useful technique in a wide variety of applications.

Finally, we may note briefly the application of the scintillation method to the detection of high-energy particles arising from cosmic rays or high-energy accelerators. Wouters[143] has described the merits of scintillation counters in conjunction with particle accelerators. He points out that in an "average" organic scintillator of 1 cm thickness the energy lost by a proton is such that one can expect to count protons in the energy interval 5 to 350 Mev. Much smaller pulse heights are expected from mesons as a result of their lower rate of ionization. The ionization energy loss of mesons in NaI has been investigated experimentally by Bowen[26]; the results were in good agreement with theory. A plot of probable energy loss of a meson in a NaI(Tl) crystal (1.51 cm thick) passes through a broad minimum near a meson energy of 5 Mc^2, where the energy loss in the crystal is about $6\frac{1}{2}$ Mev.

Many of the applications of the scintillation method to high-energy experiments involve the use of several counters operated in coincidence as a counter telescope. Frequently the experiment is designed so that the counters respond to one or more of the decay products resulting from the disintegration of the high-energy particle. As an example, Harrison and co-workers[66] discuss the application of a large liquid scintillator (300 liters volume) to cosmic-ray studies. The decay of a μ-meson could be detected in this counter by recording the pulses from the electron that results from the meson decay. The end-point energy of the electron is 53 Mev, with a range of 35 cm in the scintillator. Since the dimensions of the cylindrical scintillator tank are 75 cm diameter by 75 cm high, there is a good chance that the electron will remain in the scintillator. Using this counter, they measured the mean life of the μ-meson as 2.10 $\pm$ 0.02 μsec, in good agreement with a previous determination.

An interesting example of quite a large solid scintillation counter is provided in an experiment described by Button et al.[25] designed to detect antineutrons. The counter was constructed to contain the 2 bev of energy released upon antineutron annihilation. It was constructed of 48 identical cells measuring 24 × 12 × 2 in., each with a sensitive area of 12 × 12 in. Each cell contained alternate layers of plastic scintillator and lead sheets. An RCA 6810 photomultiplier viewed each cell end-on through a lucite light pipe. The active volume of the counter formed a cube roughly 2 ft on a side; the assembled counter weighed 2.5 tons.

Cerenkov counters, which are similar in some respects to scintillation counters, are widely used in high-energy counting experiments. The subject of Cerenkov detectors is treated in a separate chapter.

2. Detection and spectroscopy of gamma rays and electrons. The

subjects of gamma-ray and electron counting and spectroscopy are treated in Chapter 5. Accordingly, the discussion given here is limited to a few additional remarks on gamma-ray spectroscopy.

A considerable effort has been devoted to the problem of obtaining a gamma-ray scintillation spectrometer whose "peak-to-total" ratio is a maximum, hopefully approaching unity. The peak-to-total ratio represents the fraction of the total counts, in a gamma-ray pulse-height spectrum, which occurs in the main peak corresponding to the full energy of the incident gamma. Several means are available for improving the peak-to-total ratio. These include (a) use of quite a large NaI(Tl) crystal, perhaps 9 in. in diameter × 10 in. high, (b) surrounding a medium-size NaI(Tl) crystal by an anticoincidence tank which responds to gammas escaping from the NaI(Tl), and (c) use of a multiple-crystal Compton or pair spectrometer. The use of large NaI(Tl) crystals is probably the most direct method for increasing the peak-to-total ratio. The improvement that is realized in going to larger crystals is demonstrated in Fig. 32, which illustrates pulse-height spectra from Cs^{137} gamma rays on cylindrical crystals of NaI(Tl) measuring 1½ in. diameter × 1 in. high, 2 × 2 in., and 3 × 3 in. The reason for the improvement observed is simply that the probability of multiple Compton processes, resulting in the total loss of photon energy in the crystal, increases with crystal size. In Fig. 32 the peak-to-total ratio was found to be 33% for the 1½ × 1 in. detector and 55% for the 3 × 3 in. crystal. The use of a much larger crystal (9 × 10 in.), with the source located in a well drilled in the interior of the crystal, results in a peak-to-total ratio of 88% for Cs^{137} gammas.[27]

Davis and co-workers[35] have described an anticoincidence arrangement in which a NaI(Tl) crystal 4¾ in. in diameter × 5 in. high is contained within a 28-in. sheet-iron tank which is filled with a solution phosphor.

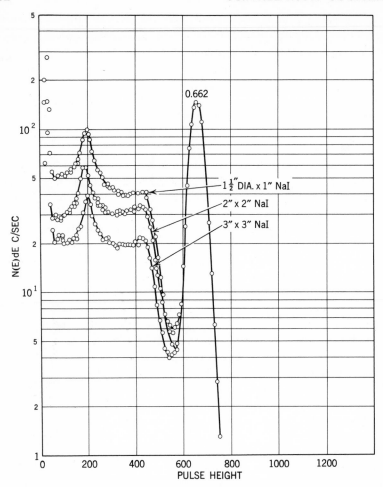

Fig. 32.   Pulse-height spectra from Cs[137] gammas on several crystals of NaI(Tl) illustrating effect of increasing crystal size on the Compton distribution. Spectra have been normalized at the full-energy peak.   Source distance = 10 cm.   From Heath.[68]

(See Fig. 33.) A $\frac{1}{4}$-in. hole is drilled in the crystal to its center, and the gamma-ray source is positioned at the bottom of this well. The organic solution is viewed by five DuMont 6364 5-in. photomultipliers, and the NaI(Tl) crystal is coupled to a single 6364. If a gamma ray suffers a Compton event in the crystal and scatters to the solution, where it is counted, an anticoincidence circuit rejects the crystal pulse. If a gamma ray is completely absorbed in the crystal (or if a Compton-scattered gamma escapes detection in the solution), the crystal pulse is recorded. This scheme provides strong discrimination against the Compton background. With Zn^{65} gamma rays (1.12 Mev), the peak-to-total ratio was found to be 88 %.[27]

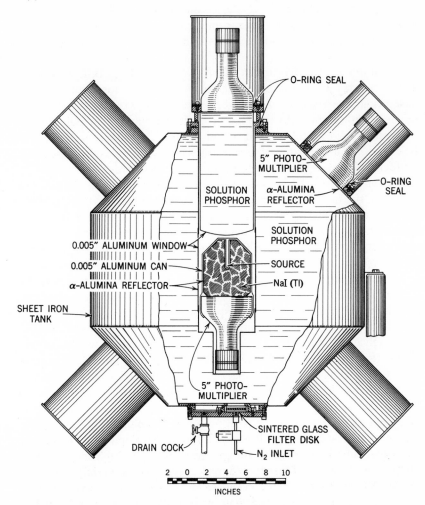

O-RING SEAL

5" PHOTO-MULTIPLIER

O-RING SEAL

SOLUTION PHOSPHOR

α-ALUMINA REFLECTOR

SOLUTION PHOSPHOR

0.005" ALUMINUM WINDOW

0.005" ALUMINUM CAN

α-ALUMINA REFLECTOR

SOURCE

NaI (Tl)

SHEET IRON TANK

5" PHOTO-MULTIPLIER

SINTERED GLASS FILTER DISK

DRAIN COCK

N_2 INLET

2 0 2 4 6 8 10
INCHES

Fig. 33. Anticoincidence tank surrounding NaI(Tl) crystal. From Davis et al.[35]

The two-crystal Compton spectrometer[67] and the three-crystal pair spectrometer[28] have considerably lower detection efficiencies than a single crystal but offer favorable peak-to-total ratios in certain energy intervals. The detection efficiency of the Compton spectrometer passes through a maximum at about $\frac{1}{2}$ Mev and decreases monotonically with increasing energy. The pair spectrometer, on the other hand, has a threshold at 1.02 Mev, and its efficiency increases rapidly with increasing energy. The peak-to-total ratio of a Compton spectrometer at 662 kev is about 80%, which is better than that of a single crystal of dimensions up to 4 × 4 in. The peak-to-total ratio of a pair spectrometer can be quite high; it reaches about 99% at 1.4 Mev, and decreases to 84% at 2.76 Mev and to 55% at 6.1 Mev.[97]

The motivation for the various efforts to improve the peak-to-total ratio arises primarily from the problems encountered in "unscrambling" the pulse-height spectrum from a source emitting several gamma rays. If a monoenergetic gamma ray produced a single sharp line in the pulse-height spectrum (peak-to-total = 1), it would be relatively simple to determine the energies and intensities of gamma rays from a complex decay scheme. In practice, however, the Compton distribution from a high-energy gamma can obscure the full-energy peaks from lower energy photons; in order to determine the incident gamma spectrum, it is then necessary to "unfold" the observed pulse-height distribution. To perform the unfolding, it is necessary to know the shape of the pulse-height spectrum resulting from monoenergetic gamma rays in the energy region of interest on the particular crystal in use. With this information, the unfolding procedure is performed by fitting the high-energy end of the complex spectrum with the appropriate distribution for a monoenergetic gamma and subtracting its Compton tail from the complex spectrum. The resulting spectrum is operated on similarly, etc., until the initial pulse-height distribution is completely accounted for. A description of this procedure, with a number of illustrations, is given by Lazar.[92] A recent report by Heath[68] is of great value to those engaged in such analysis. This report presents pulse-height spectra from a large number of gamma sources on a 3 × 3 in. NaI(Tl) crystal. These spectra can be directly superposed on an observed pulse-height spectrum (on a semilog plot) to facilitate the unfolding process.

Several laboratories (e.g., Refs. 70, 145) are developing techniques for spectrum unfolding suitable for programming on high-speed digital computers. The core of this procedure is a large matrix (perhaps 60 × 60) whose elements describe the response of a particular spectrometer to monoenergetic gammas. The unfolding of an observed pulse-height spectrum to yield the incident gamma-ray spectrum then involves operations with the inverse of the foregoing matrix.

3. Detection and spectroscopy of slow neutrons. A rather large number of techniques involving scintillation counters has been proposed and used for the detection of slow neutrons. The basis of the detection mechanism in all cases is the release of a measurable amount of energy in the scintillator upon neutron capture. Examples of such reactions include the (n, α) reaction in B^{10} or Li^6, the (n, p) reaction in He^3, the (n, γ) reaction in various nuclei, and fission. The energy measurement of slow neutrons must be accomplished by information in addition to that supplied by the scintillation detector. As an example, the energy may be predetermined by placing the detector at a particular Bragg angle with respect to a crystal in a slow-neutron crystal spectrometer. In the case of a slow-neutron chopper, the arrival time at the detector specifies the neutron energy.

Bollinger and Thomas[17] have described an organic liquid scintillator loaded with boron which is used as the detector in the Argonne chopper. The solvent is made of equal parts methyl borate and toluene. As a result of the low α/β ratio of organic liquids, the pulse height resulting from a $B^{10}(n, \alpha)$ reaction is quite small and can be lost in the sea of photomultiplier noise pulses. Several steps are taken to combat this problem. Photomultipliers are selected for low noise and operated below room temperature (55° F) to reduce the noise level even further. The solution is viewed by several photomultipliers, and coincidences are required to identify a neutron count. (Noise pulses are random in time and do not result in a coincidence.) The full width at half-maximum of the peak resulting from slow-neutron capture ranged from 65 to 95% in various counters. The detection efficiency of such a counter is about 50% for neutrons of 1 kev energy and more than 90% for 1-ev neutrons.

The $B^{10}(n, \alpha)Li^7$ reaction has also been used for slow-neutron counting in a mixture of boron-loaded plastic and ZnS(Ag) phosphor.[129] Best results were achieved with a ZnS(Ag) to boron-plastic weight ratio of 2 to 1. The scintillator thickness giving maximum counting rate was found to be 1.2 mm. For greater thicknesses, the scintillator tends to become opaque to the emitted light. The detection efficiency of such a counter for thermal neutrons is of the order of 20 to 30%. Greater detection efficiencies could be realized with the use of enriched B^{10} rather than natural boron, which is 19% B^{10}.

The detection of slow neutrons by the $B^{10}(n, \alpha)Li^7$ reaction in gas scintillation counters has already been discussed. Probably the chief advantage of a gas counter is its fast decay time and relatively low sensitivity to gamma-ray backgrounds. Slow-neutron detection in a gas scintillator could also be accomplished by counting fission events or by the $He^3(n, p)T$ reaction in a He^3-Xe gas mixture.

Another nuclear reaction that is useful for slow-neutron detection is the $Li^6(n, \alpha)T$ reaction with an energy release of 4.78 Mev. This high Q-value results in a large scintillation pulse, in a LiI(Eu) crystal, which is easily distinguishable from background counts. With a good LiI(Eu) crystal and a selected photomultiplier, a slow-neutron peak of 6% width can be achieved. (See Fig. 34.) Crystals of $Li^6I(Eu)$ enriched to 96% Li^6 concentration are available commercially. An enriched crystal of 2-mm thickness has a high detection efficiency for slow neutrons, of the order of 40% for a 1-ev neutron.

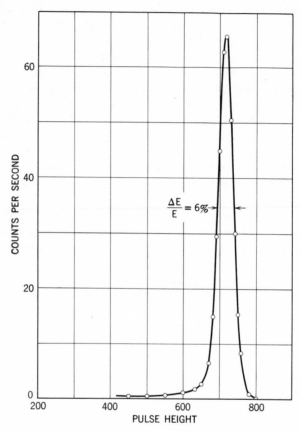

Fig. 34.   Scintillation response of LiI(Eu) crystal to slow neutrons.   From Schenck.[116]

Scintillating glasses, containing either boron or lithium, have been developed in recent years and offer distinct promise of a high-efficiency detector for slow neutrons. The pulse height resulting from slow-neutron capture in a particular boron-loaded glass[151] was found to be equivalent to that from a 17-kev electron in NaI(Tl) and is thus well above photomultiplier noise. Neutron-sensitive glass scintillators may prove to be particularly suitable for use with slow-neutron choppers where detectors of large area and high efficiency are required.

4. Detection and spectroscopy of fast neutrons. The detection of fast neutrons by scintillation techniques depends upon the interaction of the neutron to give (a) a recoil particle from a scattering event, such as a recoil proton, (b) nuclear reaction products from, say, an (n, α) or (n, γ) reaction, or (c) a combination of the foregoing events. It is also possible to determine the energy distribution of fast neutrons by the scintillation method with the use of appropriate counters and techniques. Numerous schemes involving scintillation counters have been proposed and used for fast-neutron counting and spectroscopy. We consider only a limited number. References to other methods may be found elsewhere.[75,98,109,130]

One of the simplest scintillation counters for fast neutrons is an organic scintillator which responds to recoil protons from n-p scattering events in the scintillation material itself. This class of counter may include plastics, organic liquids, or organic crystals such as anthracene or stilbene. The n-p scattering process is isotropic in the center-of-mass system for neutron energies up to about 10 or 12 Mev; as a result, the spectrum of recoil protons from monoenergetic neutrons of energy E_n is a continuous distribution in energy from 0 to E_n. Neglecting other effects, the pulse-height spectrum from monoenergetic neutrons on an organic scintillator should consist of a flat distribution of pulses up to the pulse height corresponding to E_n, at which point it should drop to zero. The drop is not expected to be perfectly sharp because of the resolution of the scintillation counter. In practice, the observed pulse-height response demonstrates a rise in counting rate with decreasing pulse height. (See Fig. 35.) This is the result of several effects, including loss of protons from the surfaces of the crystal, backgrounds, and, especially, the nonlinear response of organic scintillators to protons. Such counters are useful as detectors but apparently have limited application to fast-neutron spectrometry. The use of this technique in the measurement of a complex neutron spectrum involves considerable work in interpretation of the data, since the incident spectrum is given (even for an *ideal* counter) by the derivative of the observed pulse-height distribution. The use of stilbene as a fast-neutron spectrometer has been discussed by Swartz and co-workers.[131] One feature of such counters very much in their favor is the high neutron detection efficiencies that are possible. A stilbene crystal 1 cm thick has a detection efficiency of about 17% for 1-Mev neutrons and about 7% for 5-Mev neutrons. Much higher detection efficiencies are possible, of course, with thicker counters, particularly plastic or liquid scintillators.

A similar type of counter, which has been proposed and studied as a fast-neutron spectrometer, is the so-called "total-absorption spectrometer," in which the *total* neutron energy is lost by multiple proton collisions. The detecting element of such a counter consists of a liquid organic scintillator to which has been added a slow-neutron capturing element like cadmium or boron. The liquid may be viewed by several photomultipliers for efficient light collection. A fast neutron incident on the liquid is slowed down by successive proton collisions; ideally, the sum of the individual recoil proton pulses provides a direct measure of the incident neutron energy. The slow neutron is then captured and is identified by the capture

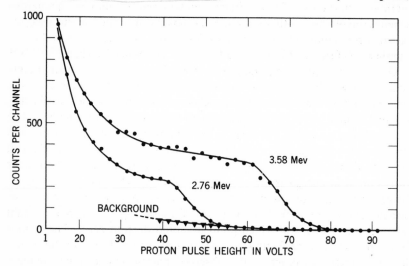

Fig. 35. Observed pulse-height spectra from monoenergetic $D(d, n)He^3$ neutrons on stilbene crystal 1 cm diameter × 1 mm thick. From Swartz et al.[131]

pulse from, say, the $B^{10}(n, \alpha)$ reaction or capture gamma rays from cadmium. A count is accepted only if it is followed within a characteristic time by the slow-neutron capture pulse. This method thus requires the use of delayed coincidence techniques; the delay time may be of the order of a few microseconds. Counters of this type have been successfully used as high-efficiency fast-neutron detectors. Their use as spectrometers, however, is based on the assumption that the light output of the liquid is a linear function of proton energy. As noted previously, this is far from true for known organic scintillators. The resulting distortion in the pulse-height spectrum from such counters has been discussed by Andrews.[2] In addition, a spectrometer of this type must be fairly large to prevent the escape of the neutron in the slowing-down process; a typical counter might be many inches in diameter.[98] As a consequence, such counters have a high gamma-ray detection efficiency with the concomitant background problems. A further discussion may be found elsewhere.[33,34]

An efficient fast-neutron detector with good discrimination against gammas and electrons has been developed by Hornyak.[64] This detector consists of a suspension of ZnS(Ag) in lucite; recoil protons from hydrogen in the lucite excite the ZnS(Ag) grains. The optimum design for such a scintillator was found to be 1.5 grams of ZnS(Ag) in 10 grams of lucite. A typical "button" was formed as a cylinder of 1-in. diameter × $\frac{5}{8}$ in. high. The initial decay time of the light pulses was about 0.1 μsec. The detection efficiency as a function of discriminator setting for various neutron sources

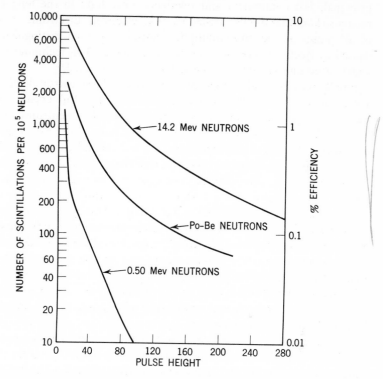

Fig. 36. Integral pulse-height spectrum showing detection efficiency for neutrons on a "Hornyak button." From Hornyak.[64]

is shown in Fig. 36. A corresponding plot of scintillations per 10^5 gamma rays versus pulse height demonstrates the very low efficiency of this counter to gammas: the curve from 2.9-Mev gammas crosses the abscissa at a pulse height of 16 and that from 17.6-Mev gammas crosses at a pulse height of about 40. This type of detector has also been studied and used as a fast-neutron dosimeter.

A very powerful method for discriminating against gamma-ray background counts in organic neutron detectors arises from the fact that the shape of a pulse resulting from a neutron event is significantly different from that following a gamma-ray event. This difference exists in organic crystals (e.g., stilbene and anthracene), organic liquids, and plastic scintillators. Scintillation pulses from organic counters in general contain a fast component whose decay time is of order 10^{-8} to 10^{-9} sec, followed by components whose decay time is significantly longer. A pulse from a recoil proton (or other heavy particle) contains relatively less light in the principal, fast component and relatively more light in the longer components than does a pulse arising from an electron. Electronic inspection of all pulses at the photomultiplier output may then distinguish those caused by electrons, and these pulses are rejected. This technique is being widely used and has been reviewed by several authors.[152]

Finally we may note the use of $Li^6I(Eu)$ as a fast-neutron detector and spectrometer.[95] The detection efficiency of a $Li^6I(Eu)$ crystal for fast neutrons is, of course, much less than that for slow neutrons, since the $Li^6(n, \alpha)T$ cross section is of the order of 0.1 barn in the Mev region but hundreds of barns for slow neutrons. Even so, the efficiency of a $Li^6I(Eu)$ crystal of several millimeters thickness is of the order of 0.1 % for neutrons in the Mev region. The efficiency decreases monotonically with increasing energy in the region above 1 Mev and is determined from the known $Li^6(n, \alpha)T$ cross section as a function of energy. This cross section has been the subject of study in several laboratories; the first measurements in the Mev region were reported by Ribe,[113] and several workers have reported more recent results.[54,89,99] With knowledge of the absolute value and energy dependence of the (n, α) cross section, it is possible to use a $Li^6I(Eu)$ scintillator as an absolute counter for fast neutrons. An example of this application is given by Kreger and Kern,[90] who counted 16.3-Mev neutrons in a cross section determination.

One of the disadvantages of using $Li^6I(Eu)$ as a fast-neutron spectrometer is that the fast-neutron peak in the pulse-height spectrum is quite wide, considerably broader than the slow-neutron peak. This behavior is attributed to the difference in scintillation efficiency of the crystal to the alpha and triton. For the fast-neutron-induced reaction, both the alpha and triton have a range of energies available to them, since the energy division between the reaction products depends upon their angular distribution. For very slow neutrons, however, the energy distribution between the alpha and triton is uniquely specified, so that the slow-neutron peak appears as a sharp Gaussian. The width of the fast-neutron peak is reduced considerably by cooling the crystal to liquid nitrogen temperature.[95] An example of a pulse-height spectrum from monoenergetic neutrons is given in Fig. 37. In this case an attempt was made to reduce the slow-neutron background, so that the crystal was not optically coupled to the photomultiplier by a light pipe. As a result, the peak width is somewhat

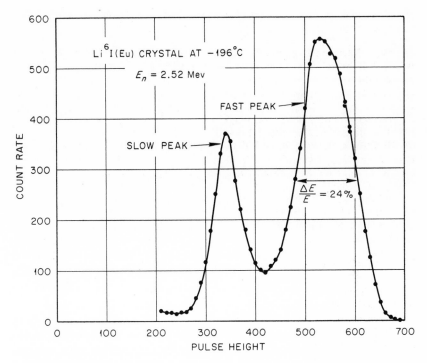

Fig. 37. Pulse-height spectrum from $T(p, n)He^3$ neutrons on Li^{6}I(Eu) crystal at $-196°$ C. Slow-neutron peak arises from neutrons moderated by scattering from nearby equipment, walls, etc.

broader than that obtainable under the best circumstances. In spite of this, the fast-neutron peak is clearly distinguishable. It appears that Li^{6}I(Eu) may be useful as a fast-neutron monitor and spectrometer in experiments in which sharp resolution is not required.

REFERENCES

1. Armour Research Foundation, *Final Progress Report on Project No. A-084* (June 1958).
2. P. T. Andrews, *Rev. Sci. Instr.*, **28**, 56 (1957).
3. J. B. Birks, *Scintillation Counters* (McGraw-Hill, New York, 1953).
4. P. R. Bell, article in *Beta- and Gamma-Ray Spectroscopy*, K. Siegbahn Ed., (North Holland Press, Amsterdam, 1955).
5. H. E. Buckley, *Crystal Growth*, (Wiley, New York, 1951).
6. J. Bonanomi and J. Rossel, *Helv. Phys. Acta*, **25**, 725 (1952).

7. S. Bashkin, R. R. Carlson, R. A. Douglas, and J. A. Jacobs, *Phys. Rev.*, **109**, 434 (1958).

8. J. B. Birks, *Phys. Rev.*, **84**, 364 (1951); *Proc. Phys. Soc. (London)*, **A-64**, 874 (1951).

9. W. L. Buck and R. K. Swank, *Nucleonics*, **11**, No. 11, 48 (1953).

10. E. J. Bowen, E. Mikiewicz, and F. W. Smith, *Proc. Phys. Soc. (London)*, **A-62**, 26 (1949).

11. J. B. Birks, *Phys. Rev.*, **94**, 1567 (1954).

12. F. D. Brooks, chapter in *Progress in Nuclear Physics*, **5**, O. R. Frisch, Ed. (Pergamon Press, New York, 1956).

13. J. B. Birks, *Phys. Rev.*, **95**, 277 (1954).

14. J. B. Birks and F. D. Brooks, *Proc. Phys. Soc. (London)*, **B-69**, 721 (1956).

15. L. J. Basile, *J. Chem. Phys.*, **27**, 801 (1957).

16. W. L. Buck and R. K. Swank, *Rev. Sci. Instr.*, **29**, 252 (1958).

17. L. M. Bollinger and G. E. Thomas, *Rev. Sci. Instr.*, **28**, 489 (1957).

18. W. Bennett, V. Hughes, and C. S. Wu, Progress Report, Nuclear Physics Laboratories, Columbia University, CU-149, 19 (1956); also *Bull. Am. Phys. Soc.*, Ser. II, **2**, No. 1 (1957).

19. L. E. Beghian, G. H. R. Kegel, and R. P. Scharenberg, *Rev. Sci. Instr.*, **29**, 753 (1958).

20. P. R. Bell, R. C. Davis, and W. Bernstein, *Rev. Sci. Instr.*, **26**, 726 (1955).

21. C. E. Crouthamel, Ed., *Applied Gamma-Ray Spectrometry* (Pergamon Press, New York, 1960).

22. E. Breitenberger, chapter in *Progress in Nuclear Physics*, **4**, O. R. Frisch, Ed. (Pergamon Press, New York, 1955).

23. G. P. Boicourt and J. E. Brolley, Jr., *Rev. Sci. Instr.*, **25**, 1218 (1954).

24. W. R. Bennett, Jr., *Rev. Sci. Instr.*, **28**, 1092 (1957).

25. J. Button, T. Elioff, E. Segre, H. M. Steiner, R. Weingart, C. Wiegand, and T. Ypsilantis, *Phys. Rev.*, **108**, 1557 (1957).

26. T. Bowen, *Phys. Rev.*, **96**, 754 (1954).

27. C. J. Borkowski, *IRE Trans. Nuclear Sci.*, **NS-3**, 71 (1956).

28. J. K. Bair and F. C. Maienschein, *Rev. Sci. Instr.*, **22**, 343 (1951).

29. C. L. Cowan, Jr., F. Reines, F. B. Harrison, H. W. Kruse, and A. D. McGuire, *Science*, **124**, 103 (1956).

30. S. C. Curran, *Luminescence and the Scintillation Counter* (Academic Press, London, 1953).

31. G. W. Clark, F. Scherb, and W. B. Smith, *Rev. Sci. Instr.*, **28**, 433 (1957).

32. D. J. Chleck and C. A. Ziegler, *Rev. Sci. Instr.*, **28**, 466 (1957).

33. M. R. Cleland, *National Bur. Standards Report 2036* (1952).

34. C. L. Cowan, Jr., and F. Reines, *Los Alamos Report, LAMS-2100* (1956).

35. R. C. Davis, P. R. Bell, G. G. Kelley, and N. H. Lazar, *IRE Trans. Nuclear Sci.*, **NS-3**, 82 (1956).

36. F. Eby and W. Jentschke, *Phys. Rev.*, **96**, 911 (1954).

37. J. O. Elliot, S. H. Liebson, and C. F. Ravilious, *Phys. Rev.*, **79**, 393 (1950).

38. C. Eggler and C. M. Huddleston, *IRE Trans. Nuclear Sci.*, **NS-3**, 36 (1956).

39. D. Engelkemeier, *Rev. Sci. Instr.*, **27**, 589 (1956).

40. R. W. Engstrom, R. G. Stoudenheimer, and A. M. Glover, *Nucleonics*, **10**, No. 4, 58 (1952).

41. R. W. Engstrom, R. G. Stoudenheimer, H. L. Palmer, and D. A. Bly, *IRE Trans. Nuclear Sci.*, **NS-5**, 120 (1958).

42. H. Enz and J. Rossel, *Helv. Phys. Acta*, **31**, 25 (1958).

43. L. C. Greene, D. C. Reynolds, S. J. Czyzak, and W. M. Baker, *J. Chem. Phys.*, **29**, 1375 (1958).
44. W. Franzen, R. W. Peelle, and R. Sherr, *Phys. Rev.*, **79**, 742 (1950).
45. E. C. Farmer, H. B. Moore, and C. Goodman, *Phys. Rev.*, **76**, 454 (1949).
46. J. Franck and R. Livingston, *Rev. Mod. Phys.*, **21**, 505 (1949).
47. M. Furst and H. Kallman, *Phys. Rev.*, **97**, 583 (1955).
48. M. Furst and H. Kallman, *Phys. Rev.*, **85**, 816 (1952).
49. C. B. Fulmer, *Phys. Rev.*, **108**, 1113 (1957).
50. J. S. Fraser and J. C. D. Milton, *Nuclear Instr.*, **3**, 275 (1958).
51. J. E. Francis and P. R. Bell, *Oak Ridge National Laboratory Report 1975*, 70 (1955).
52. R. H. Gillette, *Rev. Sci. Instr.*, **21**, 294 (1950).
53. G. F. J. Garlick, *Luminescent Materials* (Oxford University Press, London, 1949).
54. F. Gabbard, R. H. Davis, and T. W. Bonner, *Phys. Rev.*, **114**, 201 (1958).
55. B. Hahn and J. Rossel, *Helv. Phys. Acta*, **26**, 803 (1953).
56. R. Hofstadter, *Nucleonics*, **6**, No. 5, 70 (1950).
57. B. Hahn and J. Rossel, *Helv. Phys. Acta*, **26**, 271 (1953).
58. H. Hinrichs, *Z. Naturforsch.*, **9a**, 617 and 625 (1954).
59. J. E. Hardy, *Rev. Sci. Instr.*, **29**, 705 (1958).
60. F. N. Hayes, B. S. Rogers, and P. C. Sanders, *Nucleonics*, **13**, No. 1, 46 (1955).
61. F. N. Hayes, D. G. Ott, V. N. Kerr, and B. S. Rogers, *Nucleonics*, **13**, No. 12, 38 (1955); also, *ibid.*, **14**, No. 1, 42 (1956).
62. J. I. Hoover and C. F. Dohne, *Rev. Sci. Instr.*, **25**, 922 (1954).
63. C. C. Harris and P. R. Bell, *IRE Trans. Nuclear Sci.*, **NS-3**, 87 (1956).
64. W. F. Hornyak, *Rev. Sci. Instr.*, **23**, 264 (1952).
65. F. N. Hayes, *IRE Trans. Nuclear Sci.*, **NS-5**, 166 (1958).
66. F. B. Harrison, C. L. Cowan, Jr., and F. Reines, *Nucleonics*, **12**, No. 3, 44 (1954).
67. R. Hofstadter and J. A. McIntyre, *Phys. Rev.*, **78**, 619 (1950).
68. R. L. Heath, *Atomic Energy Comm. Research and Development Report, IDO-16408* (1958).
69. H. G. Hanson, J. J. Manning, and R. B. Murray, *Oak Ridge National Laboratory Report 2609*, 138 (1958).
70. J. H. Hubbell and N. E. Scofield, *IRE Trans. Nuclear Sci.*, **NS-5**, 155 (1958).
71. J. I. Hopkins, *Rev. Sci. Instr.*, **22**, 29 (1951).
72. L. W. Johnston, R. D. Birkhoff, J. S. Cheka, H. H. Hubble, Jr., and B. G. Saunders, *Rev. Sci. Instr.*, **28**, 765 (1957).
73. P. D. Johnson and F. E. Williams, *Phys. Rev.*, **81**, 146 (1951).
74. H. V. Watts, L. Reiffel, and M. D. Jones, *Bull. Am. Phys. Soc.*, Ser. II., **5**, 201 (1960).
75. C. H. Johnson and C. C. Trail, *Rev. Sci. Instr.*, **27**, 468 (1956).
76. S. Z. Kyropoulos, *Z. anorg. Chem.*, **154**, 308 (1926).
77. See, for example, C. Kittel, *Introduction to Solid State Physics*, Second Edition, Ch. 18 (Wiley, New York, 1956).
78. H. Knoepfel, E. Loepfe, and P. Stoll, *Helv. Phys. Acta*, **29**, 241 (1956); *ibid*, **30**, 521 (1957); also W. Beusch, H. Knoepfel, E. Loepfe, D. Maeder, and P. Stoll, *Nuovo cimento*, Ser. 10, **5**, 1355 (1957).
79. H. Kallman, *Phys.Rev.*, **75**, 623 (1949).
80. F. H. Krenz, *Trans. Faraday Soc.* (*London*), **51**, 172 (1955).
81. H. Kallman and G. J. Brucker, *Phys. Rev.*, **108**, 1122 (1957).

82. J. Kirkbride, *Nature*, **171**, 564 (1953).
83. H. Kallman, M. Furst, and F. H. Brown, *IRE Trans. Nuclear Sci.*, NS-3, 51 (1956).
84. L. Koch and R. Lesueur, *J. phys. radium*, **19**, 103 (1958).
85. H. Knoepfel, E. Loepfe, and P. Stoll, *Z. Naturforsch.*, **12a**, 348 (1957).
86. A. Meyer and R. B. Murray, *IRE Trans. Nuclear Sci.*, NS-7, 22 (1960).
87. G. G. Kelley, P. R. Bell, R. C. Davis, and N. H. Lazar, *IRE Trans. Nuclear Sci.*, NS-3, 57 (1956).
88. P. G. Koontz, G. R. Keepin, and J. E. Ashley, *Rev. Sci. Instr.*, **26**, 352 (1955).
89. B. D. Kern and W. E. Kreger, *Phys. Rev.*, **112**, 926 (1958).
90. W. E. Kreger and B. D. Kern, *Bull. Am. Phys. Soc.*, Ser. II., **3**, 188 (1958).
91. S. H. Liebson, *Nucleonics*, **10**, No. 7, 41 (1952).
92. N. H. Lazar, *IRE Trans. Nuclear Sci.*, NS-5, 138 (1958).
93. C. T. Schmidt, *IRE Trans. Nuclear Sci.*, NS-7, 25 (1960).
94. W. E. Mott and R. B. Sutton, *Encyclopedia of Physics*, *XLV*, 86, S. Flügge and E. Creutz, Eds. (Springer-Verlag, Berlin, 1958).
95. R. B. Murray, *Nuclear Instr.*, **2**, 237 (1958).
96. C. O. Muehlhause and G. E. Thomas, Jr., *Nucleonics*, **11**, No. 1, 44 (1953).
97. F. C. Maienschein, Oak Ridge National Laboratory, private communication.
98. C. O. Muehlhause, *IRE Trans. Nuclear Sci.*, NS-3, 77 (1956).
99. R. B. Murray and H. W. Schmitt, *Phys. Rev.*, **115**, 1707 (1959).
100. C. G. Bell and F. N. Hayes, Eds., *Liquid Scintillation Counting* (Pergamon Press, New York, 1958).
101. K. P. Nicholson and G. F. Snelling, *Brit. J. Appl. Phys.*, **6**, 104 (1955).
102. J. A. Northrop and R. A. Nobles, *IRE Trans. Nuclear Sci.*, NS-3, 59 (1956).
103. R. A. Nobles, *Rev. Sci. Instr.*, **27**, 280 (1956).
104. J. A. Northrop, *Rev. Sci. Instr.*, **29**, 437 (1958).
105. J. A. Northrop, J. M. Gursky, and A. E. Johnsrud, *IRE Trans. Nuclear Sci.*, NS-5, 81 (1958).
106. J. A. Northrop and J. C. Gursky, *Nuclear Instr.*, **3**, 207 (1958).
107. T. R. Ophel, *Nuclear Instr.*, **3**, 45 (1958).
108. D. G. Ott, F. N. Hayes, J. E. Hammel, and J. F. Kephart, *Nucleonics*, **13**, No. 5, 62 (1955).
109. W. J. Price, *Nuclear Radiation Detection* (McGraw-Hill, New York, 1958).
110. R. W. Pringle, L. D. Black, B. L. Funt, and S. Sobering, *Phys. Rev.*, **92**, 1582 (1953).
111. J. T. Randall and M. H. F. Wilkins, *Proc. Roy. Soc. (London)*, A-184, 369 (1945).
112. A. R. Ronzio, C. L. Cowan, Jr., and F. Reines, *Rev. Sci. Instr.*, **29**, 146 (1958).
113. F. L. Ribe, *Phys. Rev.*, **103**, 741 (1956).
114. D. C. Stockbarger, *Rev. Sci. Instr.*, **7**, 133 (1936).
115. R. S. Storey, W. Jack, and A. Ward, *Proc. Phys. Soc. (London)*, **72**, 1 (1958).
116. J. Schenck, *Nature*, **171**, 518 (1953).
117. E. C. Stewart, Harshaw Chemical Co., private communication.
118. R. C. Sangster and J. W. Irvine, *J. Chem. Phys.*, **24**, 670 (1956).
119. R. K. Swank and W. L. Buck, *Phys. Rev.*, **91**, 927 (1953).
120. R. K. Swank, *Ann. Rev. Nuclear Sci.*, **4**, 111 (1954).
121. H. H. Seliger, C. A. Ziegler, and I. Jaffe, *Phys. Rev.*, **101**, 998 (1956).
122. H. H. Seliger and C. A. Ziegler, *IRE Trans. Nuclear Sci.*, NS-3, 62 (1956).
123. H. Kallman and M. Furst, chapter in *Liquid Scintillation Counting*, Ref. 100.
124. R. K. Swank, W. L. Buck, F. N. Hayes, and D. G. Ott, *Rev. Sci. Instr.*, **29**, 279 (1958).

125. A. Sayres and C. S. Wu, *Rev. Sci. Instr.*, **28**, 758 (1957).
126. N. Schaetti and W. Baumgartner, *Helv. Phys. Acta*, **24**, 614 (1951).
127. A. H. Sommer, *IRE Trans. Nuclear Sci.*, **NS-3**, 8 (1956).
128. J. Sharpe, *Brit. Comm. Electronics*, **4**, 484 (1957).
129. K. H. Sun, P. R. Malmberg, and F. A. Pecjak, *Nucleonics*, **14**, No. 7, 46 (1956).
130. C. D. Swartz, *NYO-Report 3863* (1954).
131. C. D. Swartz, G. Owen, and O. Ames, *NYO Report 2053* (1957).
132. C. J. Taylor, W. K. Jentschke, M. E. Remley, F. S. Eby, and P. G. Kruger, *Phys. Rev*, **84**, 1034 (1951).
133. G. E. Thomas, Jr., *Rev. Sci. Instr.*, **27**, 878 (1956).
134. W. J. Van Sciver, *HEPL Report No. 38*, Stanford University (1955); also *IRE Trans. Nuclear Sci.*, **NS-3**, 39 (1956).
135. W. J. Van Sciver and R. Hofstadter, *Phys. Rev.*, **87**, 522 (1952).
136. W. J. Van Sciver and L. Bogart, *IRE Trans. Nuclear Sci.*, **NS-5**, 90 (1958).
137. A. E. Villaire and L. F. Wouters, *Phys. Rev.*, **98**, 280 (1955).
138. F. E. Williams, *Advances in Electronics*, **5**, 137 (1953).
139. G. T. Wright, *Phys. Rev.*, **91**, 1282 (1953).
140. J. B. Birks, *IRE Trans. Nuclear Sci.*, **NS-7**, 2 (1960).
141. A. Whetstone, B. Allison, E. G. Muirhead, and J. Halpern, *Rev. Sci. Instr.*, **29**, 415 (1958).
142. G. T. Wright, *J. Sci. Inst.*, **31**, 377 (1954).
143. L. F. Wouters, *Nucleonics*, **10**, No. 8, 48 (1952).
144. L. F. Wouters, *UCRL 4516* (1955).
145. W. Zobel, R. W. Peelle, T. A. Love, and G. M. Estabrook, *Oak Ridge National Laboratory Report 2389*, 97 (1957).
146. E. H. Thorndike and W. J. Shlaer, *Rev. Sci. Instr.*, **30**, 838 (1959).
147. H. Fleishman, H. Einbinder, and C. S. Wu, *Rev. Sci. Instr.*, **30**, 1130 (1959).
148. L. Cathey, *IRE Trans. Nuclear Sci.*, **NS-5**, 109 (1958).
149. R. B. Murray and J. J. Manning, *IRE Trans. Nuclear Sci.*, **NS-7**, 80 (1960).
150. C. D. Zerby, A. Meyer, and R. B. Murray, *Nuclear Instr.*, to be published (1961).
151. L. M. Bollinger, G. E. Thomas, and J. Ginther, *Rev. Sci. Instr.*, **30**, 1135 (1959).
152. See, for example, F. D. Brooks, R. W. Pringle, and B. L. Funt, *IRE Trans. Nuclear Sci.*, **NS-7**, 35 (1960).
153. R. L. Becker, *Phys. Rev.*, **119**, 1076 (1960).
154. A. Bisi and L. Zappa, *Nuclear Instr.*, **3**, 17 (1958).

3 A SURVEY OF CERENKOV COUNTER TECHNIQUE

BURTON J. MOYER
Lawrence Radiation Laboratory, Berkeley, California

A. Characteristics of Cerenkov Radiation
B. Types of Cerenkov Counters
C. Efficiency and Resolution Considerations

The Cerenkov effect[1] and the complete theoretical description[2] of the origin and emission characteristics of the Cerenkov light have been known for a period of more than twenty years, but the practical realization of particle counters based upon this principle awaited the development of the photomultiplier tube and of techniques of wide-band amplification that have come within the past decade.

Because of its attribute of responding selectively on the basis of velocity to high-speed charged particles, the Cerenkov counter has become a prominent instrument in the investigations of high-energy particle physics and cosmic rays. In addition to this discrimination in response, the temporal sharpness of the light pulse is compatible with the precise time resolution frequently required in present-day experiments in accelerator physics.

The first application of the Cerenkov radiation in high-energy physics was the precise determination by Mather[3] of the proton energy at the Berkeley cyclotron to an accuracy of about 0.24%. This work, however, was not "particle counting," which is the domain of the present discussion.

Present-day usefulness of Cerenkov counters is particularly in the techniques of high-energy particle identification. If a momentum selection of a beam of mixed particles is effected by magnetic bending, then a determination of velocity by an appropriate counter or by flight time will select particles of a particular mass (assuming known charge). Velocity-selecting Cerenkov counters are thus employed in some cases to identify particles of interest among others that constitute an unwanted background and in other cases to reject, usually by functioning in anticoincidence with other counters, the flux of unwanted particles. The fact that the Cerenkov light yield is proportional to the square of the charge carried by the radiating particle is also a basis for distinguishing among various particles.

Summaries and review articles covering experience in design and counting techniques up to the dates of their writing have been provided by

Marshall[4] and Jelley.[5] Jelley, in Ref. 5a has included a comprehensive review of the theory of the Cerenkov effect. Further, more recent summaries of experience with such counters appear in the CERN reports.[15]

A. Characteristics of Cerenkov Radiation

Cerenkov radiation is the electromagnetic shock wave that arises from a charged particle moving through a transparent medium at a speed greater than that of light within the medium. Thus only if the particle relative

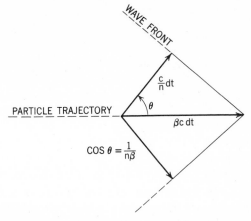

Fig. 1.   Illustration of the Cerenkov angle. The wavefront lines are the intersections of the cone with the plane of the diagram.

velocity $\beta = v/c$ and the refractive index n of the medium are such that $n\beta > 1$ will the radiation exist. When this condition is fulfilled, the Cerenkov light is emitted at the angle given by

$$\cos \theta = \frac{1}{n\beta} \tag{1}$$

where θ is the angle between the velocity vector for the particle and the propagation vector for any portion of the conical radiation wavefront, as illustrated in Fig. 1.

The spectral intensity of the radiation from a particle of charge ze is

$$\frac{d^2W}{dx\,d\nu} = \frac{4\pi^2 z^2 e^2 \nu}{c^2}\left(1 - \frac{1}{n^2\beta^2}\right)$$

in ergs per centimeter per unit frequency interval. In terms of photon emission, this becomes

$$\frac{d^2N}{dx\,d\nu} = 2\pi\left(\frac{e^2}{\hbar c}\right)\frac{z^2}{c}\left(1 - \frac{1}{n^2\beta^2}\right) = \frac{2\pi}{137}\cdot\frac{z^2}{c}\sin^2\theta \tag{2}$$

in photons per centimeter per unit frequency interval. Thus, for familiar transparent substances, for which n is not strongly a function of frequency over the visible region, the photon emission is nearly the same at all frequencies.

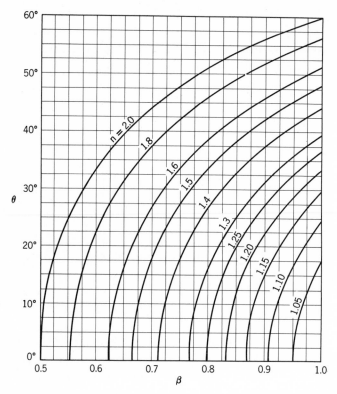

Fig. 2.   The Cerenkov angle, θ, versus particle relative velocity, β, for various values of refractive index, n.

The polarization of the radiation is such that the electric vector lies in the plane defined by the particle trajectory and the ray of light under observation and thus points toward or away from the moving charged particle.

Equation 2 indicates that over a frequency interval $dv = 3.2 \times 10^{14}$ sec^{-1}, corresponding to the range 4000–7000 A, the photon production will be (assuming a constant value for $n\beta$)

$$\frac{dN}{dx} = 490z^2\left(1 - \frac{1}{n^2\beta^2}\right) \quad \text{photons/cm.}$$

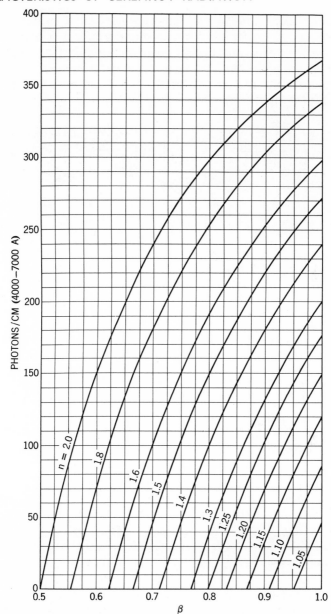

Fig. 3. Photons per centimeter of path versus β for the wavelength interval 4000–7000 A for various values of n. (Singly charged particle assumed.)

The number of photons that actually emerge from the medium, and the emergent spectrum, will depend upon the spectral absorption properties of the medium and the path lengths therein.

The angle of emission is, of course, not quite unique but varies slightly with frequency through the dependence of n upon the latter. However, this effect is but one among three effects intrinsic to the physical situation

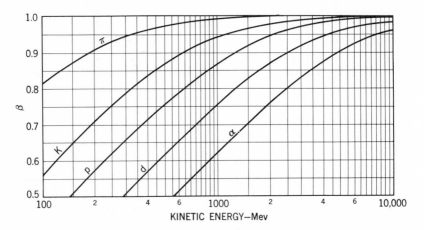

KINETIC ENERGY—Mev

Fig. 4. Relative velocity β versus kinetic energy for (1) π-mesons, (2) K-mesons, (3) protons, (4) deuterons, and (5) alpha particles. Electrons are, of course, at $\beta = 1$ in this energy region.

that produce imprecision of the angle: namely, optical dispersion, multiple scattering, and slowing down of the particle. All these effects are discussed in Sec. C.

Figures 2 and 3 present data in graphical form calculated from (1) and (2), and Fig. 4 relates relative velocity to kinetic energy for various particles. In the application of such data, the experimenter must also be cognizant of the effects of self-absorption of the Cerenkov light by the medium, of the photon collection efficiency of his optical system, and of the spectral efficiency of the photomultiplier tube. These are discussed in a subsequent section.

B. Types of Cerenkov Counters

Quite generally, various Cerenkov counters may be classified as either *focusing* or *nonfocusing* types, depending upon whether or not the rays of light form an image or quasi-image of the emitting region. In the non-focusing counters the lower velocity limit for counter response is established simply by the refractive index of the medium, and in some cases an upper limit is provided by a utilization of total internal reflection. For the focusing types a specific requirement on ray directions is imposed which can be met only by radiation from particles moving within a limited solid angle and within a small interval of velocity.

I. Nonfocusing counters: velocity threshold determined by n. Frequently the only discrimination required of a counter is the suppression of response to a "background" flux of particles, which are predominantly at low velocities, while retaining the ability to detect the passage of all charged particles above a certain critical velocity. Typical of such requirements is the need to count electrons or mesons of relativistic speeds in the midst of an intense flux of fast neutrons. A scintillation counter in such a situation will often be glutted with response to the proton recoils, whereas a Cerenkov counter with a properly selected radiating medium can be essentially free from response to neutron effects.

The construction of nonfocusing counters is simple, in principle; it involves merely the enclosure of the radiating medium in a container possessing walls of high reflectivity, either specular or diffuse, and the optical coupling of the photocathode to a clear window through which the medium can be viewed. The designer must, however, estimate the amount of effective photocathode area which must view the medium in order to collect an adequate number of photons to give desired pulse strengths. This estimate will involve wall reflectivity and absorption of the light in the medium as well as the basic photon production and photocathode efficiency data. These factors are further discussed in Sec. C.

The transparent solids and liquids which may be used to provide desired response thresholds by their various refractive indices are manifold in the region of index values greater than 1.4; we list here in Table 1 a few that provide low refractive index values.

TABLE I. SOME LIQUIDS OF LOW REFRACTIVE INDEX
USEFUL IN CERENKOV COUNTERS

Material	n	Threshold β	Protons	Pions	Electrons
			\multicolumn{3}{c}{Threshold Kinetic Energies}	
Liq. N_2	1.205	0.830	760 Mev	112 Mev	410 kev
Liq. O_2	1.221	0.819	710 Mev	104 Mev	380 kev
FC-75*	1.277	0.782	580 Mev	86 Mev	315 kev
Water	1.332	0.751	500 Mev	73 Mev	265 kev

* A fluorochemical available from Minnesota Mining & Mfg. Co. (Composition $C_8F_{16}O$).

The use of liquid nitrogen or oxygen is particularly simple in certain instances when it is possible to use a standard-size Dewar flask which nicely accommodates a photomultiplier tube 2 in. diameter in its throat.

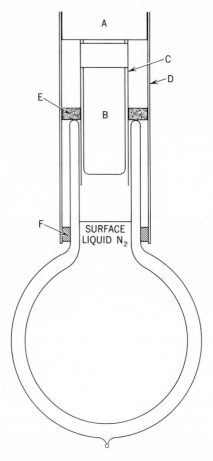

Fig. 5. Cerenkov counter for liquid N_2 or O_2, employing laboratory Dewar flask. Parts identified are A—mounting base unit for photomultiplier tube and its magnetic shield; B—photomultiplier tube, 6810-A; C—aluminum sleeve to distribute heat; D—mu-metal sleeve, for magnetic shield; E—sponge rubber, black; and F—black felt.

The vessel is an excellent photon reflector by virtue of its silvered walls, and the low-temperature condition of the phototube provides low tube noise. Figure 5 illustrates a design used by the author with excellent results. It is important, however, that the photocathode not be too cold in order that it shall not alter its semiconducting properties and become such a poor conductor that it will be unable to recover its potential after loss of electrons. In experience, a spacing of at least 2 in. between photo-cathode and the liquid N_2 surface proved satisfactory in the counter of Fig. 5.

In the use of nonfocusing water Cerenkov counters, a distinct gain may be achieved by the addition of a soluble fluor that will absorb some of the ultraviolet primary radiation and emit the absorbed energy in a spectral region for which the glass window and tube envelope are more transparent. Such a material found by Marshall[6] is 2-amino-6,8 naphthalene-disul-phonic acid, disodium salt, dissolved in the water to the extent of about 20 mg/liter. This additive is most useful in a counter in which the original directional properties of the light cannot be used to advantage to enhance light collection, since the fluorescent light is isotropic. Experience with a water counter in which the medium is viewed from one side as the particles pass through has shown a pulse-height gain by a factor of nearly 2 attri-butable to the additive.

The range of refractive index between unity and 1.20 is impossible to achieve with liquids, but this region may be continuously covered by the compression of an appropriate substance at a temperature slightly above its critical temperature. Various substances may be selected, depending upon pressures and temperatures allowed by other requirements of the experiment.

Hess and Nobles[7] have constructed a counter which employed Freon-13 under conditions that provided a refractive index of 1.10. Their determination of n versus density for this material at a temperature of 29° C is shown in Fig. 6. These data were obtained by counting interference fringe shifts produced by a Fabry-Perot interferometer placed within the chamber as the Freon-13 was slowly admitted and compressed, beginning with an initial condition of vacuum.

Frisch[8] and his colleagues have utilized the fluorochemical FC-75 (see Table 1) whose critical conditions are $T_c = 228°$ C, $p_c = 236$ lb/in^2 absolute, to achieve refractive indices between 1.01 and 1.05. With a temperature of 257° C they obtained $n = 1.018$ at a pressure of 125 lb/in^2, and $n = 1.045$ at a pressure somewhat in excess of 250 lb/in^2. Their counter is described later under the focusing counters.

For very low values of n, the compression of gases at ordinary tempera-tures is a common practice for counters designed for very high velocity thresholds. Such counters, and the above-critical-temperature systems previously described, require thick windows of clear optical glass or quartz to withstand the pressure load and yet transmit efficiently the Cerenkov light.

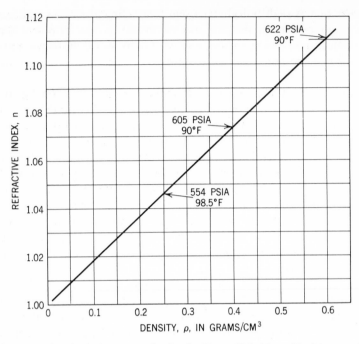

Fig. 6.   Refractive index versus density for Freon 13.[7]   The critical temperature is 83.9° F, and the critical pressure is 561 psia.

2. A nonfocusing type with upper limit of velocity. It was early noted by Bernardini, and the principle was subsequently independently utilized by Fitch,[9] that a choice of refractive index and geometric arrangement is possible so that light from directed particles exceeding a certain velocity cannot emerge into free space from the downstream face of the medium because of incidence at angles greater than critical. Thus, if it is arranged that only those photons that emerge into free space beyond the normal end-face are collected, it is possible to arrange a response only to particles whose velocity is less than a certain limit. Figure 7 illustrates the principle of the "Fitch counter."

The polarization of the Cerenkov light is such as to favor its emergence from the end face when the incidence angle is less than critical, and under these conditions very little is internally reflected; the change from efficient emergence to complete cut-off is in principle quite abrupt as the velocity is increased through the limiting value. Factors that tend to dissipate this abruptness are angular departure of the particle trajectories from normal with respect to the end face, optical dispersion, and the fact that the polarization condition is not in general so favorable for light that has experienced side wall reflections along paths skewed with respect to the axis. Such polarization effects are discussed by Marshall.[4a] Multiple scattering contributes to angular spread in particle trajectories in addition to any divergence pre-existing in the beam.

Elaborations of this type of counter have been proposed in which two media in juxtaposition, with an optically plane interface normal to the

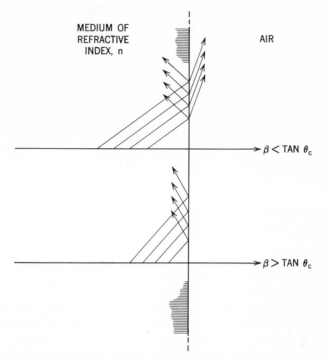

Fig. 7. Fitch counter principle for establishing upper velocity limit of response.

beam direction, allowed almost arbitrary adjustment of the cut-off velocity through choice of the two refractive indices.

3. Focusing counters: velocity selection by emission angle. The conical pattern of wavefront, with cone angle specifically related to velocity and with the relatively small angular spread due to optical dispersion, has allowed considerable play of ingenuity in the devising of optical systems for efficiently gathering the light arising from particles within a desired small velocity interval.

The usual drawback of such systems is the fact that the focusing principle is strictly valid only for particle trajectories exactly along the axis of cylindrical symmetry of the system. The radial aperture and angular aperture are both typically small in a relative sense; that is, the effective radial aperture must be small compared to the radial size of the optical focusing system. This will be immediately obvious upon examination of the following examples. The problem has been treated quantitatively by Marshall[4a] and is briefly reviewed in Sec. C of this discussion.

a. The Getting counter (as modified by Jelley). The earliest proposal for a counter of this type is that of Getting[10] whose scheme is illustrated in Fig. 8 in a form proposed by Jelley.[11]

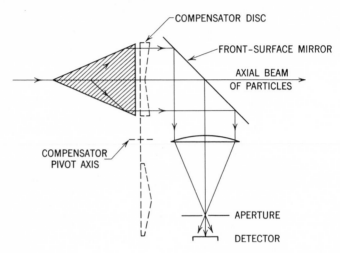

Fig. 8. Schematic optical diagram for Jelley's modification of the Getting counter.

On-axis particles of the velocity for which the cone is designed (defined by the generating angle of the cone being one half the Cerenkov angle for the desired velocity) will yield light that focuses at the focal point of the lens; whereas particles of a different velocity, even though on-axis, will produce a ring focus. Off-axis trajectories give rise to aberrations that diffuse the image, and the velocity resolution will thus depend upon the beam diameter relative to the cone diameter. Adjustment to various desired velocities is suggested by Jelley by use of compensators as indicated in Fig. 8.

In the reference cited Jelley calculates that for a lucite cone ($n = 1.5$) of 10 cm base diameter, traversed by a proton beam of 1 cm diameter at a kinetic energy of 950 Mev (total energy $W = 1890$ Mev), the relative resolution in proton total energy is not poorer than $dw/W = 16\%$. This figure can be reduced in direct proportion to the ratio of beam diameter (radial aperture) to cone-base diameter. In actual experience with this counter Jelley has subsequently reported[15c] a half-height width of 12% in the experimental energy-resolution curve.

b. Marshall counter. This counter (Fig. 9) utilizes refraction by a spherical surface to direct the parallel rays emanating from an on-axis trajectory toward a ring focus, which, because of the refractive index value 1.5 of the lucite of which the sphere consists, will be at a distance of two sphere radii from the surface. There is then provided a cylindrical mirror to reflect the rays converging toward the focal ring back into an axial point. The device is, in principle, capable of accommodating a wide range of

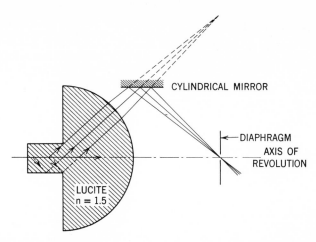

Fig. 9. Schematic diagram illustrating the principle of the Marshall counter for an axial particle trajectory.[4a]

velocities, any value of which may be selected by choice of the axial image point at which the detector is to be located. The resolution with which velocity can be selected is limited by the aperture allowed, which determines the degree of spherical aberration present through the existence of rays not passing through the center of the sphere. The experimental results in velocity resolution shown in the curve of Fig. 10 are taken from Ref. 4a. In this reference Marshall also analyzes the principles that relate aperture and resolution, utilizing an ingenious argument based upon conservation of the angular momentum of photons with respect to the axis of a cylindrically symmetric optical system.

In practice, it was found desirable to interpose plane reflectors to separate the light converging toward the axial focal point into two final image positions. This allowed rejection of phototube noise fluctuation pulses which compete in size with the Cerenkov effect but which would

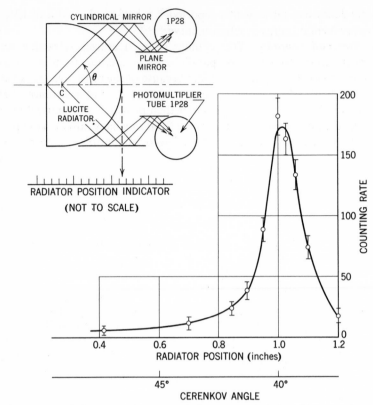

Fig. 10. Resolution curve for a Marshall counter of design illustrated in upper left.[4a] The curve was obtained with 145 Mev pions.

only very infrequently give coincident pulses within the resolution time required by the coincidence circuit.

c. *The Frisch counter.* A focusing counter, in the low-refractive-index region which has received a considerable amount of successful use in work with high-energy pions and K-mesons is that developed by the Massachusetts Institute of Technology group under Frisch.[8] The provision of the medium of low index is accomplished by the means discussed in Sec. B1.

The optical system is presented schematically in Fig. 11. The rays shown in the figure lie in a plane defined by the central axis of cylindrical symmetry and the trajectory of the charged particle which is considered to be moving parallel to the axis. Rays thus defined from various particle trajectories will give rise to a ring focus by action of the lens system. Those rays not lying in planes containing the central axis of symmetry, and which are

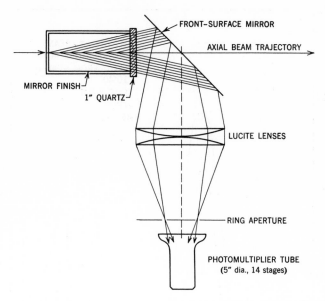

Fig. 11. Schematic diagram of optical principle of Frisch counter, for axial beam trajectory.

therefore skewed with respect to this axis, will not pass precisely through the ring focus but will pass close to it if their "impact parameters" with respect to the axis are small compared to the radius at which they enter the lens. The interposition of the ring aperture ahead of the phototube allows selection of the velocity interval desired.

Information concerning resolution available may be inferred from the data of Fig. 12, which portrays the response of the counter to a beam of π^--mesons of 1.8 bev/c momentum as a function of the pressure of the vapor of the fluorochemical FC-75, the temperature being held constant as indicated. The angular interval accepted by the ring aperture is stated in the legend. The resolution is probably better than this curve suggests, since some of this breadth is caused by the momentum spread of the pion beam, which was not given with these data.

d. The Chamberlain-Wiegand counter. A somewhat simpler optical system, involving only a cylindrical mirror to form axial images for various velocities and an opaque disk to limit the accepted rays to those belonging to the desired velocity interval, has been employed by Chamberlain, Segre, et al., in their antiproton selection system.[12] This counter was more fully described in the report by Chamberlain and Wiegand[15d] at the 1956 CERN Symposium.

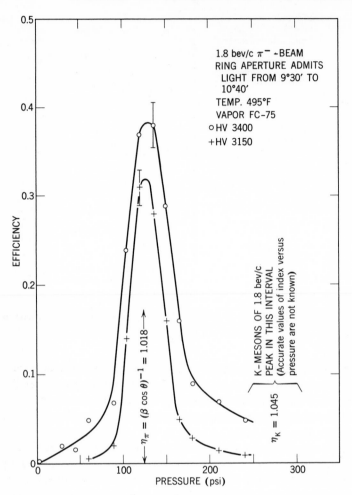

Fig. 12.   Response versus fluid pressure for a particular Frisch-type counter.[8]

Its principle is illustrated by Fig. 13.   Emanating from the end face of the cylindrical radiator, at any azimuthal direction, will be parallel rays at an angle with respect to the axial direction determined by the Cerenkov angle and refraction at the end face of the radiator.   An image of the end face, diffused somewhat by the "caustic curve" effect (cylindrical aberration), will be produced at the appropriate axial distance.   In order to keep the photomultiplier tubes out of the beam and to provide coincidence reduction of noise pulse counting, the converging rays are intercepted by three plane mirrors, 120° apart, to form three images off-axis, as shown.   As used in the

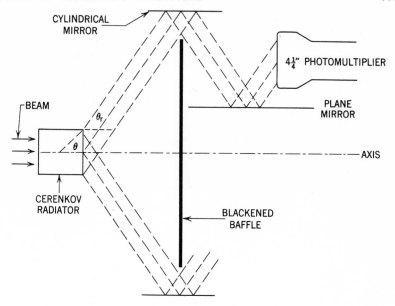

CYLINDRICAL MIRROR

$4\frac{1}{4}''$ PHOTOMULTIPLIER

BEAM

θ_r

PLANE MIRROR

θ

AXIS

CERENKOV RADIATOR

BLACKENED BAFFLE

Fig. 13. Schematic diagram of the Chamberlain-Wiegand counter used in antiproton selection system. Three plane mirrors and photomultipliers were spaced azimuthally at 120° about the axis.

cited reference, the radiator was a fused quartz cylinder, and the velocity interval accepted was between $\beta = 0.75$ and $\beta = 0.78$.

e. Kinsey's sharp threshold, focusing counter. A counter design due to B. B. Kinsey has the feature of maximizing the optical efficiency at threshold where the Cerenkov angle is very small. This is accomplished by the optical scheme indicated in Fig. 14. Particle trajectories parallel to the axis give rise near threshold to photons whose paths depart but slightly from the axial direction. Thus, although relatively few in number, the threshold photons are efficiently collected from a long extent of medium and throughout a wide aperture.

This kind of counter is useful in achieving sharp discrimination between kinds of particles, e.g., positive pions and protons, in a momentum-analyzed beam at high energies where velocities all converge toward $\beta = 1$. High-pressure gas is a usual Cerenkov medium in such applications. In Fig. 14 a response curve is displayed as a function of CO_2 pressure for such a counter in a beam of pions at 3.2 bev/c momentum.

In the design suggested by Fig. 14 the glass envelope of the photomultiplier tube must be capable of withstanding the gas pressure. The small, 1P21 tube successfully withstood the pressure indicated in Fig. 14. Use of the larger, end-window types would likely require the light to be

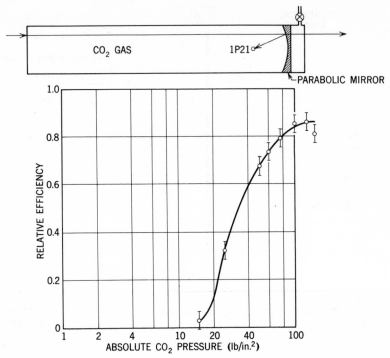

Fig. 14.   Schematic diagram of Kinsey counter and threshold response curve for a particular CO_2 gas counter in a beam of 3.2 bev pions.

directed by a small diagonal mirror at the focal point through a pressure-sustaining window in the counter chamber wall.

4. Photon (or electron) spectrometer counters. It is attractive to consider the possibility of containing within the volume of a dense transparent material the entire electronic shower development due to an entering high-energy photon or electron. Since a large fraction of the incident energy is expended in the form of relativistic motion of electrons and positrons, the total Cerenkov light development should be correlated usefully to the energy delivered by the incident photon or electron.

For such a device, one requires a medium that is dense and of rather high effective atomic number, yet as transparent as possible to light in the spectral region useful to the photomultiplier tubes. Various glasses containing oxides of lead and ranging in density from 3.5 grams/cm³ to 6 grams/cm³ are available from leading glass manufacturers. They vary greatly, however, in their suitability for this purpose. Among samples from various sources having similar densities and possessing nominally closely similar content of lead the variation in spectral transmission can be considerable.

Three types of glass which have been used in instruments such as this are described in the following table:

TABLE 2. SOME GLASSES EMPLOYED IN
SPECTROMETER CERENKOV COUNTERS

Manu-facturer	Desig-nation	Wt. % of PbO	Density grams/cm³	n_d	Radiation Length cm	Remarks
Corning[a]	No. 8392	52	3.89	1.649	2.77	Slightly yellow
Hayward[b]	EDF-3	62	4.49	1.720	2.00	Distinctly yellow
Schott[c]	SF-1	62	4.44	1.717	2.01	Clear

[a] Corning Glass Works, Corning, New York.
[b] Hayward Scientific Glass Corp., Whittier, California.
[c] Schott Glass Co., Germany; through Fish-Schurman Corp., New Rochelle, New York.

The characteristics of two "total" absorption spectrometer Cerenkov counters are described, respectively, by Brabant, Moyer, and Wallace[13] and by Swartz.[14] The energy resolution with which incident high-energy electrons are measured is typically about 30% (full width at half-height of pulse-height distribution curve). This applies to a glass cylinder of approximately 1 ft diameter and 14 in. long, with electrons of 1 bev energy incident.

A plot from Ref. 13, showing characteristic pulse height versus incident electron energy, as determined by Brabant et al., is shown in Fig. 15. The slight curvature is the result of the energy-dependence of the shower-containment efficiency; this is discussed by the authors. Filosofo and Yamagata report similar results.[15e]

Because of the weight of glass plus the extensive magnetic shielding required for the large phototubes that view the glass, this type of instrument is quite massive. It is probably desirable to use several tubes of moderate size rather than one of the large, 16-in. diameter photocathode types, since magnetic shielding is particularly difficult to accomplish. Also, its pulse rise time is poor because of the large and variable electron collection paths between the photocathode and the first dynode.

If materials suitably transparent, yet with greater density and higher effective atomic number, were available, the practicality of the spectrometer Cerenkov counter would be enhanced. Hofstadter[15b] reports the use of a crystal of TlCl, 5½ in. long and 5½ in. in diameter, viewed by a 10½-in.-diameter photomultiplier tube. Resolution was 26% with electrons of a few hundred Mev energy, and the peak position varied linearly with

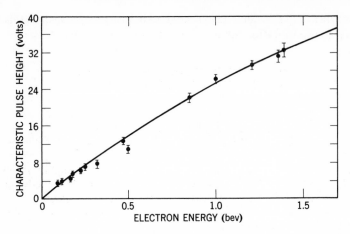

Fig. 15.   Characteristic pulse height versus electron energy for the Pb-glass Cerenkov counter.[13]

electron energy in the range of 200 to 300 Mev. The general problem of shower containment may be considered by means of the empirical work of Kantz and Hofstadter.[16]

C. Efficiency and Resolution Considerations

The physical aspects of Cerenkov radiation are predicted exactly by theory in their relation to particle charge and velocity and to the medium traversed. The practical realization of this inherent specificity is limited by the effects of multiple scattering, energy degradation, definition of beam-particle trajectories, and the fact that the light yield is relatively small and the conversion efficiency of the photons is low. These factors are now to be considered.

I. Photon economics and conversion efficiency. The problem of the development of electrical output pulses of useful size from the photomultiplier tube (or tubes) applied to a Cerenkov counter involves the following elements in succession:

(a) The number of photons produced, within the useful spectrum interval, per particle traversing the counter.

(b) The optical collection efficiency with which photons are directed to the photocathode, including the effects of absorption and back-reflection at boundary surfaces.

(c) The efficiency with which photons that reach the photocathode produce useful photoelectrons.

(d) Electron multiplication by the stages of the multiplier.

In reverse order, we may begin, by way of numerical example, by requiring a certain pulse voltage amplitude to be delivered by the photomultiplier into a transmission line leading to a pulse amplifier, which will in turn usually feed one input of a coincidence circuit. A nominal requirement, close to common practice, is 2 volts pulse height at the photomultiplier anode, working into a line of 125 ohms characteristic impedance. Typical pulse duration would be 10^{-8} sec. These conditions demand the delivery to the anode of a charge pulse of 10^9 electrons. A 14-stage multiplier tube, operated conservatively, can provide a charge multiplication of 10^8 between photocathode and anode. We are thus left with the requirement of 10 photoelectrons to be liberated into useful trajectories at the photocathode.

In the photocathode conversion efficiency of various tubes, even of the same type, there is considerable variation, ranging from 5 to 20%. A representative value for contemporary end-window photocathodes, assuming suitable focusing potentials, wouldbe 10% for the photons within the spectrum interval of response. Hence we require about 100 photons incident upon the photocathode to obtain a 2-volt output pulse from a 14-stage multiplier. The statistical variation in the number of photoelectrons will clearly be relatively large when the characteristic number is as small as 10, and this will typically control the output pulse uniformity.

From the foregoing numbers it is apparent that efficient collection of photons, and delivery to the photocathode, is necessary in order that the desired pulses may compare favorably with the fluctuational peaks of noise in the photomultiplier. In many applications it is not possible to provide Cerenkov pulses which can themselves be distinguished from noise. Consequently, it is almost always necessary to operate the Cerenkov counter in coincidence with other counters that help to select the eligible events upon which the former is to discriminate.

The spectral efficiency of conversion is illustrated by Fig. 16 for the S-11 type of phototube response. If, as a function of frequency, the photon flux is uniform, as indicated by (2), $n\beta$ being considered constant, then the average value of the ordinate of Fig. 16 is the effective conversion efficiency for the frequency interval of response. Evidently its value is about 0.10. However, this efficiency cannot be directly employed in most cases, for the absorbing properties of the medium are interposed between the creation of the light with its production spectrum and intensity and its arrival at the phototube entrance window.

For the nonfocusing type of counter, all the techniques of reflection, optical continuity, and light "piping" familiar in scintillation counting are to be employed in the effort to conserve photons. Even so, in practical experience it is difficult to achieve a full 100% efficiency in detection

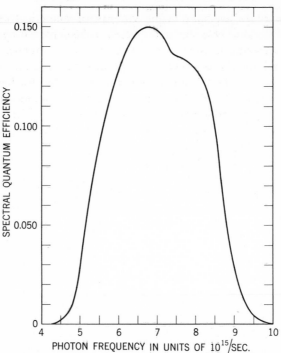

Fig. 16. Representative spectral dependence of quantum efficiency (including transmission and reflection losses due to the glass window) versus photon frequency for the S-11 type of response. The ordinate is the useful electron emission from the photocathode per photon incident upon the tube face.

because of statistical fluctuation in photoelectron numbers. This matter is, of course, strongly a function of design and technique.

In the focusing counters, which can be employed only when good definition of particle trajectories exists, the fraction of photons that may be collected depends upon the ratio of beam diameter to optical system diameter. Jelley has estimated,[11,15c] the fraction to be 25 % for Marshall's counter of the type previously described and 90 % for Jelley's design of the Getting conical counter. For any particular type, the fraction may be increased by increasing the size of the optical system relative to the beam so that the aberrations are reduced.

2. Factors controlling velocity resolution. Both in the focusing counters and in those of the Fitch type the precise character of the Cerenkov angle is the basis for discrimination of velocity. Any factor that degrades this angular precision, or limits its accurate observation, will proscribe the resolution attainable.

To begin with, the angular divergence or indetermination of the incident beam may be limiting; but this is not a characteristic of the counter and is not further discussed.

The factors fundamental to the counter in principle are the following: (a) transverse size of beam and the aberrations contingent upon it; (b) optical dispersion; (c) diffraction; (d) multiple coulomb scattering; and (e) slowing down of particles through energy loss.

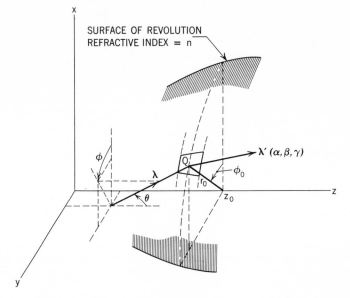

Fig. 17. Sketch illustrating the refraction of a skew ray, originating internally in a medium of index n, at a surface of revolution.

a. Beam size and aberrations. The optical systems of present concern are all of an axially symmetric type, with a central trajectory of the particle beam as the axis. The refracting or reflecting surfaces are figures of revolution about this trajectory. By the use of Snell's law (or the law of reflection, if reflection is the case), we may calculate the change in direction of a ray incident in an arbitrary manner upon any selected element of surface of the optical system. Thus Cerenkov photons whose propagation vectors possess any desired moment about the axis may be "surveyed" through the system.

In Fig. 17 the z-axis is the axis of symmetry. An element of surface of the refracting medium (of index n) is pictured at position Q whose coordinates are r_0, ϕ_0, and z_0. The contour of the surface at this point is specified by the value of $dr/dz = r_0'$. Incident upon the surface, from within, at Q is a ray of Cerenkov light whose unit propagation vector is λ with direction cosines $\sin \theta \cos \phi$, $\sin \theta \sin \phi$, and $\cos \theta$, respectively, relative to the x-, y-, and z-axes.

The refracted ray, with unit propagation vector λ' can now be shown to have direction cosines:

$$\alpha = n\left[\sin \theta \cos \phi + \cos \phi_0\left(F + \sqrt{F^2 - \left(1 - \frac{1}{n^2}\right)(1 + r_0'^2)^{-1}}\right)\right]$$

$$\beta = n\left[\sin \theta \sin \phi + \sin \phi_0\left(F + \sqrt{F^2 - \left(1 - \frac{1}{n^2}\right)(1 + r_0'^2)^{-1}}\right)\right] \quad (3)$$

$$\gamma = n\left[\cos \theta - r_0'\left(F + \sqrt{F^2 - \left(1 - \frac{1}{n^2}\right)(1 + r_0'^2)^{-1}}\right)\right]$$

where

$$F = \frac{r_0' \cos \theta - \cos (\phi_0 - \phi) \sin \theta}{1 + r_0'^2}.$$

If the surface at Q is a reflecting surface or if total internal reflection occurs, the equations in (3) reduce to

$$\alpha = \sin \theta \cos \phi + 2F \cos \phi_0,$$
$$\beta = \sin \theta \sin \phi + 2F \sin \phi_0, \quad (4)$$
$$\gamma = \cos \theta - 2r_0' F.$$

The "skewness" of a ray may be evaluated by the moment of its unit propagation vector with respect to the z-axis. For the initial ray λ, the moment is

$$M_z = r_0 \cos \phi_0 \sin \theta \sin \phi - r_0 \sin \phi_0 \sin \theta \cos \phi.$$

After refraction or reflection at Q, the moment will be

$$M_z' = r_0 \beta \cos \phi_0 - r_0 \alpha \sin \phi_0.$$

By use of the expressions in (3) and (4) we obtain

for refraction: $\qquad\qquad M_z' = nM_z$

for reflection: $\qquad\qquad M_z' = M_z \qquad (5)$

The equations in (5) are the relations that Marshall[4a] inferred very simply from conservation of angular momentum. They establish the fact that if d and d' are, respectively, the distances of closest approach to the z-axis before and after refraction (or reflection), they are related by

for refraction: $\qquad\qquad d' \sin \theta' = nd \sin \theta$

for reflection: $\qquad\qquad d' \sin \theta' = d \sin \theta \qquad (6)$

where θ and θ' are the polar angles of the ray directions.

Many of the questions regarding efficiency of light collection can be answered by appealing to relation (6). However, the actual tracing of rays to identify exactly the effects of the aberrations and to locate the position and direction of a ray at any value of z will require the use of the equations in (3) or (4) or their equivalent.

The calculation of velocity resolution for a focusing counter involves calculation of image shape and size, as determined by the optical system, and of the diffuseness of this image caused by the aberrations induced by finite beam diameter and the other effects yet to be discussed; and also calculation of the shift of image position resulting from an incremental change in velocity. The velocity increment that shifts the image position by an amount as great as the diffuse image size may be defined as the limit of velocity resolution. An example of an approximate calculation of this type is given by Jelley.[11]

Aberrations due to finite beam size may be reduced to arbitrarily small values by increasing the radii of the optical surfaces responsible for focusing. For this gain in resolution, however, one must pay the price of increased bulk and possibly of increased absorption of the light within the refracting medium.

b. Effects of optical dispersion. The angular dispersion arising from optical dispersion will in principle produce an uncertainty in the Cerenkov angle determination. The magnitude of the effect is less than that contributed by finite beam size in most counters.

From (1) we obtain the angular dispersion:

$$\frac{d\theta}{d\lambda} = \frac{1}{n^2\beta \sin \theta} \cdot \frac{dn}{d\lambda} = \frac{1}{\sqrt{n^2\beta^2 - 1}} \cdot \frac{1}{n} \frac{dn}{d\lambda}.$$

The dispersion is typically less than $1°$ of angle for wavelengths separated by the visible bandwidth; however, near threshold the effect can be large as the denominator in the foregoing expression approaches zero.

In his CERN report[15a] Marshall presents the dependence of n upon frequency for several substances useful in Cerenkov counting. He shows that over the visible spectrum the index change of lucite is from 1.493 to 1.513 and that for a relativistic particle ($\beta \simeq 1$) the angular change is thus only $0.68°$. Focusing counters operating near threshold, such as the Kinsey type described in Sec. B3e, may be distinctly limited in resolution by this effect, even though in this particular type of counter the finite size of the beam does not produce aberration.

The multiple coulomb scattering for particles of high energies (such as protons of energy greater than a few hundred Mev) moving in usual radiator materials is sufficiently small, as is also their energy degradation, to permit optical dispersion to be the major source of Cerenkov angle uncertainty aside from the effects of beam width and angular divergence. (See paragraph (d).)

c. Diffraction. Since the linear extent of particle trajectory over which coherence will prevail is limited by the quantum nature of photon emission, and also by particle scattering, a certain imprecision of angle is inherent because of diffraction. Although this is of theoretical interest, the coherent intervals of path length are sufficiently great to render the effect of no practical consequence in resolution.

d. Multiple coulomb scattering. The extent of the distribution in the directions of particle motions after they have penetrated a depth of material without appreciable energy loss can be represented by the mean squared angle of scattering. The familiar relation for estimating this parameter (assuming unit charge) is

$$\overline{\theta^2} = \left(\frac{E_0}{\beta^2 E}\right)^2 t (\text{radians})^2$$

where

E_0 = a constant energy parameter = 21 Mev
E = total energy of the particle
β = relative velocity, v/c
t = depth penetrated, measured in units of the "radiation length" L, which is characteristic of the medium and is defined by

$$\frac{1}{L} = 4NZ^2 \left(\frac{e^2}{\hbar c}\right) \left(\frac{e^2}{mc^2}\right)^2 \ln \left(\frac{183}{Z^{1/3}}\right) \quad \text{cm}^{-1}$$

where N is the number of atoms per cm³ of atomic number Z, and the other symbols have their usual meaning.

We are more precisely concerned with the root-mean-squared *projected* angle of scattering (i.e., the angular distribution projected upon a plane containing the incident trajectory of the particle), which is

$$\delta_p = \sqrt{\overline{\theta_p^2}} = \frac{1}{\sqrt{2}} \frac{E_0}{\beta^2 E} \sqrt{t} \ (\text{radians}).$$

The smearing of observed Cerenkov angles will be related to $2\delta_p$, since scattering in either direction in the plane of projection is effective in broadening the spread. The extent of this spread will increase in proportion to the square root of the distance traversed in the medium. For a proton that has traversed 5 cm of lucite, for which the radiation length L is

34 cm, the values of δ_p for a few energies (kinetic) are listed with the relative velocity uncertainty induced by this effect alone in lucite.

KE (proton, Mev)	δ_p	$\dfrac{d\beta}{\beta}$
400	0.0084 radian = 0.48°	0.62%
600	0.0059 radian = 0.34°	0.75%
1000	0.0039 radian = 0.22°	0.65%
1500	0.0028 radian = 0.16°	0.52%
2000	0.0022 radian = 0.124°	0.44%

The last column is calculated from

$$\frac{d\beta}{\beta} = 2\delta_p\sqrt{n^2\beta^2 - 1} ,$$

with $n = 1.5$.

e. Effect of particle energy loss. Besides affecting slightly the velocity resolution by a gradual decrease of the Cerenkov angle with decreasing velocity, the energy loss also reduces photon yield. Neither effect is of much practical consequence for relativistic energies in which the energy-loss rate is minimum and the light yield does not rapidly change. However, at lower energies the increase in specific ionization and the stronger dependence of velocity upon energy cause both effects to be of concern.

The rate of change of Cerenkov angle is related to energy-loss rate by

$$\frac{d\theta}{dx} = \frac{(n^2 \cos^2\theta - 1)^{3/2}}{n \sin\theta} \cdot \frac{1}{Mc^2}\frac{dE}{dx} ,$$

but it is probably more instructive to display the Cerenkov angle plotted as a function of residual range, as is done in Fig. 18 for pions moving in lucite. Included there also is the photon yield per centimeter. Marshall has suggested[15a] the design of a Cerenkov radiator consisting of a bundle of tapered hexagonal rods, with axes parallel, having an angle of taper that will compensate by action of the total internal wall reflections for the change in Cerenkov angle and thus lead to a unique emergent angle at the exit face of the bundle.

In summary of the factors that affect the velocity resolution, it may be stated that the finite width of the beam is the controlling factor in most counters of practical design. The factors intrinsic to the medium—namely, dispersion, multiple scattering, and slowing down—make contributions whose relative values vary with the identity of the particle, its energy, and the density, mean atomic number, and optical character of the medium.

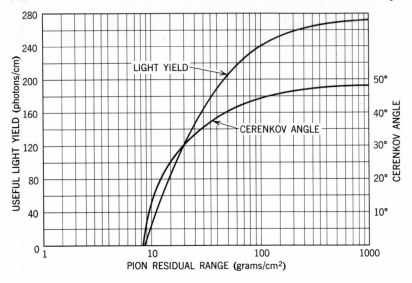

Fig. 18. Cerenkov angle and light yield (4000 to 7000 A) in photons per centimeter versus residual range for pions moving in lucite ($n = 1.50$).

The contributions from factors intrinsic to the medium are roughly similar in magnitude; only rarely is one factor strongly dominant.

Instructive tabulations of the contributions to resolution width from the intrinsic factors for a few different media at various energies are presented by Marshall.[15a] An analysis of energy resolution parameters for the Jelley-Getting type counter is given by Jelley.[15c]

REFERENCES

1. P. A. Cerenkov, *Compt. rend. acad. sci. U.R.S.S.*, **2**, 451 (1934).
2. (a) I. Frank and Ig. Tamm, *Compt. rend. acad. sci. U.R.S.S.*, **14**, 109 (1937). (b) Ig. Tamm, *J. Phys. U.S.S.R.*, **1**, 439 (1939). (c) E. Fermi, *Phys. Rev.*, **57**, 485 (1940).
3. R. L. Mather, *Phys. Rev.*, **84**, 181 (1951).
4. (a) J. Marshall, *Phys. Rev.*, **86**, 685 (1952). (b) J. Marshall, "Cerenkov Counters", in *Ann. rev. Nuclear Sci.*, J. G. Beckerley, Ed., Vol. 4, 141 (Annual Reviews, Stanford, California, 1954).
5. (a) J. V. Jelley, "Cerenkov Radiation", Ch. 4 in *Progress in Nuclear Physics*, O. R. Frisch, Ed., Vol. 3, 84 (Academic Press, New York, 1953). (b) J. V. Jelley, *Brit. J. Appl. Phys.* **6**, No. 7, 227 (1955).
6. E. Heiberg and J. Marshall, *Rev. Sci. Instr.*, **27**, 618 (1956).
7. Private communication. Work of W. N. Hess, R. Nobles, and S. Kaplan at Berkeley, California.

8. Private communication with D. Frisch. The counter was employed in experimentation at the Berkeley bevatron.
9. Use of the principle mentioned by V. Fitch and R. Motley, *Phys. Rev.*, **101**, 496 (1956); also *Phys. Rev.*, **105**, 265 (1956).
10. I. A. Getting, *Phys. Rev.*, **71**, 123 (1947); also R. H. Dicke, *Phys. Rev.*, **71**, 737 (1947).
11. J. V. Jelley, *A.E.R.E. NP/R 1770*, Harwell, August, 1955.
12. O. Chamberlain, E. Segre, C. Wiegand, and T. Ypsilantis, *Phys. Rev.*, **100**, 947 (1955).
13. J. M. Brabant, B. J. Moyer, and R. Wallace, *Rev. Sci. Instr.*, **28**, 421 (1957).
14. C. Swartz, *IRE Trans. Nuclear Sci.*, **NS-3**, No. 4, 65 (1956).
15. *Proceedings of the CERN Symposium*, Vol. 2, 1956:
    (a) J. Marshall, p. 63;
    (b) R. Hofstadter, p. 75;
    (c) J. V. Jelley, p. 76;
    (d) O. Chamberlain and C. Wiegand, p. 82;
    (e) I. Filosofo and T. Yamagata, p. 85.
16. A. Kantz and R. Hofstadter, *Nucleonics*, **12**, No. 3, 36 (1954).

4 ELECTROMETERS AND AMPLIFIERS

EDWARD FAIRSTEIN*

Oak Ridge National Laboratory
Oak Ridge, Tennessee

The output of a radiation detector can be determined from d-c measurements or pulse measurements. Direct-current measurements give information about the total amount of ionization produced in the detector by the incoming radiation but tell nothing about the disintegration rate or the energy spectrum of the radiation source. Pulse measurements, on the other hand, permit measurements of all three quantities.

The first part of this chapter deals with d-c electrometers, the second part with pulse amplifiers.

PART I ELECTROMETERS

A. The Measurement of Ionization Currents
B. Choice of Method
C. Quartz-Fiber Electrometers
D. The Lindemann Electrometer
E. Vacuum-Tube Electrometers
F. Grid Current in Electron Tubes
G. Tubes Suitable for Electrometer Use
H. Operating Point
I. Practical Electrometer Circuits
J. Feedback in Direct-Current Amplifiers
K. Practical Circuits Employing Feedback
L. Vibrating-Capacitor Electrometer
M. Noise in Vibrating-Capacitor Electrometers
N. Insulators
O. Properties of Several Insulating Materials
P. Reduction of Insulator Leakage by Choice of Circuit
Q. Switches

In the detectors pertinent to this section the interaction of the incoming radiation with the active region of the detector manifests itself at the output terminals as a quantity of charge. The charge is collected under the influence of the polarizing voltage applied to the detector, the rate of charge collection being proportional to several things, among which is the intensity of the radiation field.

* Now with Tennelec Instrument Co., Oak Ridge, Tennessee.

The collection of charge over a period of time constitutes a current flow. The currents of interest are quite feeble, being in the range between 10^{-8} and 10^{-14} amp. Since the maximum sensitivity of suspension galvanometers is approximately 10^{-11} amp, galvanometers are of limited usefulness in the measurement of ionizing radiation. Electrometers are necessary.

The term "electrometer" is applied here to those instruments which are used to measure very small currents and in which the operation depends upon the interaction of charged particles with an electric field, as opposed to galvanometers, in which the operation depends upon the interaction of a current with a magnetic field. The instruments to be described in this section are the quartz fiber, vacuum tube, and vibrating-capacitor electrometers.

Before describing these instruments, the two commonly used methods of small-current measurement are discussed.

A. The Measurement of Ionization Currents

The two types of current measurement are known as the IR-drop method and the loss-of-charge (or rate-of-drift) method.[1] The circuit shown in Fig. 1 will suffice to illustrate both.

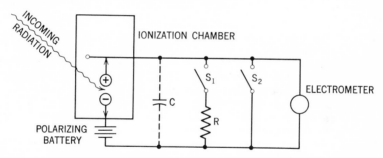

Fig. 1.   Ionization chamber connections.

C represents the total capacitance appearing across the ionization chamber. The load resistor R is used only in IR-drop measurements, hence the switch S_1. The switch S_2 is used to protect the electrometer during the application of the chamber polarizing voltage and to discharge C at the start of a measurement.

A polarizing voltage of 20 volts or more is usually sufficient to collect all of the ions produced in the ionization process. When this condition exists, the electrical equivalent of the ion chamber is a current source having infinite internal resistance. The magnitude of the current is proportional to the rate of production of ions, which in turn is proportional to the intensity of the radiation field. Unless stated otherwise, it is assumed that the total ion current is constant and of magnitude I.

When both switches in Fig. 1 are closed, the ion current flows through S_2 and produces no indication on the electrometer. If S_2 is opened, the current flow is transferred to the RC network, and the voltage drop across it builds up according to the equation

$$v_0(t) = IR(1 - e^{-t/RC}), \tag{1}$$

where $v_0(t)$ = the electrometer reading in volts,

$\qquad I$ = the total ionization current, I_+ and I_-, in amperes,

$\qquad R$ = the load resistance in ohms,

$\qquad C$ = the load capacitance in farads,

$\qquad t$ = the time, in seconds, measured from the instant of switching.

Note that

$$\lim_{t \to \infty} v_0(t) = IR. \tag{2}$$

These two equations describe the IR-drop method.

If at the start of the measurement both S_1 and S_2 are opened, the current flowing into C produces a signal expressed by

$$v_0(t) = \frac{1}{C} \int_0^t I \, dt = It/C, \tag{3}$$

where the symbols have the same meaning as before. Equation 3 describes the loss-of-charge method. The word "loss" is used because the current flow is always in the direction to neutralize the charge placed on the chamber by the polarizing battery. This being the case, the ratio of the maximum value of $v_0(t)$ to the magnitude of the polarizing voltage should be such that complete ion collection is maintained throughout the range of $v_0(t)$.

Note that as t/RC becomes small

$$IR(1 - e^{-t/RC}) \to It/C. \tag{4}$$

The immediately obvious difference between the two measurements is that in one of them the current is measured in terms of a known voltage and a known resistance, whereas in the other it is measured in terms of a known voltage, a known capacitance, and a known time interval. Not so obvious is a difference associated with the fact that the response of the electrometer is proportional to the amount of charge existing at its input terminals at the instant of reading. In the IR-drop method charge is continuously consumed by the load resistance, whereas in the loss-of-charge method all of the charge produced in the time interval between switching and reading is available to the electrometer. Because of this the loss-of-charge method is fundamentally the more sensitive of the two.

B. Choice of Method

It was stated earlier that a current measurement by the IR-drop method requires a knowledge of the precise value of two quantities—resistance and voltage—whereas the same measurement by the loss-of-charge method requires a knowledge of three—capacitance, time, and voltage. Because of this the IR-drop method is nearly always considered first. However, it is usually limited for several reasons to currents in the range that permits the use of a load resistor of less than 10^{12} ohms. The first is that the larger the resistance value, the greater the shunting effect of unwanted insulation resistance and the greater the difficulty in making precise resistance measurements. A resistance of 10^{12} ohms seems to be the upper limit of the region where accurate measurements can be made without the use of highly specialized equipment. Also, there is some doubt of the stability of resistors greater than 10^{12} ohms. Comparable difficulties do not exist in the loss-of-charge method. The lowest capacitance value likely to be encountered is 10 pf, which can be measured with an accuracy of 1% with comparatively little effort.

Another difficulty associated with the IR-drop method when resistors larger than 10^{12} ohms are required is the response time of the system. (This shortcoming can be removed by the use of feedback, as will be shown in a later section.) From (1) it can be shown that if an error of less than 1% is required no readings should be taken sooner than $t = 4.6\ RC$ sec after the shorting switch is opened, since it takes this long for the voltage to rise to within 1% of its asymptotic value. If $R = 10^{12}$ ohms and $C = 10$ pf, the waiting period amounts to 46 sec. If the loss-of-charge method is used instead, a signal equal to the asymptotic value of the IR-drop method will be produced in a time interval of RC sec (assuming the same value of C in the two cases), corresponding to an improvement of 4.6 times.

Finally, there is the difference between the integrating times of the two methods. It was assumed earlier that the current from the ion chamber is constant with time. For a given time interval the error in this assumption becomes increasingly greater as the current gets smaller. This is so because the rate of ion production is determined by the rate at which the ionizing events interact with the chamber gas; since radioactive emission is a random process, there will be a fluctuation about the mean value in the emission rate and, therefore, in the ion current.

A large number of radioactive emitters have a disintegration rate that is closely approximated by a normal distribution.[2] With such a distribution, the root-mean-squared (rms) value of the fluctuation about the mean, or the standard deviation, is

$$\sigma = \sqrt{n\tau} = \sqrt{N}, \tag{5}$$

where σ = rms value of the fluctuation, also the standard deviation of the
   distribution,
   n = the observed counting rate in counts per second,
   τ = the period of observation,
   N = the total counts within the interval of observation.

Restated in terms of the present problem, (5) states that the rms fluctuation about the mean value of an observed counting rate (observed as a
current) will be equal to the square root of the number of counts that were
integrated over the reading interval. It is often convenient to express (5)
in a form normalized with respect to the number of counts within the
reading interval:

$$\sigma_{\text{rel}} = \frac{\sqrt{n\tau}}{n\tau} = \frac{1}{\sqrt{n\tau}} = \frac{1}{\sqrt{N}}. \tag{6}$$

The effective integrating time associated with an IR-drop measurement
can be determined from Campbell's theorem of the mean square:[3]

$$(v - \bar{v})_{\text{rms}} = \left\{ n \int_0^\infty [f(t)]^2 \, dt \right\}^{\frac{1}{2}}, \tag{7}$$

where v = instantaneous value of the response in volts,
   $\bar{v}$ = mean response in volts,
   n = counting rate in counts per second,
   $f(t)$ = response as a function of time to the stimulus of a single event.

For the case cited

$$f(t) = \frac{q}{C} e^{-t/RC}, \tag{8}$$

where q = mean charge, in coulombs, produced by a single ion-chamber
   interaction,
   C = chamber load capacitance in farads,
   R = chamber load resistance in ohms,
   t = time in seconds.

Substitution of (8) in (7) yields

$$(v - \bar{v})_{\text{rms}} = \sqrt{\frac{nq^2R}{2C}}, \tag{9}$$

which, when normalized to $\bar{v} = nqR$, yields

$$\sigma(n\tau)_{\text{rel}} = \frac{1}{\sqrt{2nRC}}. \tag{10}$$

If this is compared with (6), it follows that the effective integration time τ is

$$\tau = 2RC. \tag{11}$$

Equation 11 states that in an IR-drop measurement the circuit integrates the charge over the $2RC$-sec time interval preceding the instant of measurement. It is assumed that $n \gg 1/RC$ and that equilibrium conditions have been established in the indicator before a reading is made.

In the loss-of-charge method, on the other hand, all of the charge is integrated over the time interval between switching and reading. For example, suppose a situation in which the ion current produced by a 20 c/s, 5-Mev, alpha-particle source is to be measured. Let the electrometer have a sensitivity such that a 0.5-volt indication is convenient. Assume that the capacitance of chamber and electrometer is 10 pf. Most of the chamber fillings commonly used require a loss of energy of approximately 30 ev to produce an ion pair. It follows that the total current produced will be $(5 \times 10^6$ ev $\div 30$ ev) ion pairs $\times 1.6 \times 10^{-19}$ coulomb per electronic charge $\times 20$ alpha particles per sec $\cong 0.5 \times 10^{-12}$ amp. Evidently, a 10^{12} ohm resistor is called for in an IR-drop measurement, which in conjunction with the 10-pf input capacitance produces a 10-sec time constant. The 20-sec integrating time [from (11)] results in a normalized rms fluctuation in a series of successive readings of $(20$ c/sec $\times 20$ sec$)^{-\frac{1}{2}} = 5\%$. This fluctuation can be smoothed in several ways: (1) by taking the average of a series of readings spaced at least $2RC$ sec apart, (2) by loading the chamber with additional capacitance to increase the time constant (this is done at the cost of response time), (3) by graphically integrating a long-time recording of the electrometer output, or (4) by using the loss-of-charge method, either with additional capacitive loading to increase the time necessary to produce a 0.5-volt signal, or by biasing-off the electrometer so that it sees only the last 0.5-volt section of the signal excursion.

In the foregoing example the loss-of-charge method is probably the most convenient to use if a mean fluctuation of much less than 5% is desired.

C. Quartz-Fiber Electrometers

Quartz-fiber electrometers[4] depend for their operation upon the attractive or repulsive force existing between two conductors, one of which is charged by the signal to be measured and the other by a polarizing voltage. Restoring force is applied by the quartz-fiber suspension system.

Quartz has several attributes to recommend it for this application: it can be drawn into filaments with diameters in the micron range,[5] it has high tensile strength, low internal friction (resulting in low hysteresis), and is an excellent electrical insulator.

In recent years vacuum tube electrometers, because of their portability, ruggedness, freedom from the effects of vibration and change of position during use, and their ease of reading, have largely supplanted the quartz-fiber type. The one real advantage of the quartz-fiber instrument over its

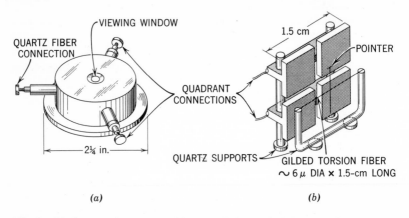

(a)   (b)

Fig. 2. Lindemann electrometer, (a) external view and (b) internal view. Only one set of quadrants is shown; the other set is placed symmetrically with respect to the moving system.

vacuum-tube competitor is its freedom from drift. Even here the vibrating-capacitor type has comparable stability and relative immunity to radio frequency fields (obtained, however, at considerable expense).

The most sensitive quartz-fiber instrument available is the Hoffman binant electrometer;[6] its sensitivity and stability are such that a steady current of 1 or 2 electrons/sec can be detected. This sensitivity is far in excess of that needed for measurements of radioactivity. The most suitable instrument for this purpose is probably the Lindemann electrometer.[7] Its sensitivity is such that a charge of 5×10^{-14} coulomb, corresponding to the ionization produced in a gas by a single alpha particle, is easily detected.

D. The Lindemann Electrometer

A sketch of the instrument is shown in Fig. 2. The pointer is viewed through the window by a microscope with a calibrated scale. Opposite the window shown in the figure is a second window that admits viewing light. The moving system is mechanically balanced, and the electrometer can be mounted in any position.

A suitable auxiliary circuit is shown in Fig. 3. The electrometer sensitivity is varied by the polarizing voltage applied to the quadrants. As the polarizing voltage is increased, a point is reached at which the moving system becomes unstable. The point of maximum usable sensitivity is

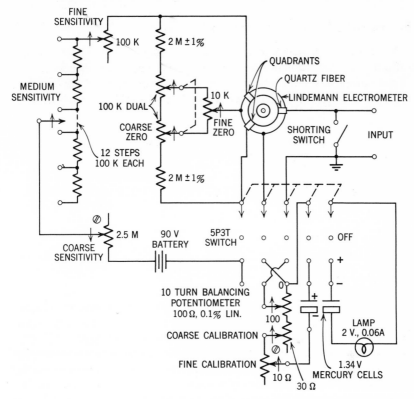

Fig. 3. Lindemann electrometer circuit.

1 to 5 volts below this point. The sensitivity controls should have scale marks on them to permit ease of resetting.

The mercury cell loading is such that the lamp current is five times the balancing current. By a suitable choice of cell size, loss of illumination can be used to signal the discharge of both the balancing cell and lamp cell.

The calibrating resistors should be adjusted to produce 1.00 volt across the balancing potentiometer.

The instrument can be used in two ways: (1) as a potentiometer, in which the unknown voltage is compared with the voltage drop across the balancing resistor, using the electrometer as a null indicator, or (2) as a direct-reading voltmeter, in which the deflection of the electrometer fiber is a measure of the input signal. The first method is preferred, since the calibration of a potentiometer is independent of the null detector sensitivity.

E. Vacuum-Tube Electrometers

A vacuum-tube amplifier containing a plate current meter whose deflection is proportional to the amplitude of the signal applied to the grid circuit constitutes, in rudimentary form, an electrometer. Circuits of this kind, an example of which is shown in Fig. 4, are imperfect because of

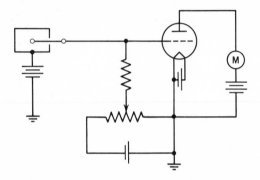

Fig. 4.   Elementary vacuum-tube electrometer circuit.

currents that flow into or out of the grid, even when no signal is present, and because of drifts in the tube characteristics and supply voltages that affect the readings. The imperfections, however, are not serious enough to prevent the measurement of low-intensity ionizing radiations. In 1933 Hafstad showed that the sensitivity of an electrometer tube was limited by the shot noise associated with the grid current[8] and/or the Johnson noise[61] associated with the grid circuit resistance. In selected tubes the noise was such that a single pulse of 1500 electrons or ions could be detected with certainty, and a steady current of 2 electrons/sec could be distinguished from the background noise. This sensitivity is comparable to that of the very best mechanical electrometers and is considerably greater than necessary for most steady-current ion-chamber measurements.

F.   Grid Current in Electron Tubes

This section is devoted to a listing of the various sources of grid current and the means of reducing it.[9,10]

1. Collection of cathode-emitted electrons. The initial energy distribution of electrons leaving the cathode extends to approximately 3 ev. Biasing the grid to approximately 2 volts negative with respect to the cathode will reduce this component of grid current to a very low value.

2. Leakage over glass or insulation. Leakage on the outside of the tube envelope and in insulators external to the tube can be reduced or eliminated by guard rings, nonwettable surface coatings, or operation in a dry atmosphere. Except for operation at low voltage, there is nothing that can be done to reduce leakage in faulty insulators within the tube envelope.

3. Collection of positive ions formed by the bombardment of residual gas in the tube by the electron stream. Operating at plate potentials below 8 volts prevents ionization of the residual gas by the electron stream.

4. Photoelectrons emitted by the control grid under the action of soft x rays produced at the plate by bombardment of the electron stream. Operating at plate potentials below 6 volts reduces x-ray production to a very low value.

5. Photoemission from the grid under the action of light, either from the cathode or from external sources. Operating the heater at a low voltage and shielding the tube from external light reduce photoemission to a negligible value.

6. Thermionic emission from the control grid caused by cathode heating. Grid heating is usually a problem only in tubes not specifically designed for electrometer use. Operating at low cathode temperatures reduces the effect.

If the tube is of a type predisposed to this effect, the grid current will increase with use because of the gradual deposition on the grid of evaporated cathode material.

7. Collection of positive ions emitted from the cathode. The emission of positive ions from the cathode is reduced by low-temperature operation of the cathode. In a multigrid tube the effect can be reduced by using one of the grids near the plate as the control grid while operating one or more of the grids near the cathode at a potential sufficiently positive to repel the ions. This is known as the "space-charge grid connection."

8. Collection of ions produced in the air in the immediate vicinity of the tube by the action of background radiation. Ion collection from the air surrounding the tube can be reduced by enclosing the grid connection in a close-fitting shield or eliminated by enclosing the tube in an evacuated container.

G. Tubes Suitable for Electrometer Use

A number of tubes has been specifically designed for electrometer applications. The oldest of these, which is still in common use, is the General Electric FP-54[9] and is capable of producing grid currents as low as 2×10^{-17} amp.[10] Because of its bulk it is not well suited to portable instruments. Modern-day subminiature types are the Victoreen 5803 triode, 5886 pentode, and 5800 space-charge tetrode and the Raytheon 5886 and 5889 pentodes. Among the tubes manufactured in Europe are the Mullard ME1401 and ME1402, the Genelex 6557, and the Philips 4065, 4066, and 4068. This listing is by no means complete.

Several of the conventional radio receiving types used for low grid-current operation ($\sim 10^{-15}$ amp) are the 954, 959,[11] 6BE6, 7A8,[12] 12BE6,[13,14] and the now obsolete 38.[11] The recently developed 12-volt automobile radio tubes, of which the 12AF6 is an example, are also suitable for this use.

The suitability of a conventional tube for electrometer use depends upon several factors: these include the length of the leakage path between the control grid connections and other electrodes in the tube, the degree to which the getter splash is shielded from the insulating surfaces, and the amplification factor of the tube when triode connected.

The length of the leakage path and the shielding of the getter splash can usually be determined by visual inspection. The gas content and insulator cleanliness can be determined only by measurement. Tubes with a high amplification factor (μ) will not draw sufficient plate current to be usable at the low electrode voltages and the optimum grid bias range necessary for low grid-current operation. In general, the lower the triode-connected μ, the greater the likelihood that the tube can be used in electrometers. This point is covered in detail on p. 279.

H. Operating Point

In all electrometer tubes the gross grid-current–grid-voltage characteristic is approximated by the graph of Fig. 5. (This curve assumes perfect insulation between the grid and the other electrodes.) The grid collects positive ions or emits electrons in the negative current region and collects electrons in the positive region. Point A is the point at which the various current components balance each other and is known as the floating-grid potential, or crossover point. For triodes A is in the region of -0.5 to -2.0 volts, being only slightly dependent on plate voltage or cathode temperature. (Decreasing the cathode temperature or the plate voltage moves the floating-grid potential towards zero bias.) In tubes using a space-charge grid the floating-grid potential is usually more negative than 2 volts because of the energy imparted to the electron stream by the first grid. If the control grid collects filament-emitted positive ions, the grid current will not go to zero at high values of V_g (as shown in Fig. 5) but, instead, will level out at a value equal to the positive ion current.

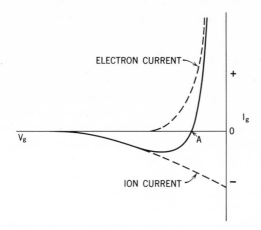

ELECTRON CURRENT

ION CURRENT

Fig. 5. Grid current versus grid bias of a vacuum tube.

The input resistance of the tube, in ohms, is numerically equal to the slope of the $V_g - I_g$ characteristic, where V_g and I_g are measured in volts and amperes, respectively. The two operating points of particular interest are the points of maximum negative grid current and floating-grid potential.

1. Point of maximum negative grid current. Since the slope of the $V_g - I_g$ curve is zero at the point of maximum negative grid current, the dynamic input resistance is infinite. The desirable feature of this operating point is that no correction for the shunting effect of input resistance need be made when using the IR-drop method of current measurement. The undesirable features are (1) the bias voltage will need readjustment with changes in chamber load resistance, the bias voltage shift being proportional to the product of grid current and load resistance, and (2) the grid current will produce a background drift that must be corrected for when using the loss-of-charge method of current measurement.

2. Floating-grid potential. At the floating-grid potential the net current through the chamber load resistance is zero, so that a change in load resistance is not accompanied by a bias shift. Also, the background drift in a loss-of-charge measurement is zero. To offset these desirable features is the need to correct for the input shunting resistance of the tube. Since the need for this correction is not apparent from a measurement of chamber current, there is the danger that the correction will be overlooked. A second shortcoming of this operating point is that the internal grid current is actually twice as great as it is at the point of maximum negative grid current, being made up of both the electron and ion current components. As a result, the rms noise level associated with the grid current will be 41% greater than it is at the former operating point. See p. 272.

I. Practical Electrometer Circuits

Sensitivity and stability are the central problems in the design and construction of electrometers. As the sensitivity of the measurement increases, the observation time must increase as well. For a given accuracy of measurement the drift rate of the system must be inversely proportional to the observation time and, therefore, to the sensitivity. In the limit, the attainable stability sets the limit on the usable sensitivity.

When the ultimate attainable sensitivity is necessary, a very good circuit is that used by Hafstad,[8] a modern version of which is shown in Fig. 6.

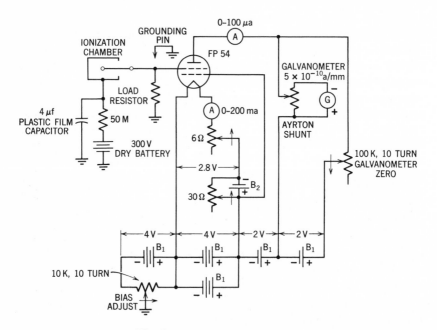

Fig. 6.   FP-54 electrometer circuit.

The batteries marked B_1 are new lead cells (old ones will be noisy) with 100 amp-hr capacities. B_2 is an Edison cell of 75 amp-hr capacity whose purpose is to provide a bucking voltage which decays at a rate that compensates for the aging of the tube and the discharge of the filament battery. Except for the filter resistor in series with the 300-volt battery and the load resistor (if one is used), all resistors should be wire-wound.

In setting up, the filament supply is connected first and the current is adjusted to approximately 100 ma. It is essential that the plate and space-charge grid circuits be opened before connecting or disconnecting the

TABLE I. TYPICAL OPERATING CONDITIONS FOR AN FP-54

Filament	2.5 volts @ 100 ma
Space charge grid	+4 volts
Control grid	−4 volts
Plate	+6 volts @ 40 μa
Mutual conductance	25 μa/volt
Amplification factor	1.0
Plate resistance	40 kilohms
Grid current	10^{-15} amp
Input capacitance	2.5 pf

filament battery; if space current flows even momentarily during the filament warm-up or cool-off period, the surface activation will be changed enough so that many hours will be needed to re-establish stable emission characteristics. The remaining electrodes are then connected and the bias voltage is adjusted to the value that gives no change in galvanometer reading when the grounding pin is opened and closed. (The galvanometer zero must be continually reset during this adjustment.) This bias setting corresponds to the floating-grid potential, which is a good operating point to use when the ultimate sensitivity is desired, even though the grid noise is higher at this point than at the point of maximim negative grid current. The next adjustment is quite time-consuming; it consists of a trial-and-error setting of the B_2 load resistor with the aim of reducing the galvanometer drift to zero. Minor readjustments will be necessary over a period of several days after the initial rough adjustments are made. Once adjusted, the electrometer will exhibit a very low drift rate ($\sim$1 mv/day)[1] for weeks at a time if operated continuously.

A typical set of operating conditions[9] for the FP-54 is given in Table 1. Filament voltage and plate current can be reduced with a corresponding reduction in grid current. An appreciable reduction in plate current will require an increase in the size of the galvanometer zeroing resistor.

By using the circuit of Fig. 6 with the operating conditions approximating those in Table 1, Hafstad was able to demonstrate the possibility of detecting a steady current of 3×10^{-19} amp, or 2 electrons/sec in an observation time of several minutes. It was necessary to house the tube in an evacuated container and to keep the apparatus in a constant-temperature oven to realize this sensitivity.

A second circuit that in principle should be almost as good as the preceding one uses two tubes in a balanced-bridge[15,16] arrangement. The basic configuration is shown in Fig. 7.

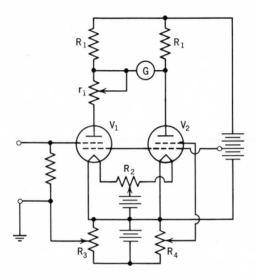

Fig. 7. Balanced-bridge electrometer circuit.

The circuit is made insensitive to small changes in filament supply voltage by the adjustment of R_2 and to small changes in plate supply voltage by the adjustment of r_1, which is placed in series with the tube having the lower plate resistance of the two. The bias of the input tube is set by R_3 and the galvanometer zero by R_4.

When using this circuit for loss-of-charge measurements, an added refinement is the connection of a well-insulated, variable capacitor in series with the second grid of V_2, which makes it possible to add a compensating rate of drift to that produced by the grid current of V_1 flowing through the input capacitance. Preferable to this technique is the operation of V_1 at the floating-grid potential.

The degree of insensitivity to tube aging is dependent upon how well the tube characteristics are matched.

When less than the ultimate current sensitivity is required, the Barth-Penick circuit[17,18] shown in Fig. 8 can be used. Its main attraction is the need for only a single battery. By suitable adjustments of R_2, R_3, and R_p, a set of conditions can be found for which the circuit is insensitive to small variations of battery voltage. Unlike the Hafstad or Wynn-Williams[16] circuits, however, the Barth-Penick circuit does not compensate for tube aging.

In the range of current measurements above 10^{-14} amp the stability of operation which can be attained in the previously described circuits is not

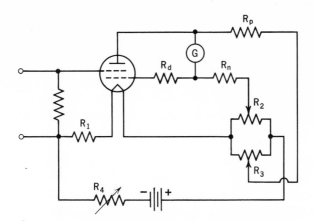

Fig. 8.   Barth-Penick electrometer circuit.

required, and it becomes advantageous to trade the stability and sensitivity for portability and operating convenience.

One of the consequences of operation at low sensitivity is the increased operating range covered by the control grid. The resulting change in grid current affects the linearity of response, which may or may not be desirable, depending upon requirements.* If the instrument is to have linear response, the effect is undesirable and can be reduced by feedback techniques.

---

* The nonlinearity of response can be used to advantage when a very wide dynamic range is required in a single-scale instrument. The electrometer is operated under floating-grid conditions, and the polarization of the ion chamber is such that the signal voltage is positive.

Since the grid bias (hence the plate current) is a logarithmic function of the grid current (which is equal to the ionization current in the absence of a grid leak) in the region between the floating-grid potential and zero bias, five to seven decades of logarithmic response can be obtained in selected tubes with a plate current change of 5 to 20 μa/decade.

J. Feedback in Direct-Current Amplifiers[1,19,20]

In Fig. 9 an unfedback amplifier, a shunt fedback amplifier, and a series fedback amplifier are compared. Units used are ohms, farads, amperes, volts, and seconds. Symbols are as follows:

I = ionization current

C_c = chamber capacitance

R_1 = chamber load resistance

C_1 = shunt capacitance of R_1

R_2 = input resistance of electrometer tube and leakage resistance to ground. In most cases $R_2 \gg R_1$

C_2 = input capacitance of electrometer tube and capacitance to ground of the input circuit wiring

ϵ = equivalent voltage source (offset voltage) appearing in series with the input tube as a result of cathode temperature variations or contact potential variations. These variations arise from supply-voltage drifts and/or aging effects in the tube

$v_i(I, t, \epsilon)$ = input voltage to the electrometer tube as a function of ionization current, time, and offset voltage

$v_0(I, t, \epsilon)$ = output voltage from the amplifier as a function of ionization current, time, and offset voltage

A = amplification between the input and output terminals, defined as $\lim_{\Delta v_0 \to 0} \Delta v_0 / \Delta v_i$. It is assumed that the amplifier has a flat frequency response over an infinite bandwidth. The symbol $+A$ denotes the same relative polarity of corresponding input and output terminals and the symbol $-A$, the opposite polarity.

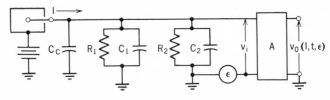

(a)

$$v_i(I, \epsilon) = I \frac{R_1 R_2}{R_1 + R_2} + \epsilon \qquad \cong I R_1 + \epsilon, \quad \text{if} \quad R_2 \gg R_1$$

$$v_0(I, t) = AI \frac{R_1 R_2}{R_1 + R_2} (1 - e^{-t/T}) \quad \cong AIR_1(1 - e^{-t/T}), \quad \text{if} \quad R_2 \gg R_1$$

$$T = \frac{R_1 R_2}{R_1 + R_2} (C_c + C_1 + C_2) \cong R_1(C_c + C_1 + C_2), \quad \text{if} \quad R_2 \gg R_1$$

$$v_0(\epsilon) = A\epsilon$$

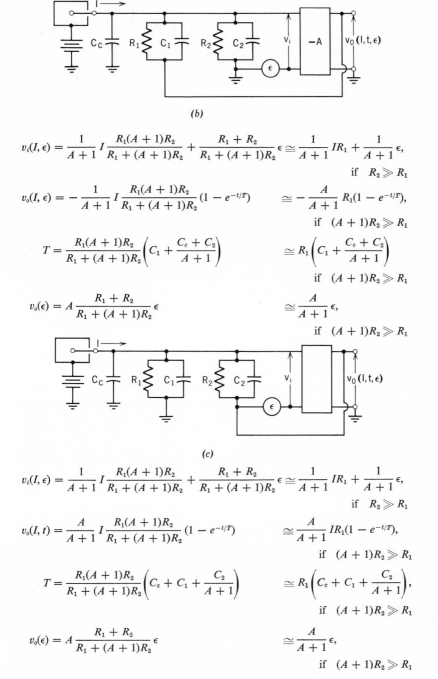

$$v_i(I, \epsilon) = \frac{1}{A+1} I \frac{R_1(A+1)R_2}{R_1+(A+1)R_2} + \frac{R_1+R_2}{R_1+(A+1)R_2} \epsilon \cong \frac{1}{A+1} IR_1 + \frac{1}{A+1} \epsilon,$$
$$\text{if} \quad R_2 \gg R_1$$

$$v_o(I, \epsilon) = -\frac{1}{A+1} I \frac{R_1(A+1)R_2}{R_1+(A+1)R_2} (1 - e^{-t/T}) \qquad \cong -\frac{A}{A+1} R_1(1 - e^{-t/T}),$$
$$\text{if} \quad (A+1)R_2 \gg R_1$$

$$T = \frac{R_1(A+1)R_2}{R_1+(A+1)R_2}\left(C_1 + \frac{C_c + C_2}{A+1}\right) \qquad \cong R_1\left(C_1 + \frac{C_c + C_2}{A+1}\right)$$
$$\text{if} \quad (A+1)R_2 \gg R_1$$

$$v_o(\epsilon) = A \frac{R_1+R_2}{R_1+(A+1)R_2} \epsilon \qquad \cong \frac{A}{A+1} \epsilon,$$
$$\text{if} \quad (A+1)R_2 \gg R_1$$

$$v_i(I, \epsilon) = \frac{1}{A+1} I \frac{R_1(A+1)R_2}{R_1+(A+1)R_2} + \frac{R_1+R_2}{R_1+(A+1)R_2} \epsilon \cong \frac{1}{A+1} IR_1 + \frac{1}{A+1} \epsilon,$$
$$\text{if} \quad R_2 \gg R_1$$

$$v_o(I, t) = \frac{A}{A+1} I \frac{R_1(A+1)R_2}{R_1+(A+1)R_2} (1 - e^{-t/T}) \qquad \cong \frac{A}{A+1} IR_1(1 - e^{-t/T}),$$
$$\text{if} \quad (A+1)R_2 \gg R_1$$

$$T = \frac{R_1(A+1)R_2}{R_1+(A+1)R_2}\left(C_c + C_1 + \frac{C_2}{A+1}\right) \qquad \cong R_1\left(C_c + C_1 + \frac{C_2}{A+1}\right),$$
$$\text{if} \quad (A+1)R_2 \gg R_1$$

$$v_o(\epsilon) = A \frac{R_1+R_2}{R_1+(A+1)R_2} \epsilon \qquad \cong \frac{A}{A+1} \epsilon,$$
$$\text{if} \quad (A+1)R_2 \gg R_1$$

Fig. 9. Comparison between unfedback (*a*), shunt fedback (*b*), and series fedback (*c*) amplifiers.

211

The shunt fedback circuit of Fig. 9*b* (so named because the current from the feedback path and the current from the ion chamber are added at a common point, called the "summing junction") is the one commonly used for making current measurements. However, the series fedback circuit of Fig. 9*c* (so named because the feedback voltage is applied in series with the incoming signal) is also used and has the desirable characteristic of not requiring a direct connection between the feedback resistor and the signal source. A cathode follower is an example of a series fedback circuit.

In an estimate of the three circuits several bases for comparison are possible. In the following it is assumed that each of the circuits is adjusted to produce a given output voltage in response to a given ion current. If A, R_2, and C_2 are assumed equal in the three circuits, then the only means of sensitivity adjustment is by variation of R_1. The capacitance C_1, being a geometric property of the resistor R_1, is independent of the value of R_1. With these conditions in mind it can be shown that

(a) for a given input sensitivity R_1 in Figs. 9*b* and 9*c* must be $(A + 1)$ times greater than in Fig. 9*a*. As a result,

(b) the response time of the two fedback circuits is greater than that of the unfedback one in the ratio $[(A + 1)C_1 + C_c + C_2]/[C_1 + C_c + C_2]$.

(c) The offset voltage appearing in the output of the fedback circuits is only $1/(A + 1)$ times that in the unfedback circuit.

(d) Variations in amplifier gain affect the output of the fedback circuits only $1/(A + 1)$ times as much as in the unfedback circuit. Gain variations may arise from tube aging or from the nonconstancy of the A versus v_0 characteristics (nonlinearity) of the circuit.

(e) The loading effect of the input resistance of the electrometer tube is the same for all three circuits.

Feedback, then, reduces zero drift, calibration drift, and nonlinearity; it also makes possible close control over the operating potentials and currents of the electrometer tube, but it does so at the sacrifice of fast response time and low-valued chamber load resistance.

No loss in response time need be suffered if a correction network[21] is added to the feedback circuit as shown in Fig. 10. If R_3C_3 is made equal to R_1C_1 ($R_3 \ll R_1$), the capacitive multiplication due to the feedback is cancelled exactly, and the time constant becomes $R_1(C_1 + C_c + C_2)/(A + 1)$. The action of the added network is to short-circuit the feedback for sudden changes in input signal. This improvement in response time is accompanied by a high-frequency noise level increase of $(A + 1)$ times, but this can usually be tolerated.

Another source of noise to which shunt fedback amplifiers are particularly vulnerable is that generated by the flexing of the cable which connects the detector to the amplifier in some instrument systems. The lagging effect of the $R_1(C_c + C_2)$ network prevents the feedback from becoming effective until some time after the noise signal appears at the amplifier output. This phenomenon sets the upper limit to the value of A in many electrometer systems.

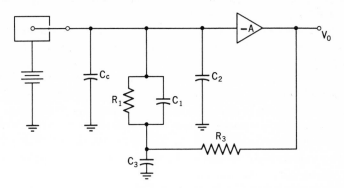

Fig. 10.   Time-constant reduction by feedback compensation.

The circuits of Figs. 9 and 10 are oversimplified in that A is assumed to have infinite frequency response. In practice, of course, this is never the case—there will be at least one additional time constant within the amplifier that affects the high frequency response. If there is only one additional time constant, its presence is largely of academic interest because it cannot cause the system to become unstable. In certain regions of operation this time constant may cause the electrometer to exhibit a damped, oscillatory response (ringing response), but the ringing frequency will be higher than can be followed by a meter or recorder and therefore will go unnoticed.

K.   Practical Circuits Employing Feedback

An excellent circuit developed by Moody[22] for use in a portable radiation monitor is shown in Fig. 11. By "bootstrapping" the plate circuit of the electrometer tube with the output cathode follower, a combination of high loop gain (60), low output impedance, and low battery drain results—a combination that has more than adequate linearity of response and calibration stability for the intended purpose of the instrument. In addition, the use of guard rings plus a switching circuit in which unused chamber load resistors are grounded minimizes the effects of insulator leakage.

Full-scale current ranges are 4×10^{-11}, 4×10^{-12}, and 4×10^{-13} amp. The grid current of the 5886 is less than 10^{-14} amp. When used with a chamber with a volume of approximately 700 cc, the full-scale beta and gamma sensitivities are 12, 120, and 1200 mr/hr. Hearing-aid batteries with a life of about 400 hr are used. Zero drift is approximately 2%/day. The resistors in the filament circuit of V_1 provide a means of adjustment for gross variations in the input tube.

Several circuit designs have been published in which selected radio receiving tubes are used as the electrometer tube in power-line operated instruments.[13,14] To get the necessary stability, it is necessary to regulate the heater power. An alternate arrangement is one in which a true electrometer tube is used at the input, followed by one or more conventional radio tubes to increase the loop gain to the desired value. Considering (1) the cost of regulating a 150-ma heater circuit versus a 10-ma filament, (2) the cost of the tubes, and (3) the performance in terms of attainable grid current, it is doubtful that the use of selected radio tubes can be justified.

An example of a circuit that uses both electrometer tubes and radio tubes[23] is shown in Fig. 12. Regulation is obtained with a constant-voltage power transformer. The most sensitive full-scale current setting is 3×10^{-13} amp, obtained with a feedback voltage of 0.3 volt, and a load resistance R of 10^{12} ohms. The drift on this range is about 4%/24 hr. On the higher current ranges the feedback voltage alternates between 1.0 and 3.0 volts, the drift being approximately 2%/24 hr. The output level is fixed at 5 volts, full scale, with a current capability of 5 ma. The input voltage necessary to produce this output level is less than 5 mv.

L. Vibrating-Capacitor Electrometer

The potential difference developed across the terminals of a capacitor C storing a charge Q is

$$V = Q/C. \tag{12}$$

If the plates of the capacitor are perfectly insulated from each other, a variation of capacitance will be accompanied by a variation in voltage according to the equation

$$\frac{dV}{dC} = \frac{Q}{C^2} = \frac{V}{C} \tag{13}$$

$$\frac{dV}{V} = \frac{dC}{C}. \tag{13'}$$

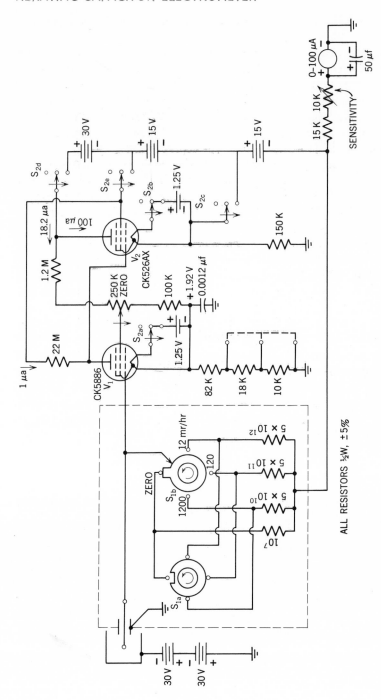

Fig. 11.   Portable radiation monitor.

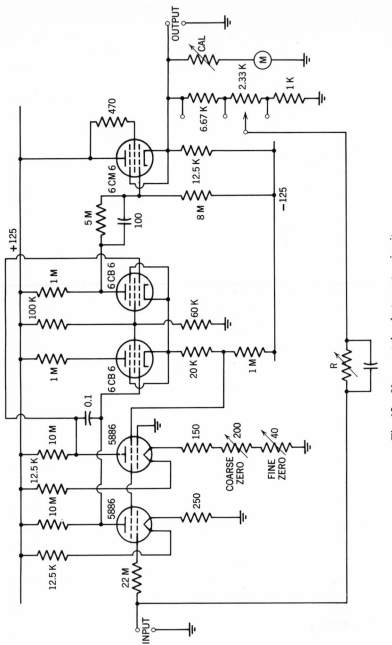

Fig. 12. Vacuum-tube electrometer circuit.

This relationship is used as the basis for a vibrating capacitor (or dynamic condenser) electrometer with a very low drift rate and a very high input impedance.[24,25] A block diagram of the instrument appears in Fig. 13. (Unless otherwise stated, it is assumed that S is in position 1.)

A cursory examination of Fig. 13 shows that the signal voltage developed by the ion chamber appears at terminal P, where it is modulated by the vibrating capacitor C_a. The resulting a-c signal is amplified by A, rectified by the synchronous detector, and fed back to C_a in such a way as to

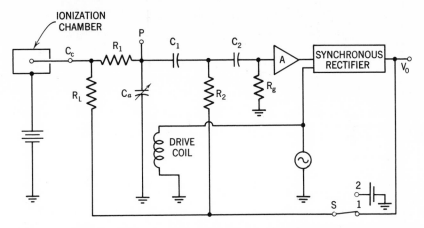

Fig. 13.   Basic circuit of a vibrating-capacitor electrometer.

reduce the voltage at P to a value approaching zero. If the current to be measured is so low that an impractically large value of R_L is required, R_L can be open-circuited and the measurement can be made by the loss-of-charge method described in Sec. B.

The input capacitance of a vibrating-capacitor electrometer is approximately 10 pf and the drift rate is approximately 0.1 mv/day. In the best vacuum-tube electrometer, the input capacitance is about 5 pf and the drift rate is about 1 mv/day. Since the ultimate sensitivity is inversely proportional to the product of input capacitance and drift rate, it is evident that the vibrating-capacitor instrument is superior to the other.

In the conventional vacuum-tube electrometer, both signal and input-tube variations are amplified alike, there being no means for distinguishing one from the other during a measurement. In the vibrating-capacitor instrument, however, the pass-band extends to direct current for the desired signal only. Most of the noise of the input tube and all of its drift are concentrated in regions outside the pass-band of the amplifier and detector; it is this basic difference in operation that accounts for the difference in stability between the two instruments.

The main source of drift is in the dynamic capacitor itself, and it is due to a variation in contact potential with time. If this drift is to be kept below 0.1 mv/day, the plates of the capacitor must have surfaces that are as identical chemically as it is possible to make them, and the capacitor must be sealed either in a dry, nonreactive atmosphere, or (preferably) in a vacuum. Vacuum sealing has the advantage of making the condenser

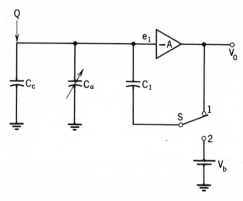

Fig. 14. Equivalent input circuit of a vibrating-capacitor electrometer (loss-of-charge connection).

insensitive to alpha-emitter contamination of the metal parts. In one version of the instrument, the capacitor plates are made of polished steel which are coated with several layers of gold, initially by plating and finally by evaporation. The plates are kept scrupulously clean throughout all phases of construction, and assembly is completed in a dust-free room. Mainly because of the involved and skilled processing required, the instrument costs three to four times more than its simpler vacuum-tube counterpart.

A detailed discussion of the input circuit of Fig. 13 follows.

If the d-c to a-c conversion efficiency is to approach the theoretical maximum of 71%,* the change in capacitance of C_a during a cycle of vibration must be large compared with the fixed capacitance of the system. [This follows from (13′).] This condition can be realized if the amplitude of vibration is large and if C_a is electrically isolated from ground. The isolation is accomplished by R_1, R_2 and R_g. (R_g is the grid leak of the first amplifier tube.) If the time constants R_1C_a, R_2C_1, and R_gC_2 (in ohms × farads) are each large compared with the period of vibration (in

---

* Practical efficiencies rarely exceed 10%.

seconds), the desired isolation is obtained. It should be noted, however, that the speed of response of the system is affected by these time constants and determines the practical upper limit of their size.

There are several ways in which the feedback signal can be returned to the input circuit. The method shown in Fig. 13 has three features to recommend it: (1) the "anvil" of the vibrating capacitor can be grounded, (2) the load resistor R_L can be open-circuited or short-circuited without disturbing the feedback signal by a significant amount, and (3) the bias of the first tube is not affected by the feedback voltage.

In analyzing the circuit operation, consider first the loss-of-charge method, in which R_L is open-circuited. If the transient conditions accompanying the sudden appearance of a charge at the output terminals of the chamber (of capacitance C_c) are neglected and if the conditions of vibrating-capacitor isolation discussed above are met, then the equivalent circuit can be simplified to the form shown in Fig. 14. The voltage e_1, developed at the input of the amplifier, is the sum of two components: the first, due to Q, is

$$v_1 = \frac{Q}{C_c + C_a + C_1}. \tag{14}$$

The second, due to v_0, is

$$v_2 = v_0 \frac{C_1}{C_c + C_a + C_1}. \tag{15}$$

The total voltage is

$$e_1 = v_1 + v_2 = \frac{Q + v_0 C_1}{C_c + C_a + C_1}. \tag{16}$$

Since $e_1 = v_0/(-A)$,

$$v_0 = -\frac{A}{A+1} \frac{Q}{C_1 + \dfrac{C_c + C_a}{A+1}}, \tag{17}$$

where A can be measured in the following way.

Throw S to position 2, connecting the battery v_b and breaking the feedback loop. When this is done,

$$A = \frac{v_0}{v_b} \frac{C_1}{C_c + C_a + C_1}. \tag{18}$$

C_1, C_a, and C_2 can be measured either directly with a capacitance bridge or indirectly by substituting several known values for C_c and solving the set of simultaneous equations for C_1 and C_2 that result from the repeated application of (18). This method of gain measurement includes the conversion efficiency of C_a.

From (17) it is apparent that as long as $C_1 \gg (C_c + C_a)/(A + 1)$, the input capacitance of the system is nearly equal to C_1. It is usual for A to be 1000 or more.

Evidently, C_1 must be chosen with care. Too small a value results in excessive loss of a-c signal (due to the dividing action of the input-tube capacitance acting in conjunction with C_1) and too large a value results in a loss in charge sensitivity, since C_1 determines the input capacitance. A size of 10 pf represents a good compromise between the two extremes. It is also necessary that the leakage of C_1 be very low, since it serves to isolate C_a from the charge-dissipating part of the circuit. Fortunately, the small capacitance makes possible the use of a well-insulated, air-dielectric capacitor.

The coupling capacitor C_2 (Fig. 13) is important in that it prevents the d-c component of the input-tube grid current from flowing into R_2, where it would produce an offset voltage. This condition can be prevented by choosing a capacitor whose leakage resistance is large compared with R_2.

The second case to be considered is a current measurement by the IR-drop method, which requires the connection of R_L to the circuit.

Analysis shows that the output of the electrometer will be $IR_L A/(A + 1)$, where I is the current to be measured. If $C_1 \gg (C_c + C_a)/(A + 1)$, then $IR_L A/(A + 1)$ is the asymptotic value of an exponential having $(R_L + R_2)C_1$ as its time constant.

M. Noise in Vibrating-Capacitor Electrometers

When the sensitivity of the electrometer is high, the output signal is observed to fluctuate in a random fashion. This fluctuation (noise) arises from several sources: (1) from thermal agitation of the electrons in the resistors associated with the input circuit, (2) from the shot effect of the grid current in the first tube in the amplifier, and (3) from the shot effect of the plate current in the same tube. (A fourth source of noise, which will not be considered further, is that due to ion currents arising from background radiation.) The noise signals fall into two definite frequency bands, as shown in Fig. 15. The high-frequency band is centered on f_0, the frequency at which the vibrating capacitor and synchronous detector operate. The noise falling into this band is called the "direct" contribution and consists largely of the shot noise generated at the plate of the first amplifying tube. The noise falling into the low-frequency band is called the "indirect" contribution and consists largely of the resistor and grid-current noise signals. The indirect contribution (usually the larger of the two) is transformed into the pass-band of the synchronous rectifier by the modulating action of the vibrating capacitor. The noise level can be computed by using the methods developed in Part 2 of this chapter. The reader is also referred to the analyses made by Palevsky, et al.[24] and Ritsma.[26]

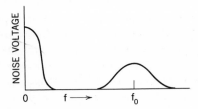

Fig. 15.   Noise spectrum of a vibrating-capacitor electrometer.

The elimination of the indirect component of grid-current noise can result in a substantial improvement in the over-all signal-to-noise ratio. Several schemes for doing this exist.[26,27,28,29] The one due to Ritsma[26] is described.

In the arrangement shown in Fig. 16 the vibrating capacitor consists of two fixed plates, P_1 and P_2, placed close to a vibrating reed. The

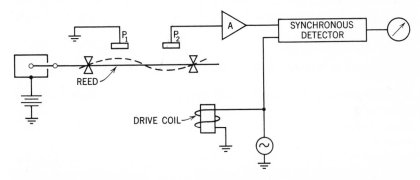

Fig. 16.   Dual vibrating-capacitor for the elimination of the indirect component of grid-current noise.

reed is forced to operate at the first overtone of its natural period, and the plates are positioned at the point of maximum reed displacement. It is clear from the drawing that as the capacitance between the reed and one plate increases the capacitance between the reed and the other decreases. The plates are adjusted to keep the capacitance between P_2 and ground constant during a cycle of vibration. The low-frequency component of the voltage difference between P_2 and ground produced by grid current in the first tube of the amplifier will not be modulated by the vibrating reed, whereas signal voltage developed between the reed and ground will be.

N. Insulators

The sensitivity of an electrometer makes it susceptible to insulation difficulties not present in less sensitive current measuring devices.

A fundamental requirement of an insulator is that the current flowing through it be negligibly small compared with the current flowing through the conductors that it supports. Before discussing this in detail, a second requirement, associated with stored charge, is covered.

Once charged, the surface of a good insulator is not easily discharged. Surface charges can be developed by mechanical stresses in the insulator, by charged particle bombardment, or simply by the rubbing of one surface against another. Conductors under the influence of the electrostatic field surrounding a charged insulator will have induced in them an image charge. If a conductor connected to the input of an electrometer is movable (e.g., a switch rotor) and if the motion disturbs the field, a spurious signal will result. This undesirable situation can be avoided (1) by interposing a grounded electrostatic shield between the insulator and all conductors that either move or are connected to the electrometer input terminal or (2) by so placing the insulator that it is not likely to pick up a surface charge.

The remainder of this section is devoted to the properties of insulating materials; it consists largely of a summary of the findings of Curtis[30] and Field.[31]

The resistivity of an insulator has two components—volume resistivity and surface resistivity. Volume resistivity is defined as the resistance between opposite faces of a cube of material 1 cm on edge, and surface resistivity as the resistance between opposite boundaries of a square of surface.

The volume resistivity of a pure material is an intrinsic property of the material. Since no material is perfectly pure, any measurement of a physical sample must include the resistivity of both the material and its impurities.

Impurities fall into two categories: (1) those which are a permanent part of the material, such as inclusions in a sheet of mica and (2) those which can change with environment, such as water absorbed from the air. Permanent impurities need not be troublesome if the impurities have a high intrinsic resistance of their own or if the impurities are contained in isolated pockets. Transient impurities, of which water is by far the commonest, can be very troublesome. A good insulator is impermeable to water vapor, or can be made impermeable by suitable surface treatment, or its structure is such that water is contained in isolated pockets.

The measurement of volume resistivity is usually complicated by several side effects that must be taken into consideration.

I. Dielectric absorption.[32] In many solids the displacement current does not obey the simple exponential charging characteristic of an RC circuit. The initially exponential inrush of current may be accompanied by an extended tail that will be mistaken for leakage current in a hurried measurement. The higher the insulation resistance, the more important this component becomes. There is no means of avoiding it, if it exists, except to wait until the polarization process is complete.

2. Surface leakage. This is discussed as a separate topic.

3. Slow moisture absorption. Resistivity measurements made on a slightly permeable material near the end of a long dry season may be much higher than those made near the end of a long wet season, for obvious reasons.

The surface resistivity of an insulator, unlike the volume resistivity, is not an intrinsic property of the material but depends entirely upon the thickness and exact composition of the water and/or oil film that usually exists on its surface. If such a film does not exist, the surface resistivity is infinite. A moisture film will form within a few minutes after exposure to air on all wettable surfaces. The resistivity ranges from 10^{14} to 10^9 ohms at 50% relative humidity (RH) and down to 10^7 ohms at 90% RH. In insulators of interest to electrometer users the surface resistivity is always lower than the volume resistivity in wettable materials exposed to the air when the RH exceeds 50%. A graph of the logarithm of the surface resistivity versus RH is approximately linear for RH $>$ 50% and is always an inverse function of RH.

The water film on the surface of a perfectly clean insoluble solid can be expected to contain carbon dioxide and ammonia dissolved from the air. Although it might be suspected that these gases would increase the conductivity, Curtis[30] found that such was not the case. The conductivity of the surface film is essentially that of distilled water. However, exceedingly small traces of a soluble salt have a very large effect. The salt can come from the solid itself (if it is soluble), from air-borne dust particles, or from contact with the skin. This fact emphasizes the importance of never touching an electrometer insulator with bare hands.

O. Properties of Several Insulating Materials

The surface resistivity of a wettable insulator is a highly variable quantity, depending upon the humidity, the cleanliness of the insulator surface, and the amount and kind of soluble material contained in the solid. This dependence on cleanliness is demonstrated in Fig. 17, which shows the resistivity of a sample of fused quartz before and after thorough cleaning.[30]

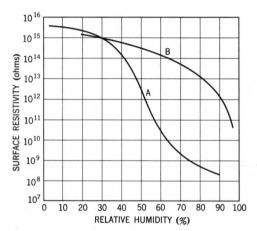

Fig. 17.   Surface resistivity of fused quartz (A) cleaned by wiping with a dry cloth, and (B) cleaned in a strong chromic acid solution, followed by distilled water.

Table 2 lists the insulating materials best suited to electrometer use. An exception is the soda-lime glass, which is listed only to show the importance of ascertaining the type of glass before using it in a high-resistance circuit. The table is separated into three categories: vitreous materials, plastics, and water-repellant materials.

The vitreous materials are desirable for their mechanical rigidity and for the fact that they can be freed of volatile impurities by high-temperature baking. All of them are water-wettable, however, and if high-humidity operation is contemplated they should be treated with one of the water-repellent compounds or contained in hermetically sealed enclosures.

The plastics are desirable for their high volume resistivity and for their ease of fabrication.

The figures on surface resistivity were taken almost entirely from papers of Curtis[30] and Field.[31] Curtis cleaned his samples by wiping with a dry cloth or dusting with a brush. Field cleaned his by washing in grain alcohol.

The following section is devoted to a detailed discussion of the materials listed in Table 2.

I. Vitreous materials. *a. Glass.* Of the various glasses listed, the soda-lime variety is the least desirable. The fact that its water solubility is higher than that of the other glasses probably accounts for its relatively poor surface resistivity.

The high-K glass of unspecified formulation was probably a high-lead glass.

The surface resistivity of the glasses is much improved by treatment with one of the water-repellent compounds.

b. Mica. As the table indicates, mica is quite variable in its electrical properties. This variability, combined with its fragility, limits its usefulness in electrometer applications.

c. Porcelain and steatite. These materials are available in many grades and exhibit large variations in electrical properties. They are important to electrometer users because of their availability in the form of rotary switch decks, tube sockets, and stand-off insulators. The poor surface properties can be markedly improved by proper treatment.

Probably the best of the surface treating agents is a silicone compound known as Dri-Film SC-77. This material, formulated specifically for ceramics, is discussed in Sec. O3a, p. 229.

Another method of treatment consists of coating the surface with polystyrene "coil dope."[33] The ceramic parts are first scrubbed in carbon tetrachloride with a stiff brush, rinsed in ethyl alcohol, and finally in distilled water. The parts are then vacuum baked for 2 h at 100° C, following which they are immersed, still hot, in a half-and-half mixture of polystyrene cement and thinner. Excess cement is slung off and the parts allowed to air-dry for at least 3 h before use. To avoid contamination the treated insulators should be stored in distilled water until needed. At no time after the cleaning process has begun should the insulators be touched with bare hands. Polystyrene, once contaminated, is never successfully cleaned. The leakage resistance of a treated insulator exceeds 10^{15} ohms at a relative humidity of 95%. This method of treatment is only temporarily beneficial in the case of insulators subjected to high voltage ($>$ 1 kv), since the surface film separates from the body after several months of high voltage operation.

d. Quartz. See Sec. C, pp. 199, 200.

e. Titanates. The titanates are of interest because of their use as the dielectric material in ceramic capacitors.

2. Plastics. *a. Methylmethacrylate.* Methylmethacrylate is a hard transparent plastic that machines well. Although its properties are adequate for many electrometer applications, polystyrene is generally used in its place.

TABLE 2. INSULATING PROPERTIES OF DIELECTRIC MATERIALS SUITABLE FOR ELECTROMETER USE

Vitreous Materials	Reference	Dielectric Constant	Volume Resistance	Surface Resistivity		
				60% RH*	90% RH*	100% RH*
Glass						
Soda-lime 0080 (general purpose)	(1)	7.2	2×10^{12} Ω	2×10^{11} Ω	8×10^{7} Ω	
Borosilicate 7052 (kovar sealing Pyrex)		5.1	10^{17}	10^{12}	8×10^{9}	
7070 (low-loss electrical)		4.0	$>10^{17}$			
7740 (Pyrex glassware)		4.6	10^{15}			
96% Silica 7900 (high temperature)		3.8	10^{17}			
High-lead 8870 (sealing or electrical)		9.5	$>10^{17}$			
Glass (high dielectric constant)	(3)			3×10^{13}	3×10^{10}	3×10^{9} Ω
Mica		5.6–6.6				
Brown African, clear	(2)		2×10^{15}	3×10^{12}	3×10^{9}	
spotted	(2)			10^{11}	10^{9}	
India ruby, clear	(2)			3×10^{12}	3×10^{9}	
stained	(2)		5×10^{13}	3×10^{9}	10^{8}	
Clear mica, unspecified source	(2)		2×10^{17}	2×10^{12}	10^{10}	
Clear mica, unspecified source	(3)			6×10^{12}	2×10^{10}	3×10^{9}
Porcelain						
Unglazed (chemical dish)	(2)		3×10^{14}	10^{11}	3×10^{7}	
Glazed (knife switch base)	(2)			10^{11}	3×10^{8}	
Glazed	(3)			2×10^{12}	2×10^{10}	4×10^{9}
Quartz	(3)	5.5–7.5	10^{13}–10^{15}			2×10^{6}
Quartz, fused	(2)		$>5 \times 10^{18}$	See Fig. 17		
Steatite						
(L-3)	(3)					2×10^{9}
(L-4)	(3)					6×10^{8}
(L-4)	(3)					3×10^{8}
Titanates (Ba, Sr, Ca, Mg, Pb)		15–12,000	10^{8}–10^{15}			

Plastics

Material	Ref.	Dielectric constant	Volume resistivity			
Methylmethacrylate (Lucite, Plexiglass, Perspex)		2.7–3.2	10^{13}–10^{16}			
Polyethylene		2.3	10^{13}–10^{15}			
Polyethylene	(3)			2×10^{14}	2×10^{10}	10^{9}
Polystyrene	(3)	2.4–2.8	10^{15}–10^{19}			
Sheet	(3)			$>2 \times 10^{14}$	$>2 \times 10^{14}$	8×10^{9}
Plasticized	(3)			2×10^{14}	2×10^{12}	5×10^{9}
Plasticized	(3)			$>2 \times 10^{14}$	4×10^{10}	2×10^{9}
Molded	(3)			2×10^{14}	2×10^{10}	2×10^{9}
Tetrafluoroethylene (Teflon)		2.0	10^{15}–10^{17}			
Tetrafluoroethylene	(3)					3.6×10^{12}
Trifluorochloroethylene (Chemelec 500, Fluorothene, Kel-F)	(3)	2.0–3.0	10^{15}–10^{17}			

Water-Repellent Materials

Material	Ref.	Dielectric constant	Volume resistivity			
Dri-Film	(2)	2–5	See text, pp. 229, 230			
Wax						
Ceresin (melting point 69° C)	(2)		$>5 \times 10^{18}$	$>5 \times 10^{18}$	$>5 \times 10^{18}$	
Paraffin (Parowax, MP 52° C)	(2)			10^{16}	10^{16}	
Hydrocarbon wax (type unspecified)	(2)			3×10^{13}	10^{11}	2×10^{10}

* RH: Relative humidity.

References: (1) Corning Glass Works, (2) Curtis,[30] (3) Field.[31]

Trade names: Pyrex—Corning Glass Works; Lucite, Teflon—E. I. duPont de Nemours and Co.; Plexiglass—Rohm and Haas; Perspex—ICI Ltd.; Chemelec 500—U.S. Gasket Co.; Kel-F—M. W. Kellogg Co.; Dri-Film—General Electric Co.

b. Polyethylene. Polyethylene is a soft plastic commonly used to insulate wires and cables. Polyethylene-covered wires usually have an additional vinyl jacket whose electrical properties are not as good as those of the plastic it protects. The vinyl jacket should be stripped back from the end of the wire to expose approximately $\frac{1}{4}$ in. of the polyethylene, care being taken to avoid touching the polyethylene with bare fingers.

c. Polystyrene. Polystyrene is a clear plastic that machines well and is slightly harder than methylmethacrylate. Despite several shortcomings, it is one of the most frequently used insulating materials in systems involving electrometers. Its volume resistivity, although quite variable (depending upon the amount of plasticizer used in its fabrication), even at its worst is adequate for nearly all electrometer applications.

The table indicates a highly variable surface resistivity at high humidities. Part of this variation is due to the method of manufacture and part is probably due to handling prior to measurement. As was stated earlier, a polystyrene insulator once contaminated can never be thoroughly cleaned. This characteristic is one of its major shortcomings. A second one is the surface charge produced by mechanical stress. The stress is usually produced either in the fabrication process or in the method of mounting. It can be relieved by annealing for an hour at 65° C.

In machining a polystyrene insulator,[33] light clamping pressure should be used and light cuts should be taken (to avoid stresses) with a sharp tool that has been thoroughly degreased. Cutting lubricants should not be used. The part close to the vise or chuck should be discarded. After machining, the part should be polished, first with a nonmetallic abrasive and then with talc until an optically clear surface is obtained. The polishing agents should be applied with a lint-free cloth moistened with distilled water. Finished parts should be stored in distilled water. Insulators machined in this manner and not touched with bare fingers will consistently exhibit surface resistivities exceeding 10^{15} ohms at 95% RH.

Polystyrene should never be washed with carbon tetrachloride, since it causes crazing. A delay of a week or more usually occurs before the crazing becomes visible. Grain alcohol may be used as a cleaning agent, but its effectiveness is limited.

d. Tetrafluoro- and trifluorochloroethylene. Among the various materials suitable for insulation in electrometer circuits the fluorocarbons are probably the most useful. The two discussed here range in color from white to gray or brown. They are opaque and are much softer than methylmethacrylate (but cold-flow only slightly). They have a slick feel and are very easily machined. Their volume resistivities, although not as high as those of the best grades of polystyrene, are adequate for nearly all electrometer systems. They are much superior to polystyrene in that mechanical stresses do not produce long-lived surface charges.* Furthermore, contaminated insulator surfaces are easily cleaned (with grain alcohol and distilled water), machined surfaces need no polishing, the softening temperatures are several hundred degrees higher than that of polystyrene, and the materials are water repellent.

3. Water-repellent materials. *a. Dri-Film.* Dri-film is the trade name† for a series of silicone compounds intended for use as coating materials. Two of them are especially useful for their electrical properties.

DRI-FILM SC-77. This compound is a mixture of methyl-chloro-silanes formulated specifically for the treatment of ceramics.[34] Its action is to combine with the water adsorbed on the surface of the ceramic to form HCl and a residual silicone. The HCl evaporates, leaving a very hard, abrasion-resistant, completely water-repellent film several hundred molecules thick. Under dew-point conditions, condensed water vapor forms in isolated droplets and high surface resistivity is maintained. In an early investigation of the electrical properties of the material, a resistivity $>2 \times 10^{11}$ ohms under these conditions was found. Unfortunately, this figure was limited by the available resistance bridge; it is more than likely that the surface resistivity of a treated ceramic exceeds 10^{17} ohms at all humidities.

The coating should be applied to a ceramic part whose surface moisture is in equilibrium with air in the RH range of 50 to 90%. The unheated part is treated by subjecting it to a stream of 25° C air which has bubbled through a container of the treating agent, also at 25° C. The surface film forms in a few minutes of exposure. An additional 10 min are required for the evaporation of most of the HCl formed in the process. Metal parts subject to corrosion by HCl should be removed before treatment. When necessary, the film can be cleaned with carbon tetrachloride without damaging it.

DRI-FILM SC-87. This compound was formulated specifically for glass and quartz but may be used on plastics as well. It is much less volatile than the SC-77 formulation and is usually applied full strength to a previously cleaned surface by wiping it on with a cloth moistened with a few drops of the compound. After an oily film forms, the excess is removed with a dry cloth and the surface polished until dry.

The compound is acidic while wet and may cause corrosion of metallic parts. To reduce the corrosion rate, SC-87 should be diluted in an organic

---

* Another form of "stress" current is due to relative motion between an insulator and its metal support. This component can be eliminated by applying graphite to all parts of the insulator in contact with the metal.

† General Electric Company

solvent to a concentration of 5 to 10%, applied to the insulator by dipping or spraying, then dried rapidly by baking for 15 to 30 min at a temperature of 100° C.

b. Wax. Although waxes are quite variable in their electrical properties, many of them are very useful in the surface treatment of other insulating materials. In particular, pure ceresin is completely water repellent and has insulating properties equaled by few other materials.

Because of their softness, the waxes should be considered as temporary treating agents. Some of them (such as beeswax) lose their surface-insulating properties after continued exposure to ultraviolet light. All of them collect dust, which eventually ruins them as insulators. In temporary set-ups this may be acceptable, since the surface is easily scraped to expose fresh material.

Unlike the dri-films, the waxes do not combine chemically with surface moisture; unless the moisture is driven off before treatment, no great improvement will result.

P.   Reduction of Insulator Leakage by Choice of Circuit

A frequently used means of reducing insulator leakage is the guard-ring technique. This is illustrated in Fig. 18. In Fig. 18a, leakage current through the insulator returns to the polarizing battery via the load resistor R, where it causes a spurious signal. In Fig. 18b the insulator is divided into sections that are separated by a conducting cylinder. The cylinder intercepts the leakage current and returns it directly to the battery. There may still be a leakage current through the inner part of the insulator due to the signal voltage, but since the signal voltage is small compared with the polarizing voltage the leakage current will be small as well. It can be further reduced by feedback from a low impedance point in the electrometer to the guard ring, the feedback signal being such as to keep the potential difference between the guard ring and the center electrode small compared with the signal developed across R.

Since the leakage current through the body of the insulator is usually negligible, the guard ring in most cases can be limited to a ring of conductive material applied to the surface of the insulator. Whether both inner and outer surfaces need be guarded depends upon the moisture content of the filling gas.

Because the leakage current through (or over the surface of) an insulator is usually proportional to the voltage drop across it, it is always desirable to choose a circuit configuration that results in low voltage across critically located insulators. For example, in the three circuits of Fig. 9 that of Fig. 9b is the best with regard to leakage currents between the center conductor of the chamber and ground because in this circuit the feedback keeps the voltage difference between this conductor and ground small compared with the signal voltage developed across the load resistor R_1. Similarly, in the circuit of Fig. 3 it is better to use the electrometer as a null detector rather than as a voltmeter. Both the guard-ring and voltage-reduction-by-feedback techniques are used in the circuit of Fig. 11.

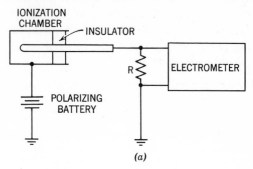

(a)

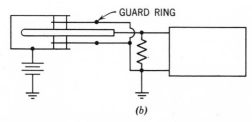

(b)

Fig. 18.   Ionization chamber connections (a) without and (b) with a guard ring.

The extent to which leakage resistance can be tolerated in a feedback circuit can be judged from the equation for $v_o(I, t)$ in Fig. 9b, where R_1 is the load resistance and R_2 is the leakage resistance. Evidently, as long as $(A + 1)R_2 \gg R_1$, very little of the ion current flows through R_2, even though R_1 may be comparable in size to R_2. Of course, a high value of R_1/R_2 will reduce the feedback signal by voltage dividing action; the effect of this feedback reduction on the linearity, gain stability, and time response of the electrometer amplifiers must be considered before using low-grade insulators or very high-valued chamber load resistances.

Q. Switches

A switch haphazardly connected to the input of an electrometer will more often than not cause a transient voltage of large amplitude to occur upon operation. The transient is usually caused by one or more of the following.

I. Frictional electricity due to rubbing insulators. This effect probably marks man's introduction to electrical phenomena, yet it is frequently overlooked in making high impedance measurements. Wherever possible, rubbing insulators should be avoided. If they cannot be avoided, the insulators should be electrostatically shielded from signal leads, or the rubbing surface should be coated with a conductor, such as evaporated metal, conducting paint, colloidal graphite, or even soft pencil lead, and the conductor should be grounded.

2. Thermally generated voltages due to sliding contacts. This effect is of consequence only when measurements are being made in the 0–20 mv range. Sliding contacts should be avoided wherever possible. If they cannot be avoided, the mating surfaces should be made of the same metal.

3. Amplification of contact potential by capacitive variation. This effect requires a detailed explanation.

Figure 19 is an electromechanical diagram of a typical electrometer input circuit. S is the switch under consideration, 1 and 2 are the switch arm and contact, respectively; V_1 is the electrometer tube, and $\mathcal{C}$ is an imaginary contour enclosing all parts of the circuit that remain connected to the grid of V_1 after S is opened. If 1 and 2 are made of different metals, the difference in their work functions (the contact potential)[35],[36] will manifest itself as a voltage between point 2 and ground, symbolized by the battery e_c. As a result of e_c, the portion of the grid circuit within $\mathcal{C}$ will be charged according to the equation

$$Q = Ce_c, \tag{19}$$

where Q = the charge in coulombs,

   C = the capacitance to ground of the conductors within $\mathcal{C}$,

   e_c = the contact potential in volts.

If S is opened, the change in geometry of the switch contacts will change the capacitance C by an amount ΔC. If the charge is conserved, the transient resulting from this change will be

$$\Delta e_c = \frac{Q}{C + \Delta C} - e_c. \tag{20}$$

Obviously, it is desirable to reduce Δe_c to a minimum. One way of doing this is to make 1 and 2 of the same material. This is easy to say but hard to do, since traces of surface contamination can produce marked differences in surface properties. Gold and platinum are good surface materials because of their low chemical activity. Sliding contacts should be avoided not only because of thermal emf's but also to avoid surface abrasion.

In experimental work it is not always feasible to use ideally designed switches. For instance, commercially available rotary switches are poorly

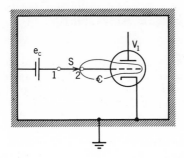

Fig. 19. Circuit for illustrating switching transients.

designed from the standpoint of electrometer use, but their availability and compact construction make them convenient to use for range selection. In such a situation it is desirable to provide a second, transient-free, single pole switch to short the electrometer input while operating the range selecting switch. An application of classical electrostatic principles[37]

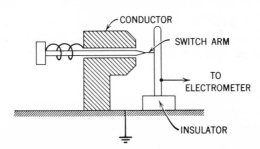

Fig. 20. Electrometer grounding switch.

tells us that it is possible to determine the capacitance between two conducting regions from a computation of the electric flux existing between the regions. Thus in Fig. 19 the flux of interest is that passing through $\mathfrak{C}$. It follows that a desirable switch is one in which the motion of the switch arm produces the least possible disturbance in the electric field distribution and, therefore, in the capacitance. Such a switch is illustrated in Fig. 20.

The arm consists of a stiff wire of minimal diameter located in a low-field region. The motion of the grounding wire should be limited to a few wire diameters. If possible, the wire and electrometer input connection should be gold or platinum plated.

PART 2 PULSE AMPLIFIERS

A. Total Activity Measurements
B. Energy Measurements
C. Amplifier Pulse Shaping
D. Need for a Clipping Network
E. Location of the Clipping Network
F. RC Clipping Network
G. Choice of T_1/T_2
H. Pulse Flattening Techniques
I. Delay-Line Clipping
J. Shorted-Line Pulse Formers
K. Blocking
L. Amplifier Noise
M. Noise Reduction Techniques. Removable Noise
N. Noise Reduction Techniques. Irremovable Noise
O. Optimization of the Signal-to-Noise Ratio
P. Grid-Current Noise in Receiving Tubes
Q. Selection of Tubes and Operating Conditions
R. Practical Operating Conditions
S. Input Circuits
T. Noise Measurements
U. Amplifier Linearity
V. Techniques for Attaining Good Linearity
W. Measurement of Linearity

The block diagram of a pulse counting system is shown in Fig. 21. This system is usually used to make two kinds of measurements: (1) total activity measurements and (2) spectral distribution measurements.

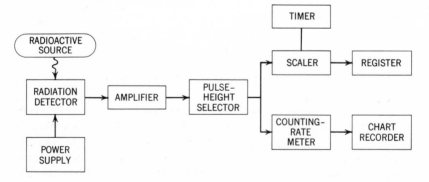

Fig. 21. Pulse counting system.

A. Total Activity Measurements

The purpose in making a total activity measurement is to determine the disintegration rate of a sample of radioactive material. To do this, it is first necessary to have a radiation detector that converts to electrical signals a known fraction of the radiation leaving the sample. The signals manifest themselves at the output of the detector as packets of electrons or ions. Each packet corresponds to one disintegration in the radioactive sample. (Occasionally two packets arrive so close together that they cannot be distinguished as separate pulses, but the probability of this occurrence is calculable and is of no concern for the moment.) Usually the packets of charge are integrated by the capacitance existing at the output of the detector, and in the idealized case they are converted to voltage steps of magnitude Q/C, where Q is the total charge in the packet and C is the capacitance. The detector is followed by an amplifier and

TABLE 3. DETECTOR CHARACTERISTICS

Detector	Output Signal	Energy Dependent	Supply Voltage Dependent
Geiger-Muller counter	0–10 volts	No	Yes
Proportional counter	0–50 mv	Yes	Yes
Pulse ion chamber	0–10 mv	Yes	No
Scintillation	0–100 volts	Yes	Yes

then by a trigger circuit. The signal amplification required between the detector and the trigger circuit depends upon the output level of the former and the sensitivity of the latter. The output level of the commonly used detectors is given in Table 3. A load capacitance of 20 pf is assumed.

There are three classes of trigger circuits[38,39,40,41] which are characterized by limiting sensitivities of 5 volts, 100 mv, and 1 mv, respectively. (These sensitivities are based on a drift rate of 1%/day.) It would appear that the use of a trigger circuit with a sensitivity of 1 mv in most cases obviates the need for an amplifier because each of the detectors listed in Table 3 can produce a signal exceeding 1 mv over at least part of its operating range. At the present writing, however, the 1-mv class of circuit has several shortcomings that limit its application to measurements of total activity. When energy measurements are necessary, trigger circuits of the 5-volt class are generally used, necessitating amplifier gains at least as high as 5000.

If the trigger circuit is adjustable by means of a calibrated control, it is

known as an integral discriminator[42,43] or integral pulse-height selector
(PHS). The trigger circuit has two important functions: (1) it establishes
a pulse-amplitude threshold, permitting discrimination against noise
pulses, and (2) it produces standardized pulses for the reliable operation
of the following scaler-register or counting-rate-meter-recorder combination. An idealized graph of counting rate versus PHS level is shown in
Fig. 22.

In the region between A and B virtually all of the pulses leaving the
detector are counted. In the region above B some of the pulses fall below
the threshold level of the trigger and are not counted. In the region below

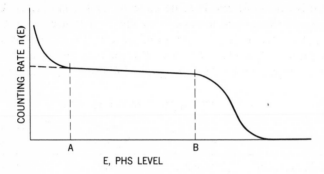

Fig. 22.   Counting rate versus PHS setting.

A amplifier noise pulses exceed the PHS setting and are counted in addition
to the pulses leaving the detector.

The region between A and B is known as the "plateau." In an ideal
apparatus the plateau is long enough to cover up the expected sensitivity
variations and of sufficiently low slope so that a small error in the setting
of the PHS level has a negligible effect on the measured counting rate.
The plateau length is affected by the amplifier and detector characteristics
and by the spectral distribution of the measured radiation. It is especially
important that the amplifier produce no satellite pulses under overload
conditions, since these pulses are difficult to distinguish from detector
pulses. The effect of satellite pulses is to limit the extent of the plateau.

B.   Energy Measurements

Energy measurements are made (1) to determine the modes of decay of
a known radioactive material or (2) to identify samples of unknown
material. The block diagram of the required equipment is the same as that
for the total activity measurement, but the characteristics of the blocks
must meet conditions not required of those in a simple counting apparatus.

The radiation detector must be a type in which output signal is proportional to the energy lost in it by the incident radiation. (This requirement rules out the use of a conventional G-M counter, in which the avalanche type of discharge that takes place with each triggering event produces pulses of equal height, regardless of the energy of the initiating event.)

The amplifier must also be a type in which the output level is proportional to the input level. Usually the amplifier has a linear[44,45] characteristic (i.e., one whose output obeys the law $V_o = KV_{in}$, where V_o is the

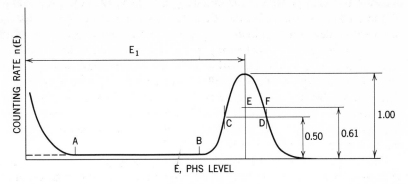

Fig. 23. Spectrum of Fig. 22.

output pulse height, V_{in} is the input pulse height, and K is a constant referred to as the amplifier gain), but in some applications a logarithmic or other type of response may be preferred.

Instead of accepting all pulses whose amplitudes exceed the threshold setting, the PHS accepts only those pulses whose peaks fall into a narrow region between two trigger-level settings. This type of PHS is known as a differential PHS, differential discriminator, or kicksorter.[46] The acceptance region is known as the slit, window, or channel, and its edges are defined by the upper and lower trigger levels. Differential PHS circuits may be single channel or multichannel. With both types, the recorded information approximates the derivative of the curve shown in Fig. 22. The new curve is illustrated in Fig. 23.

The region below A corresponds to the amplifier noise. The region of interest is usually the peak whose mid-point lies E_1 energy units along the E-axis and is a measure of the energy of the radiation entering the detector. The peak width is usually measured at half-maximum intensity and corresponds to the line CD in the figure. Resolution* is expressed as the fraction CD/E_1. Since the peaks are usually Gaussian in shape, the

* This term, though in common use, is a poor one. The fraction CD/E_1 is actually a measure of the lack of resolution.

standard deviation σ is also of interest. It is measured by the line EF at the level indicated in the figure. The line CD is related to σ by the equation $CD = 2.355\sigma$.

C. Amplifier Pulse Shaping. General Considerations

The packet of charge that results from the interaction of a radiation event with the radiation detector appears at the output terminal of the detector as a voltage step of magnitude Q/C_1, where Q is the total charge of the packet in coulombs and C_1 is the capacitance in farads existing between the detector terminals. (C_1 includes the input capacitance of all circuits connected to the detector.) If the detector were isolated from its surroundings and if the insulation between its terminals were perfect, none of the charge would leak off; successive events would eventually build up a retarding field that would prevent the further accumulation of charge. To prevent this, the detector is connected to a load resistor that leaks off at least part of the charge between successive events, giving rise to the pulse shape shown in Fig. 24.

The rise time of the pulse is defined as the time required for the output voltage to rise from 10 to 90% of its maximum value and is determined by the rate at which charge is accumulated at the output terminals of the detector. The rate of charge accumulation is largely independent of the system capacitance and load resistance, depending instead upon the characteristics of the detector and, in the case of an ion chamber, on the orientation of the primary track of ionization with respect to the collector.

The fall time of the pulse is determined by the product of the load resistance and the system capacitance. It is customary to make the fall time much longer than the rise time; when this is the case, the pulse shape is approximated by the equation

$$v = \frac{Q}{C_1} e^{-t/R_1 C_1}, \tag{21}$$

where $v =$ the output signal in volts,
$\quad Q =$ charge in coulombs produced by the ionizing event,
$\quad t =$ time in seconds,
$\quad R_1 =$ system load resistance in ohms,
$\quad C_1 =$ system capacitance in farads.

The collection of charge in the detector constitutes a current whose mean value is

$$i = nQ, \tag{22}$$

where $\bar{\imath}$ = mean current in amperes,

$\quad n$ = mean counting rate in counts per second,

$\quad Q$ = mean charge per pulse in coulombs.

This current flowing through the load resistor R_1 produces an average voltage of value:

$$\bar{v} = nQR_1. \tag{23}$$

The voltage $\bar{v}$ can also be obtained from Campbell's theorem of the mean:[3]

$$\bar{v} = n\int_0^\infty f(t)\,dt, \tag{24}$$

where $f(t)$ = time response of the system to a single event. Equation 24 reduces to (23) if (21) is substituted for $f(t)$.

Fig. 24.　Output pulse from a radiation detector.

The pulses obtained from the detector are not suitably shaped for transmission through a counting system, partly because of the overlap that occurs between pulses at high counting rates and partly because of the frequency response required of the system to transmit the pulses. The first effect is illustrated in Fig. 25a, which is typical of the waveform observed at the junction of the radiation detector and the input terminals of the amplifier. To be counted as an individual event, a pulse must cross the trigger threshold in a positive direction. It is evident that only a fraction of the pulses shown in Fig. 25a meets this condition.

The mean pulse height can be calculated from (24). If the system is a-c coupled, no average component can be transmitted and a base line is established at the mean level. However, because the pulses arrive at random times, the mean level fluctuates from instant to instant; this fluctuation *can* be transmitted through the system. The rms fluctuation can be computed by using Campbell's theorem of the mean square:

$$(v - \bar{v})^2 = n\int_0^\infty |f(t)|^2\,dt, \tag{25}$$

where v = instantaneous value of the mean voltage,

$\quad \bar{v}$ = long-time value of the mean (base line).

When the pulse shape can be described by (21), the rms fluctuation of the mean becomes

$$(v - \bar{v})_{\mathrm{rms}} = \frac{KQ}{C_1} \sqrt{\frac{nR_1C_1}{2}} \tag{26}$$

where K is the amplification between the detector and the point in the amplifier at which the measurement is made. Because of the statistical

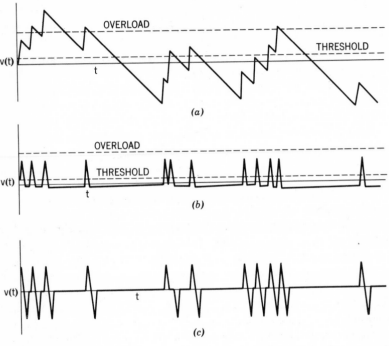

Fig. 25. Amplifier pulse shapes. The base line is determined by the mean pulse heights (see text).

nature of the fluctuation, the instantaneous pulse pile-up may exceed the rms value by several times, and it must be provided for in the design of the system. The probability that the pile-up will exceed 2.5 times the rms level is approximately 1%,[47] and 2.5 is a reasonable factor to use. The system, then, should be operable in the range

$$v = \frac{KQ}{C_1}\left(1 \pm 2.5\sqrt{\frac{nR_1C_1}{2}}\right). \tag{27}$$

It must be emphasized that the foregoing analysis is valid (1) only when the average pulse spacing is not more than the time constant of recovery of an individual pulse and (2) only as long as none of the pulses overloads the system. The second point is discussed further in a later section.

D. Need for a Clipping Network*

The useful information in a detector pulse is contained in its leading edge and its top. The long tail that follows contains little (if anything) of interest and, if accurately reproduced, makes the system subject to pile-up errors at high counting rates. In addition, the low-frequency response required of the amplifier makes it susceptible to the effects of hum, microphonics, and flicker noise. The use of a clipping network, which in its simplest form is an interstage RC coupling network whose time constant is much smaller than any of the others, simultaneously clips the tail of the pulse and degrades the low-frequency response of the amplifier.

The choice of the optimum clipping time depends upon the time constant associated with the amplifier rise, which in turn depends upon the collection time in the detector and upon the type of measurement being made.

In ion chambers the collection time is dependent on the orientation of the initial track of ionized gas particles with respect to the collecting electrode. Unless collimation is used, the orientation, hence the collection time, varies from pulse to pulse. If the amplifier rise and clipping times are made comparable with the collection time, variations in orientation of incoming events will produce variations in measured pulse height. If spectral measurements are being made, these variations may limit the attainable energy resolution. It can be shown[48] that if the time constants which control the amplifier rise and fall are made equal and if these time constants are at least twice as great as the longest collection time that can occur, then variations in pulse height due to variations in track orientation will be less than 1%. It can also be shown that the amplifier signal-to-noise ratio (S/N) is optimized when the time constants controlling the rise and fall are equal. (It is assumed that a single time constant controls the amplifier rise. In practice, this may not be the case.)

If the pulse-amplitude measurements are unimportant, the amplifier time constants can be reduced to the average detector time constant with no appreciable loss in S/N and with a considerable increase in permissible

---

* Also known as a "differentiating network" because the resulting output signal approximates the mathematical derivative of the input signal. Since the analogy is far from exact, the term "clipping network" is used in this text. It refers here to time clipping and should not be confused with a voltage clipping network.

counting rate. The same condition applies to scintillation counters, whether or not energy measurements are made, because there is no rise-time dependence upon the direction of the incoming radiation.

E. Location of the Clipping Network

The performance of an amplifier is strongly dependent on the location of the clipping circuit. If it is located at the input, the full amplifier gain is available to amplify the noise level of the input tube. If it is placed near the output, the section preceding the clipper will be subject to overload from pile-up. It is evidently necessary to balance one effect against the other in deciding the location.

F. RC Clipping Network

It was stated earlier that clipping may be accomplished by giving one RC coupling network in the amplifier a shorter time constant than any of the others. Several consequences of this arrangement are now considered; the clipping network plus one additional interstage coupling network are used as the basis of the discussion.

The response to a unit step of two cascaded RC coupling networks which are separated by an isolating stage is

$$v(t) = \frac{1}{1 - T_1/T_2}\left(e^{-t/T_1} - \frac{T_1}{T_2}e^{-t/T_2}\right), \tag{28}$$

where $v(t) =$ time response of the system,

   $T_1 = RC$ product in ohms $\times$ farads ($=$ seconds) of the clipping network,

   $T_2 = RC$ product in ohms $\times$ farads ($=$ seconds) of the coupling network.

If $T_1 = T_2 \equiv T$, the response becomes*

$$v(t) = e^{-t/T}(1 - t/T). \tag{28'}$$

Equation 28 is graphed in Fig. 26 for $T_1/T_2 = 1$ and $T_1/T_2 = 0.1$. The base line crossing occurs at

$$t_1 = \frac{T_1 T_2}{T_2 - T_1}\ln\frac{T_2}{T_1}, \tag{29}$$

which yields

$$t_1 = T, \quad \text{if } T_1 = T_2 \equiv T. \tag{29'}$$

---

* Equation 28' may be derived from (28) by using l'Hospital's rule to resolve the indeterminate that results from setting $T_1/T_2 = 1$. See a mathematics text.

The peak of the undershoot occurs at

$$t_2 = 2t_1 \tag{30}$$

and has a magnitude of

$$|v(t_2)| = \left(\frac{T_1}{T_2}\right)^{\frac{T_2+T_1}{T_2-T_1}} \tag{31}$$

which yields

$$|v(t_2)| = e^{-2}, \quad \text{if } T_1 = T_2. \tag{31'}$$

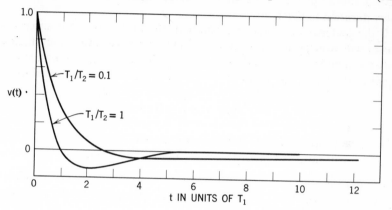

Fig. 26. Response of two cascaded RC coupling networks to a unit step.

Examination of (31) shows that the ratio of the peak of the undershoot to the peak of the primary pulse approaches T_1/T_2 as T_1/T_2 approaches zero.

The mean value of (28) or (28'), as calculated from (24), is zero, as is to be expected from the d-c blocking action of an RC coupling network. It follows that the area of the primary pulse is equal to the area of the undershoot. Pulses with a small undershoot will have a long recovery time and vice versa.

When three interstage coupling networks are used, it is found that an overshoot follows the undershoot. Since the overshoot has the same sign as the primary pulse, it will be counted as a second pulse under adverse conditions. Fortunately, the magnitude of the overshoot compared with the magnitude of the primary pulse is small under ordinary conditions. If T_1 is the clipping time constant and T_2 and T_3 are additional coupling time constants, it can be shown that the ratio of the overshoot to the primary pulse height approaches $(T_1/T_3)^2$ for the values of T_2 in the range $T_1 \leqslant T_2 \leqslant T_3$.

As additional coupling networks are added, additional undershoots and overshoots with successively decreasing amplitudes and increasing durations will appear. If N coupling networks are used, there will be $N - 1$ base-line crossings.

G. Choice of T_1/T_2

Returning to the case in which only one coupling network in addition to the clipping network is used, the question arises whether it is better to have a low-amplitude, long-duration undershoot, or a large-amplitude, short-duration undershoot.

If the undershoot has a long duration, the probability that successive pulses will overlap is relatively high. The measured amplitude of these pulses will be lower than the true amplitude by an amount approximately equal to the duty cycle times the amplitude. The duty cycle is defined as

$$\text{duty cycle} \equiv n \int_0^{t_1} f(t)\, dt, \tag{32}$$

where n = mean pulse rate in pulses per second,

t_1 = duration of pulse as defined in (29) and (29′).

In addition, the measured amplitude of the pulses will be modulated by the undershoot from instant to instant by an amount whose rms value is, by Campbell's theorem,

$$V_{\text{rms}} = \left[n \int_{t_1}^{\infty} |f(t)|^2\, dt \right]^{1/2}. \tag{33}$$

(It must be emphasized that (32) and (33) are applicable only if the duration of the primary pulse is short compared with the duration of the undershoot and if the mean spacing between pulses is such that appreciable overlap between successive pulses occurs. It should also be noted that under overload conditions the shape of $f(t)$ changes appreciably because of amplifier saturation. In applying (32) and (33), it is necessary to use the $f(t)$ existing at that point in the amplifier under consideration.)

If, on the other hand, the undershoot is large and of short duration, the probability of having pulses overlap is relatively small, and the counting rate at which amplitude shifts and modulation effects become important is much higher than for the condition of small undershoot.

The undershoot of the largest amplitude and shortest duration occurs when two of the coupling networks have time constants that are equal to each other and smaller than those of the remaining coupling networks. The resulting pulse shape is shown in Fig. 25c. Not only is the maximum usable counting rate increased by the use of double clipping, but it also becomes possible to place one clipper near the input of the amplifier to reduce the effects of pile-up and the second clipper in a later stage to reduce the low-frequency noise generated in the early stages. Unfortunately, these features complicate the amplifier design, since an amplifier employing double clipping must be built to transmit pulses of both polarities.[49]

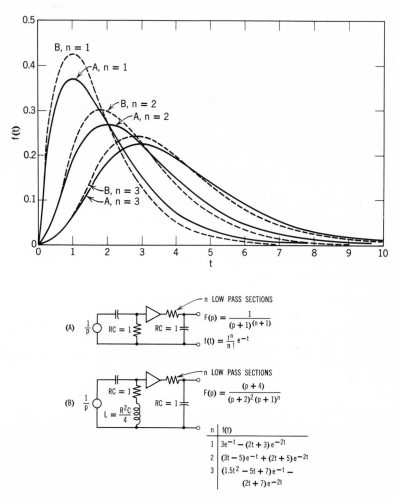

Fig. 27. *RC* network response to a unit step; single clipper.

Figures 27 and 28 show in detail the response of an amplifier having *RC* and *RLC* shaping networks to a unit voltage step. In both figures the time scale is in units of *RC*. It is assumed that the high-frequency response of an amplifier stage can be described by a simple *RC* low-pass network,

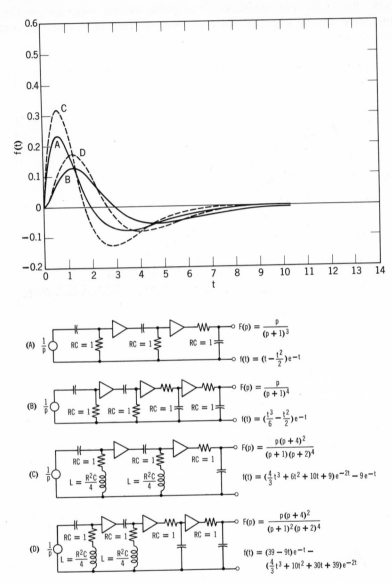

Fig. 28.   *RC* network response to a unit step;   double clipper.

that each of the networks is connected between stages having zero output impedance and infinite input impedance, and that the stage gain is 1.00.

Figure 27 shows the response to a unit voltage step of an amplifier with a single clipping network of time constant $RC = 1$ and one, two, three, or four low-pass networks each of time constant $RC = 1$. Compensating the clipping network with an inductance chosen to produce critical damping has the desirable effect of reducing both the peak signal attenuation and the recovery time.

Figure 28 shows the response to a unit voltage step of an amplifier with two clipping networks, each of time constant $RC = 1$, and one or two low-pass networks, each of time constant $RC = 1$. As in Fig. 27, inductive compensation improves the response.

Since clipping networks are usually located near the input of the amplifier, the compensating inductances, if used, must be shielded to prevent the pickup of electromagnetic radiation.

The attractive features of RC or RLC clipping networks are their small size, low cost, ease of adjustment, and relative freedom from external noise pickup. Unfortunately, the pulse shape produced by an RC network is far from ideal. When precise pulse-height measurements are important, the short duration of the peak requires a faster PHS circuit than is necessary for a pulse with a flat top. Also, under overload conditions, the portion of the pulse close to the base line comes into prominence; the exponential decay characteristic results in an amplifier recovery time that is proportional to the overload and always excessively long compared with that of a rectangular pulse. The situation is especially serious in the case of double RC or RLC clipping; because of the asymmetry of the positive and negative halves of the pulse, the area balance is destroyed under overload conditions.

H. Pulse Flattening Techniques

There are several methods for flattening the top of a pulse. One, due to Glenn,[50] is shown in Fig. 29. An incoming positive pulse charges the output capacitor through the lower diode to the fraction $R_2/(R_1 + R_2)$ of the pulse height available from V_1. The charge remains on the capacitor until the output of V_1 drops to the level that permits the upper diode to conduct. The capacitor is subsequently discharged through the upper diode. It is desirable that the cathode potential of V_1 be at ground level.

This method has limited application because undershoots and negative-polarity noise peaks produce long, negative-polarity pedestals. The circuit is also nonlinear at low pulse heights because of the diode characteristics.

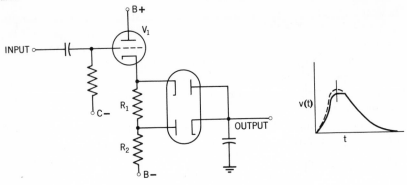

Fig. 29.   Glenn circuit for pulse flattening.

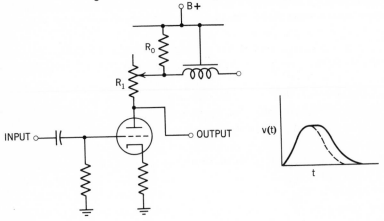

Fig. 30.   Kelley stretching circuit.

Another method of pulse flattening is due to G. G. Kelley* and is shown in Fig. 30. In this circuit the pulse is stretched by using the in-phase reflection of an open-circuited delay line. The line length must be such that the reflection returns to the driving point at the instant the incident pulse reaches its peak. If this condition is met, the leading edge of the reflection adds to the trailing edge of the incident wave, producing a short voltage plateau. R_0 must be adjusted to absorb all of the reflected wave to prevent further reflections. R_1 permits an adjustment of the magnitude of the reflected wave as compared with the incident wave to take care of the usual difference in shape between the leading and trailing edges of the incident pulse.

This circuit also has limited application because of the precise and tedious adjustments that are necessary and because of the limited amount of stretching that can be attained.

* Personal communication.

I. Delay-Line Clipping

Neither of the methods in Sec. H prevents pulse broadening under overload conditions. By the use of delay-line clipping,[51,52,53] it is possible to obtain a pulse that is essentially rectangular and not subject to broadening. In addition, its height can be measured with relative ease, compared with the RC case.

The pulse-shaping feature of a delay line (transmission line) is derived from three properties:

(a) The input impedance of a perfect line has the characteristic resistance

$$R_0 = \sqrt{L/C}, \qquad (34)$$

where R_0 = characteristic resistance in ohms,

L = the inductance per unit length of line in henrys,

C = the capacitance per unit length of line in farads.

(b) A signal transmitted down a perfect line will not have its shape distorted but will be delayed by an amount

$$T_d = \sqrt{LC}, \qquad (35)$$

where T_d = the delay per unit length in seconds.

(c) The signal, upon reaching the end of the line, will be reflected with a reflection coefficient of

$$\rho = \frac{Z - R_0}{Z + R_0}, \qquad (36)$$

where Z = shunt terminating impedance seen by the end of the line.

Figure 31 illustrates three ways in which a unit step may be converted to a rectangular pulse by means of a delay line. In each case it is assumed that the time required for the wavefront to traverse the line from terminal 1 to terminal 2 is T and that the internal impedance of the step generator is zero.

In Fig. 31a the driving-point resistance of the line in conjunction with the input terminating resistor constitute an attenuator that halves the input voltage. This signal is impressed on one side of a difference amplifier, which produces an output. When the signal reaches terminal 2, both difference-amplifier inputs see the same signal level and the output signal is canceled. In accordance with (36), no reflection is produced.

In Fig. 31b the full input signal is impressed on the first grid and half on the second. The infinite terminating impedance at terminal 2 results in a reflection coefficient of $+1$. When the reflected signal reaches terminal 1, the inputs to the difference amplifier are equalized, thereby canceling the output signal.

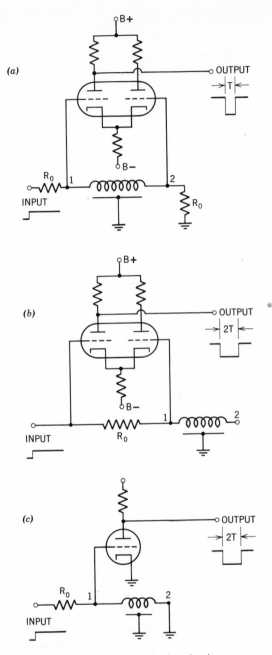

Fig. 31. Delay-line clipping circuits.

In Fig. 31c half the input signal is impressed on the grid. The zero terminating impedance at terminal 2 produces a reflection coefficient of −1. The reflection, upon reaching terminal 1, cancels the input signal to the amplifier. This configuration is the one most commonly used.

Any transmission line can in principle be used for a pulse-forming network. Ordinary flexible coaxial cables have characteristic impedances of 50 to 250 ohms and a delay constant of about 1.6 mμsec/ft. These cables are useful for producing pulse widths in the range of 1 to 100 mμsec. For pulse widths in the range of 0.1 to 10 μsec, delay cables are used which differ from ordinary coaxial cables in that the central conductor is spiraled to increase the inductance per unit length, thereby increasing both the delay per unit length and the characteristic impedance. Although the following discussion is limited to delay lines, much of the information is also applicable to ordinary coaxial cable.

J. Shorted-Line Pulse Formers

Consider the test circuit in Fig. 32, in which the terminating resistance R is adjusted to match the cable. It is assumed that the generator has an internal impedance small compared with R and that the line length is chosen to produce a 1-μsec pulse. The cables under consideration are listed in Table 4 (p. 257). Depending upon the kind of cable used, the observed waveform will have one or the other of the shapes shown in Fig. 33. (Note the difference in the amplitude scales between the two graphs.)

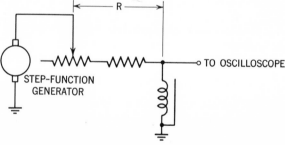

Fig. 32. Pulse forming circuit.

In Fig. 33a the top of the pulse is smooth, as is the region following the main pulse, except for a series of low-amplitude wiggles occurring at multiples of the clipping time. This pulse shape is characteristic of delay lines in which the central helix has a diameter approximately one third that of the outer sheath. These lines have a comparatively short delay per unit length.

In Fig. 33*b* the latter part of the main pulse "rings," whereas the region following it exhibits large-amplitude wiggles having only a slight correlation with the clipping time. This waveform is characteristic of lines in which the diameter of the central helix is only slightly less than that of the outer sheath. These lines have a comparatively long delay per unit length. In pulse amplifiers that are used for precise amplitude measurements, when measurements of wide dynamic range are important, cables

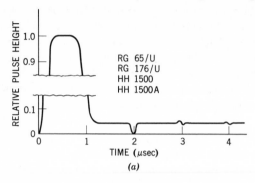

(a)

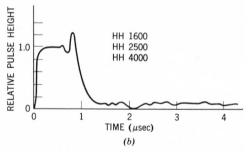

(b)

Fig. 33. Delay-line clipped pulses.

of the second type cannot be used unless something is done to improve their pulse-forming properties. (A method of improvement is discussed in a later section.) The wiggles in Figs. 33*a* and 34*a* are reflections that arise partly from end effects in the line (the end few turns of the helix have mutual coupling with other turns from one direction only) and partly because of the capacitive discontinuity introduced by external loading. The impedance matching can be improved by connecting in series with the line a small coil (10 to 100 μh) whose inductance in conjunction with the external circuit capacitance constitutes a filter half-section having the same characteristic impedance as the line. The resulting improvement is shown in Fig. 34*b*, in which L represents the compensating inductance and C_s is the external loading capacitance. A further improvement results from the shunting of L with a damping resistance, R_d, of value 2000 to 7000 ohms. Care must be exercised to add a minimum of excess capacitance by the addition of the compensating components; it is quite possible to nullify the expected improvement by careless wiring. The optimum values of L and R_d are best arrived at by trial and error.

A second salient feature of Fig. 33a is the pedestal that follows the main pulse. The pedestal is caused by line losses that reduce the amplitude of the reflected wave to a value less than that of the incident wave, thereby resulting in incomplete signal cancellation. The important losses arise from three sources: (1) The resistance of the central conductor, (2) the resistance of the outer conductor, and (3) the magnetic core.

The loss due to the central conductor resistance is important in all types of delay line and is calculable from the equation

$$v_l = v_i e^{-rl/2R_0}, \tag{37}$$

where v_l = the voltage at a distance l from the input of the line,

$\quad v_i$ = the voltage at the input of the line,

$\quad r$ = the resistance per unit length of the central conductor,

$\quad R_0$ = the nominal characteristic resistance $\sqrt{L/C}$.

In the case of a shorted line, the contribution to the pedestal due to the central conductor resistance is

$$v_p = v_i(1 - e^{-R/R_0}) \tag{38}$$

$$\cong v_i R/R_0, \qquad \text{if } R_0 > 10R, \tag{39}$$

where R = the measured d-c resistance of the line.

The manner in which the outer-conductor resistance contributes to the pedestal shape depends upon the construction of the outer conductor. In RG176/U and HH1500A it consists of a sheath of separately insulated wires that are parallel to each other and nearly parallel to the cable axis. In this type of construction there is no magnetic coupling between the central helix and the outer conductor; only longitudinal current flow can exist. Since the resistance of the sheath is negligible compared with the resistance of the helix and since the magnitude of the current in the sheath and the helix are the same, the sheath resistance contributes almost nothing to the pedestal height. The shape of the pedestal corresponds to that of C in Fig. 35.

In RG65/U and in HH1500 the sheath consists of a braid of uninsulated wires, which permits a circumferential component of current in addition to the axial component. The sheath appears to the helix as a magnetically coupled, short-circuited turn of inductance λ and resistance ρ. The

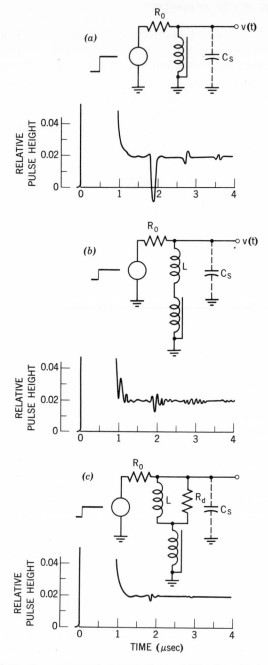

Fig. 34. Effects of a compensating network on a delay-line clipping circuit. The clipper consisted of 4 ft 6 in. of RG176/U.

induced current in the sheath decays with a time constant λ/ρ. As a result, the effective helix inductance and resistance change with time, varying the pedestal height as shown by A in Fig. 35. The situation can be improved by making ρ either zero or infinite. In the former case, the time constant is made so large compared with the initial pulse duration that there is no measurable change in the pedestal during the period of interest, and in the latter case (corresponding to a sheath of parallel, separately insulated wires) the change is instantaneous.

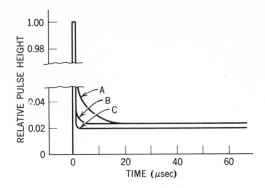

Fig. 35. After-effects of a delay-line clipped pulse.

The resistance of the sheath can be made essentially zero by substituting copper tubing for the wire braid. If this is done with HH1500, the resulting waveform corresponds to that of B in Fig. 35. The residual curvature is due to the magnetic core and does not exist in RG65/U under similar operating conditions; neither does it exist in magnetic-cored lines when a parallel-insulated-wire sheath is used. The magnetic-core effect is usually so small that it causes no trouble in most measurements.

The pedestal following a delay-line-shaped pulse is as undesirable as the exponential recovery of an RC-shaped pulse. A common method for eliminating the pedestal is to drive the line through a capacitor whose size will cause the primary pulse to decay by an amount equal to the pedestal height. The resulting waveform, shown in Fig. 36, indicates that this is not a good solution because of the undershoot that is introduced. Another and better method is the balanced-bridge technique shown in Fig. 37. In this circuit the signal from the clipper is applied to one terminal of a difference amplifier and a signal equal in height to the pedestal to the other. $R_1/(R_1 + R_2)$ determines the magnitude of the latter signal. If the pedestal exhibits a decaying component, as shown in Fig. 35, compensation can be obtained with the network R_3C_3.

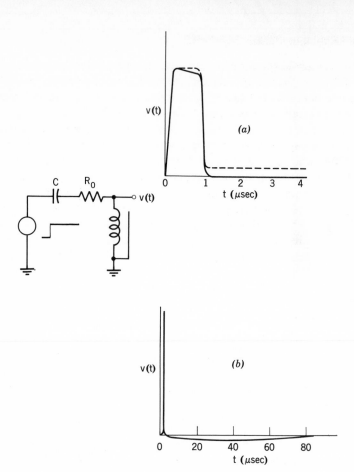

Fig. 36. Pedestal compensation by series C.

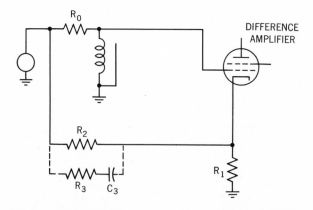

Fig. 37. Pedestal compensation by balanced-bridge technique.

The balanced-bridge technique permits complete elimination of the pedestal. Because the adjustments are critical, it is desirable to choose a delay line that does not exhibit a decaying pedestal and one in which the pedestal is small to begin with. Table 4 lists the commonly available delay lines and the ratio R/R_0, which is a measure of the pedestal height. The best lines for pulse-forming purposes are, in the order of preference, HH1500A and RG176/U. Unfortunately, the separately insulated parallel-conductor sheath used in these lines gives no shielding against stray electromagnetic fields. Shielding can be obtained by coiling the line and enclosing it completely in a conducting container* or by sheathing the line with $\frac{1}{2}$ in. thin-walled, soft-drawn copper tubing. The tubing reduces the characteristic impedance and the delay per unit length by approximately 20%, but it has the advantage of simpler and less bulky packaging.

TABLE 4. COMMONLY USED CONTINUOUS DELAY CABLES

Cable	R_0-ohms	Specific Length ft/μsec	Specific Resistance ohms/μsec	Spec. R / R_0	Outer Conductor	Magnetic Core	3-db Bandwidth 1-μsec Delay
RG65/U	950	23.8	167	0.176	CS*	No	4 Mc
HH1500	1600	13.3	102	0.064	CS	Yes	5
HH1500A	1500	12.5	30	0.02	SIPW†	Yes	15
HH1600	1700	1.0	75	0.044	SIPW	Yes	6
RG176/U (HH2000)	2280	9.1	70	0.032	SIPW	Yes	15
HH2500	2800	1.67	125	0.045	SIPW	Yes	8
HH4000	4000	1.0	85	0.021	SIPW	Yes	6

* Conducting sheath.
† Separately insulated parallel wires.

The foregoing techniques, carefully applied, make it possible to construct a delay-line clipper in which all spurious responses measured at a point 2.5 pulse widths (or more) from the start of the pulse are lower in amplitude than the main pulse by a factor of 1000.

When pulse widths of several microseconds are necessary, or when dynamic range can be sacrificed for compactness, the lines having a high specific delay become attractive. The jaggedness of both the top of the pulse and the pedestal (shown in Fig. 33b) can be eliminated almost

* Screws or other conducting fasteners that join opposite faces of the container must not be located so as to pass through the spiral formed by the coiled line. To do so would inductively couple the container to the line, thereby destroying the shielding action.

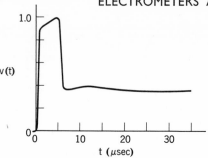

Fig. 38.   Pulse shape obtained with six feet of HH4000 in 1/2-in. OD copper tube. Termination adjusted for optimum impedance match.

completely by sheathing the lines with copper tubing as previously described. The reduction in specific delay and characteristic impedance that occurs with a close fitting sheath is about 50% in these lines. Although the small-period variations can be eliminated, the pulse shape will have distortions as shown in Fig. 38.

A nearly ideal pulse shape for transmission through an amplifier can be obtained by the double-clipping networks. The symmetry of the pulse, shown in Fig. 39, is such that the area balance between positive and negative

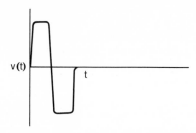

Fig. 39.   Pulse shape obtained from a double-delay-line clipping network.

pulse halves is changed hardly at all by overload, assuming that the amplifier saturates symmetrically. Two methods for obtaining the desired pulse shape are shown in Fig. 40.

The circuit of Fig. 40a permits the clippers to be placed at different points in the amplifier, whereas the circuit of Fig. 40b (due to Maeder in Koch and Johnston[53]) requires only a single piece of line (whose length is equal to the combined lengths of the lines in Fig. 40a).

If the lines are matched in the circuit of Fig. 40a and if the pedestal produced by each is $1/n$ as great as the main pulse, the combined pedestal will be only $(1/n)^2$ as great, making it unnecessary to use pedestal compensation in many cases.

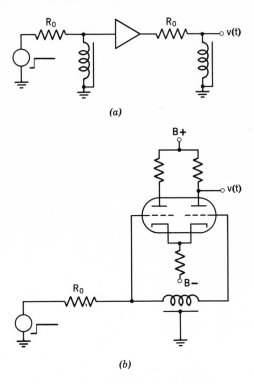

(a)

(b)

Fig. 40.   Networks for double clipping.

K.   Blocking

Blocking is the term used to describe a condition of temporary amplifier paralysis that follows an overload pulse. The advent of the scintillation counter, with its very wide dynamic range, brought the problem of blocking into prominence. In recent years much of the effort in amplifier design has been devoted to the elimination of this effect.

Blocking is usually caused by grid current in an RC-coupled amplifier stage. In Fig. 41 it is assumed that the input pulse to V_1 is negative and of sufficient amplitude to cause the plate swing of V_1 to be limited by the grid current of V_2. The input resistance of V_2 is low when its grid is conducting and in most cases negligible in comparison with R_L. When this is true, the coupling capacitor charges with a time constant of $R_L C$ sec. Upon the recovery of the input pulse, the grid of V_2 no longer conducts, and C must discharge with a time constant of $(R_L + R_g)C$ sec. The ratio of recovery time to pulse duration is evidently $(R_L + R_g)/R_L$. In early amplifier designs R_g was usually 10 to 40 times greater than R_L.

The simplest way of reducing the effect is by reducing R_g to a value comparable with that of R_L.[54] (The size of the coupling capacitor must then be increased to maintain the $(R_L + R_g)C$ product at its original value).

Pulse shaping by double clipping also reduces blocking by providing a pulse of opposite polarity to hasten recovery.

In a third method of blocking reduction, the coupling capacitor is eliminated by the use of d-c coupling between stages.[55,56,57] Because of

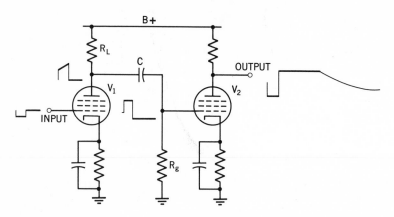

Fig. 41.   Waveforms in an RC-coupled amplifier under overload conditions.

the normal drifts in vacuum tubes, this technique is practical only if over-all d-c feedback is used to stabilize the operating points of the tubes.

A fourth method of blocking reduction prevents the flow of grid current, either by limiting the amplitude of positive pulses or by providing circuits that can accept them without going into the positive-grid region. A clamp circuit for limiting the amplitude of positive pulses is shown in Fig. 42. The diode-biasing arrangement keeps the diode nonconducting for small-signal swings but limits the positive-pulse amplitude to a value equal to the sum of the voltage drops across R_1 and r, where r is the forward conduction resistance of the diode. The resistor R_1 is connected to the plate of V_1 rather than to ground to make the bias voltage relatively independent of the d-c plate voltage of V_1. It is usual to make R_1 approximately 10 times larger than R_L, and it is necessary that the $R_L C$ product be large compared with the width of the input pulse. At high counting rates charging effects in C cause a shift in clamping level.

Another circuit for the prevention of grid current is shown in Fig. 43. The tubes V_2 and V_3 are connected as a "long-tailed pair" (cathode-coupled amplifier).[58] For small-signal swings the resistance seen by the cathode of V_2 is essentially that of the internal resistance of V_3, namely, $1/g_m$ ohms, where g_m is the transconductance of V_3 in mhos. For large positive signals V_3 is cut off, and the cathode resistance seen by V_2 is the very much larger value R_k. By a judicious choice of operating conditions, it becomes possible for V_2 to absorb 100-volt positive pulses without drawing grid current.

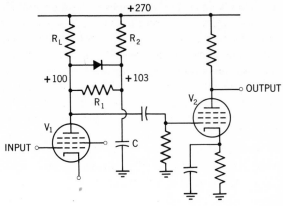

Fig. 42.   Pulse-limiting circuit.

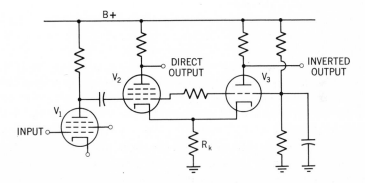

Fig. 43.   Long-tailed pair.

To avoid the wasteful IR-drop in R_k, it may be desirable to replace all or part of it with an inductor. If V is the voltage swing seen by the inductor L during an overload pulse and if T is the width of the pulse, then the size of L should be such that the current change (VT/L) will be small compared with the quiescent current.

Unless double clipping is used, the inductor makes the circuit subject to duty-cycle shifts.

L. Amplifier Noise. General Considerations

Amplifier noise affects the accuracy of measurement of low-level signals. The effects of the noise interference depend upon the nature of the measurement being made. If the amplifier is part of a simple counter, the noise introduces spurious counts, and the lowest level of detectable signal is approximately equal to the noise level. If the amplifier is part of a spectrometer, the situation is different in that noise signals are not counted directly but are observed as a broadening influence on spectral lines. If the spectral line under consideration has a Gaussian pulse-height distribution with a standard deviation of σ_1 volts and the amplifier noise also has a Gaussian pulse-height distribution with a root-mean-square (rms) amplitude level of σ_2 volts, then the measured spectral line width will exhibit a standard deviation equal to the quadratic sum of these components $(\sigma_1{}^2 + \sigma_2{}^2)^{1/2}$. For the line to be broadened by not more than 10% the rms noise level must be less than half as great as the standard deviation of the line. In the case of α-particle spectra, σ_1 may be only 1% of the average pulse height; this would require the pulse-height level to be approximately 200 times greater than the rms noise level if no appreciable line broadening is to occur. Evidently spectral measurements impose a much severer requirement on the noise level of amplifiers than do simple counting measurements.

Noise can be a result of poor engineering or construction, or it can be a result of the fundamental properties of electron flow in resistors and vacuum tubes.

In the first category, contributing causes can be faulty circuit components, hum, microphonics, and electromagnetic and electrostatic pickup from sources external to the measuring equipment.

In the second category are the noise sources arising from the thermal motion of electrons in the detector load resistor and the noise arising in the input tube due to grid current, flicker effect, and shot effect. One or more of the last three components nearly always determine the lowest noise level that can be obtained from an amplifier.

M. Noise Reduction Techniques. Removable Noise

1. Hum. Hum can be eliminated by using a d-c supply for heater circuits, by using well-filtered d-c plate supplies, and by physical isolation from a-c magnetic fields. Constant-voltage transformers have high leakage fields and care should be taken to isolate them from input circuits.

With care in wiring, it is possible to use an a-c heater supply and still maintain a low hum level. The least possible hum pickup is attained when the heater circuit is connected as shown in Fig. 44. Note in particular that the wiring to the first one or two stages is shielded, that the electrical mid-point of the filament supply is connected to a point 20 to 50 volts different from the cathode potential (either positive or negative), and that the mid-point is well bypassed to ground. Additional bypassing from either

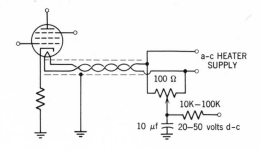

Fig. 44.   A-c heater connections for minimum hum pickup.

side of the filament supply to ground should not be used because the action of this bypassing conflicts with that of the hum balance control.

The wiring to the input tube should be as shown in Fig. 45. The aim here is to reduce the a-c induction field to a minimum, which can be accomplished by minimizing the area enclosed by the heater forward and return circuits. In particular, heater wiring should cross rather than surround a tube socket. The grid resistor, cathode resistor, and cathode bypass capacitor should be grounded at a common point, preferably at the input connector. The use of a grounding bus common to several stages is not recommended, since its use may lead to unwanted interstage coupling.

Depending upon the gain and low-frequency cutoff of the amplifier, the wiring may be successively simplified to a system in which the mid-point of the heater supply is grounded, to one in which one side is grounded, and finally, to one in which one of the heater wires is replaced by a chassis-return system.

2. Microphonics. Microphonic noise arises in tubes and signal-carrying wires as a result of mechanical vibration. Ruggedized tubes were designed to minimize this effect and should be used wherever necessary. Shock mounting can be used in severe cases. The resonant frequency of a shock-mounted component should be made as low as possible by using a compliant support and by weighting the component. When the input tube in a preamplifier is the offender, the tube should be rigidly fastened to the detector and the whole system shock mounted, since relative motion between the input tube and the detector will usually generate a spurious signal.

3. External pickup. Noise pickup from sources external to the measuring equipment can be minimized by proper shielding and by avoiding multiple grounds. In noisy locations it is necessary to use double-shielded cable between the preamplifier and main amplifier.

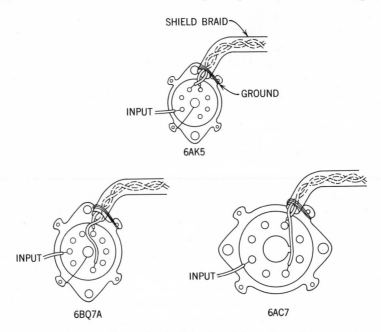

Fig. 45. Heater circuit wiring for minimum hum pickup.

The outer shield should be grounded at the outside surface of the chassis at the point of entry rather than at the inside. Multiple grounds should be avoided because of the possibility that potential differences may exist between them. Noise currents flowing between ground points in a cable shield induce voltages in the signal-carrying leads within the shield. Ideally, the system should be grounded at one point only, usually the preamplifier. When many instruments are used in a measuring system, a single ground is rarely possible, and the best grounding arrangement must be determined by trial and error. A common source of trouble is the ground loop inherent in a system (such as that of Fig. 21) in which the high-voltage supply to the radiation detector is separate from the amplifier supply. In cases of severe noise pickup, the use of electrostatically shielded isolation transformers may be necessary.

N. Noise Reduction Techniques. Irremovable Noise

Current flow consists of the movement of charged particles. This movement exhibits statistical fluctuations about a mean value,[59] and these fluctuations constitute a noise signal that can be minimized by the choice of operating conditions, but which can never be completely eliminated.

To consider amplifier noise independently of the input signal is of little value. The parameter of interest is the signal-to-noise ratio (S/N), a dimensionless number which may be expressed for present purposes as the ratio of *peak* signal volts (or charge) to *rms* noise in volts (or charge). The importance of considering S/N rather than noise alone stems from the fact that the networks that control the amplifier's bandwidth control the signal and noise levels to differing degrees. In the usual case a shaping network that minimizes the noise level of an amplifier does not maximize the desired peak signal.

After a set of shaping networks has been selected for an amplifier, it is expedient to discuss amplifier noise in terms of equivalent noise charge. *The equivalent noise charge is that quantity of charge which if deposited on the input terminal of the amplifier in a time short compared with the response time of the amplifier would produce an output pulse of peak amplitude just equal to the rms noise level.* This definition is desirable because (1) it includes the concept of S/N ratio and (2) because the unit of charge is consistent with the nature of the detector signal. The latter point is of particular importance because the size of a detector pulse in terms of charge can be computed in advance of an experiment from a knowledge of the energy loss of the incoming particle (or ray) in the detector and the energy required to produce an ion pair in the active region of the counting volume. If the equivalent noise charge is known as well, it is a relatively simple matter to predict such factors as the optimum level at which to set the discriminator bias in a counting experiment, the background noise counts that will result from the setting, and the effect of the noise level on the line width in a spectral measurement.

Traditionally, noise equations have been derived in terms of mean-squared currents or voltages and this practice will be continued here. At any point in the discussion the reader may convert to mean-squared noise charge by multiplying the equation for mean-squared noise voltage by $C_1{}^2$, where C_1 is the total amplifier input capacitance (with detector connected) *measured with the power removed from the amplifier.*

In computing the S/N ratio existing at the output of an amplifier, it is necessary to know (1) the signal waveform, (2) the spectral density of each of the noise sources, and (3) the transfer function of the amplifier. In principle, it makes no difference whether the computation is carried out in the time domain or in the frequency domain. In practice, the computation proceeds best if the signal waveform is described as a function of time and the noise sources are described as functions of frequency.

At the output of the amplifier the signal voltage appears in the form

$$v_0(t) = \mathscr{L}^{-1}V_i(p)F(p), \tag{40}$$

where $v_0(t)$ = output signal (in volts) expressed as a function of time,
  $V_i(p)$ = Laplace transform[60] of the desired signal at the amplifier input,
  $F(p)$ = Laplace transform of the transfer function of the amplifier,
  $\mathscr{L}^{-1}$ = inverse of the Laplace transform.

The peak signal can be found analytically as that value of $v_0(t)$ for which dv_0/dt vanishes or from a point-by-point evaluation of $v_0(t)$.

Most of the irremovable noise appearing at the output of the amplifier arises from four sources: (1) the chamber load resistor (thermal agitation noise[61,62]), (2) grid current in the first tube (grid-current noise[8]), (3) statistical fluctuations in plate current of the first tube (shot noise[63,64]), and (4) random changes in cathode emission of the first tube (flicker noise[65]). The noise signals are assumed to have normal amplitude distributions and to be independent of each other. These characteristics permit their mean-squared (ms) values to be added arithmetically. Since the noise voltages are random in character, each has an infinite frequency distribution. For analytical purposes, each of the noise voltages is expressed in the form of a ms noise voltage per unit bandwidth, $d\bar{v}^2/df$. The total rms noise voltage appearing at the output of an amplifier is

$$v_{0(\text{rms})} = \left[\sum_{k=0}^{n} \frac{1}{2\pi} \int_0^{\infty} \bar{v}_k^2 |g(\omega)|^2 \, d\omega \right]^{\frac{1}{2}}, \tag{41}$$

where $v_{0(\text{rms})}$ = the total noise signal in rms volts,
  $\bar{v}_k^2$ = one of the n noise components in ms volts per cycle per second,
  $g(\omega)$ = the transfer characteristic of the amplifier as a function of ω,
  $\omega = 2\pi f$, where f = cycles per second.

The constant $1/2\pi$ converts ms volts per cycle per second to ms volts per radian per second.

In the following sections the computations for a typical case are carried through. For a more extensive treatment of amplifier noise and related problems the reader is referred to the excellent monograph by Gillespie.[48]

I. Equivalent circuits. In considering tube and resistor noise, it is convenient to think of the pulse-forming parts of the amplifier as being completely separate from the amplifying parts. This concept is illustrated in Fig. 46, in which all of the pulse-forming parts are contained in the box labeled $F(p)$ and the amplifying parts are contained in the triangles. The amplifying parts are assumed to generate no noise and to have infinite input and zero output impedance. Except for the input tube, which is considered later, the amplifying parts are assumed to contribute nothing to the S/N ratio and serve only to isolate the various pulse-forming networks.

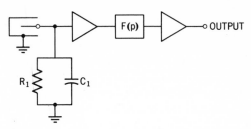

Fig. 46.   Equivalent circuit of a pulse amplifier.

The network $R_1 C_1$ in Fig. 46 represents the equivalent circuit of the detector, its load, and the input impedance of the first tube in the amplifier. The input signal can be approximated as either a voltage step of Q/C_1 volts introduced in series with C_1 or as a charge-step of Q coulombs applied across the terminals of C_1. This approximation is valid as long as the rise-time of the step is short compared with the rise-time of the amplifier. When this is not the case, a closer approximation results from the assumption that the step has a finite rate of rise, linear in the case of an ion chamber or exponential in the case of a scintillation detector. These waveforms and their Laplace transforms are illustrated in Fig. 47.

The waveform of Fig. 47a is assumed in the example. An RC clipping circuit is used, and it is assumed that the high-frequency response of the amplifier is controlled by a single RC circuit. It can be shown that the best S/N ratio exists when the time constants of the clipping and low-pass sections are equal, and this condition is assumed as well. With these conditions, the equivalent circuit shown in Fig. 48 applies to the problem.

The signal appearing at the amplifier input terminal is

$$V_1(p) = \frac{Q}{C_1} \frac{1}{p} \frac{p}{(p + 1/T_1)} \tag{42}$$

$$v_1(t) = \frac{Q}{C_1} e^{-t/T_1}, \tag{42'}$$

where $T_1 = R_1 C_1$.

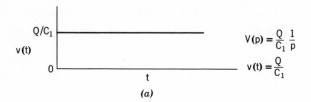

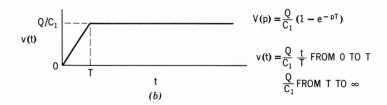

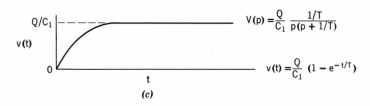

Fig. 47.   Radiation detector waveforms.

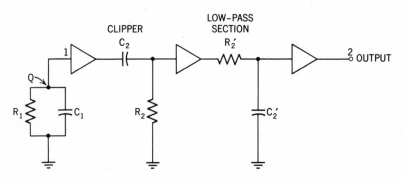

Fig. 48.   Pulse amplifier equivalent circuit.

The transfer function of the amplifier is

$$F(p) = \frac{p}{T_2(p + 1/T_2)^2},$$ (43)

where $T_2 = R_2C_2 = R_2'C_2'$.

The output signal is

$$V_2(p) = \frac{Q}{C_1} \frac{p}{T_2(p + 1/T_1)(p + 1/T_2)^2}$$ (44)

$$v_2(t) = \frac{Q}{C_1} \frac{T_1/T_2}{(t_1/T_2 - 1)^2} \left\{ e^{-t/T_2} \left[1 + \frac{1}{T_2}\left(\frac{T_1}{T_2} - 1\right)t \right] - e^{-t/T_1} \right\}.$$ (44')

In general, the peak value of this signal cannot be explicitly determined, but as T_1/T_2 varies between 1 and ∞ the peak signal varies between $0.231Q/C_1$ and $0.368Q/C_1$.

2. Thermal noise. The random motion of free electrons in the detector load resistor[61,62] R_1 gives rise to a noise voltage of constant spectral density whose ms amplitude is

$$\frac{d\bar{v}_t^2}{df} = 4kT_eR_1,$$ (45)

where $\bar{v}_t^2$ = mean-square thermal noise in (volts)^2,

f = frequency in cycles per second,

k = Boltzmann's constant, 1.37×10^{-23} joule/$^\circ$ K,

T_e = absolute temperature in $^\circ$ K,

R_1 = resistance in ohms.

For computational purposes it is valid to assume that all of the noise is produced by a generator connected in series with the load resistor, which itself is noiseless. The transfer function of the input circuit connected as described is

$$F_t(p) = \frac{1}{1 + pT_1}$$ (46)

$$g_t(\omega) = \frac{1}{1 + j\omega T_1}$$ (46')

$$|g_t(\omega)|^2 = \frac{1}{1 + (\omega T_1)^2},$$ (46'')

where $F_t(p)$ = transfer characteristic, expressed in operational form, of the input circuit,

$g_t(\omega)$ = transfer characteristic, as a function of ω, of the input circuit,

$T_1 = R_1C_1$ in ohms $\times$ farads,

$\omega = 2\pi f$ cps.

The ms amplitude of the spectral density of the noise voltage appearing at the input of the amplifier is the product of (45) and (46″), or

$$\frac{d\bar{v}_t^2}{df} = \frac{4kT_eR_1}{1 + (\omega T_1)^2} .$$ (47)

Equation 47 can be integrated to give the total noise voltage seen by the amplifier input:

$$\bar{v}_t^2 = \frac{2kT_eR_1}{\pi} \int_0^\infty \frac{d\omega}{1 + (\omega T_1)^2} ,$$ (48)

$$= \frac{kT_e}{C_1}$$ (48′)

where $d\omega = 2\pi \, df$.

It is evident that the total noise depends only on the capacitance of the input circuit and not on the value of the load resistance.

Equation 48′ is useful because it gives the upper limit of the thermal noise which can exist at the input of the amplifier. If an input capacity of 20 pf and a temperature of 290° K are assumed, then (48′) gives an rms voltage of approximately 14 μv. Because of the finite amplifier bandwidth, the effective rms thermal noise will always be less than $(kT_e/C_1)^{1/2}$ and can be computed from

$$\bar{v}_t^2 = \frac{2kT_eR_1}{\pi} \int_0^\infty \frac{|g(\omega)|^2 \, d\omega}{1 + (\omega T_1)^2}$$ (49)

where $g(\omega)$ = the transfer characteristic of the pulse-shaping networks in the amplifier, excluding the input circuit.

For the amplifier shown in Fig. 48 the transfer function given in (43) becomes, when expressed in the frequency domain,

$$g_1(\omega) = \frac{j\omega}{(1 + j\omega T_2)^2}$$ (50)

the square of whose absolute value is

$$|g_1(\omega)|^2 = \frac{\omega^2}{[1 + (\omega T_2)^2]^2} .$$ (50′)

Substituting (50′) in (49) and integrating gives the result

$$\bar{v}_t^2 = \frac{kT_eR_1}{2} \frac{T_2}{(T_1 + T_2)^2} .$$ (51)

3. Shot noise. The random variations in mean plate current of a triode give rise to a signal known as shot noise.[63,64] The spectral density of this noise voltage for receiving tubes, referred to the input, is

$$\frac{d\bar{v}_s^2}{df} = \frac{0.24e}{g_m},$$ (52)

where $\bar{v}_s^2$ = ms shot noise in (volts)^2,
  e = the electronic charge, 1.6×10^{-19} coulomb.
  g_m = grid-to-plate transconductance in amperes per volt,

which, by a rearrangement of constants, can be written

$$\frac{d\bar{v}_s^2}{df} = 4kT_e\frac{2.5}{g_m},$$ (53)

where T_e is assumed to be 290°.

Equation 53 states that the shot noise generated in a tube produces the same disturbance in an amplifier as would the thermal noise generated in a resistor of magnitude $2.5/g_m$ ohms and temperature 290° K placed in series with the grid of a noiseless tube having zero input capacitance. It is this value of resistance that is usually referred to as the equivalent noise resistance. Since the electron stream of the tube generates the noise, its amplitude and spectral distribution are independent of the electrical network to which the grid is connected.

The shot noise of a pentode is higher than that of a triode, partly because the presence of the screen grid reduces the transconductance by robbing the plate of a fraction of the cathode current and partly because this division of current is itself subject to random fluctuations. The latter contribution to the excess noise is known as partition noise. For a pentode (53) becomes

$$\frac{d\bar{v}_s^2}{df} = 4kT_e\left(\frac{2.5}{g_{m(\text{pent})}}\frac{I_p}{I_k}\right)\left(1 + 8\frac{I_{c(2)}}{g_{m(\text{pent})}}\right)$$ (54)

$$= 4kT_eR_{eq},$$ (54')

where g_m = grid-to-plate transconductance in amperes per volt,
  I_p = plate current in amperes,
  I_k = cathode current in amperes,
  $I_{c(2)}$ = screen current in amperes,
  R_{eq} = equivalent noise resistance in ohms.

The term in the first bracket represents the equivalent noise resistance that the tube would have if it were triode-connected, and the term in the second bracket represents the excess-noise factor due to pentode operation.

Equation 54 can also be written in the form

$$\frac{d\bar{v}_s^2}{df} = 4kT_eR_{eq(\text{tri})}\left(1 + 3.2\,R_{eq(\text{tri})}\frac{I_{c(2)}}{I_p}\,I_k\right),\qquad (54'')$$

where $R_{eq(\text{tri})}$ = the equivalent noise resistance of the tube triode-connected.

The noise appearing at the output terminals of the amplifier is affected by the shaping networks in accordance with the equation

$$\bar{v}_s^2 = \frac{2kT_eR_{eq}}{\pi}\int_0^\infty \frac{(\omega T_2)^2\,d\omega}{[1 + (\omega T_2)^2]^2}\qquad (55)$$

$$= \frac{kT_eR_{eq}}{2T_2}.\qquad (55')$$

As in the case of thermal noise, the condition $T_1 = T_2$ is of interest.

If the input time constant is made equal to the two time constants that ordinarily shape the signal, no change in the shot-noise level will be observed because, as stated earlier, the input circuit configuration cannot affect the shot-noise level. If the input network is used as a pulse shaper in place of the clipping network ordinarily used, the shot noise must increase because the clipping circuit is no longer available to limit the low-frequency response of the amplifier. The ms noise level becomes

$$\bar{v}_s^2 = \frac{2kT_eR_{eq}}{\pi}\int_0^\infty \frac{d\omega}{1 + (\omega T_2)^2}\qquad (56)$$

$$= \frac{kT_eR_{eq}}{T_2}.\qquad (56')$$

4. Grid-current noise. The important sources of grid current in input tubes commonly used for pulse amplifiers are the same as those encountered in electrometer tubes. (See p. 203.)

The grid current flowing through the input circuit gives rise to a signal at the grid whose spectral density is

$$\frac{d\bar{v}_g^2}{df} = 2e(\Sigma\,I_g)\frac{R_1^2}{1 + \omega^2 T_1^2},\qquad (57)$$

where $\bar{v}_g^2$ = ms grid-current noise in (volts)^2,

ΣI_g = the arithmetic sum of the grid-current components in amperes.

The ms voltage appearing at the amplifier output is

$$\bar{v}_g{}^2 = \frac{e(\Sigma I_g)R_1{}^2}{\pi} \int_0^\infty \frac{\omega^2 T_2{}^2 \, d\omega}{(1 + \omega^2 T_1{}^2)(1 + \omega^2 T_2{}^2)^2} \tag{58}$$

$$= \frac{e(\Sigma I_g)R_1{}^2}{4} \frac{T_2}{(T_1 + T_2)^2}. \tag{58'}$$

If $T_1 \gg T_2$, (58') reduces to

$$\bar{v}_g{}^2 = \frac{e(\Sigma I_g)T_2}{4C_1{}^2}. \tag{59}$$

If $T_1 = T_2$, (58') becomes

$$\bar{v}_g{}^2 = \frac{e(\Sigma I_g)T_2}{16C_1{}^2}. \tag{60}$$

If T_1 is used instead of the normally used clipping network, the grid-current noise is

$$\bar{v}_g{}^2 = \frac{e(\Sigma I_g)T_2}{4C_1{}^2}. \tag{61}$$

5. Choice of R_1. At this point the effects of R_1 on thermal noise, grid-current noise, and output pulse shape have been established, making it possible to choose the optimum value of R_1.

If $T_1 \geq T_2$, the value of R_1 which makes the thermal noise equal to the grid-current noise is, from (51) and (58'),

$$R_1 = \frac{2kT_e}{e(\Sigma I_g)} = \frac{5 \times 10^{-2}}{\Sigma I_g} \text{ ohm} \tag{62}$$

at $T_e = 290°$ K.

If R_1 is made 10 times larger than this critical value the rms thermal noise becomes negligible (0.01 times as great) by comparison with the grid-current noise.

Separate from the noise consideration is the effect of R_1 on the pulse shape. If a singly clipped pulse with a small undershoot is desired, it is necessary that

$$R_1 \gg T_2/C_1. \tag{63}$$

The upper limit on the value of R_1 is usually determined by the permissible pile-up at the input grid. However, grid-current flow in the grid-leak resistor may be the limiting factor, since the current flow causes a bias shift V of magnitude:

$$V = (I_{g^-} + I_{g^+})R_{gl}, \tag{64}$$

where V is in volts,

$I_{g^-} + I_{g^+}$ = algebraic sum of grid-current components,

$\quad R_{gl}$ = grid-leak resistance in ohms.

The effect of this bias shift on the operating point of the input tube must be considered in the circuit design.

When double clipping is used, it may be desirable to make R_1 part of the first clipper. The consequences of this arrangement are that (1) the thermal noise level is at its maximum possible value, being equal to

$$v_{t(\max)}^2 = \frac{kT_e}{8C_1} ; \tag{65}$$

(2) the undershoot is at its maximum possible value, being equal to 0.135 of the primary pulse height, and (3) the primary pulse height is approximately halved compared with the case in which $T_1 \gg T_2$. The desirable features of this arrangement are (1) pulse pile-up is held to its lowest possible value and (2) base-line shifts are minimized. The rms thermal noise, although at its highest value, may still be acceptable, being only 5 μv for a 20-pf input capacitance.

When the detector load circuit is used for pulse shaping, it is necessary to ensure that the R_1C_1 product remain constant with changes in detectors or connecting cables.

It is of passing interest to note that half of the thermal noise appearing at the input of the amplifier exists in the region below $\omega = 1/T_1$ and half above. In the region $\omega \ll 1/T_1$ the ms spectral noise density is proportional to R_1 and independent of frequency. In the region $\omega \gg 1/T_1$, the ms spectral noise density is inversely proportional to R_1 and inversely proportional to ω^2.

6. Flicker noise. The modulation of the cathode current by sudden changes in potential drop across the boundary layer of an oxide-coated cathode gives rise to a form of noise known as flicker noise.[65] The fundamental reasons for the potential variations are not well understood, but the characteristics of the resulting noise are. It is known that the flicker noise referred to the grid is nearly the same for all tube types;* it is independent of the grid circuit used and is nearly independent of the plate current as long as the tube is operated under space-charge limited conditions. The spectral density of the ms noise voltage referred to the grid is inversely proportional to the frequency in the range from well below 1 cps to 50 kc and has the value

$$\frac{d\bar{v}_f^2}{df} = \frac{10^{-13}}{f} , \tag{66}$$

where $\bar{v}_f^2 =$ ms flicker noise in (volts)^2.

---

* Tubes with small grid-to-cathode spacing have a slightly lower flicker noise than those with large grid-to-cathode spacing.

When operated on by the shaping networks, the output noise voltage becomes

$$\bar{v}_f^2 = 10^{-13} \int_0^\infty \frac{\omega T_2^2 \, d\omega}{(1 + \omega^2 T_2^2)^2} \tag{67}$$

$$= 0.5 \times 10^{-13} \, (\text{volt})^2,$$

whose rms value is 0.22 μv. The level does not change when $T_1 = T_2$.

O. Optimization of the Signal-to-Noise Ratio

The dependence of the S/N ratio on the parameters affecting it can be written in the form

$$\text{S/N} \propto \frac{v_{\text{max}(t)}}{(\bar{v}_t^2 + \bar{v}_f^2 + \bar{v}_s^2 + \bar{v}_g^2)^{1/2}}, \tag{68}$$

where $v_{\text{max}(t)}$ = the peak response of the shaping networks to the desired input signal in volts,

$\bar{v}_t^2$ = ms thermal noise in (volts)^2,

$\bar{v}_f^2$ = ms flicker noise in (volts)^2,

$\bar{v}_s^2$ = ms shot noise in (volts)^2,

$\bar{v}_g^2$ = ms grid-current noise in (volts)^2.

It has been shown that $\bar{v}_t^2$ can be reduced to negligibility by choosing a sufficiently high-valued detector load resistance. It has also been stated that the flicker noise is independent of the operating conditions of the input tube. If the amplifier shaping network is known, the amplifier transfer function can be established. The problem of optimizing the S/N ratio then becomes one of minimizing the sum of the shot and grid-current noise components, which are dependent upon the circuit used for the input tube, the tube type used in the circuit, and the operating conditions of the tube.

Certain of the properties of shot noise and grid-current noise are common to all types of tubes and circuits. In particular, the transconductance of a tube is proportional to its plate (and cathode) current, thereby resulting in an inverse relationship between the shot noise and the cathode current. Also, the grid current is proportional to the cathode current. Evidently it is possible to reduce the shot noise at the expense of grid-current noise and vice-versa. The ms shot noise can be expressed as

$$\bar{v}_s^2 = k_1 I_k^{-m} \tag{69}$$

and the grid-current noise as

$$\bar{v}_g^2 = k_2 I_k^n, \tag{70}$$

where k_1 and k_2 denote constants of proportionality, I_k is the cathode current, and m and n are exponents in the range 0 to 2.

If (69) and (70) are substituted in (68), it can be shown that the best S/N ratio occurs when

$$\frac{\bar{v}_g{}^2}{\bar{v}_s{}^2} = \frac{m}{n}. \tag{71}$$

For a given set of shaping networks, then, the best S/N ratio is obtained by adjusting the operating parameters of the input tube to meet the condition stated in (71).

Measurements on many tubes show that if the tube is triode-connected and if the plate voltage is adjusted to the lowest value that permits a grid bias more negative than the floating-grid potential at a given cathode current then m and n have values of approximately 0.85 and 1.1, respectively, at a cathode current of 1 ma or less. As the cathode current is increased to 10 ma, m drops to 0.5 or less, whereas n increases to 2. If the tube is pentode-connected, m has a value of approximately 0.7 at a cathode current of 1 ma, decreasing towards zero as the cathode current is increased. In some tubes a current of 10 ma results in a negative value for m. The value of n is not affected by the change in tube connections.

It can also be shown that the cathode current which results in the highest S/N ratio is inversely proportional to the rise and clipping times of the amplifier. When the time constant controlling the rise or clipping time is 3 μsec or more, the required cathode current is usually less than 10 ma. When the time constant is less than 3 μsec, the required cathode current may exceed the capabilities of the input tube, in which case the shot noise will limit the attainable S/N ratio, the grid-current noise being negligible by comparison.

The following section covers in greater detail the grid-current and shot-noise properties of receiving tubes available in 1959.

P.   Grid-Current Noise in Receiving Tubes

In Fig. 49 the grid-current versus cathode-current characteristics of a triode-connected 6AJ5 (selected for low grid current and operated at a grid bias more negative than the floating-grid potential) are shown for several values of grid-to-plate voltage and two values of heater voltage. The shape of the curves is typical of receiving tubes. The following three points should be noted:

(a) The grid current is directly proportional to the cathode current over a wide range of cathode currents. At very low values of cathode current this direct proportionality may be destroyed by the masking effect of positive ions released by the cathode, by thermionic emission from the grid, or by photoemission, but can usually be restored by reducing the cathode temperature and shielding the tube from external light.

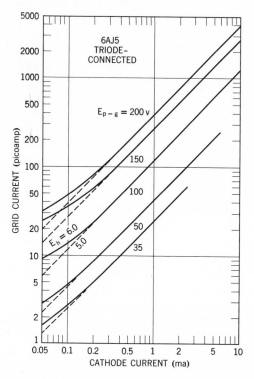

Fig. 49.   Grid current versus cathode current of a triode-connected 6AJ5.

(*b*) At high values of cathode current the direct proportionality displayed in the graph may be destroyed by the electron component of the grid current. (This effect is not shown in Fig. 49.)

(*c*) At a given cathode current the grid current is proportional to the $\frac{3}{2}$-power of the grid-to-plate (screen) voltage in the range of voltages commonly used for the input tube of a pulse amplifier.

The art of tube construction has advanced to the point that grid current is determined not by residual gas in the tubes,* as it was only a few years ago,[66] but by photoelectric emission from the grid. The photoelectrons are produced by soft x rays generated at the screen grid and plate

* This is true as long as the tubes are operated at less than three fourths of rated plate dissipation. Above this level outgassing of the tube parts becomes significant.

as a result of bombardment by cathode-emitted electrons. Since the difference in geometry and materials of construction between various tube types is not very great, it is not surprising to find that all small tubes exhibit approximately the same grid current when operated at a given current and voltage.[67] This fact is demonstrated in the histogram of Fig.

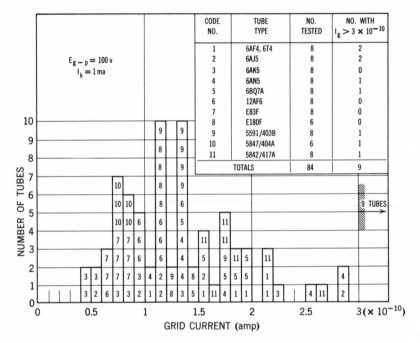

CODE NO.	TUBE TYPE	NO. TESTED	NO. WITH $I_g > 3 \times 10^{-10}$
1	6AF4, 6T4	8	2
2	6AJ5	8	2
3	6AK5	8	0
4	6AN5	8	1
5	6BQ7A	8	1
6	12AF6	8	0
7	E83F	8	0
8	E180F	6	0
9	5591/403B	8	1
10	5847/404A	6	1
11	5842/417A	8	1
TOTALS		84	9

Fig. 50. Grid-current spectrum of several tube types.

50, which gives numbers of tubes exhibiting a particular grid current as a function of grid current. Each of the 84 tubes tested was first aged for 24 hr at 150 volts plate voltage and 10-ma cathode current. The tubes were tested as triodes, with a grid-to-plate potential difference of 100 volts and a cathode current of 1 ma. On the basis of this and other tests, it is reasonable to expect that 75% of a randomly selected group of tubes will exhibit grid currents that are within a factor or two of

$$I_g = E_{g-p}^{3/2} I_k \times 10^{-10} \text{ amp,} \qquad (72)$$

where I_g = grid current in amperes,
      E_{g-p} = grid-to-plate voltage in volts,
      I_k = cathode current in amperes,

if (1) the grid bias is at least 0.5 volt more negative than the floating-grid potential, (2) the positively biased elements in multigrid tubes are all at the same voltage, (3) the control-grid temperature is low enough so that the grid does not emit electrons thermionically (this effect is important only in high figure-of-merit tubes with very close grid-to-cathode spacing), (4) the tube is operated at less than three fourths of rated plate dissipation, and (5) the tube is shielded from external light (at grid currents of less than 10^{-10} amp).

Q. Selection of Tubes and Operating Conditions. General Considerations

The curves of Fig. 49 show that if low grid current is important it is necessary to operate at a plate (screen) voltage as low as possible. For a triode

$$I_k = G(E_p + \mu E_g)^{3/2}, \tag{73}$$

where I_k = cathode current in amperes,

G = perveance in units of amperes per (volt)$^{3/2}$,

E_p = plate-to-cathode voltage in volts,

μ = amplification factor,

E_g = grid-to-cathode voltage in volts.

If a negative bias of 1 volt is assumed (which is close to the floating-grid potential), then (73) can be rearranged in the form

$$E_p = \left(\frac{I_k}{G}\right)^{2/3} + \mu. \tag{74}$$

Because of the dependence of grid current on plate voltage, it is evident from (74) that the most desirable tube types from the standpoint of grid current are those that combine low μ and high perveance. Since G is also a measure of transconductance, a tube with high perveance will also exhibit low shot noise.

The exact value of grid bias to be used has an important bearing on circuit performance. The floating-grid potential is the lowest bias value practical for input tube use and has two features to recommend it: (1) the bias value can be easily obtained by floating the grid and (2) the accompanying low plate (screen) voltage results in low grid current. The bad feature is that because of the electron current component the total grid current is nearly twice that obtainable by operating at a slightly more negative bias. In the sections that follow, the standard operating point for low-noise input stages is considered to be at a bias 0.5 volt more negative than the floating-grid potential.

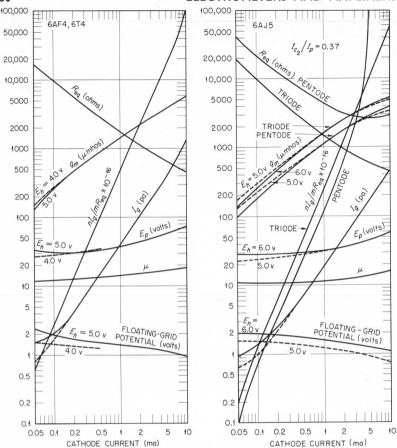

Fig. 51a.   Tube characteristics.   Types 6AF4, 6T4, and 6AJ5.

R. Practical Operating Conditions

Figure 51 provides the information necessary to determine the operating conditions resulting in the best S/N ratio for several tube types that are likely to be used as input tubes.

Each tube was the best of a randomly selected batch of eight, the criterion for selection being the ratio of g_m to I_g at a cathode current of 1 ma and a plate-to-grid potential of 100 volts. The tubes were triode-connected for this test.

It should be stressed that these are not graphs of average performance. Although there is no assurance that other batches of eight will yield tubes whose performance is as good as those shown, it is not unlikely

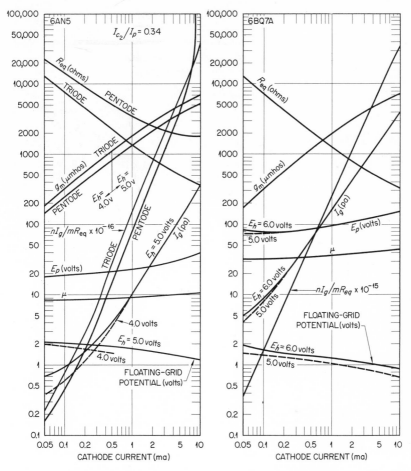

Fig. 51*b*.   Tube characteristics.   Types 6AN5 and 6BQ7A.

that even better tubes can be found if selection is made from larger batches.

In general, parameters were measured at two heater voltages, as indicated on the graphs.   All curves were obtained from actual measurements except for the nI_g/mR_{eq} curves, which were computed from the measured parameters.   In both cases the computation was based on the heater voltage that resulted in the least total noise voltage.

Measurements were made at a bias level 0.50 volt more negative than the floating-grid potential.   If the tube is operated at the floating-grid potential, the E_p, I_g, and nI_g/mR_{eq} figures will change but not the μ, g_m,

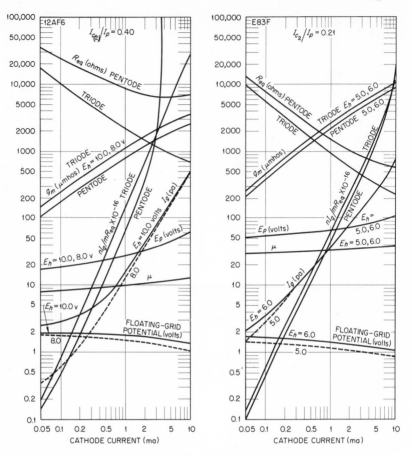

Fig. 51c. Tube characteristics. Types 12AF6 and E83F.

or R_{eq} figures. At a given I_k, the I_g value (taking into consideration the doubling effect due to the electron-current contribution) can be computed from

$$I_{g(\text{fgp})} = 2\left(1 - \frac{\mu}{2E_p}\right)^{\!3/2} I_g, \tag{75}*$$

where $I_{g(\text{fgp})}$ = the grid current at the floating-grid potential,
μ = the amplification factor given by the curves,
E_p = the plate voltage given by the curves,
I_g = the grid current given by the curves.

* Formula (75) is derived from (72) and (73), pp. 278 and 279, respectively.

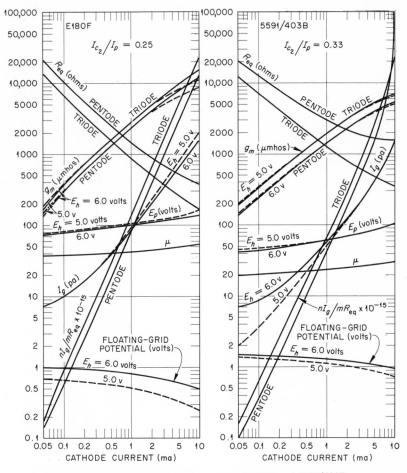

Fig. 51d. Tube characteristics. Types E180F and 5591/403B.

The following paragraphs explain the meaning of the nI_g/mR_{eq} curves. From (54′), p. 271, it follows that the ms shot noise is

$$\bar{v}_s^2 = R_{eq}\frac{2kT_e}{\pi}\int_0^\infty |g(\omega)|^2\,d\omega \tag{76}$$

and from (57) it follows that the ms grid-current noise is

$$\bar{v}_g^2 = (\Sigma I_g)\frac{eR_1^2}{\pi}\int_0^\infty \frac{|g(\omega)|^2\,d\omega}{(1 + \omega^2 T_1^2)}, \tag{77}$$

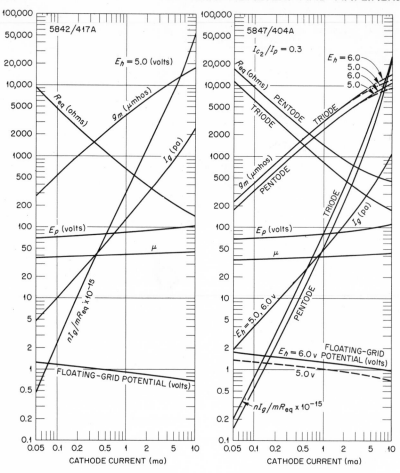

Fig. 51e.   Tube characteristics.   Types 5842/417A and 5847/404A.

where $g(\omega)=$ the transfer function of the shaping networks, not including
the input circuit,

$T_1=$ the input time constant,

$R_1=$ the input load resistance.

From (71), p. 276, it was shown that the best S/N results from the
condition

$$\frac{\bar{v}_g^{\,2}}{\bar{v}_s^{\,2}}=\frac{m}{n}\,,\tag{78}$$

where $m=$ the slope of the $\bar{v}_s^{\,2}$ versus I_k curve,*

$n=$ the slope of the $\bar{v}_g^{\,2}$ versus I_k curve.

* The quantity m is also the negative of the slope of the R_{eq} versus I_k curve.

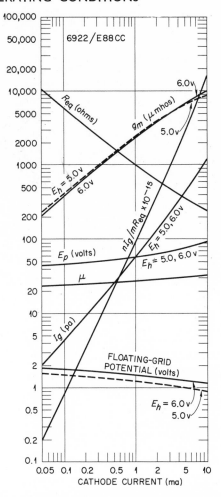

Fig. 51*f*. Tube characteristics. Type 6922/E88CC.

Combining (76), (77), and (78) gives the result

$$\frac{n \Sigma I_g}{m R_{eq}} = \frac{2kT_e}{eR_1^2} \frac{\displaystyle\int_0^\infty |g(\omega)|^2 \, d\omega}{\displaystyle\int_0^\infty \frac{|g(\omega)|^2 \, d\omega}{(1 + \omega^2 T_1^2)}} \cdot \tag{79}$$

The term on the left of the equation is a function of the operating conditions of the input tube and is given in Fig. 51. The term on the right is a function of the shaping network parameters. Equation 79 permits the designer to select the operating conditions of the input tube from a knowledge of the shaping networks. The following numerical example shows how the preceding design information can be used to compute the resolution of a spectrometer.

Suppose an amplifier is to be built for use in an alpha-particle spectrometer. An ionization chamber[68] with a capacitance of 15 pf and an electron collection time of approximately 3 μsec is to be used. Pulse shaping will be done by equal-valued RC clipping and integrating networks. To keep variations in collection time from having more than a

TABLE 5.   E83F PARAMETERS AT I_k = 2.35 ma AND 2.7 ma

	Triode	Pentode
I_k	2.35 ma	2.7 ma
E_h	6.0 volts	6.0 volts
E_p	77 volts	77 volts
E_{c1}	−1.81 volts	−1.79 volts
g_m	4.8 ma/volt	4.3 ma/volt
R_{eq}	520 ohms	880 ohms
I_g	102 pa	120 pa

0.5% effect on the pulse size,[48] the time constants of the shaping network will be made 10 μsec. An E83F (input capacity = 11 pf) is selected as the input tube.[69]

From (76) and (55′)

$$\int_0^\infty |g(\omega)|^2 \, d\omega = \frac{\pi}{4T_2}.$$ (80)

From (77) and (58′)

$$\int_0^\infty \frac{|g(\omega)|^2 \, d\omega}{(1 + \omega^2 T_1^2)} = \frac{\pi T_2}{4(T_1 + T_2)^2}.$$ (81)

With the condition that $T_1 \gg T_2$, the simultaneous solution of (79), (80), and (81) gives

$$\frac{nI_g}{mR_{eq}} = \frac{2kT_e}{e} \frac{C_1^2}{T_2^2} = 0.05 \frac{(15 + 11)^2 \times 10^{-24}}{10^{-10}}$$

$$= 338 \times 10^{-15}.$$

This value of nI_g/mR_{eq} results in a set of operating conditions for the E83F that is summarized in Table 5.

The ms shot noise is computed as 0.10 $(\mu v)^2$ and 0.18 $(\mu v)^2$ for triode and pentode operation, respectively, and the ms grid-current noise as 0.06 $(\mu v)^2$ and 0.07 $(\mu v)^2$. The flicker noise is 0.05 $(\mu v)^2$.

From (62) the critical value of the grid resistor R_1 is $(5 \times 10^{-2})/(102 \times 10^{-12})$ = 500 megohms. If R_1 is made 2000 megohms, the thermal noise will be negligible, the effect of the input network on the pulse height will be negligible, the effect on the pulse shape will produce a 4% undershoot, and, from (64), the effect on the operating point of the input tube will produce a 0.2-volt bias shift. Assuming that this value of R_1 is acceptable, the various noise voltages may be summed to give ms voltages of

$$\overline{v_s^2} \qquad \overline{v_g^2} \qquad \overline{v_f^2}$$

$$\overline{v_{n(\text{tri})}^2} = 0.10 + 0.06 + 0.05 = 0.21 \ (\mu v)^2 \tag{82}$$

$$\overline{v_{n(\text{pent})}^2} = 0.18 + 0.07 + 0.05 = 0.30 \ (\mu v)^2. \tag{82'}$$

The next step is to determine the signal voltage produced by the ion chamber.

If a gas ionization potential of 30 ev is assumed, a 5.0-Mev alpha-particle will produce 1.67×10^5 ion pairs. The peak signal produced at the output of the detector is

$$\frac{Q}{C_1} = \frac{Ne}{C_1} = \frac{1.67 \times 10^5 \times 1.6 \times 10^{-19}}{(15 + 11) \times 10^{-12}} = 1.03 \text{ mv} \tag{83}$$

where N is the number of ion pairs per pulse and e is the charge of the electron. The shaping networks attenuate the signal by the factor $e^{-1} = 0.37$, resulting in an effective peak signal of

$$V_0 = 0.37 \ Ne/C_1 = 0.38 \text{ mv}. \tag{84}$$

At this point the S/N ratio can be determined from (82), (82'), and (84). However, before the resolution can be computed, one more factor must be considered. This is the statistical variation in the number of ion pairs produced per alpha pulse. This variation has the property of a noise signal in its effect on the spectrometer resolution and is treated as such.

If each ion pair produced in the ionization process were completely independent of every other, the statistical variations would be closely approximated by a normal distribution having as its variance the mean number of ion pairs produced per pulse. However, the variance is a fraction F of this value,[70] where F lies between $\frac{1}{3}$ and $\frac{1}{2}$. The value $F = \frac{1}{3}$ agrees well with the experimental results[71] and is the figure used here.

The variance in the number of ion pairs per pulse, when expressed as a signal voltage, is numerically equivalent to a ms noise voltage in its effect on the spectrometer resolution. This voltage can be computed from

$$\bar{v}^2 = g_{max}^2 (t) \frac{FNe^2}{C_1^2} \tag{85}$$

$$= (0.37)^2 \frac{1.67 \times 10^5 \times (1.6 \times 10^{-19})^2}{3[(15 + 11) \times 10^{-12}]^2} = 0.28 \, (\mu v)^2 , \tag{85'}$$

where $\bar{v}^2$ = equivalent mean square voltage due to statistical variations in the number of ion pairs per pulse,

$g_{max}(t)$ = peak response of the shaping networks to a unit voltage step,

F = Fano factor,[70]

N = number of ion pairs per pulse,

e = electronic charge,

C_1 = total input capacitance.

Equation 85 is generally applicable to counting systems involving ionization chambers.

By adding (85') to (82) and (82'), the equivalent ms voltages become 0.49 $(\mu v)^2$ and 0.58 $(\mu v)^2$ for triode and pentode operation, respectively, leading to equivalent rms voltages of 0.70 μv and 0.76 μv. These figures combined with the peak signal computed in (84) yield S/N ratios of 543 and 500, the reciprocals of which, 0.185% and 0.2%, respectively, correspond to the relative standard deviations of the measured alpha-particle spectra. The resolution of this spectrometer at 5 Mev can be found by multiplying these figures by 2.355 (see Fig. 23) to yield 0.42 and 0.47% for triode and pentode operation, respectively.

For purposes of comparison it is customary to express the input tube noise in terms of equivalent ion pairs; that is, the number of ion pairs which, when collected in the chamber in an infinitesimal time, would produce the same peak signal at the output of the amplifier as the rms noise produced by the input tube. This quantity is

$$N_e = \frac{v_{n(rms)} C_1}{e g_{max}(t)} , \tag{86}$$

where N_e = equivalent ion pairs,

$v_{n(rms)}$ = rms noise voltage at the output of the amplifier due to the first stage,

C_1 = total input capacity in farads,

e = electronic charge, 1.6×10^{-19} coulomb,

$g_{max}(t)$ = peak response of the shaping networks to a unit step of charge appearing at the ion-chamber output terminals.

If (86) is applied to the preceding example, N_e becomes 200 and 238 ion pairs for triode and pentode operation, respectively.

In Fig. 52 two of the tube types that are likely to be used as input tubes are compared for noise over a likely range of shaping-network time constants. The noise figures were computed by the method previously described. It should be noted that the difference between triode and

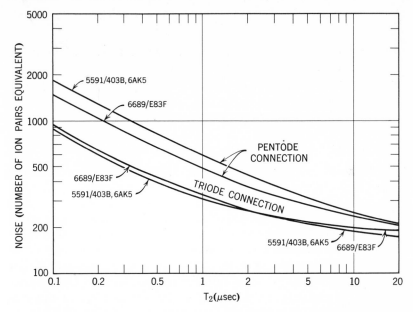

Fig. 52. Sensitivity comparison between 5591/403B, 6AK5, and 6689/E83F.

pentode performance is lower for the E83F than for the 5591/403B (as is to be expected from the low I_{c2}/I_p ratio for this tube) and that the difference is inversely proportional to the shaping-network time constants.

The graphs of Fig. 51 imply that no one tube has a clear-cut advantage (regarding noise) over any other. This is misleading, however. Certain tubes, such as the 6AF4, 6AN5, 6BQ7A, 6T4, 12AF6, and 404A can give the low grid-current operation shown in the graphs only if the heater voltage is carefully adjusted. A heater voltage that is too high causes grid current by thermionic emission (partly due to deposition of cathode material on the grid), whereas a heater voltage that is too low causes short tube life by cathode-interface[72] formation (except for the 404A). The four most desirable ones, from the standpoint of life, uniformity, and relative freedom from critical heater-voltage adjustment, are, in the

order of preference, the E83F, 5842/417A, 6922/E88CC, and 5591/403B.*
In the range below 0.5 μsec, where grid current is unimportant, the choice
goes to the 5842/417A and 6922/E88CC on the basis of high transconductance and long life.

With tubes such as the 6689/E83F and 6922/E88CC, measured and
predicted performance figures agree within 5 to 10% for selected tubes in
the time constant region below 4 to 8 μsec. For longer time constants the
expected improvement in the S/N ratio is not attained for reasons that
have yet to be determined. It may be that flicker effect contributes more
noise at the lower frequencies than is predicted from the $1/f$ formula.
Also, there is some reason to believe that oscillations of ionized gas molecules at the potential minima within the tube result in a small noise component. As the amplifier time constants are increased and the noise level
decreased, incidental effects, such as microphony and power line noise
pickup, become increasingly important; at a noise level below 300 equivalent electrons it is difficult to make measurements of sufficient accuracy
to permit isolation of the various noise sources.

S. Input Circuits

The three commonly used input-tube circuits are the triode, pentode,
and cascode[73] illustrated in Fig. 53.

The triode circuit has the advantage of simplicity and low noise.
However, the Miller effect,[74] which adds appreciably to the input capacity,
results in a low-gain stage. It is quite possible for the gain to be so low
that noise from the following stage limits the attainable S/N ratio.

The Miller effect does not change the S/N ratio,[75,76] since the added
input capacitance affects signal and noise equally. In computing the S/N
ratio, the capacitance of the grid to all other electrodes, with these electrodes bypassed to ground, should be used.

The pentode circuit has a higher noise level than the triode stage, but
it does not suffer from the Miller effect. The cascode circuit combines
the advantages of the triode and pentode stages. The upper tube, by acting
as a cathode-follower voltage regulator, prevents any appreciable change
in the plate potential of the lower tube, thereby reducing the Miller effect
to negligibility. Furthermore, all of the cathode current from the lower
tube flows through the plate circuit of the upper (if the upper tube is
operated in the negative-grid region), thereby eliminating the partition

---

* LM Ericsson 5591/403B and 5847/404A tubes have an appreciably lower I_{c2}/I_p
ratio than the Western Electric prototypes. As a result, the equivalent noise resistance
under pentode operating conditions will be lower than the values shown in the curves of
Fig. 51.

effect found in pentodes. Although it is usual to use two tubes of the same type in this circuit, it is by no means necessary. Since grid-current noise cannot develop in the upper tube (because of the bypassed grid), tubes with high figure of merit can be used in this position with no loss in over-all performance.

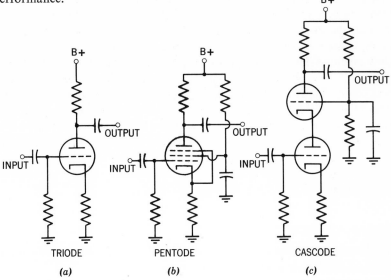

Fig. 53.   Input-tube circuits.

T.   Noise Measurements

It is frequently necessary to determine the noise in an existing system experimentally. Several methods are available; two are described.

A pulse or square-wave generator is needed for both methods. The pulse width and/or pulse-repetition period must be large compared with the time constants of the amplifier shaping networks. The generator should have a driving impedance low enough so that the loading due to the input capacitance of the amplifier will have no effect on the waveform or amplitude of the output signal. Furthermore, the shape of the leading edges of the artificial pulses should approximate the shape of the leading edges of the actual pulses coming from the radiation detector.

The first method of measurement uses a voltmeter to determine the amplifier noise. Ideally, a wide-band meter with square-law response should be used. A meter with average response can be used if it has a bandwidth at least 10 times that of the amplifier to be tested. It can be shown that a meter responding to the average energy of an incoming signal, and which is calibrated to read the rms value of a pure sine wave, will yield the rms value of a random noise signal if its reading is multiplied by 1.129.[77]

The first problem is to determine the capacitance of the detector. This can be done by the obvious method of disconnecting it from the amplifier and measuring it with a capacitance bridge. Should this be impractical, a substitution technique can be used.

With the detector connected, the generator is connected to the input of the system by a capacitor approximately equal to the capacitance of the detector. The output pulse level is then noted with the aid of an

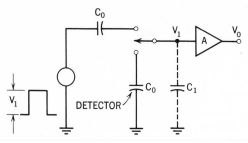

Fig. 54.   Noise-test circuit.

oscilloscope or pulse-height discriminator. A variable capacitor is substituted for the detector and its value is adjusted to produce the same output signal as before. The variable capacitor can then be removed and its value measured on a capacitance bridge. Its capacitance, of course, will be the same as that of the detector.

Next, the generator is disconnected, the detector reconnected, and a radioactive source with a known spectral line is exposed to the detector. The amplifier gain is adjusted to produce an output signal that is within the linear operating range of the amplifier. The peak output voltage corresponding to the energy of the spectral line is then noted with the aid of a calibrated oscilloscope or pulse-height discriminator.

The detector is disconnected and the generator is connected to the amplifier input through a fixed capacitor having the exact value of capacitance measured earlier. The connections are shown in Fig. 54, in which C_0 is the detector capacitance and C_1 the amplifier input capacitance. The generator is adjusted to produce the same output level, $v_{o(\text{peak})}$, as the detector signals.

The immediate problem is to determine the charge produced by the detector under the influence of spectral line radiation. The signal voltage produced at the amplifier input by the detector is

$$v_1 = \frac{Q}{C_0 + C_1} \tag{87}$$

and by the generator

$$v_1' = V_1 \frac{C_0}{C_0 + C_1}. \tag{88}$$

Equating (87) and (88) yields

$$Q = V_1 C_0. \tag{89}$$

Evidently, if V_1 and C_0 are known, Q can be determined.

The next step is to remove the input signal while retaining a shunt capacitance of C_0 across the amplifier input terminals. The output rms noise voltage is then measured. It follows that the rms amplifier noise referred to the input, in units of charge, is

$$Q_{\text{rms}} = \frac{v_{o(\text{rms})}}{v_{o(\text{peak})}} Q = \frac{v_{o(\text{rms})}}{v_{o(\text{peak})}} V_1 C_0. \tag{90}$$

The sum of shot and flicker noise can be determined by observing the rms noise voltage remaining in the output after connecting a capacitor large compared with $C_0 + C_1$ across the input, thereby removing the grid-current and thermal noise.

If the bandwidth of the a-c voltmeter is not greater than the frequency components appearing in the amplified pulses, it becomes necessary to use the second noise-measuring method. In this method a pulse-height analyzer is substituted for the a-c voltmeter and the noise voltage is determined from the width of an artificial spectral line.

The first part of the earlier measurement is repeated to establish the quantities in (89). The next step is to reduce the output of the generator while increasing the amplifier gain until a point is reached at which the modulation of the generator voltage by the amplifier noise is appreciable. The spectrum of the generator output is then measured by the pulse-height analyzer as if it were a spectral line. If the measured peak is Gaussian in shape, the rms noise level, $v_{o(\text{rms})}$, at the amplifier output, will be equal to σ, in volts, of the measured peak. The standard deviation is measured as half the peak width at 0.607 of the peak height. The rms noise in units of charge, referred to the input, is

$$Q_{\text{rms}} = \frac{v_{o(\text{rms})}}{v_{o(\text{peak})}} \frac{A_1}{A_2} \frac{V_2}{V_1} C_0, \tag{91}$$

where A_1 = the initial amplifier gain setting,
A_2 = the final gain setting,
V_2 = the final pulse generator setting,
V_1 = the initial generator setting,
C_0 = the detector capacitance.

U. Amplifier Linearity. General Considerations

A linear amplifier is one in which the ratio of output signal to input signal is constant (i.e., one in which the gain is constant) over the rated output range. In spectrometer applications strict linearity is important

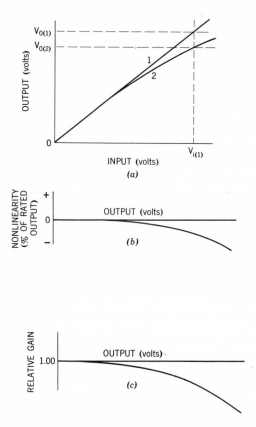

Fig. 55. Amplifier linearity curves.

because departures from linearity introduce spectral distortions.* For example, a decrease in gain over part of the output range causes the pulse-height analyzer channels in that region to subtend a larger part of the spectrum than in a region of normal gain. The result is a false bump in

---

* At this writing, linear amplifiers are used almost universally. However, amplifiers having logarithmic or square-root response have desirable features also and will probably become more popular as time goes on.

the spectral response combined with a compression of the energy axis in the region of nonlinearity.

To distinguish between the effects on energy-axis and intensity distortions, two kinds of linearity are defined: integral and differential.

Integral linearity, of interest in connection with energy-axis distortion, is a measure of the departure of the output versus input characteristic (transfer characteristic) of an amplifier from the ideal straight line and is usually expressed as a percentage of rated maximum amplifier output. This is illustrated in Fig. 55, in which the nonlinearity is

$$L = \frac{100 \left(v_{o(1)} - v_{o(2)} \right)}{v_R}, \tag{92}$$

where L = the nonlinearity in per cent,

$v_{o(1)}$ = the ideal amplifier output for a given input $v_{i(1)}$,

$v_{o(2)}$ = the measured amplifier output,

v_R = the rated maximum output.

Since L is usually in the neighborhood of 1 %, a graphical display of the type shown in Fig. 55a cannot be read with high accuracy. A better presentation is shown in Fig. 55b, in which the *departure* of the measured output from the ideal output is plotted in terms of the measured output.

Differential linearity, as the name implies, is proportional to the derivative of the measured transfer characteristic and is therefore proportional to the amplifier gain. The differential linearity is usually displayed as in Fig. 55c, in which the measured gain, normalized to the gain at a specified output voltage, is plotted as a function of the output voltage.

V. Techniques for Attaining Good Linearity

Because of the dependence of transconductance on cathode current, nonlinearities arise in amplifier stages that are subjected to current excursions of large amplitude. In a practical amplifier the points of danger are the preamplifier output stage, the stage immediately preceding the gain control, and the main amplifier output stage. The most commonly used technique for reducing nonlinearity is negative feedback.[78,79,80] Improvement factors of 5 to 50 are common but may be insufficient. Further improvement by feedback may be impractical because of the instabilities that usually result from its too-generous application. It then becomes necessary to limit the current swing in the offending stages or to provide compensating nonlinearities in other parts of the amplifier. Of these two methods, the first is preferable.

A brute-force method of holding tube current constant is the use of a high-voltage B_+ supply combined with a high-valued plate load resistor for the offending stages. This is wasteful of power. A preferable method

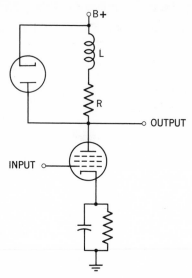

Fig. 56.   Constant-current circuit for the improvement of amplifier linearity.

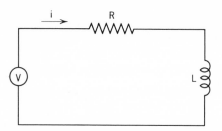

Fig. 57.   Equivalent circuit of Fig. 56.

is the use of a series inductor, which takes advantage of the constant-current characteristics associated with the energy storage properties of the inductor. A typical circuit is shown in Fig. 56. The diode is used to limit positive excursions of the output pulse to the d-c voltage drop across R.

For analytical purposes the circuit of Fig. 56 may be replaced by the equivalent circuit of Fig. 57. The signal current which flows under pulsed conditions is

$$i = \frac{v}{R}(1 - e^{-(Rt/L)}), \tag{93}$$

where i = current in amperes,

    v = pulse voltage in volts,

    t = time in seconds, measured from the start of the pulse.

If L/R is made large compared with the pulse width T, it follows from the series expansion of (93) that the change in plate current that results from an output of pulse magnitude v and duration T will be approximately equal to vT/L.

In cases in which L must be impractically large a further improvement may be had by the addition of the cathode-follower shown in Fig. 58,

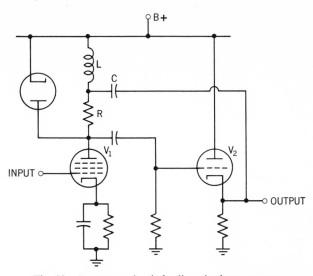

Fig. 58.   Bootstrap circuit for linearity improvement.

The extra tube, V_2, acts like a bootstrap circuit[81] in keeping the voltage drop across R, and therefore the current through V_1, constant. Since in this circuit L serves only as an isolating impedance, it can be replaced by a resistor if the accompanying d-c voltage drop and added cathode-follower loading are acceptable. The capacitance of C should be large enough to ensure that under pulsed conditions the voltage change across it will be small compared with the pulse voltage.

In a typical case[82] an amplifier that produced a 100-volt, 1-μsec pulse exhibited a differential nonlinearity of approximately 7%. The addition of the circuit of Fig. 58 ($L = 125$ mh, $C = 0.05$ μf) reduced this figure to less than 0.1%.

One way of compensating a nonlinearity is by loading the amplifier stage preceding the offending stage to the point at which its current swing is equal to that in the offending stage.[49] Because of the signal inversion in a grounded-cathode amplifier, the current swings in the two stages will be of opposite polarity and therefore compensatory. The resulting improvement in linearity will be comparable to that which can be obtained in a push-pull arrangement. This method is effective but imposes the condition of low-gain operation on the driving stage.

W. Measurement of Linearity

Three methods of linearity measurement are now described.

The first method, suitable for integral linearity measurements, requires a calibrated pulse generator, a Schmitt trigger circuit with a calibrated bias adjustment, and an output indicator, such as an oscilloscope, counting-rate meter, or scaler.

The circuit diagram of a pulse generator[83] well suited to the measurement is shown in Fig. 59. It operates by alternately charging and discharging the 3-μf capacitor. The capacitor is charged from a stable, adjustable, d-c supply and discharged through the output attenuator circuit. The output pulse has a rise time of less than 7 mμsec, a fall time of 300 (or more) μsec, and a maximum amplitude of 10 volts. The linearity (integral) of adjustment is 0.1%. An external terminating resistor of 100 ohms is required. A capacitor shunting the output can be applied to slow the rise time to a value comparable to that of the radiation detector to be used. It is assumed that the clipping circuit is part of the amplifier.

The circuit diagram of a suitable Schmitt trigger is shown in Fig. 60. The tube types used will depend upon the pulse width available from the amplifier. Type 6AK5 tubes are suitable for 1-μsec (or more) delay-line clipped pulses; type 404A or E180F tubes will be necessary for 1-μsec RC-clipped pulses. It is essential that the trigger circuit be fast enough to exhibit true switching action.[84]

The voltage drop across the bias control is made equal to the rated maximum amplifier output by means of the span adjustment. The bias control is zero-adjusted by the following procedure.

The generator and trigger dials are set to 500 (full scale = 1000). The attenuator and normalize controls in the generator are set to the point at which the trigger circuit is actuated by the amplifier at half the repetition rate of the generator output (half-triggering point, or HTP). This setting corresponds to equality between the trigger bias setting and the output pulse height from the amplifier. The generator dial is then set to 250, and the bias dial is set to the HTP. If the reading of the bias dial is different from 250 at this point, the zero-set control is readjusted and the process is repeated until the 250 and 500 points on the generator and bias dials agree with each other.

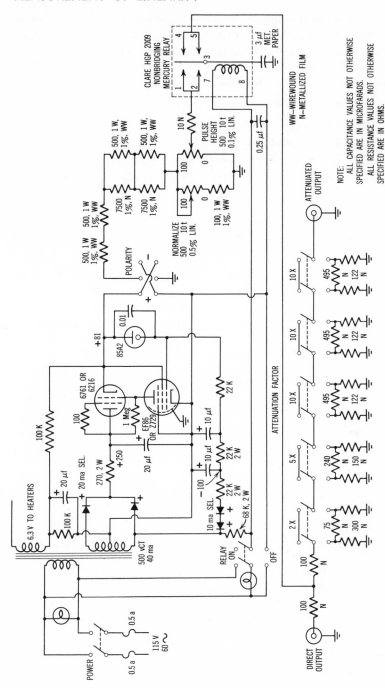

Fig. 59. Mercury relay pulse generator.

The remainder of the linearity check is quite simple; it consists of a series of observations of the differences in dial readings between the generator and trigger circuit as the trigger bias dial is moved from 0 to 1000, the generator being adjusted for the HTP at each stopping point. It is helpful to graph the information in the form shown in Fig. 55*b*.

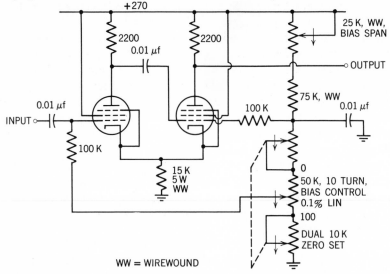

WW = WIREWOUND

Fig. 60.   Schmitt trigger circuit.

The limiting accuracy of this method is determined by the accuracy of the pulse generator and trigger bias controls. The best practical linearity for each is approximately 0.1 %, leading to a probable error in the determination of any one point of about 0.15 % of the rated amplifier output. In a measurement of differential linearity it is necessary to take successive differences between points separated by approximately 1 % of the rated output. This procedure leads to probable errors of 20 % in the determination of any one differential linearity point and rules out the use of the foregoing method for differential linearity measurements.

The second method of measurement is best suited for the determination of differential linearity but can also be used for integral linearity. It requires a differential discriminator of known precision, a scaler, and a pulse generator whose output level is varied by a sweep circuit with a very constant (0.1 % or better) rate of change of voltage. Such a sweep is best obtained from a high-gain d-c amplifier connected as an integrator. The measurement is made by setting the discriminator bias to the amplifier output levels of interest and sweeping the pulse-generator signal across the discriminator window. The number of pulses per sweep recorded at each of the discriminator settings is inversely proportional to the amplifier gain at that output level.

A third method of linearity measurement is applicable to feedback amplifiers. The method is an indirect one and must be applied to one feedback group at a time. It tells nothing about the linearity of amplifier sections to which it is not applied.

As in the first method, a calibrated pulse generator is required. The amplifier output indicator, however, need be only an oscilloscope. The input to the amplifier is adjusted to give the desired output level, and the generator dial reading is noted. (The output level is considered to be the topmost part of the output pulse.) Next, the feedback in the amplifier section under test is disabled in such a way that amplifier loading and d-c operating levels are not affected. (In some circuits this condition may be difficult to meet, and this is one of the shortcomings of the method.) A marked increase in amplifier output will be observed. The output is restored to its original level by readjusting the generator, and its new dial reading is noted. This procedure is repeated over the range of outputs of interest. The meaning of the recorded information should become apparent from the following.

Assume an output reference voltage of $v_{o(1)}$ volts for the feedback loop under consideration. The input voltage corresponding to this output is $v_{i(1)}$ and the ratio of these two voltages defines a straight line passing through the origin, of slope

$$K_1 = \frac{v_{o(1)}}{v_{i(1)}} = \frac{\mu_1\beta}{1 + \mu_1\beta}, \tag{94}$$

where K_1 = gain of the feedback group in its normal state,
  μ_1 = gain of the group with the feedback disabled,
  β = fraction of the output voltage fed back to the input.

Unless the amplifier is perfectly linear, the point of rated maximum output will not fall on this reference line but will define another one passing through the origin of slope

$$K_2 = \frac{v_{o(2)}}{v_{i(2)}} = \frac{\mu_2\beta}{1 + \mu_2\beta}. \tag{95}$$

From (92), p. 295, the nonlinearity at the output $v_{o(2)}$ is

$$L = 100\,\frac{K_1 v_{i(2)} - v_{o(2)}}{v_{0(2)}} = 100\,\frac{K_1 - K_2}{K_2}\,\%. \tag{96}$$

From (94) and (95)

$$L = 100 \frac{\frac{1}{\mu_2\beta} - \frac{1}{\mu_1\beta}}{1 + \frac{1}{\mu_1\beta}} \%. \tag{97}$$

If $\mu_1\beta \gg 1$,

$$L \cong 100 \left(\frac{1}{\mu_2\beta} - \frac{1}{\mu_1\beta} \right) \%. \tag{97'}$$

It remains to determine the values of $\mu_1\beta$ and $\mu_2\beta$ from the generator dial readings.

With the loop closed, the generator voltage necessary to produce $v_{o(1)}$ is $v_{i(1)}$. From (94) the gain is $\mu_1/(1 + \mu_1\beta)$. With the loop open, the new generator voltage required to produce the same output is $v'_{i(1)}$, with a corresponding gain of μ_1. Evidently, $v'_{i(1)}/v_{i(1)} = (1 + \mu_1\beta)$, from which $\mu_1\beta$ can be determined.

This method of linearity determination has two features to recommend it:

(a) At any one point the accuracy of the output-level determination does not affect the accuracy of the linearity measurement, since the output level is held constant.

(b) Although not obvious from the preceding derivation, the effect of errors in pulse generator setting is reduced by the feedback $(1 + \mu\beta)$. If $(1 + \mu\beta) > 10$, it is possible to make differential linearity measurements as well as integral measurements.

REFERENCES

1. K. Kandiah and D. E. Brown, "High-Gain D.C. Amplifiers," *Proc. Inst. Elec. Engrs.*, II, **99**, 314 (1952).
2. A. H. Jaffey, *Nuclear Instruments and Their Uses*, Vol. II, A. H. Snell, ed. (Wiley, New York). In press; also L. J. Rainwater and C. S. Wu, "Application of Probability Theory to Nuclear Particle Detection," *Nucleonics*, **1**, 60, September 1947.
3. N. R. Campbell and V. J. Francis, "A Theory of Valve and Circuit Noise," *J. Inst. Elec. Engrs.* (*London*), III, **93**, 45 (1946).
4. H. V. Neher, *Procedures in Experimental Physics*, John Strong, Ed. (Prentice-Hall, New York, 1943).
5. T. J. O'Donnell, "Drawing and Working Quartz Fibers," *Nuclear Science Ser.*, (Natl. Acad. Sci., Natl. Research Council, Washington D.C., 1958).
6. B. Zipprich, "Uber eine Neukonstruktion des Vakuum-Duantenelektrometers," Part II, *Physik Z.* **37**, 36 (1936).
7. F. A. and A. F. Lindemann and T. C. Keeley, "A New Form of Electrometer," *Phil. Mag.*, **47**, 577 (1924).

8. L. R. Hafstad, "The Application of the FP-54 Pliotron to Atomic Disintegration Studies," *Phys. Rev.*, **44**, 201 (1933).
9. G. E. Metcalf and B. J. Thompson, "A Low Grid-Current Vacuum Tube," *Phys. Rev.*, **36**, 1489 (1930).
10. P. A. Macdonald, "The Thermionic Amplification of Direct Currents," *Physics*, **7**, 265 (1936).
11. C. E. Nielsen, "Measurement of Small Currents: Characteristics of Types 38, 954, and 959 as Reduced Grid-Current Tubes," *Rev. Sci. Instr.*, **18**, 18 (1947).
12. J. R. Prescott, "The Use of Multigrid Tubes as Electrometers," *Rev. Sci. Instr.*, **20**, 553 (1949).
13. H. S. Anker, "Stabilized D.C. Amplifier with High Sensitivity," *Electronics*, **20**, 138 (June 1947).
14. V. J. Caldecourt, "An Electrometer Amplifier," *Rev. Sci. Instr.*, **20**, 748 (1949).
15. Wold, U.S. Patent 1232879 (1916).
16. C. E. Wynn-Williams, "A Valve Amplifier for Ionization Currents," *Proc. Cambridge Phil. Soc.*, **23**, 811 (1927).
17. G. Barth, "Uber ein Neuartiges Röhrengalvanometer," *Z. angw. Physik*, **87**, 399 (1934).
18. D. B. Penick, "Direct-Current Amplifier Circuits for Use with the Electrometer Tube," *Rev. Sci. Instr.*, **6**, 115 (1935).
19. H. W. Bode, *Network Analysis and Feedback Amplifier Design* (Van Nostrand, New York, 1945).
20. G. E. Valley, Jr., and H. Wallman (Eds.), *Vacuum Tube Amplifiers*, (McGraw-Hill, New York, 1948), Chapters 9–11.
21. I. Pelchowitch and J. J. Zaalberg van Zelst, "A Wide-Band Electrometer Amplifier," *Rev. Sci. Instr.*, **23**, 73 (1952).
22. N. F. Moody, "An Improved dc Amplifier for Portable Ionization Chamber Instruments," *Rev. Sci. Instr.*, **22**, 236 (1951).
23. J. Praglin, "A New High Stability Micromicroammeter," *IRE Trans. on Instr.*, **I-6**, 144 (June 1957).
24. H. Palevsky, R. K. Swank, and R. Grenchik, "The Design of Vibrating Capacitor Electrometers," *Rev. Sci. Instr.*, **18**, 298 (1947).
25. S. A. Scherbatskoy, T. H. Gilmartin, and G. Swift, "The Capacitive Commutator," *Rev. Sci. Instr.*, **18**, 415 (1947).
26. R. J. Ritsma, "An Electrometer Amplifier with Two Dynamic Condensers," *Appl. Sci. Research*, **6B**, 429 (1957).
27. H. den Hartog and F. A. Muller, "Reduction of Spontaneous Fluctuations in V-T Electrometer Circuits Through Mechanical Conversion," *Physica*, **10**, 167 (1943).
28. P. J. Van Heerden, "Vermindering van het Geruis van een Radiobus bij het Meten van Ladingen," *Physica*, **11**, 151 (1944).
29. H. den Hartog and F. A. Muller, "Verwijdering van den Ruisch in Thermionische Electrometers met Mechanische Conversie," *Physica*, **11**, 161 (1944).
30. H. L. Curtis, "Insulating Properties of Solid Dielectrics," *Bull. Bur. Standards*, **11**, 387 (1915).
31. R. F. Field, "How Humidity Affects Insulation," *Gen. Radio Experimenter*, **20**, 6 (July, August 1945).
32. L. Page and N. I. Adams, *Principles of Electricity* (Van Nostrand, New York, 1931), pp. 67–69.
33. F. M. Glass, "Methods for Reducing Insulator Noise and Leakage," *Rev. Sci. Instr.*, **20**, 239 (1949).

34. F. J. Norton, "Organo-Silicon Films," *Gen. Elec. Rev.*, **47**, 6 (August 1944).
35. L. Page and N. I. Adams, *op. cit.*, pp. 228, 229.
36. J. Millman and S. Seely, *Electronics* First Edition (McGraw-Hill, New York), pp. 157–161.
37. L. Page and N. I. Adams, *op. cit.*, Chapters 1–3.
38. W. C. Elmore and M. Sands, *Electronics* First Edition (McGraw-Hill, New York, 1949), pp. 99–103.
39. *Ibid.*, pp. 106–107.
40. K. Kandiah, "A Sensitive Pulse Trigger Circuit with a Stable Threshold," *Proc. Inst. Elec. Engrs.*, II, **101**, 239 (1954).
41. S. Barabaschi, C. Cottini, and E. Gatti, "High Sensitivity and Accuracy Pulse Trigger Circuit," *Nuovo cimento*, **II**, 1042 (1955).
42. W. C. Elmore and M. Sands, *op. cit.*, pp. 202–206.
43. A. B. Van Rennes, "Pulse-Amplitude Analysis in Nuclear Research, Part I," *Nucleonics*, **10**, No. 7, 20 (1952).
44. W. C. Elmore and M. Sands, *op. cit.*, pp. 164–171.
45. W. H. Jordan and P. R. Bell, "A General Purpose Linear Amplifier," *Rev. Sci. Instr.*, **18**, 703 (1947).
46. A. B. Van Rennes, "Pulse Amplitude Analysis in Nuclear Research, Part II," *Nucleonics*, **10**, No. 8, 22 (1952).
47. Handbook of Chemistry and Physics (Chemical Rubber Publishing Co., Cleveland, Ohio) Table of Probability of Occurrence of Deviations.
48. A. B. Gillespie, *Signal, Noise and Resolution in Nuclear Counter Amplifiers*, (McGraw-Hill Book Co., New York, or Pergamon Press, London, 1953) pp. 62–70.
49. E. Fairstein, "Nonblocking Double-Line Linear Pulse Amplifier," *Rev. Sci. Instr.*, **27**, 475 (1956).
50. W. E. Glenn, Jr., "Pulse Height Distribution Analyzer," *Nucleonics*, **4**, No. 6, p. 50.
51. W. C. Elmore and M. Sands, *op. cit.*, pp. 38–45, 132–134.
52. I. A. D. Lewis and F. H. Wells, *Millimicrosecond Pulse Techniques* (McGraw-Hill, New York, or Pergamon Press, London, 1955), Chapter 2.
53. H. W. Koch and R. W. Johnston, Eds., *Multichannel Pulse Height Analyzers* (*Natl. Acad. Sci., Natl. Research Council, Publ.* 467, Washington, D.C., 1957), pp. 19–33.
54. G. E. Valley, Jr. and H. Wallman, Editors, *Vacuum Tube Amplifiers*, (McGraw-Hill, New York, 1948), pp. 116–117.
55. W. M. Brubaker, "D-C Amplifier," *Bull. Amer. Phys. Soc.*, **14**, No. 6 (1939). (Program for the Univer. California Meeting.)
56. E. L. Ginzton, "D-C Amplifier Design Techniques," *Electronics*, **27**, 98 (1944) or V. Zeluff and J. Markus, Editors, *Electronics Manual For Radio Engineers* (McGraw-Hill, New York, 1949), First Edition, pp. 257–262.
57. G. E. Valley and H. Wallman, *op. cit.*, Chapter 11.
58. R. L. Chase and W. A. Higinbotham, "A Flexible Pulse Amplifier with Good Overload Properties," *Rev. Sci. Instr.*, **23**, 34 (1952).
59. D. A. Bell, "Fluctuations of Electric Current," *J. Inst. Elec. Engrs., Part III (London)*, **93**, 37 (1946). This is an excellent review paper and lists 37 references to earlier work.
60. J. C. Jaeger, *An Introduction to the Laplace Transformation* (Wiley, New York, or Methuen, London, 1955).
61. J. B. Johnson, "Thermal Agitation of Electric Charge in Conductors," *Phys. Rev.*, **32**, 97 (1928).

62. H. Nyquist, "Thermal Agitation of Electric Charge in Conductors," *Phys. Rev.*, **32**, 110 (1928).

63. W. Schottky, "Über spontane Stromschwankungen in verschiedenen Elektrizitäts-leitern," *Ann. Physik*, **57**, 541 (1918).

64. D. O. North, "Fluctuation Noise in Space Charge Limited Currents at Moderately High Frequencies," *R C A Rev.*, **4**, 441 (1940); **5**, 106 (1940); **5**, 244 (1940).

65. W. W. Lindemann and A. van der Ziel, "New Mechanism for the Generation of Flicker Noise in Tubes with Oxide-Coated Cathodes," *J. Appl. Phys.*, **27**, 1179 (1956).

66. A. B. Gillespie, *op. cit.*, pp. 33–40.

67. E. Fairstein, "Grid Current in Electron Tubes," *Rev. Sci. Instr.*, **29**, 524 (1958).

68. D. H. Wilkinson, *Ionization Chambers and Counters* (Cambridge University Press, 1950), pp. 128–131.

69. C. Cottini, E. Gatti, G. Gianelli and G. Rozzi, "Minimum Noise Preamplifier for Fast Ionization Chambers," *Nuovo cimento*, **3**, 473 (1956).

70. U. Fano, "Ionization Yield of Radiations. II. The Fluctuations of the Number of Ions," *Phys. Rev.*, **72**, 26 (1947).

71. D. W. Engelkemeir and L. B. Magnusson, "Resolution of Alpha-Particle Spectra by Ionization Pulse Analysis of Collimated Samples," *Rev. Sci. Instr.*, **26**, 295 (1955),

72. L. S. Nergaard and R. M. Matheson, "Studies of the Interface Layer in Oxide Cathodes," *R C A Rev.*, **15**, 335 (1954).

73. H. Wallman, A. B. Macnee, and C. P. Gadsden, "A Low-Noise Amplifier," *Proc. I. R. E.*, **36**, 700 (1948).

74. F. Langford-Smith, Editor, *Radiotron Designer's Handbook* (Radio Corporation of America, Harrison, New Jersey, or Iliffe and Sons, London, 1952) Fourth Edition, p. 52 and pp. 493–494.

75. G. E. Valley and H. Wallman, *op. cit.*, Section 13.11.

76. A. B. Gillespie, *op. cit.*, pp. 54–56.

77. L. L. Beranek, *Acoustic Measurements* (Wiley, New York, or Chapman and Hall, London, 1949) p. 453.

78. H. W. Bode, *Network Analysis and Feedback Amplifier Design* (Van Nostrand, New York, 1945).

79. F. Langford-Smith, *op. cit.*, Chapter 7.

80. G. E. Valley and H. Wallman, *op. cit.*, Chapter 9.

81. J. Millman and H. Taub, *Pulse and Digital Circuits* (McGraw-Hill, New York, 1956), Chapter 7.

82. E. Fairstein, "Improving the Linearity of Pulse Amplifiers," *Rev. Sci. Instr.*, **25**, 1134 (1954).

83. "Instrumentation and Controls Division Semiannual Progress Report for Period Ending July 31, 1956" (Oak Ridge National Laboratory, Report No. ORNL-2234, Oak Ridge, Tennessee) pp. 22–24. This instrument and others like it are commercially available.

84. E. Fairstein, "Effect of Driving Pulse Shape on the Performance of a Schmitt Trigger Circuit," *Rev. Sci. Instr.* **27**, 483 (1956).

5 COUNTING METHODS FOR THE ASSAY OF RADIOACTIVE SAMPLES

ELLIS P. STEINBERG
Argonne National Laboratory
Argonne, Illinois

A. General Considerations
B. Beta Counting
C. Alpha Counting
D. Gamma Counting

The general availability of radioisotopes has placed a powerful tool in the hands of investigators in many fields of science, and it is the purpose of this chapter to aid these workers in the design of meaningful experiments utilizing radioactivity. An understanding of the various factors that may contribute to errors in measurement is essential for the choice of appropriate techniques and measuring devices and for the proper evaluation of experimental data. This chapter is not intended as a treatise on the measurement of radioactivity, but it is hoped that the presentation of a handy guide to some of the problems involved and the techniques generally employed in avoiding or correcting for them, together with references to the pertinent literature, will provide an adequate orientation and introduction to the subject.

A. General Considerations

Although a variety of techniques is available for the assaying of the radioactive strength of samples of various kinds, we herein limit our discussion to methods that employ particle counting and omit reference to photographic methods, calorimetry, charge collection, colloid deposition, crystal coloring, and other techniques of rather specialized application. Different techniques may, of course, involve somewhat different error analyses; however, the problems associated with the determination of the absolute disintegration rate of a radioactive source by counting techniques afford an excellent example of the commonly encountered difficulties.

Such a determination involves a knowledge of the decay scheme of the radioactive nuclide and the efficiency of the detector for the particles or rays emitted by the source. Thus it is necessary to know the fraction of the radiation leaving the source that enters the sensitive volume of the detector ("geometry factor") and the intrinsic efficiency of the detector for the radiation. The interactions of radiation with matter alter the simple geometrical relationship between the source and detector by processes of absorption and scattering in the material of the sample itself, its support, any covering material, the space between the sample and the counter, the counter window, and the housing of the detector unit. These effects are complex and depend critically on the size and material of the sample and its support and on the energy and type of the radiation. Special techniques are required to minimize these effects and limit errors in the determination of disintegration rates to a few per cent.

For many purposes an experiment can be designed so that relative counting rates of samples of a particular nuclide will suffice. It is then only necessary to count under nearly identical conditions to obtain precisions of the order of 1 to 2 per cent. This criterion, in practice, is relatively simple to meet, and, whenever possible, comparative counting is therefore recommended. Of course, if it is necessary to compare the activity of sources that differ in chemical or physical nature or in the energy of their radiations, these differences must be taken into account.

Much time and effort may be saved by the judicious application of published correction factors for the individual and combined effects of backscatter, sample thicknesses, etc., on counting determinations. However, it is extremely important to be aware of the sensitivity of the effects to experimental conditions. When high accuracy is desired, it is usually advisable for each investigator to determine the correction for his own conditions or to employ techniques that minimize the effects.

In some cases, the radioactivity of the nuclide of interest may be complicated by the presence of isotopic or genetically related species that are also radioactive. Corrections for the presence of these species may be made, in general, by taking advantage of the differences in the half-lives, energies, and, perhaps, types of radiation involved. Even in the case of a pure nuclide, different types of radiation may be emitted (e.g., β^-, e^-, x, or gamma rays) and their contributions to the observed counting rates must be evaluated.

Any detector will record counts, even in the absence of a sample, due to the presence of cosmic rays and of ionizing radiation in the materials of construction and in the laboratory air (thoron, radon, etc.). This background rate may vary with laboratory conditions and must be determined under conditions duplicating those under which the sample is counted. It must be subtracted from the sample counting rate. Since the background rate limits the sensitivity of the detector, it is advisable to reduce it to a level that is low in comparison with sample counting rates. The background rate is dependent on the size of the detector. For standard end-window Geiger-Müller and proportional counters (about $1\frac{1}{4}$ in. diameter $\times$ 2 in. long) backgrounds of 30 to 50 counts per minute (c/m) are common. This rate may be reduced by a factor of two to three by the common practice of enclosing the detector in a lead or iron housing 1 to 2 in. thick.

Further shielding of beta counters from penetrating cosmic radiation may be achieved by surrounding the detector with a ring of additional counters connected so that the detector will not record a count that is coincident with one in the protective ring. The entire assembly is enclosed in an iron, lead, or mercury shield. Such an arrangement—referred to as anticoincidence shielding[1]—may reduce the background rate to as low as 1 to 2 c/m. Additional corrections may be necessary for the variation in efficiency of the detector with time (as determined by the routine counting of a suitable standard) and for the finite resolving time of the detector. (See Appendix 2.)

Radioactive decay is a random process, and inherent fluctuations in the disintegration rate of any source limit the ultimate accuracy of counting data. These fluctuations follow well-known statistical laws and the statistical accuracy of a set of data can be readily calculated.

B. Beta Counting

I. End-window counters. Although many specially designed counters are employed to satisfy particular needs,[118] the end-window Geiger-Müller counter has probably been the most universally used detector for beta radiation. Consequently, much of the experimental work on the problems of beta counting has been carried out with this detector. Although the Geiger-Müller counter still finds useful application, it is generally being replaced with the flow-type, end-window proportional counter, which has many advantages. Since it is operated at atmospheric pressure, a thin window (usually 0.5 to 1.0 mg/cm² plastic foil* coated with a conducting film of Aquadag or evaporated metal) can be used; hence the range of application can be extended to lower energy betas while the convenience of counting samples externally is retained. Geiger-Müller counters are usually operated at a pressure of about 10 cm Hg, and window thicknesses greater

---

* For example, rubber hydrochloride, available from Originality House, Inc., 480 Avalon Avenue, Akron, Ohio, or Mylar (polyethylene terephthalate), available from E. I. du Pont de Nemours & Co., Wilmington, Delaware.

than about 2 mg/cm² are most usual. Moreover, the proportional counter permits a much wider range of source strengths to be used, since the dead-time losses are of the order of 1% per 10^5 c/m compared with losses of about 0.5% per 10^3 c/m in a Geiger-Müller counter. Proportional counters require associated electronic equipment of somewhat greater complexity than Geiger-Müller counters (e.g., stable high-voltage supplies and non-overloading amplifiers), but these are readily available. Considerable experience with proportional counters has proved them to have long lifetimes and excellent stability.

Fortunately, the size and shape, as well as the commonly employed holder and shelf arrangement, are very nearly identical for the Geiger-Müller and end-window proportional counters, and the extensive studies of various effects in beta counting carried out with Geiger-Müller counters are in most cases directly applicable to the proportional counter. Of course, there will be differences in some cases in which the window thickness plays a significant role, but even here the effects will be qualitatively the same. It cannot be overemphasized that the greatest contribution of the many studies of beta counting reported in the literature lies in their elucidation of the complex effects encountered and the presentation of methods of correction. The quantitative data presented are useful for approximate corrections and general orientation. However, for the highest accuracy, the quantitative factors should be determined for the particular experimental arrangement being used.

The importance of absorption and scattering phenomena in the detection of beta particles was pointed out as early as 1910 by Kovarik and others.[2] Many aspects of the problem of the determination of absolute disintegration rates from counting data have since been investigated experimentally. The complexity of the problem has prevented successful theoretical development, and the magnitude of the effects must usually be determined from empirical data. Although it is not always necessary to obtain absolute disintegration rates, the investigator should be aware of the factors that may contribute to errors in counting determinations.

When particle emission accompanies each decay, a counting yield, Y, may be defined[3] as the ratio of the net counting rate observed (corrected for resolution losses and background activity) and the true disintegration rate. Thus

$$Y = \frac{\text{counts per minute (c/m)}}{\text{disintegrations per minute (d/m)}}.$$

For simplicity, the present discussion is limited to the case of a simple beta-emitter (such as P^{32} or C^{14}). More complex decay schemes with gamma rays, x rays, and conversion electrons, as well as beta branching, are discussed later. Although the factors that enter into the determination of Y are not simple and not easily separable experimentally, they can, in principle, be treated independently. Then,[3,4]

$$Y = \frac{c/m}{d/m} = (I)(G) f_W f_A f_C f_B f_H f_S,$$

where $I =$ detection probability, $G =$ geometry, $f_W =$ factor for the absorption effect of the counter window and air between source and window, $f_A =$ factor for the scattering effect of the air, $f_C =$ factor for the effect of any covering material over the sample, $f_B =$ factor for the effect of backscattering by the material supporting the source, $f_H =$ factor for the effect of the sample and tube-supporting structure and the walls of the housing or shield in scattering counts into the counter, and $f_S =$ factor for the effect of the finite mass of the source ("self-absorption" and "self-scattering").

a. I (detection probability). Ideally, every particle that passes through the window of an end-window Geiger or proportional counter will form at least one ion-pair, initiate a Townsend avalanche, and register a count. Actually, however, there is a finite probability that an ion-pair will not be formed. This probability may be calculated[4] and is dependent on the specific primary ionization constant of the counter gas, the pressure of the gas, the energy, and the path length of the particle through the volume of the counter. In general, the detection probability is close to unity, and no corrections are required except for work of extremely high accuracy. For cases of high geometry and energetic betas the path length obliquely through the corners of the counter may be too short to produce sufficient ionization to register a pulse. This will result in a shift of the knee of the voltage plateau to higher values. Defining apertures in front of the window may counteract this effect by collimating the particles, but these apertures may also introduce scattering effects from the edges. It may be more advisable to reduce the geometry of counting by increasing the source to tube distance if the added path length does not introduce an absorption problem.

Effects such as these illustrate the care that should be exercised in the choice of operating voltage. Voltages just above the plateau knee for weak betas may be below the plateau for energetic betas, since the specific ionization of electrons decreases with increasing energy over the energy range generally encountered. On the other hand, the resolving time of the counter increases with increasing voltage along the plateau, and a voltage that ensures a high detection probability may introduce higher resolution losses.

In practice, this problem is generally met by determining the geometry of the source position with standards having approximately the same energy and counting rate as the sources to be measured. In this case, a "geometric efficiency" is actually determined in which the detection probability and resolution losses cancel.

b. G (geometry). Radiation is emitted isotropically from a point source, and, in the absence of absorption and scattering phenomena, the fraction of the solid angle of 4π radians subtended by the sensitive volume of the counter at the source will represent the fraction of the emitted radiation that is counted. This fraction is known as the "geometry" or "physical geometry" and is determined simply by the dimensions of the system. Formulas may also be derived for the geometry of extended sources. These are given in Appendix 1.

The geometry is generally determined by counting standards of known disintegration rates (determined by coincidence counting, 4π counting, or other techniques) in the desired position. In order to minimize the corrections for absorption and scattering, standards are prepared in thin, uniform deposits on thin backings.[4,5,6,59e] The ratio of the counting rate of the standard (suitably corrected for absorption and scattering effects, as well as background activity and any resolution losses) and the known disintegration rate gives the geometric efficiency.

It has been reported[4,5,7] that the observed geometric efficiency is slightly lower than that calculated from the dimensions of the counting system. This may arise from the collection of part of the charge on the ball at the end of the wire, but it has also been interpreted as indicating that the active volume of the counter begins a few millimeters behind the window. A "defined geometry" technique employing a brass collimator has been suggested[7,8,9] to avoid this difficulty. However, Fried et al.[10] observed significant increases in the curvature of absorption curves of Co^{60} and RaE at low absorber thicknesses and demonstrated that when appropriate corrections for absorption in the window and gas path are applied the observed and calculated geometries do, indeed, agree within the accuracy of the measurements.

The geometric efficiency for extended sources has been evaluated empirically and shown to agree well with the calculated geometry.[4,11–14]

Although, as previously pointed out, it is desirable to use standards having the same energy as the sources of interest, errors in the extrapolation of absorption curves (see Sec. c, f_W) to zero thickness may result from differences in the beta spectra shapes of two nuclides with the same maximum beta energy. Manov[15] suggests that many standards may be required for the accurate calibration of sources of general interest and has reviewed the status of the work on the standardization of radioactive sources to 1954.

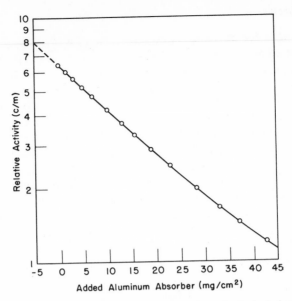

Fig. 1.   Illustration of extrapolation of initial portion of a typical absorption curve to correct for 5.0 mg/cm² absorption in tube window and air path. (Factor f_W.)

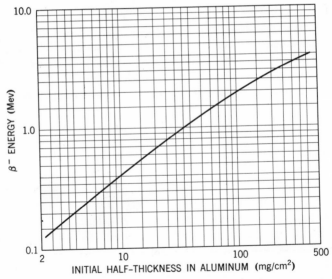

Fig. 2.   Energy versus half-thickness in aluminum for beta particles. [These data were obtained for samples weighing about 20 mg, mounted over a 2-cm² area on filter paper, and covered with 3 mg/cm² cellophane. They were counted on the first shelf (geometry factor = 25% of 4π) of a standard Geiger counter (tube window = 3.0 mg/cm²).]

312

c. f_W (factor for air and counter-window absorption). Since beta particles are easily scattered in passing through matter, an absorbing material placed between the source and detector may reduce the intensity of radiation reaching the counter by true absorption or by scattering particles out of their normal paths toward the detector. On the other hand, some particles may be scattered into the detector, increasing the apparent intensity. These effects are critically dependent on the relative positions of source, absorber, and detector.[4,16-19] If the absorbing material is close to the counter window, scattering effects are minimized, and true absorption effects are observed. The fractional reduction in counting rate due to the window and air, f_W, will be dependent on the energy of the radiation and the thickness* of the window and air path. The factor f_W is determined from an absorption curve by extrapolation to a negative value of added absorber corresponding to the average thickness of air and window (i.e., to zero total absorber). (See Fig. 1.) In determining such a curve, the absorbing foils should always be placed close to the counter window. Since the average atomic number of air and plastic counter-window materials is close to that of the conveniently prepared aluminum absorbers, aluminum is usually used for absorbing foils. The fact that the air is an extended absorber and scattering medium is neglected here, but it is taken into account in the discussion of the factor f_A.

Serious errors may arise in the extrapolation of absorption curves to zero total absorber. It is often stated that the absorption of beta particles is nearly exponential. This statement can be misleading. The complex nature of beta spectra and absorption and scattering phenomena do, in many cases, give rise to absorption curves that are exponential over the initial portions. In fact, initial half-thickness values or absorption coefficients are conveniently used to determine corrections for absorption analytically (i.e., $N = N_0 e^{-\mu t}$). (For approximate calculations a curve of initial half-thickness versus energy may be useful and is given in Fig. 2.) Careful determinations of absorption curves, however, particularly when using the thin window proportional counters, have indicated that the exponential character of beta absorption is not a valid generalization, and the absorption curves of many nuclides indicate initial curvatures. Zumwalt[4] has suggested a formula for calculating the extrapolated counting rate in terms of the initial slope of the absorption curve and the curvature. In determining the factor f_W graphically, it is obviously necessary to obtain a sufficient number of points on an absorption curve

---

* It is convenient to express the "thickness" of absorbing material in terms of surface density (mass per unit area), since on this basis the absorption of beta particles is nearly independent of the nature of the material, particularly for absorbers of low atomic number.

as close to zero absorber as possible in order to increase the accuracy of the extrapolation. Since the absorption is nearly exponential in many cases, it is convenient to use semilog paper for the graphical presentation.

d. f_A (factor for scattering effect of air). The effect of the air in scattering particles into the counter was determined by Zumwalt[4] indirectly by the use of thin polystyrene films placed between the source and counter. The magnitude of the effect increases with distance from the counter and with decreasing energy of the beta particle. With the sample on the first shelf position (0.5-cm air path), he found that the factor varied from 1.001 for UX_2 (2.3-Mev β) to 1.005 for Co^{60} (0.3-Mev β), and on the fourth shelf (5.3-cm air path), from 1.012 for UX_2 to 1.060 for Co^{60}.

e. f_C (factor for effect of sample covering). In many cases, samples are covered with thin protective plastic films. Since these are close to the sample, scattering effects are important, and the counting rate is usually increased somewhat over what would be observed if only absorption were taking place. This "forescattering" effect was first observed and qualitatively explained by Kovarik.[2] (See also Refs. 4, 20.) The effect is a function of the thickness and atomic number of the absorbing foil, the energy of the beta radiation, and the distance between the sample and the detector. For a given covering material (3 mg/cm² of polystyrene) Pappas[20] found that the forescattering factor was negligible for a source-to-counter distance of 5.3 mm and equal at 21.3, 37.3, and 53.3 mm. He defines the factor as the ratio of counts with the cover on the sample to that with the cover near the counter window (where it acts only as an absorber). The factor decreases with increasing energy of the beta particles from about 1.11 at 0.2 Mev to $\sim$1.01 at 2.2 Mev. Zumwalt[4] examined the forescattering effect (defined as the difference between the counting rate with absorber directly on the source and near the window expressed as a percentage of the counting rate of the sample with no absorber) for second and fourth shelf positions with various beta rays and absorbers. In general, the forescattering effect increases to a maximum with increasing thickness of absorber and then decreases again. The maximum tends to shift toward thicker absorbers as the beta energy increases and as the atomic number of the absorber decreases. The initial slope of the forescattering curves increases with decreasing beta energy and with increasing atomic number of the absorber. The maximum forescattering increases somewhat with decreasing geometry.

Studies of the angular distribution of scattered radiation[21] indicate that the spatial distribution follows a cosine law. The isotropic emission expected from an isolated source is modified, so that the radiation is concentrated in the direction of the detector.

Corrections for the effect of any covering on the sample may be made for the first shelf position by considering the cover as added absorber and extrapolating the absorption curve as in the case of the air and counter-window correction. (See Sec. c, f_W.) At lower geometries, the scattering effects must also be taken into account. These act to compensate the loss by absorption in the cover, and, in many cases, the two effects nearly cancel, giving a value of f_C near unity.

f. f_B (factor for effect of backscattering). Many experimental studies of the backscattering of electrons have been reported.[2,4,5,22–32] These data indicate the dependence of the effect on the nature and thickness of the scattering material, the electron energy, and the geometry of the source.

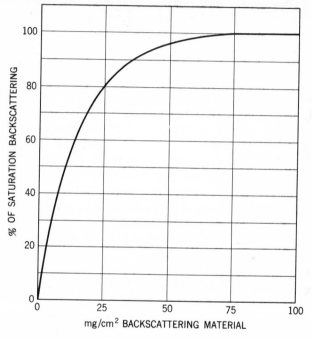

Fig. 3.   Typical backscattering "growth" curve.

The counting rate of a sample is increased by contributions from radiation initially directed away from the counter but scattered back by the material on which the source is mounted. This contribution increases with the thickness of the backing to a saturation value that occurs at a thickness equivalent to about 15 to 25 % of the range of the beta particles in the material (Fig. 3). (The fraction of the range at which saturation backscattering occurs decreases with increasing beta energy and, to a lesser extent, with increasing atomic number of the scatterer.) The per cent increase in counting rate at saturation increases with increasing atomic number of the scatterer (Fig. 4). When appropriate corrections are made for the difference in absorption of the backscattered radiation (which is degraded in energy) in the air and counter window, it is seen that the saturation backscattering for a given scatterer is independent of energy over the range investigated (0.17 to 1.7 Mev).[4,5,26]

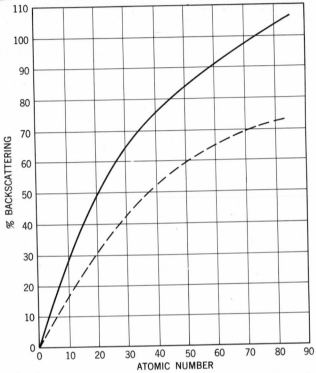

Fig. 4. Saturation backscattering of beta radiation as a function of the atomic number of the backscattering material. The solid line represents data for the source directly on the surface of the backscatterer and the broken line represents data for the source on a thin film separating it from the backscatterer.

Most data on backscattering have been obtained with sources on thin films and scattering materials placed very close to or in contact with the film. Significant increases in the backscattering effect are obtained with the sources placed directly on the scattering materials, possibly as a result of surface imperfections.

The degradation in energy that takes place as a result of inelastic collisions in the process of backscattering is a function of the atomic number of the scatterer.[4,17,26,30] Experimental data on the energy degradation of backscattered radiation indicate somewhat greater energy degradation on scattering from materials of low atomic number than from high. These data are presented in Fig. 5 in terms of the relative half-thicknesses of scattered and unscattered radiation.

Experimental investigations of the angular distribution of backscattered radiation have shown it to be anisotropic.[4,21,25,27,32] The angular aniso-tropy is a function of the atomic number of the backscatterer,[25,27,32] and

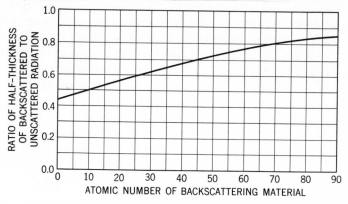

Fig. 5. Energy degradation of backscattered radiation as a function of the atomic number of the backscattering material.

Seliger[27] has shown that the distribution can be conveniently interpreted on the basis of "diffusion" and "side-scattering" effects, the former increasing with atomic number Z, whereas the latter is relatively constant. For material of low Z the energy degradation is much larger at a scattering angle of 90° than at 10°, whereas for high Z both are about the same.

g. f_H (factor for the effect of the housing). Scattering from the walls of the counter shielding and sample support structure contributes negligibly to the observed counting rate of a sample mounted on thin backing except for positions near the base of the housing.[4] The effect increases with energy of the beta ray, and on the fourth shelf (11 mm from the base of an aluminum-lined lead shield and about 53 mm from the tube window) Zumwalt observed an increase from a factor of 1.045 for Co^{60} to 1.102 for UX_2.

This effect is dependent on the materials used for construction of shield linings and sample supports. Materials of low Z should be employed whenever possible to minimize the scattering.

h. f_S (self-absorption and self-scattering factor). It is not always convenient or possible to prepare samples that are effectively "weightless." In many experiments samples of low specific activity are encountered or carriers are used, and it is necessary to count samples of appreciable weight. In such samples scattering and absorption of radiation take place within the source material itself. The effects depend in a complex manner on sample thickness, the effective atomic number of the source material, the energy of the radiation, and the geometry. The largest error in the determination of beta disintegration rates probably lies in the determination of f_S.

Although a number of attempts has been made to generalize the effects of self-absorption and self-scattering and some equations and graphs have been published,[25,33–55,126] the data are, in general, applicable only to experimental conditions duplicating those under which the effects were studied. They are, of course, extremely useful in illustrating the nature of the effects and can be used for approximate corrections. For more accurate work, however, the corrections should be determined empirically by each investigator.

Self-absorption in thick samples is fairly well represented by an equation that assumes exponential absorption and no self-scattering. The activity A_t observed from a sample of thickness, t mg/cm², is given by[39,40]

$$A_t = A_0 \frac{(1 - e^{-\mu t})}{\mu t},$$

where A_0 is the activity that would be observed from a weightless source, and μ is the mass absorption coefficient measured in cm²/mg. For geometries of less than 2π the angular distribution of scattered radiation gives rise to the "forescattering effect" discussed in connection with added absorbers. With increasing weight of a uniformly radioactive source, the specific activity (counts per minute per milligram) rises initially as a result of self-scattering, reaches a maximum (at about 5 to 10% of the range of the beta radiation), and then decreases in accordance with the self-absorption equation (Fig. 6). It is obvious that if sufficient data are not obtained at small thicknesses, or if the simple self-absorption equation is applied to data beyond the maximum, the extrapolated counting rate at zero weight may be in error. In an extreme case the error may be as much as a factor of two. Baker and Katz[52] have shown that such a curve can be described as the product of self-scattering and self-absorption curves. The self-scattering curve is determined from measurements of the angular distribution of the radiation from thick sources and is expressed in terms of the ratio $N_{0,x}/\bar{N}_x$, where $N_{0,x}$ is the activity measured in a direction normal to the plane of the sample of thickness x and $\bar{N}_x$ is the activity averaged over all angles. Although sufficient data to establish a dependence on atomic number were not obtained, a single curve described $N_{0,x}/\bar{N}_x$ as a function of sample thickness (expressed as fraction of the range). Walton[53] derived equations describing the combined effects of self-absorption, self-scattering, and backscattering, which account fairly well for observed

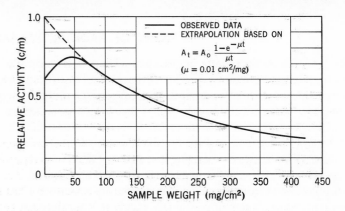

Fig. 6. Illustration of self-absorption and self-scattering effects as a function of sample weight.

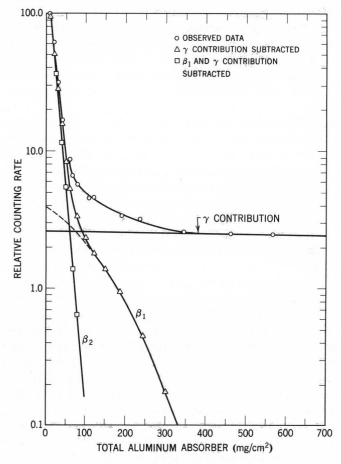

Fig. 7. Analysis of a complex absorption curve.

319

results. It is significant to note that sources with smooth flat surfaces were essential in order to obtain reproducible results in Walton's work. This illustrates the necessity of maintaining standardized conditions in relative counting rate determinations. A similar study has been carried out by Lerch.[54]

The foregoing discussion of the factors that may contribute to errors in beta counting illustrates the complexity of the problem of determining the disintegration rate of even a simple beta emitter from a thick source. When other radiations from the nuclide of interest or genetically related species are present, their contribution to the observed counting rate must be evaluated. In general, absorption techniques are combined with decay measurements to analyze multicomponent systems, and the radiations of interest are corrected for the effect involved. These measurements may introduce additional errors arising from uncertainties in the half-lives of the activities involved and difficulties in analyzing absorption curves (Fig. 7).

2. Suggested techniques for end-window counting. *a. Absolute beta counting.* The most accurate method of determining beta disintegration rates, using end-window counters, is to prepare essentially weightless sources mounted on thin backing and to count in a position of known or calibrated geometry. If the geometry has been determined by the use of some standard (such as RaE [6]) or is calculated, it will be necessary to apply corrections for absorption and scattering effects. Of course, if a geometric efficiency for the radiation has been determined, no corrections will be needed (other than background and any resolution loss). Such techniques should give errors of the order of 5 % or less.

When it is necessary to determine absolute disintegration rates from thick sources within a reasonable degree of error, for example, the order of 10 % or less, it is essential to prepare calibration standards. A high specific activity source of the activity of interest should first be prepared and its disintegration rate determined by 4π counting, coincidence counting (if applicable), or the counting of a weightless source on thin backing in a position of known geometry. Equal aliquots of the activity are added to solutions containing varying known amounts of the element of interest. The compound to be measured is precipitated, the chemical yield determined, and the sample mounted and counted under the desired conditions. The observed counting rates are corrected for chemical yield, background, and resolution losses. A comparison of the observed activity of these samples with the known disintegration rate of the aliquot added gives an over-all counting efficiency for the conditions of the measurement. The counting efficiency for each sample may be plotted graphically as a function of sample weight, and a calibration curve that can be readily applied to the determination of disintegration rates of other samples measured under the same conditions will thereby be obtained. It is, of course, important to ensure reproducibility of the sample mounting technique by determining a number of samples at each weight. Similar curves must be obtained for each activity or compound to be measured.

If it is not possible to obtain a source of high specific activity, or if errors of the order of 20% will suffice, correction factors or equations reported in the literature[25,31–55,126] may be used. In general, these factors have been determined under conditions that should not be difficult to reproduce rather closely. Examples of such correction factors for S^{35} ($\beta^- = 0.167$ Mev, precipitated as $BaSO_4$) and P^{32} ($\beta^- = 1.7$ Mev, precipitated as $MgNH_4PO_4 \cdot 6H_2O$) are given in Fig. 8. The curves represent data[119] for precipitates of different weights collected over a 2-cm² area on filter paper, mounted on cardboard cards, and covered with rubber hydrochloride 0.5 mg/cm² thick. The samples were counted in the first shelf position (geometry factor = 36% of 4π) of a standard end-window flow pro-portional counter assembly, using a counting tube with a 0.6-mg/cm² window. The disintegration rate of an aliquot of a solution of the radionuclide was determined by 4π counting. Equal aliquots were incorporated in precipitates of varying weight and the counting rates were determined. The observed counting rates were corrected for the chemical yield in the precipitation (i.e., the fraction of the added carrier actually mounted) and for the absorption effects of the sample covering, the air path, and the counter window. The correction factor F represents the ratio of the disintegration rate to the corrected counting rate of the samples. Figure 9 gives the correction factor F as a function of beta-particle energy for precipitates of 10 mg/cm² thickness. Differences in the average effective atomic number of precipitates other than those used in determining the curve of Fig. 8 may be ignored for approximate calculations when errors of the order of 10% may be tolerated. The factor is essentially constant for source thicknesses over the range 5 to 15 mg/cm².

Bayhurst and Prestwood[137] have pointed out that the average beta energy, which is dependent on the shape of the beta spectrum, is a better parameter for correlation with counting efficiency than the maximum energy as used in Fig. 9. They have prepared a number of standardized sources and constructed counting efficiency curves as a function of average energy and sample weight by a procedure similar to that outlined above. They estimate an error of the order of 3% for the determination of absolute disintegration rates with this technique.

In some instances, if the activity level permits, a solution of a thick sample may be dissolved and relatively thin sources prepared from small aliquots.

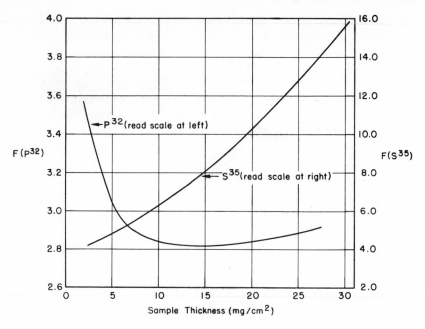

Fig. 8. Empirical correction factors for S^{35} and P^{32} to obtain disintegration rates from observed counting rates.

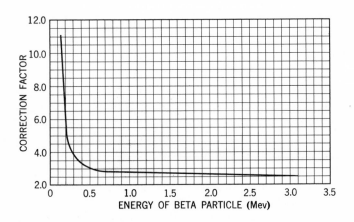

Fig. 9. Empirical self-absorption self-scattering correction factor as a function of beta energy for 10-mg/cm² sources.

b. Relative counting. The most important consideration in relative counting is the reproducibility of sample preparation and mounting techniques. In particular, sample areas and thickness should be the same. Reproducibilities with about 2% error may be expected for the relative counting rates of properly prepared samples. A number of techniques for preparing reproducible samples has been reported.[38,44,45,47,48,51,53,120,121,126] In comparing the counting rates of samples which may differ in chemical composition, weight, size, mounting, etc., corrections must be applied as previously outlined, and consequently the precision of the result may be somewhat less. In general, it is desirable to prepare either very thin samples, in which the corrections are minimized, or samples thick enough to be approaching saturation of the effects, since such samples can be most readily made reproducibly.

3. 2π counting. Counting under conditions of a solid angle of 2π radians may be carried out with external or internal samples. Since the effects of the anisotropic distribution of scattered radiation are minimized at such high geometry, the major effects of concern are true self-absorption and backscattering (including that from the sample itself). These are treated in the manner described for end-window counting, namely, by minimizing the effects, if possible, or by establishing empirical correction factors.[55-57,125]

For samples of low activity 2π counting is particularly advantageous, and numerous instruments have been utilized for this purpose. Samples may be mounted externally by wrapping around glass-walled cylindrical Geiger-Müller counters[134] or internally in a flow-type proportional counter or screen-wall counter.[58] The internal counters are, of course, desirable and sometimes necessary for the counting of very low energy betas. These instruments may be calibrated as described in Sec. B2b to determine a counting yield (or efficiency).

A typical efficiency curve[119] for a flow-type internal proportional counter using weightless samples mounted on 5-mil Pt foils is shown in Fig. 10. The fact that the efficiency falls below 50% at very low energies is probably the result of self-absorption in the sources. It is extremely difficult to prepare sources that are essentially "weightless" for radiation of such low energy. Somewhat different results would be obtained with different mounts as a result of backscattering differences. Backscattering corrections have been determined[122-124] for internal (2π) flow proportional counters as a function of the atomic number of the mounting plate; such a curve[122] is given in Fig. 11, where the backscattering factor F_B represents the ratio of the observed counting rate of a known aliquot of a solution of the radionuclide to one half the known disintegration rate of the aliquot (determined by 4π counting). In many designs of 2π counters materials of construction are close to or in contact with the sample mount. Thus it may not be possible to eliminate or minimize backscattering by the use of thin films for mounting samples, and mounting plates thick enough to

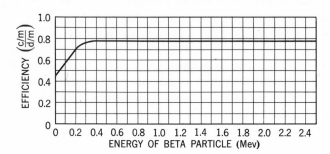

Fig. 10. Counting efficiency of an internal (2π) flow proportional counter for samples mounted on 5-mil Pt.

give saturation backscattering should be used. Even with the same mount material, some differences in backscattering may be observed because of the differences in surface conditions, and where high precision is desired this should be borne in mind.

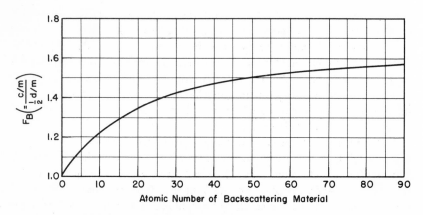

Fig. 11. Backscattering at 2π geometry.

Absolute beta disintegration rates may be determined by using internal (2π) counting technique, with suitable calibration, to an accuracy involving errors of the order of a few per cent.

Suttle and Libby[56] have shown that under conditions of close cylindrical geometry, such as obtains in the use of a screen-wall counter, the assumption of purely exponential absorption is valid for thick sources of simple beta emitters. For a sample thick with respect to λ, the reciprocal of the mass absorption coefficient of the radiation, the absolute specific radioactivity in disintegrations per minute per gram of sample is given by

$$\sigma = RG/A\lambda$$

where R is the observed counting rate in counts per minute, A is the area of the sample in square centimeters, λ is the reciprocal of the absorption coefficient of the radiation in units of grams per square centimeter, and G is the ratio of 4π to the solid angle subtended by the sensitive counter volume at the source. (It is assumed that G is not seriously dependent on the depth of sample and has been averaged over its area.) With this technique, absolute disintegration rates may be obtained with an error of about 5%.

4. 4π counting. If one event were recorded for each disintegration of a radioactive nuclide, a direct measure of the absolute disintegration rate would be readily obtained. In practice, the 4π counter comes closest to achieving this ideal condition. Designs of 4π counters, utilizing twin, facing Geiger or proportional counters, with the sample mounted between them,[59] and multiple counter arrangements,[52] have been described. Methods based on charge collection have also been reported.[60] The sample may also be homogeneously distributed through the detector in the gas phase or in solution (see sections on internal gas counting and beta scintillation counting).

When the two halves of a 4π counter are connected in parallel, coincident events [such as betas, conversion electrons, secondary (delta) rays, x rays, or gammas] will be recorded as a single pulse. The detection efficiency of Geiger and proportional counters for particles is very close to 100%, so that if particle emission (which may be β^-, β^+, conversion, or Auger electrons) accompanies every disintegration (or a known fraction of the disintegrations) the 4π counter, in principle, will record the disintegration rate directly, regardless of the complexity of the decay scheme. If excited states occur with lifetimes longer than the resolving time of the instrument, these will, of course, be recorded as independent events, and their contribution to the observed count must be determined from a knowledge of the decay scheme. Likewise, the presence of isotopic or genetically related radioactivities of the nuclide of interest will contribute to the observed counting rate, and their contribution must be evaluated. As is necessary in all counting methods, background activity and resolution losses must be corrected for.

Although the 4π counter offers a versatile and convenient method of determining absolute disintegration rates, a few sources of error must be considered, namely, absorption of radiation in the mounting film that separates the two counters, the possibility of a counting efficiency of less than 100%, and self-absorption in the sample.

Pate and Yaffe[59] have carried out a systematic survey of 4π counting techniques with twin, facing proportional counters. They have examined the problem of source-mount absorption correction and have pointed out errors in previous publications in connection with this correction. Three techniques have been used to correct for this effect: (1) a "sandwich" procedure,[61] in which the counting rate is determined for the sample on a mount of known thickness and another determination is made with a film identical to the mount covering the sample; (2) a calculation consisting of simplified assumptions of scattering and absorption effects and measurements of 2π and 4π single and sandwiched film counting rates;[62] and (3) an absorption curve method[63] in which the source is mounted on a thin film (5 to 10 $\mu g/cm^2$) and the counting rate is observed as a function of increasing mounting film thickness. Increased thicknesses of film are obtained by allowing thin films of known thickness to adhere to the back of the mounting film. The "absorption curve" is extrapolated to zero thickness to obtain the disintegration rate.

For beta energies above a few hundred kev any of these methods work quite well, since the corrections are small. However, at lower energies the absorption-curve technique appears to be the most accurate. Pate and Yaffe estimate that disintegration rates can be determined within an error of about $\pm 0.2\%$ for energies as low as 67 kev and probably to higher accuracy at somewhat higher energies. Their data are reproduced in Fig. 12 in which the ratio of observed counting rate to disintegration rate (N_T/N_0) is given as a function of beta end-point energy for a series of film thickness. These data may be used directly to obtain the source-mount correction for beta rays of known energy. It should be remembered that beta-ray spectra may differ in shape even for identical end-point energies, and unless the correction is to be applied to a nuclide for which data is given in Fig. 12 the accuracy of the disintegration rate value will not be so high as if an empirical determination of the absorption curve were made.

Geiger-Müller and proportional counters have sensitive volumes that are very nearly 100% efficient, but, as previously discussed, there may be regions of low field strength and a consequent loss in detection efficiency. This is particularly true in internal counters, when the source is mounted on a nonconducting film on which charge may accumulate and cause field distortion. Thin evaporated metal coatings should be used on all mounting films.[59b]

The most difficult correction to make is that for self-absorption in the source. The preparation of very thin sources has plagued many fields of investigation, particularly when known aliquots must be deposited. Examinations with optical and electron microscopes show evaporated sources to consist of small clusters of crystals. Additional solid (as carrier) might fill in the spaces between clusters to give a more uniform but not necessarily thicker source. Thus the technique of determining a self-absorption curve by depositing equal aliquots containing increasing weights of carrier may not be applicable. Optical measurements of S^{35} and

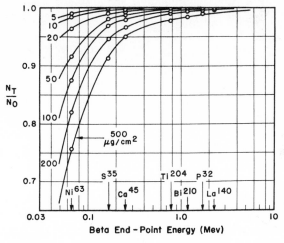

Fig. 12. Absorption parameter (N_T/N_0) as a function of beta end-point energy for a series of film thicknesses. (Pate and Yaffe.[59])

Co^{60} sources[59e] indicate that with increasing weight of carrier the number and size of crystals increase. The problem of source preparation is not easily solved, and, at present, the best that can be done, if a self-absorption curve does not appear applicable, is to examine sources of low-energy betas and estimate the self-absorption loss from the density of the deposit. Corrections of the order of a few per cent may be expected, for example, for Co^{60} (0.3 Mev). They may, of course, be less for more energetic and greater for less energetic radiation.

Methods for preparation of thin films and samples are given by Slätis,[135] Povelites,[138] and Parker et al.[139] The most satisfactory method for preparation of thin uniform samples appears to be by volatilization from a hot filament.[59e,64,140] An electrostatic spray technique[141] and the use of microexchange columns[142] have proved useful for a number of nuclides.

The 4π-counting technique is the most generally applicable method for the determination of disintegration rates of radioactive sources and is recommended for the most precise work. Methods of measurement for the calibration of a number of radioactive sources prepared at the National

Bureau of Standards are reviewed by Seliger and Schwebel.[65] This report illustrates the application of the 4π-, coincidence-, and internal-gas-counting techniques.

5. Internal gas counting. Another type of 4π counting may be achieved by incorporating the activity in the gas phase with the counting mixture in a Geiger or proportional counter[66-68] or by the use of ionization chambers.[69] For the determination of absolute disintegration rates cylindrical tubes are filled with measured quantities of counting and radioactive gases. Each measurement requires a new filling, and the counter characteristics must be checked to ensure proper operating conditions for each determination.

In addition to the corrections for background and resolution losses, the effects of field inhomogeneity at the insulated ends of the sensitive volume (end effect) and the escape of radiation originating near the cathode wall before causing ionization (wall effect) must be considered. End-effect corrections for brass wall counters having flat Lucite ends have been investigated as a function of the length-to-diameter ratio of the counter.[70]

The end effect is dependent on the tube construction and may be determined from measurements in two counters of identical construction and diameter but different length. The wall loss is a function of the energy of the radiation and is inversely proportional to the pressure in the counter and to the diameter of the tube. Backscattering and secondary electron emission from the wall tend to compensate the wall loss. The end and wall effects may be represented as additive correction terms on the actual bare wire length (L) and tube diameter (D). The active volume of the counter V is then given by

$$V = \frac{\pi(D + d)^2(L + l)}{4}$$

where d and l are the corrections to the diameter and wire length, respectively. These corrections may be determined by measurements with counters of constant length and varying diameters, and vice versa, or by measurements with standardized gas samples.

The end effect may be eliminated by the use of paired differential counters,[71] differing only in length, or by employing a movable and a fixed glass shield around the central wire anode.[72]

The wall effect may also be determined by varying the pressure P and plotting the counting rate as a function of $1/P$. The curve may then be extrapolated to $1/P = 0$.

When proper care is exercised in internal gas counting, absolute disintegration rates may be determined with errors of the order of 1% and reproducibilities to within 0.5%.

6. External gas counting. Gas samples may be prepared in cells that can be counted externally in the same manner as a solid sample.[73,74] Corrections for absorption and scattering effects as well as geometry must be made to determine disintegration rates. It is recommended that such cells be calibrated with gases of known disintegration rate if they are to be used for absolute measurements. For relative measurements, external gas counting may prove more convenient than internal counting, and it is necessary only to maintain reproducible conditions to obtain results of high precision.

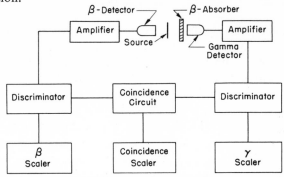

Fig. 13.   Schematic diagram of coincidence counting equipment.

7. Coincidence counting. The coincidence counting technique[9,75–77,136] may be used for absolute disintegration rate determinations in cases in which beta and gamma rays are emitted in sequence within the resolving time of the apparatus (usually of the order of 10^{-6} sec). Although the method may, in principle, be applied to any known decay scheme, it is generally limited to simple systems of a single beta particle followed by one or more gamma rays. The convenience and accuracy of the method rapidly decrease with increasing complexity of the decay scheme.

If a point source of activity (which decays through a single beta followed by a single unconverted gamma) is placed between a beta counter and a gamma counter (shielded so as to be insensitive to beta particles) and the counters are connected through a coincidence circuit, data sufficient for a determination of the absolute disintegration rate may be obtained. A schematic diagram of the apparatus is given in Fig. 13. The counting rate in the beta counter, N_β, is given by

$$N_\beta = N\epsilon_\beta$$

where N is the disintegration rate and ϵ_β is the over-all efficiency of the counter for the beta particles (including geometry). Likewise,

$$N_\gamma = N\epsilon_\gamma$$

where N_γ is the gamma counting rate and ϵ_γ is the efficiency of gamma counting. Since the coincidence counter registers only when a beta and gamma count occur simultaneously in the two counters, the counting rate of true coincidences, N_c, will be

$$N_c = N\epsilon_\beta\epsilon_\gamma$$

(assuming the coincidence circuitry has been adjusted to give unit coincidence efficiency). Then

$$N = N_\beta N_\gamma / N_c.$$

N_β, N_γ, and N_c must be derived from the observed counting rates by the application of a number of corrections. These include corrections for chance (random) coincidences, backgrounds, presence of conversion electrons, any angular correlation, and dead-time losses. In addition, for the coincidence method to be valid, at least one counter must have a constant efficiency (i.e., be equally sensitive) to radiations from all parts of the source. In general, the corrections are dependent on the particular detectors and electronic circuitry employed. It is advisable to use detectors that exhibit high efficiency for one radiation and low efficiency for the other. Thus the beta counter should be a Geiger, proportional, or thin-crystal scintillation counter, all of which are highly efficient for betas but have low gamma counting efficiency. A number of types of gamma counter with fairly high efficiencies has been developed, among which the gamma scintillation counter using thallium-activated NaI is perhaps the best. Beta detection in the gamma counter is prevented by the interposition of a suitable absorber.

Since the pulses arriving at the coincidence circuit have finite widths, two independent counts (not associated with the same disintegration) may overlap and give rise to a coincidence pulse. This random coincidence rate is given by

$$C_R = 2\tau N_\beta N_\gamma$$

where 2τ is the resolving time of the system and N_β and N_γ are the observed singles counting rates in the beta and gamma counters, respectively. [It should be noted that when the observed coincidence rate N_c is not small with respect to the observed singles rates N_β and N_γ the foregoing expression for C_R must be modified to $C_R = 2\tau(N_\beta - N_c)(N_\gamma - N_c)$.][78] The resolving time may be determined by the use of two independent sources suitably shielded from each other so that no scattered or coincident radiation is registered. Any coincidences recorded, then, will be due primarily to a background of cosmic-ray showers and the finite resolving time of the circuit. Sources of different strength should be used to determine any dependence of resolving time on counting rate. The coincidence rate is given by

$$M = B_c + 2\tau N_1 N_2$$

where B_c is the independently measured cosmic-ray-background coincidence rate, and N_1 and N_2 are the singles counting rates.

Since it is desirable to keep the chance rate below the true coincidence rate, a limitation is imposed on the source strength. For C_R to be less than N_c it is necessary that $2\tau N$ be less than unity.

Background activity must be subtracted from the observed counting rates. In the gamma counter the background is determined simply from a measurement using a blank sample mounting. (For sources of high beta activity bremsstrahlung in the beta absorber may also contribute to the gamma background.) In addition to registering normal background activity, the beta counter also records some gamma counts from the source. (In a more complex decay scheme, these gamma counts may give rise to γ-γ coincidences.) The background for the beta (and coincidence) channel is determined with an absorber (usually aluminum) shielding the beta counter so as to stop all betas from the source. The effect of the absorber on the gamma counting efficiency in the beta counter must be determined empirically. With beta counters whose gamma counting efficiency is low, the correction will be small.

Internal conversion of the gamma ray may take place. For the simple decay scheme under consideration (one beta followed by a single gamma) such internal conversion will contribute electron counts to the beta counter and N_β will be given by

$$N_\beta = N[\epsilon_\beta + a\epsilon_e(1 - \epsilon_\beta)]$$

where a is the fraction of total disintegrations leading to conversion electrons (i.e., $a = N_e/N_\beta$), and is related to the internal conversion coefficient α by $a = \alpha/(1 + \alpha)$, and ϵ_e is the efficiency of the beta counter for the counting of conversion electrons. The last term, giving β-e^- coincidences, can often be neglected if ϵ_β and ϵ_e are not too high. Likewise,

$$N_\gamma = N(1 - a)\epsilon_\gamma$$

and

$$N_c = N(1 - a)\epsilon_\gamma\epsilon_\beta.$$

The foregoing equation has no term in ϵ_e, since there can be no coincidences between the conversion electron and the converted gamma. Then

$$\frac{N_\beta N_\gamma}{N_c} = N\left(1 + \frac{a\epsilon_e}{\epsilon_\beta} - a\epsilon_e\right)$$

where it is apparent that it may be advantageous to operate with $\epsilon_\beta \approx 1$, inasmuch as a and ϵ_e are likely to be only inaccurately known. It is possible to discriminate against the conversion electrons in the beta counter by the use of appropriate absorbers when the energy of the electrons is lower than that of the betas. High-energy conversion electrons arise from the conversion of high-energy gammas, but in such cases a is generally small.

If the beta and gamma have a directional correlation in the decay process, this must be known so that the observed coincidence rate for a given orientation of sample and counters may be properly interpreted. The use of high geometry in at least one detector tends to minimize effects of angular correlation.

Dead-time losses in the counters contribute errors in N that are generally small (the order of 1 to 2%). If pulse-height selection is employed as indicated in the schematic diagram (Fig. 13), so that every pulse entering the coincidence circuit will also register in one of the singles channels, any losses that occurred at the detectors may be considered as part of the detection efficiencies. When the dead times appropriate to the singles channels are the same as those for coincidence registration (i.e., when the coincidence resolving time 2τ is negligible with respect to the dead times), the dead-time corrections cancel in the determination of N. However, this cancellation is no longer exact[78] when the coincidence resolving time is comparable to the dead times of the singles channels.

Statistical errors must be applied to the data in order to estimate the accuracy. If careful measurements are made, the coincidence method for determining disintegration rates of nuclides with simple decay schemes may be expected to yield results having an error of 1 to 2%.

When complex decay schemes are involved, the treatment must be extended. For example, if a single beta is followed by more than one gamma ray, the gamma counting efficiency is the sum of the counting efficiencies of the individual gammas with a small correction for $\gamma-\gamma$ coincidences. If both gammas are converted, their conversion coefficients must be known and applied in the equations for N_β, N_γ, and N_c. When more than one beta ray is emitted, a series of coincidence measurements is made with varying absorber thicknesses in front of the beta counter. A coincidence absorption curve is obtained, which may be extrapolated to zero total absorber, and the disintegration rate is determined from a knowledge of the beta branching ratios. Alternatively, energy discrimination in either counter may be effected by the use of pulse-height analyzers. Other combinations of coincidence measurements (such as $\gamma-\gamma$, $\gamma-e^-$, or $\beta-e^-$) may also be employed in certain cases.

The importance of a number of the correction factors discussed above diminishes when the beta detector has high efficiency. Thus, for example, with a 4π beta detector the effects of source size, angular correlations, branching ratios, and conversion electrons are minimized. Coincidence systems utilizing 4π beta detectors have been developed with proportional counters[143] and with liquid scintillation counters.[144]

8. Liquid sample beta counting. In general, counting of liquid samples is employed for relative measurements of rather energetic betas. As in solid sample counting, the conditions of counting must be reproduced accurately for meaningful results. The problems of solution counting, such as the effects of type and energy of the radiation, geometrical arrangement, wall thickness of the counting tube, and the density and atomic number of the medium, are analogous to those encountered in solid sample counting. Experimental data on these effects in liquids, however, are not very extensive. Some of the problems are reviewed by Cook and Duncan,[79] Solomon and Estes,[80] Chiang and Willard,[81] Walton,[82] and Friedman and Hume.[83]

If absolute counting of liquids is necessary, it is recommended that the counter be standardized with a source of known disintegration rate.

9. Beta scintillation counting. Beta particles may be conveniently detected with scintillating crystals,[84] plastic scintillators[85] (solid solutions of organic phosphors in plastics), or liquid scintillator solutions.[86] These detectors must be suitably coupled to a photomultiplier tube for the detection and amplification of the light emitted by the scintillator, either by direct contact or by the use of light guides. A nonoverloading amplifier, pulse-height analyzer, and scaler complete the counting system. Such detectors offer the same advantages as proportional counters in the ability to discriminate between beta rays of different energy and in having small resolving time losses. In addition, they may be used for beta rays of higher energy. In the low-energy region, however, proportional counters give somewhat better resolution.

The major problem in the use of scintillation detectors for low-energy radiation is the correction for background pulses that arise from the thermal noise of the photomultiplier tubes. If the beta spectrum is sufficiently energetic, the background may be discriminated against by suitable biasing. Cooling of the photomultiplier tube, the use of two photomultipliers in a coincidence arrangement,[87] or a combination of both techniques may be employed to reduce the background effect. In addition, techniques for increasing the light output of the scintillators may be utilized to improve the signal-to-noise ratio. For example, in liquid scintillator solutions dissolved oxygen quenches the light output,[88] and sweeping of the solution with an inert gas may be desirable. "Intermediate solvents,"[89] such as naphthalene or biphenyl, may be used as energy transferrers in liquid scintillator solutions to combat the quenching action of some solutes, particularly heavy elements. Since many materials exhibit a delayed fluorescence on exposure to ultra-violet light, caution should be exercised in the preparation of scintillation detectors. For example, m-xylene and benzene exhibit two periods of fluorescence[90] with half-lives in the region of 1 to 2 minutes and 15 to 20 minutes. The photocathode surface of the photomultiplier tubes should be protected from light, or a sufficient period of time should be allowed after exposure for the decay of the fluorescence. Backgrounds, when critical, should, of course, be determined under conditions exactly reproducing those for sample counting.

A variety of counting techniques, employing scintillation detectors with external sources to take advantage of the opportunity for obtaining increased counting efficiency, has been investigated. Samples may be evaporated on the surface of a scintillating crystal or plastic and, to secure a 4π geometry, another crystal or plastic scintillator may be placed on top to form a sandwich;[95,164] the sample may be suspended on a thin foil[91] or in the form of a fine powder[92] in a liquid scintillator medium or in a scintillating gel;[93] and samples may be placed in a well drilled in a crystal or plastic scintillator.[94] None of these techniques, however, avoids the problem of sample self-absorption, and this must be treated in the manner discussed under Geiger-Müller and proportional counting. For routine relative counting, in which reproducibility is the major criterion, these techniques may prove convenient and useful. This is particularly true for the well counter, in which tubes containing solutions of the radioactive samples may be counted without further preparation (if the beta rays are of sufficient energy to penetrate the solution and container). For some applications the suspension counting of low energy or low specific activity solid samples may be desirable. The 4π sandwich-crystal technique has been employed for absolute beta counting,[95] and it appears to be comparable with other techniques for medium and high-energy beta rays but somewhat poorer for low energy. The higher efficiency of anthracene for x rays may make this technique advantageous for the assay of electron-capture nuclides.

The greatest advantage of scintillation counting for beta rays appears to lie in the opportunity of obtaining a 4π detector for low-energy and low-specific-activity sources without sample self-absorption problems. This may be achieved by incorporating the radioactivity into the molecules of the crystal itself[96] or by dissolving the radioactive sample in a liquid scintillator solvent.[97] In the first case the applications are somewhat limited, and the technique, in general, is not suitable or convenient for assay work. The prospects for liquid scintillation counting, however, seem very promising. Steyn[98] has shown that liquid scintillation counting may be successfully employed for the absolute standardization of beta sources. He has used refrigeration to $-20°$ C to reduce the background. A 10-ml scintillator volume in a sample cell was placed directly on the face of the photomultiplier tube and covered with a hemispherical mirror. The voltage and amplification were adjusted so that more than half of the pulses saturated the nonoverloading amplifier. Under these conditions, the differential distribution of the remaining pulses was essentially constant and the integral distribution curve was a straight line that could be extrapolated to zero pulse height to give the true disintegration rate of the source. Accuracies comparable with other methods seem readily attainable with this technique.

Most elements can be prepared in a form that is soluble in a liquid scintillator medium and which does not quench the light output of the scintillator seriously. Even aqueous samples may be made compatible with the organic solutions by the use of alcohol or dioxane. Solutions of the sources may be conveniently measured and introduced into the scintillator, and a wide range of energies and sample weights may be accommodated by the adjustment of scintillator volumes. This technique, though relatively new and in the process of further development, appears to offer a satisfactory solution to the problem of the absolute assay of low specific activity and/or low-energy beta sources.[145–148]

C. Alpha Counting*

The extremely short range of alpha particles in matter necessitates the use of detectors with thin windows or provisions for the introduction of samples into the active volume (internal counters). For general alpha assay work pulse-ionization chambers or proportional counters have proven most satisfactory. Current-measuring devices have a number of disadvantages, such as the dependence of ionization current on the alpha energy and the sample thickness, the lack of distinction between the ionization due to alphas and that due to beta, gamma, or cosmic radiation, and the inability to measure very weak sources. In pulse chambers one alpha will give rise to a single pulse over a wide range of energies. Sample self-absorption is not so important, since a pulse may be detected even after a large fraction of the range has been expended. An alpha pulse can be discriminated from beta, gamma, or cosmic-ray pulses and extremely low backgrounds (<1 c/m) can be attained, thus permitting the accurate measurement of very weak samples.

* This section is based largely on the excellent and comprehensive discussion of alpha assay by A. H. Jaffey.[3]

In general, the same considerations discussed in the case of the determination of beta disintegration rates apply to alpha determinations with
quantitative rather than qualitative differences. The counting yield is
again dependent on such factors as geometry, scattering, absorption, and
detection probability.

1. Geometry factor. Two geometry factors are generally used:
"50%" (or 2π) and "low" ($<1\%$). In the 50% chamber the source is
placed inside the chamber, and, since half the particles are emitted away
from the plate, the relative solid angle is 0.5. In the low-geometry counter
the source is placed at a known distance from an aperture that opens into
the chamber. The relative solid angle is calculated from the known
dimensions of the system. (See Appendix 1.)

2. Scattering. Since alpha particles do not scatter easily, the scattering
factor may be considered as unity, even in low-geometry chambers.
However, backscattering from the sample plate does occur and must be
corrected for in 50% chambers.

3. Backscattering. Not much experimental data have been accumulated on the variation of alpha backscattering with the alpha energy and
atomic number of the scatterer. However, it is known qualitatively that
backscattering increases with increasing atomic number Z and with
decreasing alpha energy. For the most commonly used sample plates
(Pt) the backscattering factor has been determined as 1.04 in a 50%
chamber.[99,100] This result is in good agreement with theoretical predictions.[101] In a low-geometry chamber the backscattering effect is negligible,
and this instrument is useful as an absolute geometry standard.

4. Absorption. In alpha assay work it is the general practice to count
under such conditions that the effect of external absorbers is negligible.
Thus internal counters or low-geometry chambers with a total absorber
path (in gas plus window) equal to less than 90% of the alpha range are used.

For some measurements not requiring high precision it is possible to use
a foil-absorption technique to separate the contributions of mixtures of
alphas with different ranges. The sample is mounted in a 50% geometry
chamber, and the counting rate is measured as a function of the absorber
thickness placed over the sample. The alphas are absorbed linearly, and
the "peeling-off" process is used to determine the contributions of the
individual components (Fig. 14). Thin, smooth samples are necessary for
the application of the method since excessive self-absorption in the sample
results in a nonlinear absorption curve that might erroneously be interpreted as indicating more than one alpha (Fig. 15). Other methods, for
example, the use of a differential range chamber[3] or pulse analysis, may

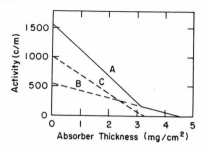

Fig. 14. Resolution of a complex curve (range measurement by foil absorption in a 50% geometry pulse chamber) into two alpha-emitting components with extrapolated ranges of 3.18 and 4.45 mg/cm², respectively.

also be utilized for the purpose of resolving a multicomponent alpha source, but they require special instrumentation.

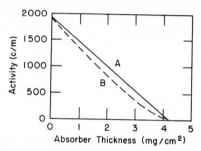

Fig. 15. Effect of excessive self-absorption due to sample thickness. Curve A shows the type of curve determined from a thin, smooth sample. Curve B shows the type of curve determined from a sample having the same type of radioactivity and the same counting rate with no absorber but with an excessive amount of foreign material (for example) carrier salt.

5. Self-absorption.[3,127-132] If visible amounts of solid are present in an alpha sample, losses in counting rate in a 50% geometry chamber may be expected because of self-absorption. In a smoothly spread sample the fraction F of alphas lost by self-absorption has been calculated[102] as

$$F = \tfrac{1}{2}t/R*$$

where t is the sample thickness and R is the effective range of the alpha particle (i.e., the maximum distance an alpha particle can travel through the source material and still register a pulse in the chamber). R is always less than the true range. Since it is difficult to prepare uniformly spread samples, the effect of sample thickness is generally larger than calculated.

* This formula applies to thicknesses less than R. For samples of greater thickness $F = 1 - (R/2t)$.

Scratches in the surface of the mounting plate may also cause losses in counting rate due to absorption of alphas emitted at low angles from the part of the sample deposited in the scratch.

In low-geometry chambers only those alphas emitted nearly vertically are effective, and, if the sample thickness (plus gas and window thickness) is less than the range of the alpha, no appreciable losses will occur. For thicknesses greater than R the fraction lost will be $F = 1 - (R/t)$. Clumping of the sample will usually make the effective thickness larger than the average thickness of the source.

Self-absorption correction curves may be determined by methods analogous to those employed in the case of beta particles. In the determination of such self-absorption curves, it should be realized that as the thickness of sample increases the plateau changes, and it is advisable to extrapolate the plateau for each sample to zero pulse height for comparison.

6. Plateaus. Although a knowledge of the proper operating conditions for the detecting instrument is assumed for the purposes of this report, a discussion of the proper operating voltage in relation to the sample properties is pertinent. Thus it may not always be desirable to use a counter at the flattest portion of its plateau. For the comparison of samples having various degrees of energy degradation (e.g., due to different self-absorption in the sources) it may be desirable to count far up on the plateau where the degraded pulses will register. For thin samples on the same backing reproducible counting can be obtained at any point along the plateau, although it is generally desirable to operate a short distance above the knee of the plateau. In internal proportional counters the counting efficiency may depend on the sample area for large samples when operating just above the plateau knee, and it is advisable to keep the samples confined to areas 1 cm in diameter or less.

7. Beta pulse pile-up. The proportional alpha counter may be used to count alpha particles in the presence of betas, since the pulse heights produced by the betas are much smaller and may be discriminated against by appropriate biasing. However, when the number of beta particles becomes great enough so that they pile up to produce pulses of sufficient magnitude to be registered, the alpha plateau is shortened and the input threshold of the instrument is affected such that a net reduction in alpha counting rate may be observed.[103] The magnitude of the reduction depends on the operating voltage, beta intensity, beta energy, alpha-pulse-amplitude distribution, input amplitude threshold, and individual instrument circuit characteristics. For a beta intensity of 3×10^7 disintegrations per minute (d/m) the reduction is about 0.5%, and for 4×10^8 d/m it is about 2%.

With sufficient beta activity, the plateau disappears and alpha counting is impossible.

8. Counting standards. The reproducibility of counting efficiency is normally checked by the use of alpha-counting standards. If it is desired to adjust the external or internal gain so that a previous counting rate of the standard is reproduced, a thick sample should be used as a standard. In such a sample a wide and continuous distribution of pulse heights is produced, and, since essentially no plateau exists, the counting rate is very sensitive to small variations in gain and may be accurately and easily reproduced. For counting a series of similar samples over a period of time it is usual to measure ratios of the counting rates of sample and a standard. These ratios are generally more reproducible than the individual counting rates.

9. Resolution losses. The corrections for coincidence or resolution losses are discussed in Appendix 2. The low-geometry counter is suggested for very active samples when the resolution loss correction in a 50% chamber is too large to be made accurately.

10. Absolute counting.[3,133,149] Absolute disintegration rates may be determined in 50% chambers when the backscattering correction is known and self-absorption in the source is negligible. The counting efficiency, however, will vary along the plateau because of the slope resulting from the backscattering effect and variations of internal amplification for tracks in different parts of the chamber. These effects limit the accuracy of such absolute determinations and introduce errors of the order of 1%.

Low-geometry counters avoid these effects, and very accurate disintegration rate determinations can be made, provided the geometry is accurately defined and calculated or the counter efficiency is calibrated with a source of known disintegration rate.

The application of liquid scintillation counting to alpha assay avoids the problem of self-absorption in the source material since the sample is homogeneously dispersed in the counting medium. Both differential and integral measurements may be made, and the technique has been shown to be essentially identical in accuracy with low and intermediate geometry counters.[150-152]

11. Relative counting. For many purposes the relative counting rates of sources is sufficient. It is then only necessary to reproduce the counting conditions (such as backscattering and self-absorption) by mounting the samples identically. It is difficult to reproduce self-absorption accurately except by making it very small. For sample thicknesses of the order of 0.1 mg/cm² it is usually possible to spread the samples sufficiently uniformly to attain reproducibilities to within a few per cent.

D. Gamma Counting

1. Relative counting. The high penetrability of gamma radiation in matter permits some simplification of relative counting techniques. The problems of absorption and sample thickness, which are extremely important in alpha and beta counting, are minimized in gamma counting. Thus relative gamma intensity measurements are particularly useful for samples that differ in chemical composition or size and for liquid samples. Of course, in measuring gamma radiation, sufficient absorber must be placed in front of the detector to screen any accompanying beta particles, and such an absorber should be of low-Z material in order to minimize the bremsstrahlung production that accompanies the stopping of the betas.

It is sometimes difficult to maintain a constant geometric relationship between source and detector when solid samples of different size are being compared. Such comparisons, however, may be made readily in solution by using, for example, a high-pressure ionization chamber detector.[104]

2. Absolute gamma counting. In the determination of absolute intensities of gamma radiation the major problem is a knowledge of the intrinsic efficiency of the detector. This efficiency is dependent on the energy of the gamma ray and the nature of the material of which the detector is made. The ordinary brass-walled, argon-filled, end-window Geiger counters have an efficiency of about 1% per Mev gamma energy. This relationship is quite linear above ~ 0.1 Mev. Below this energy the efficiency decreases less rapidly with decreasing energy and finally rises again because of the significant absorption in the gas filling. Many devices have been used to increase the efficiency of detectors for gamma radiation; for example, multiple-chamber counters, counters lined with materials of high atomic number, high-pressure ion chambers, and scintillation detectors.

Any of these detectors may be calibrated with sources of known disintegration rate, and an efficiency curve as a function of gamma-ray energy may be determined. The decay schemes of the standards used must, of course, be known, so that the number of gamma rays accompanying each disintegration may be calculated. The disintegration rate may be determined by using the methods outlined in Sec. B. The intensity of gamma radiation of known energy in a source is then determined from the counting rate of the sample and the efficiency as read from the calibration curve.

In many instances two or more gamma rays are involved in a decay process. If the energies are sufficiently different, the relative contributions may be determined from an absorption curve (usually in lead). The logarithm of the activity is plotted against the thickness of absorber. Since gamma radiation is exponentially absorbed, each component will exhibit a half-thickness characteristic of its energy. The resolution of this method is rather poor, however, and, in general, the energies must differ by about a factor of two for a successful analysis of the curve. (The resolution is somewhat better in the region of a few hundred kev, where the absorption coefficient is a more sensitive function of the energy.) For energies that do not differ sufficiently, a single exponential curve with a half-thickness characteristic of the average energy of the components is obtained.

Experimental verification of theoretical absorption coefficients may be obtained under conditions of so-called "good" geometry, that is, collimated beams with large distances separating source, absorber, and detector so that secondary radiation is not recorded.[105] Under the usual laboratory counting conditions, "good" geometry is rarely attained, and secondaries and scattered radiation may be detected. The effect on absorption curves is to alter the strictly exponential character of the absorption and to introduce curvature that may be erroneously interpreted as an additional component. The exact nature of the effect is dependent on the particular conditions involved. A satisfactory technique places one lead absorber ($\sim$1 gm/cm²) adjacent to the detector window. The position of additional absorbers between the sample and the first absorber is not critical. Such an arrangement results in exponential absorption, although the half-thicknesses observed are somewhat larger than theoretical. The efficiency curve should be determined with the same absorber in position adjacent to the detector if absolute intensities are to be determined.

3. Scintillation counting. Pulse-height analysis. Scintillation counting has proved extremely valuable for gamma counting,[106] and it is rapidly replacing other techniques. By the use of thallium-activated NaI crystals, detection efficiencies approaching 100% may be achieved. The scintillation detector may be calibrated by using standard sources and may be used for integral or differential counting. Integral counting is perhaps somewhat simpler and is not so subject to the electronic difficulties associated with pulse-height analysis. It is recommended for relative measurements or for absolute intensity measurements of samples known to emit a single gamma or x ray. (Multiple gammas may be separated by absorption, as previously described, with the same limitation on resolution.) For absolute measurements one must know the solid angle between the source and the entering face of the crystal, and also an efficiency factor which expresses the probability that a gamma quantum, after striking the crystal, produces a light pulse large enough to register over the background of noise.

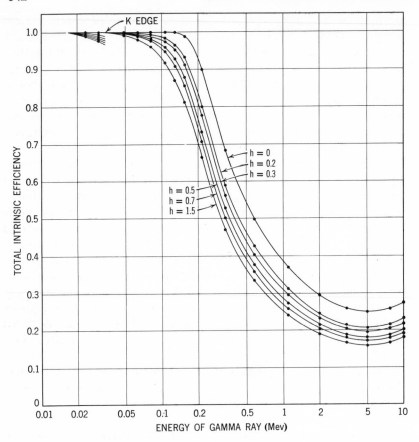

Fig. 16. The total intrinsic efficiency of a NaI(Tl) crystal 1½ in. in diameter and 1 in. high for registering gamma rays in the energy interval 0.01 to 10 Mev. The curves are calculated for source-to-crystal distances h in the range 0 to 1.5 cm., the source being centrally located above the crystal.

This "total intrinsic efficiency," as it has been called, depends upon the energy of the gamma quantum, the size and shape of the crystal, and the distance of the source from the crystal, inasmuch as the source distance affects the paths of the gamma rays in the sodium iodide. Computations have been made of the total intrinsic efficiency by using appropriate theoretical gamma-ray absorption coefficients for NaI, and results have been given by Bell, Davis, and Lazar* and more extensively by Wolicki, Jastrow, and Brooks.[107] Figures 16 to 24 give the results of Bell, Davis, and Lazar for 1½ × 1 in. crystals, 3 × 3 in. crystals, and 3 × 3 in. crystals

* Unpublished.

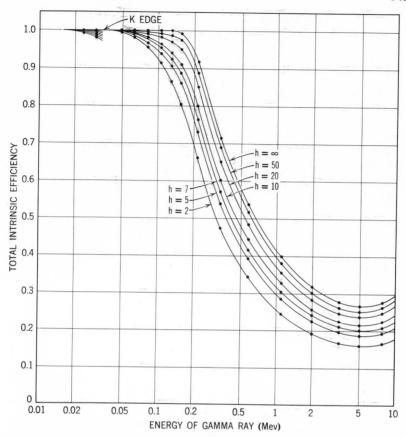

Fig. 17. Curves similar to those of Fig. 16 but calculated for source-to-crystal distances in the range $h = 2$ cm to $h = \infty$.

with the edge of the entering face beveled off to reduce the number of small pulses arising from short path lengths near the corner.

A single or (better still) a multichannel pulse-height analyzer for use with the sodium iodide crystals ensures a much more powerful position for gamma-ray measurements.[107] Not only can sources that emit gamma rays of more than one energy be dealt with, but more reliable results in absolute measurements can often be obtained.[112,113,116,117] One reason for the increased reliability lies in the fact that the pulse-height spectra consist in general of two parts: the pulse distribution from gamma rays that lose all of their energy in the crystal and the pulse distribution from gamma rays that lose only part of their energy in the crystal. The first part stands as a separate peak that is especially prominent in the larger crystals, and use

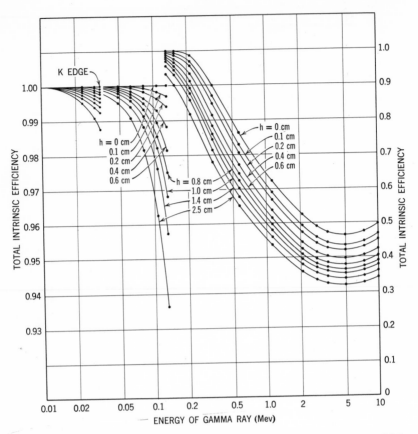

Fig. 18.   The total intrinsic efficiency of a NaI(Tl) crystal 3 in. in diameter and 3 in. high for registering gamma rays in the energy range 0.01 to 10 Mev. The curves are calculated for source-to-crystal distances *h* in the range 0 to 2.5 cm, the source being centrally located above the crystal. The ordinate scale at right applies to the curves above 0.13 Mev in gamma-ray energy.

of the area under this peak as a measure of the gamma-ray intensity insures against the measurement of scattered (and therefore degraded) gamma rays. The requirements of source surroundings then become less stringent. To do this conveniently a figure for the "intrinsic peak efficiency" is needed, that is, the probability that a gamma quantum, after striking the entrance face, loses all of its energy in the sodium iodide. Figures for intrinsic peak efficiencies have been obtained experimentally in relation to the calculated total intrinsic efficiencies by comparing, in a scatter-free geometry, the intensities of the total-energy peaks with the total intensities of the

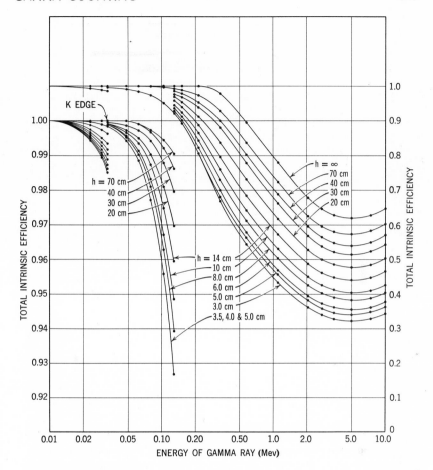

Fig. 19. Curves similar to those of Fig. 18 but calculated for source-to-crystal distances h in the range 3 to 70 cm.

scintillation spectra. Work of this kind has been carried out by Kalkstein and Hollander,[111] by Heath and Schroeder,[112] and by Lazar, Davis, and Bell.[108,109,110] The curves obtained by Lazar et al. are reproduced in Figs. 25 and 26. The curves have been checked by comparison with independently calibrated gamma-ray sources and are thought to be accurate to within 5%. To use them in an absolute gamma count, the area under the total-energy peak, as given by the scintillation spectrometer, is measured and divided by the intrinsic peak efficiency read from Fig. 25 or 26 for the appropriate crystal size, source distance, and gamma-ray energy. Finally, the solid angle factor between source and crystal is applied. In all of this

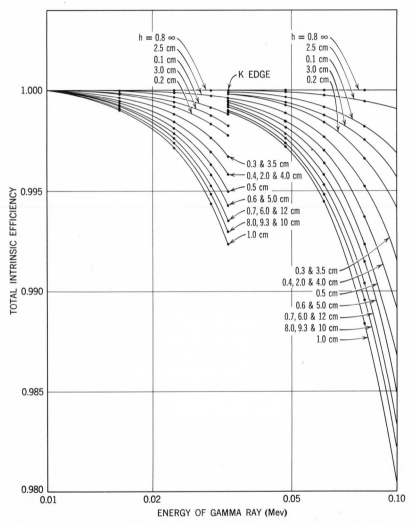

Fig. 20. The total intrinsic efficiency of a NaI(Tl) crystal 3 in. in diameter and 3 in. high, with upper edge beveled at 45° for ½ in., for registering gamma rays in the energy range 0.01 to 0.10 Mev. The curves are calculated for source-to-crystal distances between $h = 0$ and $h = \infty$.

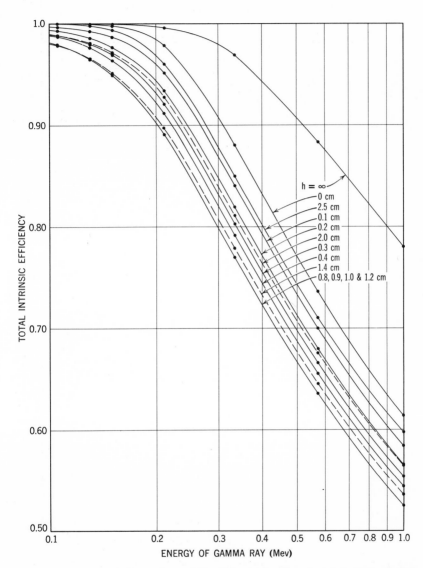

Fig. 21. Curves similar to those of Fig. 20 but giving the calculated efficiency of the 3 × 3 in. beveled crystal for gamma rays in the energy range 0.1 to 1.0 Mev and source-to-crystal distances from 0 to 2.5 cm.

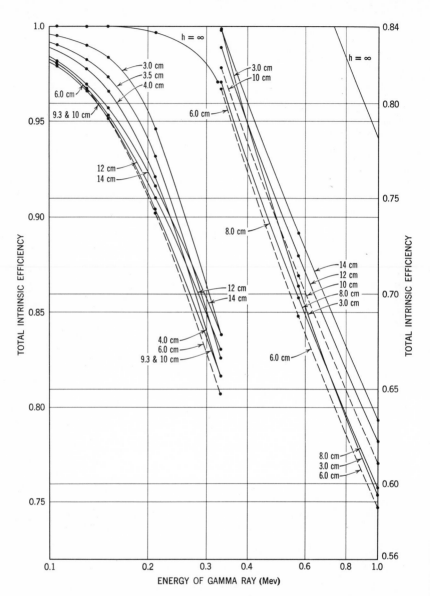

Fig. 22.   Curves similar to those of Fig. 21, but giving the calculated efficiency of the
3 × 3 in. beveled crystal for source-to-crystal distances between $h = 3$ cm and $h = \infty$.
The ordinate scale at right applies to the energy range above 0.35 Mev.

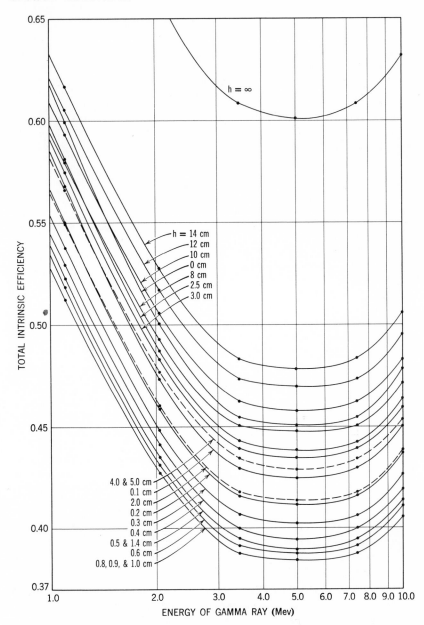

Fig. 23.   Efficiency curves for the beveled 3 × 3 in. NaI(Tl) crystal for gamma rays in the energy range 1.0 to 10 Mev. The curves are calculated for a wide range of source-to-crystal distances *h*. The source is presumed to be centrally located above the crystal.

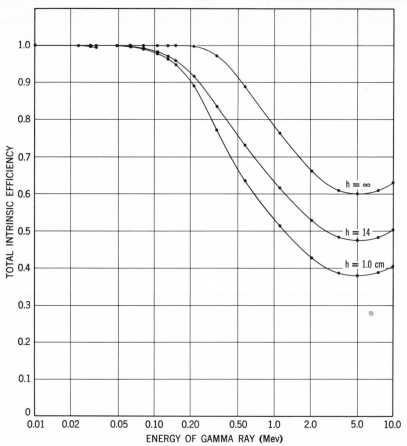

Fig. 24.   Efficiency curves, NaI(Tl) crystal 3 in. diameter and 3 in. high, with ½-in., 45° bevel around upper edge, for registering gamma rays in the energy range 0.01 to 10 Mev. The source is presumed to be located centrally above the crystal, and curves are calculated for source-to-crystal distances h of 1, 14 and ∞ cm.

work it is assumed that the source is small compared to the dimensions of the crystal and that it is situated on a prolongation of the axis of a cylindrical (perhaps beveled) crystal.

The properties of some useful standards for calibration of systems not adequately represented by the curves of Fig. 16–26 are given in Table 1.[113,114] Disintegration rates for these nuclides may be determined by 4π- or coincidence-counting techniques.

Convenient standards may not be readily available for calibration, particularly in the low energy region. In the energy region below about 150 kev essentially all of the gamma rays interact by the photoelectric

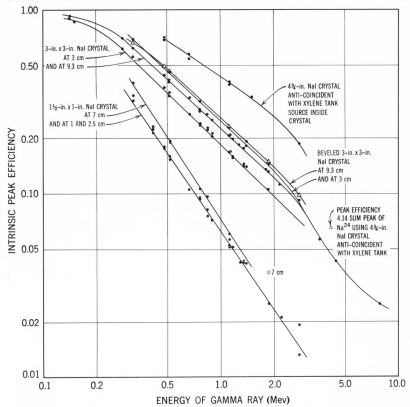

Fig. 25. Experimental curves for the "intrinsic peak efficiencies" of various NaI(Tl) crystal arrangements, expressed as functions of gamma-ray energy in the range 0.1 to 10 Mev. The "intrinsic peak efficiency" refers to the efficiency of the crystal for counting gammas in the *total energy peak* (see text). The distances given refer to the separation between gamma-ray source and entrance face of the crystal, the source being located on the prolongation of the axis of the (cylindrical) crystal. (From Lazar, Davis and Bell.)

process and the pulse-height distribution exhibits a full-energy or photo peak. Events occurring near the edges of the crystal may result in the loss of pulses from the full-energy peak. To avoid these edge effects, the crystal edges may be screened by the use of a collimator or iris. Under these conditions, the intrinsic efficiency of the crystal is essentially 100% and the geometric efficiency may be calculated from the dimensions of the system.

Iodine x rays produced near the surface of the crystal may not interact further and may leave the crystal. This loss is observable in the pulse-height distribution as an additional peak about 28 kev below the photo

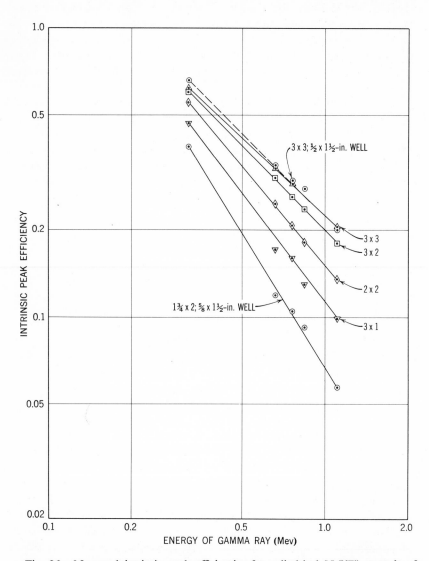

Fig. 26. Measured intrinsic peak efficiencies for cylindrical NaI(Tl) crystals of various shapes and sizes, expressed as functions of gamma-ray energy in the range 0.1 to 2.0 Mev. In two of the arrangements the gamma-ray source was placed in a recess (or *well*) drilled to a depth of $1\frac{1}{2}$ in. axially into the crystal. In the other cases the gamma-ray source was located 9.3 cm from the entering face of the crystal, on a prolongation of the crystal axis. (From Lazar, Davis and Bell).

peak for incident gamma-ray energies of less than about 150 kev (and greater than 33.2 kev, the *K*-edge of iodine). At higher incident energies the resolution of scintillation spectrometers is insufficient to distinguish a separate escape peak. The contribution of pulses in the escape peak must be added to those in the photo peak to give the total gamma intensity. The escape-peak correction may be calculated or determined empirically.

TABLE I. USEFUL STANDARD SOURCES FOR
GAMMA-INTENSITY CALIBRATIONS

Nuclide	Half-Life	Gamma Energy (Mev)	Number of Gammas per Disintegration	Beta Energy (Mev)	Method of Determination of Disintegration Rate
Na^{22}	2.60 y	1.277	1.11[a]	0.542	4π counting,
		0.511	2.00[a]		β-γ coincidence
Na^{24}	15.0 h	1.38	1.00	1.39	4π counting,
		2.76	1.00		β-γ coincidence
Sc^{46}	85 d	0.89	0.995	0.36	4π counting,
		1.12	1.00		β-γ coincidence
Co^{60}	5.27 y	1.332	1.00	0.306	4π counting,
		1.172	1.00		β-γ coincidence
Nb^{95}	35 d	0.745	1.00	0.160	4π, β-γ coincidence
I^{131}	8.14 d	0.364	0.80	0.815	4π
Au^{198}	2.69 d	0.412	0.957	0.963	4π
Hg^{203}	47 d	0.279	0.81	0.208	4π, β-γ coincidence
Tl^{208}	3.1 m[b]	2.62	1.00	1.79	α-counting
Am^{241}	500 y	0.0596	0.357	α	α-counting

[a] Number of gammas per positron.
[b] Supported by 10.6-h Pb^{212}.

Axel[115] has reviewed the problem and presents calculations of the escape-peak probability as a function of gamma-ray energy based on the approximations of infinitely wide and thick crystals and interaction involving only the photoelectric process. Both assumptions are shown to be valid for the energy range considered ($<$150 kev). Figure 27 illustrates the results for the cases of "good" geometry (gammas incident normal to plane of crystal), "intermediate" geometry (crystal subtends a cone of half angle equal to 60°), and "poor" geometry (half angle of cone equal to 90°, i.e., source in direct contact with crystal).

The defined geometry technique is not convenient to apply at higher incident gamma-ray energies, since the collimating screens become too thick and may introduce scattering effects from their edges. In addition, at higher gamma-ray energies the Compton effect becomes appreciable, and the scattered gammas may undergo multiple processes that contribute to pulses in the photo peak. Such effects are extremely difficult to calculate, and calibration techniques using standard sources are advisable for these energies.

In those cases in which two or more gamma rays are emitted within the resolving time of the instrument a peak representing the sum of the gamma-ray energies may be observed. The probability of observing such

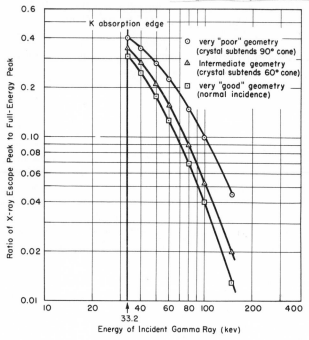

Fig. 27. The x-ray escape probabiltiy for infinitely thick, infinitely wide NaI crystal. (Gamma rays should produce x rays more than 2.5 mm from the edges or the back surface of crystal.)

a peak increases with increasing counting efficiency of the system. For absolute counting-rate determination such events must be added to the counting rate of the gamma ray of interest to give the total counting rate.

The technique of gamma-ray spectrometry utilizing multichannel pulse-height analysis is an extremely useful tool for the assay of radioactive nuclides.[153-155] The efficiency of the method is determined by means of calibrated sources, and direct assay of mixtures of radionuclides may be carried out in many cases without chemical separation.

The Compton distribution of higher energy gamma rays must be subtracted from the photopeaks of the less energetic gamma rays, and a number of systems for accomplishing this have been suggested. A "complement-subtraction method"[156] makes use of a feature of some multichannel analyzers which permits the display of an inverse spectrum.[157] When a calibrated source of a particular nuclide is then counted in the normal mode of operation, its spectrum is subtracted out. The number of counts required to erase this portion of the complemented (or inverse) spectrum completely gives the abundance of the nuclide of interest in the original mixture. The Compton distribution may be minimized by the use of large crystals[158] or, even better, by anticoincidence rejection of the radiation escaping the crystal.[159-162]

Catalogs of gamma-ray spectra have been compiled[153,163] and are useful aids in the identification of unknown radioactive samples.

ACKNOWLEDGMENTS

I should like to express my appreciation to my colleagues, Drs. D. W. Engelkemeir, M. S. Freedman, L. E. Glendenin, A. H. Jaffey, T. B. Novey, and F. T. Porter, for their comments on the manuscript and for their helpful and willing advice during its preparation. Also, the helpful suggestions of members of the Subcommittee on Instruments and Techniques and others who kindly submitted comments on a preliminary draft of the manuscript are gratefully acknowledged.

I wish to thank also P. R. Bell, R. C. Davis and N. H. Lazar of the Oak Ridge National Laboratory for permission to reproduce their data on the gamma-ray absorption efficiencies of sodium iodide crystals.

REFERENCES

1. A. Berthelot, *Compt. rend.*, **212**, 1087 (1941); *ibid.*, **216**, 806 (1943); J. L. Putman, *J. Sci. Instr.*, **26**, 198 (1949); M. I. Kalkstein and W. F. Libby, *Phys. Rev.*, **85**, 368 (1952); G. I. Mulholland and T. P. Kohman, *Phys. Rev.*, **85**, 144 (1952); W. E. Grummitt et al., *Can. J. Chem.*, **34**, 206 (1956); E. C. Anderson and F. N. Hayes, *Ann. Rev. Nuclear Sci.*, **6**, 303 (1956).
2. A. F. Kovarik, *Phil. Mag.*, **20**, 849 (1910); J. McClelland, *Sci. Trans. Roy. Dublin Soc.*, IX, Parts 1 and 2, 1 (1906); H. W. Schmidt, *Ann. Physik*, **23**, 671 (1907); H. W. Schmidt, *Jahrb. Radioak Elektronik*, IV, 4 (20), 451 (1908); J. A. Gray and W. Wilson, *Phil. Mag.*, **20**, 870 (1910); A. F. Kovarik and W. Wilson, *Phil. Mag.*, **20**, 866 (1910); W. Wilson, *Proc. Roy. Soc. (London)*, A-87, 321 (1912); B. F. J. Schonland, *ibid.*, A-104, 235 (1923), A-108, 187 (1925); J. A. Chalmers, *Proc. Cambridge Phil. Soc.*, **25**, 331 (1929), **26**, 252 (1930); P. B.

Wagner, *Phys. Rev.*, **35**, 98 (1930); J. L. Saunderson and O. S. Duffenback, *Phys. Rev.*, **60**, 190 (1941).

3. A. H. Jaffey, in *The Actinide Elements*, G. T. Seaborg and J. J. Katz, Eds., *Natl. Nuclear Energy Ser.*, Vol. 14A, Div. IV, Chap. 16 (McGraw-Hill, New York, 1954).

4. L. R. Zumwalt, *Oak Ridge National Laboratory Report*, *Mon C-397* (September 1949).

5. B. P. Burtt, *Nucleonics*, **5**, 28 (August 1949).

6. T. B. Novey, *Rev. Sci. Instr.*, **21**, 280 (1950).

7. H. O. Anger and C. A. Tobias, *Nuclear Sci. Ser.*, *Prelim. Rept. No. 8*, p. 8, (Natl. Acad. Sci., Natl. Research Council, Washington, D.C., October 1950).

8. G. I. Gleason, J. D. Taylor, and D. L. Tabern, *Nucleonics*, **8**, No. 5, 12 (1951).

9. J. L. Putman, *Brit. J. Radiol.*, **23**, 46 (1950).

10. S. Fried et al., *Phys. Rev.*, **81**, 741 (1951).

11. G. B. Cook, J. F. Duncan, and M. A. Hewitt, *Nucleonics*, **8**, No.1, 24 (1951); G. B. Cook and J. F. Duncan, *J. Chem. Soc.*, **S**, 369 (1949).

12. J. W. Healy, L. C. Schwendiman, and R. C. Thorburn, *HW-18258* (1950).

13. B. Kalmon, *Nucleonics*, **11**, No. 7, 56 (1953).

14. J. L. Putman and R. H. Boxall, *Brit. J. Rad.*, **20**, 190 (1947).

15. G. G. Manov, *Nuclear Sci. Ser.*, *Prelim. Rept. No. 13* (Natl. Acad. Sci., Natl. Research Council, Washington, D.C., July 1953); *Ann. Rev. Nuclear Sci.* **4**, 51 (1954).

16. F. Johnston and J. E. Willard, *Science*, **109**, 11 (1949).

17. T. B. Novey and N. Elliott, in *Radiochemical Studies: The Fission Products*, C. D. Coryell and N. Sugarman, Eds., *Natl. Nuclear Energy Ser.*, Vol. 9, Div. IV, Paper 3 (McGraw-Hill, 1951).

18. N. Elliott and E. Shapiro, *ibid.*, Paper 2.

19. M. Deutsch, *Phys. Rev.*, **61**, 672 (1942); M. Deutsch et al., *Phys. Rev.*, **62**, 3 (1942).

20. A. C. Pappas, *Mass. Inst. Tech.*, *Tech. Rept. No. 63* (1953); also issued as *AECU-2806*.

21. N. Elliott, D. W. Engelkemeir, and W. Rubinson, in *Radiochemical Studies: The Fission Products*, C. D. Coryell and N. Sugarman, Eds., *Natl. Nuclear Energy Ser.*, Vol. 9, Div. IV, Paper 1 (McGraw-Hill, New York, 1951).

22. S. Eklund, *Arkiv Mat. Astron. Fysik*, **33A**, 50 (1945).

23. D. W. Engelkemeir et al., in *Radiochemical Studies: The Fission Products*, C. D. Coryell and N. Sugarman, Eds., *Natl. Nuclear Energy Ser.*, Vol. 9, Div. IV, Paper 5 (McGraw-Hill, New York, 1951).

24. R. F. Cowing and E. DeAmisis, *Science*, **108**, 187 (1948).

25. L. Yaffe and K. M. Justus, *J. Chem. Soc.*, **S**, 341 (1949).

26. L. E. Glendenin and A. K. Solomon, *Science*, **112**, 623 (1950).

27. H. H. Seliger, *Phys. Rev.*, **78**, 491 (1950); **88**, 408 (1952).

28. J. G. Balfour, *J. Sci. Instr.*, **31**, 395 (1954).

29. D. Christian, W. W. Dunning, and D. S. Martin, Jr., *Nucleonics*, **10**, No. 5, 41 (1952).

30. G. L. Brownell, *Nucleonics*, **10**, No. 6, 30 (1952).

31. R. H. Muller, *Phys. Rev.*, **93**, 891 (1954); see also *Chem. Eng. News*, **34**, 4032 (1956).

32. C. H. Collie, P. F. D. Shaw, and H. J. Gale, *Proc. Phys. Soc.* (*London*), **A-63**, 282 (1950); P. F. D. Shaw and C. H. Collie, *J. Chem. Soc.*, **264**, 1217 (1949).

33. D. W. Engelkemeir et al., in *Radiochemical Studies*: *The Fission Products*, C. D. Coryell and N. Sugarman, Eds., *Natl. Nuclear Energy Ser.*, Vol. 9, Div. IV, Paper 4 (McGraw-Hill, 1951).

34. M. Perey, *J. phys. radium*, **6**, Series 8, 28 (1945).

35. T. E. Banks, *Brit. J. Radiol.*, **19**, 333 (1946).

36. M. Haissinsky and B. Pullman, *J. phys. radium*, **8**, 33 (1947).

37. G. Gueben, J. Govaerts, and A. D. M. Stoppani, *Ann. soc. sci. Bruxelles*, **61**, 250 (1947).

38. R. H. Hendricks et al., *J. Phys. Chem.*, **47**, 469 (1943).

39. F. C. Henriques et al., *Ind. Eng. Chem., Anal. Ed.*, **18**, 349, 415 (1946).

40. W. F. Libby, *Anal. Chem.*, **19**, 2 (1947).

41. A. K. Solomon, R. G. Gould, and C. B. Anfinsen, *Phys. Rev.*, **72**, 1097 (1947).

42. E. Broda et al., *Proc. Phys. Soc. (London)*, **60**, 460 (1948).

43. A. N. Wick, H. M. Barnet, and N. Ackerman, *Anal. Chem.*, **21**, 1511 (1949).

44. W. D. Armstrong and J. Schubert, *Anal. Chem.*, **20**, 270 (1948).

45. P. E. Yankwich, T. H. Norris, and J. Huston, *Anal. Chem.*, **19**, 439 (1947); *J. Chem. Phys.*, **14**, 131 (1946); P. E. Yankwich and J. W. Weigl, *Science*, **107**, 651 (1948); also see P. E. Yankwich in Calvin et al., *Isotopic Carbon* (Wiley, New York, 1949).

46. A. F. Reid, in *Preparation and Measurement of Isotopic Tracers* (J. W. Edwards, Ann Arbor, Michigan, 1946).

47. G. K. Schweitzer and B. R. Stein, *Nucleonics*, **7**, No. 3, 65 (1950).

48. C. L. Comar et al., *Nucleonics*, **8**, No. 3, 19 (1951).

49. W. L. Graf, C. L. Comar, and I. B. Whitney, *Nucleonics*, **9**, No. 4, 22 (1951).

50. A. H. W. Aten, Jr., *Nucleonics*, **6**, 68 (January 1950).

51. W. E. Nervik and P. C. Stevenson, *Nucleonics*, **10**, No. 3, 18 (1952).

52. R. G. Baker and L. Katz, *Nucleonics*, **11**, No. 2, 14 (1953).

53. G. N. Walton, J. S. Thompson, and I. F. Croall, *Brit. Atomic Energy Res. Est. Report A.E.R.E. C/R 1136* (1953); B. J. Bowles and G. N. Walton, *ibid.*, *A.E.R.E. C/R 1463* (1954).

54. P. Lerch, *Helv. Phys. Acta*, **26**, 663 (1953); C. Haenny and P. Lerch, *ibid.*, **24**, 602 (1951).

55. E. K. Gora and F. C. Hickey, *Anal. Chem.*, **26**, 1159 (1954).

56. A. D. Suttle and W. F. Libby, *Anal. Chem.*, **27**, 921 (1955).

57. J. G. Cuninghame, M. L. Sizeland, and H. H. Willis, *Brit. Atomic Energy Res. Est. Report A.E.R.E. C/R 1646* (1955).

58. W. F. Libby, *Phys. Rev.*, **46**, 196 (1934); W. F. Libby and D. D. Lee, *Phys. Rev.*, **55**, 245 (1939).

59. See B. D. Pate and L. Yaffe, *Can. J. Chem.* (a) **33**, 15 (1955); (b) **33**, 610 (1955); (c) **33**, 929 (1955); (d) **33**, 1656 (1955); (e) **34**, 265 (1956).

60. R. A. Clark and G. Failla, *Phys. Rev.*, **75**, 328A (1949).

61. R. C. Hawkings, W. F. Merritt, and J. H. Craven, *Proc. Symposium Maintenance of Standards, Natl. Phys. Lab.*, May 1951 (H. M. Stationers Office, London, 1952).

62. H. H. Seliger and L. Cavallo, *J. Research Nat. Bur. Standards*, **47**, 41 (1951); W. B. Mann and H. H. Seliger, *ibid.*, **50**, 197 (1953).

63. F. G. Houtermans et al., *Z. Physik*, **134**, 1 (1952); L. Meyer-Schütsmeister and D. H. Vincent, *ibid.*, 9 (1952); D. B. Smith, *Brit. Atomic Energy Res. Est. Report A.E.R.E. I/R 1210* (1953).

64. J. Milsted, *Brit. Atomic Energy Res. Est. Report A.E.R.E. C/R 1379* (1954).

65. H. H. Seliger and A. Schwebel, *Nucleonics*, **12**, No. 7, 54 (1954).

66. S. C. Brown and W. W. Miller, *Rev. Sci. Instr.*, **18**, 496 (1947); B. J. Fontana, *J. Am. Chem. Soc.*, **64**, 2503 (1942).

67. A. G. Engelkemeir et al., *Phys. Rev.*, **75**, 1825 (1949).

68. R. C. Hawkings, R. F. Hunter, and W. B. Mann, *Can. J. Research*, **27**, 555 (1949).

69. C. D. Jannay and B. J. Moyer, *Rev. Sci. Instr.*, **19**, 667 (1948); W. P. Jesse et al., *Phys. Rev.*, **72**, 478 (1947); H. Palevsky, R. K. Swank, and R. Grenchik, *Rev. Sci. Instr.*, **18**, 298 (1947); J. D. Roberts et al., *Anal. Chem.*, **20**, 904 (1948); G. L. Brownell and H. S. Lockhart, *Nucleonics*, **10**, No. 2, 26 (1952).

70. A. G. Engelkemeir and W. F. Libby, *Rev. Sci. Instr.*, **21**, 550 (1950).

71. W. B. Mann and G. B. Parkinson, *Rev. Sci. Instr.*, **20**, 41 (1949).

72. M. L. Eidinoff, "Conference on Absolute β Counting," *Nuclear Sci. Ser., Prelim. Rept. No. 8*, Paper 9 (Natl. Acad. Sci., Natl. Research Council, Washington, D.C., October 1950).

73. A. S. Newton et al., in *Radiochemical Studies: The Fission Products*, C. D. Coryell and N. Sugarman, Eds., *Natl. Nuclear Energy Ser.*, Vol. 9B, Div. IV, Paper 145 (McGraw-Hill, 1951); E. J. Hoagland and N. Sugarman, *ibid.*, Papers 146 and 147.

74. F. D. Rosen and W. Davis, Jr., *Rev. Sci. Instr.*, **24**, 349 (1953).

75. J. V. Dunworth, *Rev. Sci. Instr.*, **11**, 167 (1940).

76. M. L. Wiedenbeck, *Phys. Rev.*, **72**, 974 (1947); M. L. Wiedenbeck and K. Y. Chu, *Phys. Rev.*, **72**, 1164, 1171 (1947).

77. J. Barnothy and M. Forro, *Rev. Sci. Instr.*, **22**, 415 (1951).

78. M. S. Freedman et al., *Argonne National Laboratory Report 5525*, 29–34 (1956).

79. G. B. Cook and J. F. Duncan, *Modern Radiochemical Practice* (Oxford University Press, New York, 1952).

80. A. K. Solomon and H. D. Estes, *Rev. Sci. Instr.*, **19**, 47 (1948).

81. R. S. Chiang and J. E. Willard, *Science*, **112**, 81 (1950).

82. G. N. Walton, *Physica*, **18**, 1280 (1952).

83. A. J. Friedman and D. N. Hume, *Science*, **112**, 46 (1950).

84. H. Kallmann, *Natur u. Technik*, July 1947; M. Deutsch, *Phys. Rev.*, **73**, 1240 (1948); P. R. Bell, *Phys. Rev.*, **73**, 1405 (1948).

85. W. S. Koski, *Phys. Rev.*, **82**, 230 (1951); M. G. Schorr and F. L. Torney, *ibid.*, **80**, 474 (1950).

86. M. Ageno, M. Chiozzoto and R. Querzoli, *Accad. naz. Lincei*, **6**, 626 (1949) and *Phys. Rev.*, **79**, 720 (1950); M. Kallmann, *Phys. Rev.*, **78**, 621 (1950); G. T. Reynolds, F. B. Harrison, and G. Salvani, *ibid.*, **78**, 488 (1950).

87. H. Kallmann and C. A. Accardo, *R.S.I.*, **21**, 48 (1950).

88. H. H. Seliger, C. A. Ziegler, and I. Jaffe, *Phys. Rev.*, **101**, 988 (1956) and *Nucleonics*, **14**, No. 5, 84 (1956).

89. M. Furst and M. Kallmann, *Phys. Rev.*, **97**, 583 (1955).

90. B. N. Audric and J. V. F. Long, *Research (London)*, **5**, 46 (1952).

91. E. H. Belcher, *J. Sci. Instr.*, **30**, 286 (1953); O. Blüh and F. Terentiuk, *Nucleonics*, **10**, No. 9, 486 (1952); F. Terentiuk, *ibid.*, **12**, No. 1, 61 (1954).

92. F. N. Hayes, B. S. Rogers, and W. H. Langham, *Nucleonics*, **14**, No. 3, 48 (1956).

93. B. L. Funt, *Nucleonics*, **14**, No. 8, 83 (1956); C. G. White and S. Helf, *ibid.*, No. 10, 46 (1956).

94. H. O. Anger, *R.S.I.*, **22**, 912 (1951); W. S. Michel, G. L. Brownell, and J. Mealey, Jr., *Nucleonics*, **14**, No. 11, 96 (1956).

95. B. H. Ketelle, *Phys. Rev.*, **80**, 758 (1950); C. C. Smith, H. H. Seliger, and J. Steyn,

Natl. Bur. Standards J. Research, **57**, 251 (1956); W. B. Mann and H. H. Seliger, *ibid.*, 252 (1956).

96. M. S. Freedman, B. Smaller, and J. May, *Phys. Rev.*, **77**, 759 (1950); G. M. Lewis, *Phil. Mag.*, **43**, 1070 (1952); J. Sharpe and G. H. Stafford, *Proc. Phys. Soc. (London)*, A-**64**, 211 (1951); E. der Mateosian and A. Smith, *Phys. Rev.*, **88**, 1186 (1952).

97. M. D. Raben and A. Bloembergen, *Science*, **114**, 363 (1951); B. N. Audric and J. V. F. Long, *Research (London)*, **5**, 46 (1952); E. C. Farmer and I. A. Berstein, *Science*, **115**, 460 (1952) and *ibid.*, **117**, 279 (1953); F. N. Hayes, R. D. Hiebert, and R. L. Schuh, *ibid.*, **116**, 140 (1952); F. N. Hayes and R. G. Gould, *ibid.*, **117**, 480 (1953).

98. J. Steyn, *Proc. Phys. Soc. (London)*, A-**69**, 865 (1956).

99. B. B. Cunningham, A. Ghiorso, and J. C. Bindman, *The Transuranium Elements*, G. T. Seaborg, J. J. Katz, and W. M. Manning, Eds., *Natl. Nuclear Energy Ser.*, Vol. 14B, Div. IV, Paper 16.3 (McGraw-Hill, New York, 1949).

100. J. H. Parsons et al., *ibid.*, Paper 16.4.

101. J. A. Crawford, *ibid.*, Paper 16.55.

102. B. B. Cunningham, A. Ghiorso, and A. H. Jaffey, *ibid.*, Paper 16.6.

103. D. E. Miller and M. B. Leboeuf, *Nucleonics*, **11**, No. 4, 28 (1953).

104. J. W. Jones and R. T. Overman, *Atomic Energy Comm. Declassified Document, AECD-2367* (1948).

105. C. M. Davisson and R. D. Evans, *Rev. Mod. Phys.*, **24**, 79 (1952).

106. P. R. Bell and J. Cassidy, *Phys. Rev.*, **79**, 173 (1950); C. Eggler and C. M. Huddleston, *Nucleonics*, **14**, No. 4, 34 (1956); *ibid.*, **12**, No. 3, 13 (1954); R. E. Bell, *Ann. Rev. Nuclear Sci.*, **4**, 93 (1954); R. K. Swank, *ibid.*, **4**, 111 (1954); R. Hofstadter and J. A. McIntyre, *Nucleonics*, **7**, No. 3, 32 (1950).

107. E. A. Wolicki, R. Jastrow, and F. Brooks, *Naval Research Laboratory Report NRL-4833* (1956).

108. N. H. Lazar, R. C. Davis, and P. R. Bell, *Nucleonics*, **14**, No. 4, 52 (1956).

109. N. H. Lazar, R. C. Davis, and P. R. Bell, *IRE Trans. on Nuclear Sci.*, **NS-3**, No. 4, 136 (1956).

110. R. C. Davis, P. R. Bell, G. G. Kelley, and N. H. Lazar, *IRE Trans. on Nuclear Sci.*, **NS-3**, No. 4, 82 (1956).

111. M. I. Kalkstein and J. M. Hollander, *Univ. Calif. Rad. Lab. Rept.*, *UCRL-2764* (1954).

112. R. L. Heath and F. Schroeder, Phillips Petrol. Co., Atomic Energy Div., Idaho Falls, Idaho, *Report IDO-16149* (1955).

113. B. Kahn and W. S. Lyon, *Nucleonics*, **11**, No. 11, 63 (1953).

114. D. W. Engelkemeir, private communication (1956).

115. P. Axel, *Brookhaven National Laboratory Report*, *BNL-271* (1953).

116. L. Salmon, *Brit. Atomic Energy Res. Est. Report*, *A.E.R.E. C/M 206* (1954).

117. C. E. Crouthamel and C. E. Johnson, *Argonne National Laboratory Report*, *4924* (1952).

118. See, for example, S. C. Brown, *Nucleonics*, **3**, 50 (August 1948).

119. K. F. Flynn, Argonne National Laboratory, unpublished results.

120. E. L. Abers, *Nucleonics*, **3**, 43 (October 1948).

121. T. T. Hutchens et al., *Nucleonics*, **7**, No. 3, 41 (1950).

122. E. P. Steinberg and L. E. Glendenin, Argonne National Laboratory, unpublished results.

123. C. J. Borkowski and T. H. Handley, *Oak Ridge National Laboratory Report 1056* (1951).
124. D. C. Conway and J. O. Rasmussen, *Univ. Calif. Rad. Lab. Rept., UCRL-2075* (1953).
125. G. K. Schweitzer, B. R. Stein, and J. W. Nehls, *J. Phys. Chem.*, **56**, 692 (1952).
126. F. C. Larson et al., *Anal. Chem.*, **21**, 1206 (1949).
127. R. D. Evans, *Phys. Rev.*, **45**, 29 (1934).
128. G. D. Finney and R. D. Evans, *Phys. Rev.*, **48**, 503 (1935).
129. N. B. Keevil and W. E. Grashem, *Can. J. Research*, **A-21**, 21 (1943).
130. H. H. Nogami and P. M. Hurley, *Trans. Am. Geophys. Union*, **29**, 335 (1948).
131. R. D. Evans and C. Goodman, *Phys. Rev.*, **65**, 216 (1944).
132. M. Blau and H. Sinason, *Science*, **106**, 400 (1947).
133. M. L. Curtis et al., *Nucleonics*, **13**, No. 5, 38 (1955).
134. T. T. Sugihara, R. L. Wolfgang, and W. F. Libby, *Rev. Sci. Instr.*, **24**, 511 (1953).
135. H. Slätis, in *Beta- and Gamma-Ray Spectroscopy*, K. Siegbahn, Ed., Chapter VIII (II) (Interscience, New York, 1955).
136. A. C. G. Mitchell, *ibid.*, Chapters VII and VIII (I).
137. B. P. Bayhurst and R. J. Prestwood, *Nucleonics*, **17**, No. 3, 82 (1959).
138. J. G. Povelites, *Second U.N. Geneva Conference, Paper 664* (1958).
139. W. Parker, M. DeCroës, and K. Sevier, Jr., *Nucl. Instr. and Methods*, **7**, 22 (1960).
140. R. Stockendal and K. E. Bergkvist, *Nucl. Instr.*, **1**, 53 (1957).
141. D. J. Carswell and J. Milsted, *J. Nuclear Energy*, **4**, 51 (1957).
142. S. Bjørnholm, O. B. Nielsen, and R. K. Sheline, *Nature*, **178**, 1110 (1956).
143. P. J. Campion, *Intern. J. Appl. Radiation and Isotopes*, **4**, 232 (1959); R. Gunnink, L. J. Colby, Jr., and J. W. Cobble, *Anal. Chem.*, **31**, 796 (1959).
144. J. Steyn and F. J. Haasbroek, *Second U.N. Geneva Conference, Paper 1104* (1958).
145. J. D. Davidson and P. Feigelson, *Intern. J. Appl. Radiation and Isotopes*, **2**, 1 (1957).
146. D. L. Horrocks and M. H. Studier, *Anal. Chem.*, **30**, 1747 (1958).
147. K. F. Flynn and L. E. Glendenin, *Phys. Rev.*, **116**, 744 (1959).
148. C. G. Bell, Jr., and F. N. Hayes, Eds., *Liquid Scintillation Counting* (Pergamon Press, New York, 1958).
149. R. Hurst and G. R. Hall, *Analyst*, **77**, 790 (1952).
150. P. W. Wright, E. P. Steinberg, and L. E. Glendenin (to be published).
151. J. K. Basson and J. Steyn, *Proc. Phys. Soc. (London)*, **A-67**, 297 (1954).
152. J. K. Basson, *Anal. Chem.*, **28**, 1472 (1956).
153. C. E. Crouthamel, Ed., *Applied Gamma-Ray Spectrometry* (Pergamon Press, New York, 1960).
154. B. Kahn and W. S. Lyon, *Nucleonics*, **11**, No. 11, 61 (1953).
155. R. W. Perkins and J. M. Nielsen, *Second U.N. Geneva Conference, Paper 2377* (1958).
156. W. Lee, *Anal. Chem.*, **31**, 800 (1959).
157. R. W. Schumann and J. P. McMahon, *Rev. Sci. Instr.*, **27**, 675 (1956).
158. L. J. Colby, Jr., and J. W. Cobble, *Anal. Chem.*, **31**, 798 (1959).
159. P. R. Bell, *Science*, **120**, 625 (1954).
160. R. C. Davis et al., *IRE Trans. on Nuclear Sci.*, **NS-3**, No. 4, 82 (1956).
161. C. C. Trail and S. Raboy, *Rev. Sci. Instr.*, **30**, 425 (1959).
162. W. H. Ellett and G. L. Brownell, *Nucl. Instr. and Methods*, **7**, 56 (1960).
163. R. L. Heath, *Atomic Energy Comm. Report, IDO-16408* (July 1957).
164. B. Grimeland, *Intern. J. Appl. Radiation and Isotopes*, **4**, 116 (1958).

GENERAL REFERENCES ON THE MEASUREMENT OF RADIOACTIVITY

Beckerley, Ed., *Annual Reviews of Nuclear Science* (Annual Reviews, Stanford, California) Vol. 1 (1952), Vol. 4 (1954), Vol. 6 (1956).

Birks, *Scintillation Counters* (Pergamon Press, New York, 1953).

Bleuler and Goldsmith, *Experimental Nucleonics* (Rhinehart, New York, 1952).

Broda, *Advances in Radiochemistry* (Cambridge University Press, Cambridge, 1950).

Calvin et al., *Isotopic Carbon* (Wiley, New York, 1949).

Chemical Inst. of Canada, "Proceedings of Conference on Nuclear Chemistry" (held at McMaster University, Hamilton, Ontario, May 15–17, 1947).

Chemical Inst. of Canada, "Symposium on Nuclear and Radiochemistry" (held at McGill University, Montreal, September 7–9, 1955).

"Conference on Absolute Beta Counting,"*Nuclear Sci. Ser., Prelim. Rept. No. 8 (Natl. Acad. Sci., Natl. Research Council*, October 1950).

Cook and Duncan, *Modern Radiochemical Practice* (Oxford University Press, New York, 1952).

Coryell and Sugarman, Eds., *Radiochemical Studies: The Fission Products*, Vol. 9, Div. IV, Natl. Nuclear Energy Ser. (McGraw-Hill, New York, 1951).

Curran, *Luminescence and the Scintillation Counter* (Butterworths, London, 1953).

Curran and Craggs, *Counting Tubes* (Butterworths, London, 1949).

Curtiss, *Measurements of Radioactivity*, U.S. Department of Commerce-National Bur. Standards Circular 476 (1949).

Friedlander and Kennedy, *Nuclear and Radiochemistry* (Wiley, New York, 1955).

Frisch, Ed., *Progress in Nuclear Physics* (Pergamon Press, London, annually).

Glascock, *Labelled Atoms* (Interscience, New York, 1951).

Graves and Froman, Eds., *Miscellaneous Physical and Chemical Techniques of the Los Alamos Project*, Vol. 3, Div. V, Natl. Nuclear Energy Ser. (McGraw-Hill, New York, 1952).

Guest, *Radioisotopes* (Pitman, New York, 1951).

Hahn, *Applied Radiochemistry* (Cornell University Press, Ithaca, 1936).

Hevesy, *Radioactive Indicators* (Interscience, New York, 1948).

Jaffey, Kohman, and Crawford, *A Manual on the Measurement of Radioactivity*, Manhattan District Declassified Doc., *MDDC-388* (August 1944).

Jordan, *Detection of Nuclear Particles*, Ann. Rev. Nuclear Sci., **1**, 207 (1952).

Kamen, *Radioactive Tracers in Biology* (Academic Press, New York, 1957).

Kennedy, *Radioactive Atoms and Isotopic Tracers* (Pennsylvania State College, 1952).

Kohman, *Measurement Techniques of Applied Radiochemistry*, Anal. Chem., **21**, 352 (1949).

Lapp and Andrews, *Nuclear Radiation Physics* (Prentice-Hall, New York, 1954).

Lawrence and Hamilton, Eds., *Advances in Biological and Medical Physics*, Vols. I and II (Academic Press, New York, 1948, 1951).

Libby, *Radiocarbon Dating* (University of Chicago Press, 1952).

Manov, *Standardization of Radioactive Sources*, Ann. Rev. Nuclear Sci., **4**, 51 (1954).

"Nucleonics and Analytical Chemistry Symposium," Anal. Chem., **21**, 318 (1949).

Paneth, *Radioelements as Indicators* (McGraw-Hill, New York, 1928).

Pannell, *Radioactive Measurement Techniques*, Atomic Energy Comm. Declassified Doc., AECD-2270 (Nov. 13, 1947).

Roddis, Ed., *Preparation and Measurement of Isotopes and Some of their Medical Aspects* Suppl. to U.S. Naval Med. Bull. March-April, 1948).

Rossi and Staub, *Ionization Chambers and Counters*, Natl. Nuclear Energy Ser., **2** (McGraw-Hill, New York, 1949).

Seaborg and Katz, Eds., *The Actinide Elements*, Vol. 14A, Div. IV, Natl. Nuclear Energy Ser. (McGraw-Hill, New York, 1954).

Seaborg, Katz, and Manning, Eds., *The Transuranium Elements*, Vol. 14B, Div. IV, Natl. Nuclear Energy Ser. (McGraw-Hill, New York, 1949).

Siegbahn, Ed., *Beta and Gamma-Ray Spectroscopy* (Interscience, New York, 1955).

Siri, Ed., *Isotopic Tracers and Nuclear Radiation* (McGraw-Hill, New York, 1949).

Wahl and Bonner, Eds., *Radioactivity Applied to Chemistry* (Wiley, New York, 1951).

Whitehouse and Putman, *Radioactive Isotopes* (Oxford University Press, New York, 1953).

Wilkinson, *Ionization Chambers and Counters* (Cambridge University Press, Cambridge, 1950).

Wilson, Nier, and Reimann, Eds., *Preparation and Measurement of Isotopic Tracers* (Edwards, Ann Arbor, Michigan, 1946).

Yagoda, *Radioactive Measurements with Nuclear Emulsions* (Wiley, New York, 1949).

APPENDIX I. FORMULAS FOR GEOMETRY CALCULATIONS*

The "geometry" of the aperture for a point source, G_p, is defined as the fraction of the total solid angle subtended by the aperture, that is,

$$G_p = \frac{\Omega_p}{4\pi} \tag{1}$$

For the case of a point source on the axis of a circular aperture (see Fig. 1, p. 363),

$$G_{p'} = \frac{1}{2}\left(1 - \frac{Z}{D}\right) = \frac{1}{2}\left[\frac{a^2}{D(D+Z)}\right]. \tag{2}$$

For the case of a point source off the axis of a circular aperture, and $\rho/D < 1$,

$$G_p = G_{p'} - \frac{3}{8}\rho^2\frac{a^2 Z}{D^5} + \frac{15}{32}\rho^4\frac{a^2 Z}{D^9}\left(Z^2 - \frac{3}{4}a^2\right) + \cdots$$

$$= G_{p'} + \frac{1}{2}\frac{Z}{D}\sum_{n=1}^{\infty}\frac{(-1)^n(2n+1)!}{2^{4n}(n!)^2}\left(\frac{\rho^2}{D^2}\right)^n\sum_{k=0}^{n} m_k \tag{3}$$

* For a much more extensive discussion and tables of point-source geometries, see A. H. Jaffey, *Rev. Sci. Instr.*, **25**, 349 (1954). For tables of solid angles subtended by circular disks and cylinders, see A. V. H. Masket, R. L. Macklin, and H. W. Schmitt, Oak Ridge National Laboratory Report, ORNL-2170 (November 1956), and for a discussion thereof see A. V. Masket, *Rev. Sci. Instr.*, **28**, 191 (1957).

where

$$m_k = \frac{(-1)^{k+1}(4n - 2k)!}{(2n - k)!\,(2n - 2k + 1)!}\left(\frac{Z^2}{D^2}\right)^{n-k}$$

and $G_{p'}$ is taken for the same value of Z and is given by (2).

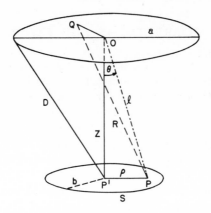

Fig. 1. Relation of source and aperture. O = origin, $PQ = R$, $OP' = Z$, $PP' = \rho$, $\cos\gamma = Z/R$, $OP = l = (Z^2 + \rho^2)^{1/2}$, $Z/l = \cos\theta = x$, $D = (Z^2 + a^2)^{1/2}$. The upper circle represents the circular aperture to a counter, and the lower circle represents a parallel disk source centered on the counter axis.

For the case of a uniformly spread circular source of radius b, coaxial with and parallel to the aperture,

$$G_s = G_{p'} - \frac{3}{16}b^2\frac{a^2 Z}{D^5} + \frac{5}{32}b^4\frac{a^2 Z}{D^9}\left(Z^2 - \frac{3}{4}a^2\right) + \cdots. \qquad (4)$$

Approximate Formulas

For small displacements the geometry of an off-axis point may often be fairly well approximated by $G_{p'}$. Likewise, when b is sufficiently small, the geometry of a uniformly spread source may be approximated by $G_{p'}$. The error introduced in these approximations may be determined from the following:

For the case of small ρ/D or b/D, approximately,

$$G_p = G_{p'}\left\{1 - \frac{3}{4}\rho^2\left[\frac{Z(Z+D)}{D^4}\right]\right\} \qquad (5)$$

and

$$G_s = G_{p'}\left\{1 - \frac{3}{8}b^2\left[\frac{Z(Z+D)}{D^4}\right]\right\}. \qquad (6)$$

If a/Z is also small,

$$G_p = G_{p'}\left(1 - \frac{3}{2}\frac{\rho^2}{Z^2}\right). \tag{7}$$

APPENDIX 2. CORRECTIONS FOR COUNTER NONLINEARITY

The instruments used to detect radioactivity have finite resolving powers, and two events that occur within a short time interval may not be distinguished and recorded separately. Thus some counts may be missed, the fraction lost increasing with increasing counting rate of the sample. This nonlinearity (sometimes referred to as "resolution loss," "dead-time loss," or "coincidence loss") may be determined in a number of ways: (1) the method of paired sources, (2) measurement of calibrated samples, (3) measurement of multiple aliquots, and (4) measurement of the decay of a sample of known half-life. Electronic methods of determining the dead time may also be used.

A. The Method of Paired Sources

Two radioactive sources of approximately equal strength are measured separately and then together. Backgrounds must be subtracted from each measurement, and care must be taken to ensure constant geometry factors for the measurements. If nonlinearity is present, the counting rate of the combined samples will be less than the sum of the individual counting rates. It is advisable to prepare the sources on sturdy material and to support them in a reproducible fashion, for example, as illustrated in Fig. 1. The sources should be small enough so that they can lie side by side,

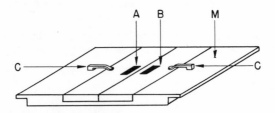

Fig. 1. Suggested source-mount for paired-sample technique. M is a metal plate holder that fits shelf of counter assembly, A and B are sources mounted on metal slides, and C is a metal clip to hold slides in position. Blank slides are used for backgrounds and to replace either sample during separate counting-rate determinations.

without touching each other, on the support. If the sources are too far apart, effects of the variation of counter sensitivity along the window diameter may be encountered.

The sequence of measurements necessary for the evaluation of the resolving time is as follows:

(a) Place both blanks in position and measure the background b.

(b) Replace one blank by sample A and measure counting rate R_A.

(c) Replace other blank by sample B (taking care not to disturb position of sample A) and measure the combined counting rates R_C.

(d) Replace sample A by blank (taking care not to disturb the position of sample B) and measure counting rate R_B. τ is then given by

$$\tau = \frac{R_A + R_B - R_C - b}{R_C^2 - R_A^2 - R_B^2}.$$

The highest statistical accuracy for a given total expenditure of time is obtained when

$$t_A : t_B : t_C : t_b = \sqrt{R_A} : \sqrt{R_B} : \sqrt{R_C} : \sqrt{b} \approx 1 : 1 : \sqrt{2} : \sqrt{b/R_A}.$$

It is convenient and desirable to count R_A, R_B, and R_C for equal periods of time to obtain the highest statistical accuracy for a given total number of counts. It is also desirable to make t_b somewhat greater than indicated by the foregoing ratio.

If a simple equation involving only one parameter relates the true and recorded counting rates, only a single set of measurements involving one pair of samples is necessary. An example of such an equation is

$$N = R + \tau R^2$$

where N is the true counting rate, R is the observed counting rate, and τ is the resolution-correction parameter or dead time.

For correction formulas involving two or more parameters more data are necessary and may be obtained by measuring a series of paired sources of different counting rates.

A complete treatment of the method of paired sources is given by T. P. Kohman in Seaborg, Katz, and Manning, "The Transuranium Elements" *Natl. Nuclear Energy Ser.*, Vol. 14B, **Div. IV**, Paper 22.50 (McGraw-Hill, 1949), and *Anal. Chem.* **21,** 358 (1949).

B. Measurement of Calibrated Samples

If the resolution-loss correction has been determined on one counter, a sample or series of samples of different counting rates can be counted with this counter and the true counting rates determined. The samples may then be used to determine the resolution-loss corrections for other counters.

C. Measurement of Multiple Aliquots

A series of samples may be prepared from a stock solution, each differing in activity by a known multiple from the others. These can then be counted, and the resolution losses may be determined from the decrease in the expected counting rate at higher activities. Of course, careful aliquoting and plating of samples are imperative for the application of this technique.

D. Measurement of the Decay of a Sample of Known Half-life

This technique, in principle, is equivalent to method C. The decay of a pure radio-nuclide with accurately known half-life is followed until the activity reaches a level at which the resolution losses are negligible and the known half-life is observed. The deviation of the initial portion of the decay curve (high counting rate) from the expected half-life gives a measure of the resolution losses.

In the application of all of these methods, small differences between large numbers are generally encountered. Thus it is necessary that counting rates be determined with high statistical accuracy. Methods B, C, and D are somewhat more convenient, since they give correction curves that can readily be applied to counting data.

6 APPLICATIONS TO RADIATION DOSIMETRY

G. S. HURST and **R. H. RITCHIE**
Oak Ridge National Laboratory
Oak Ridge, Tennessee

A. Variation of Dose with Energy for Gamma Rays and Neutrons
B. Experimental Determination of the Dose
C. Instruments and Techniques of Dosimetry

Because of the rapid increase in the number of sources of ionizing radiation being used in research and industry, it is important to have adequate means of measuring those properties of the various radiations that characterize their effect on biological systems.

The property of a radiation field that has been chosen as an approximate index of its ability to damage tissue is the physical "dose," or the energy that would be absorbed by a small volume of tissue-equivalent material if placed at a given point in the radiation field.

There are many good reviews in the literature of the dosimetry of alpha, beta, and gamma radiations.[1] Hence this chapter deals briefly with the fundamental concepts and present trends in the field of dosimetry of external sources of ionizing radiations and emphasizes recent developments in instrumentation and techniques of the dosimetry of gamma rays and neutrons. The discussion is limited to those instruments that may be used to determine the physically significant dose; devices that merely indicate the presence of radiation are excluded from consideration.

The most significant early dose measurements were made by observing the ionization arising in an air-wall ion chamber during irradiation.[2] In fact, the first international unit of dose, the roentgen, was chosen in 1928 in terms of this ionization. The roentgen is presently defined[3] as "that amount of x or gamma radiation such that the associated corpuscular emission per 0.0012393 gram of air produces, in air, ions carrying 1 esu of electricity of either sign." It was realized early in the development of the field that the quantity of energy transferred from radiation to biological material is more fundamental and important than air ionization. Accordingly, in 1950 the International Commission on Radiological Units[4] agreed that the term "dose" shall denote energy absorption per unit mass of the irradiated object. At the 1953 Copenhagen meeting of the International Commission on Radiological Units the *rad* was chosen as the unit of absorbed dose and defined as 100 ergs/gram of any medium. In using this unit, one should always specify the medium under consideration. In the following sections, unless otherwise specified, the rad dose to soft tissue is abbreviated to rad.

The roentgen equivalent physical (rep) is commonly defined as that amount of radiation corresponding to the absorption of 93 ergs/gram of soft tissue (composed approximately of 75% O, 12% C, 10% H, and 4% N by weight). It applies to any kind of radiation directly or indirectly capable of producing ionization and dissipating energy in tissue. The roentgen and the rep are sensibly equal for photons with energy less than 3 Mev and greater than 20 kev.

As the nature and energy of radiation sources become more varied in the rapid development·of nuclear physics, it becomes apparent that in general the doses of different kinds of radiation, for example, gammas and neutrons, which are required to produce comparable biological effects, are quite different. It is convenient to define the relative biological effectiveness (RBE) of a given radiation as

$$\text{RBE} = \frac{\text{dose in rads of gamma radiation from a } Co^{60}\text{* source to produce a given biological change}}{\text{dose in rads of radiation under comparison to produce same biological change}}$$

The RBE has been found to depend upon the type of biological damage under consideration, for example, cataract formation, tumor incidence, genetic change, as well as upon the nature and energy of the radiation. The picture is further complicated because the RBE can be a function of the dose rate as well as of the total accumulated dose. Also, simultaneous irradiation from two types of radiation may lead to damage different from the sum of the damages inflicted by each radiation when administered separately. It has become customary to make the simplifying assumptions[5] that

RBE = 1 for x, gamma, and beta radiation,
    = 10 for protons, fast neutrons, and alpha
    = 20 for ions of mass > 4

These values of RBE are indicative of the over-all damage to man from radiation in the energy ranges in which the radiations normally occur, that is, 50 to 1000 kev x rays, 0.01 to 3 Mev beta, 0.01 to 3 Mev gamma, 0.1 to 14 Mev protons and fast neutrons, and 4 to 8 Mev alpha. Another unit that is sometimes used as a measure of biological damage is the Rem. It is defined as (rad) times (RBE).

* 250 kvp x rays are often used as the reference radiation.

Since the RBE of different types of radiation may be greatly different, it is clear that the methods of measurement should be such that the dose due to each type of radiation is measured separately. Each radiation dose may be weighted with the foregoing RBE values to determine the biological "damage" resulting from the total irradiation.

With the advent of a still greater variety of energies and types of radiation accompanying the growth of nuclear research in the high-energy region and with increasing refinement in radiobiological experimentation, it becomes necessary that those engaged in dosimetry adopt a more sophisticated approach to the problems than has existed in the past.

The present trend in radiobiology is toward relating the RBE for a given effect and radiation to the energy lost per unit path length of the secondary ionizing radiation (LET, or linear energy transfer).[6] The average distance between excited or ionized atoms along the track of a charged particle is thought to determine to a large degree the amount of damage produced. Thus electrons originating from the interaction of gamma rays with matter and knock-on protons from the collision of fast neutrons with hydrogen atoms differ in their physical effect only in the greater average specific ionization produced by the protons. In order to relate the RBE of a given radiation for the production of a given biological effect with the LET spectrum engendered by the radiation, it will be necessary to determine the entire energy distribution of the primary radiation and, by computation, the LET spectrum that exists for the particular biological experiment. A method for measuring LET distributions is under development.[7]

Although such a determination would at present involve a rather sizeable physical research project, methods for accomplishing it are now in existence. Until much detailed measurements are carried out, it has been suggested[8] that biologists conform to a limited number of standard exposure conditions for better intercomparison of work and to facilitate analysis of these conditions.

A. Variation of Dose with Energy for Gamma Rays and Neutrons

1. First-collision dose. The x or gamma ray interacts with matter by essentially three processes for energies less than a few Mev.[9] These processes are, as is well known, photoelectric absorption, Compton scattering, and the production of electron pairs. At higher energies the gamma ray may interact directly with the nucleus, but even in the case of quantum energies as high as 100 Mev nuclear phenomena contribute negligibly to the tissue dose. In the three processes mentioned the ionizing entities produced are electrons of either negative or positive charge. These particles lose energy to tissue by ionization and excitation of atoms or molecules composing the stopping medium. In tissue these energetic particles may cause damage by direct inactivation of a cell subunit or by the formation of deleterious chemical substances. Although the complete mechanism by which the energy of a photon becomes available for producing tissue change has not been elaborated, it is assumed that the total energy dissipated in tissue by a given kind of radiation is a good index of the damage done.

Dose, being defined in terms of energy absorbed per unit mass of medium, may be determined from physical principles if the energy spectrum of the radiation is known. Given the flux and energy spectrum of primary radiation impinging upon a mass of medium that is small compared with the attenuation length of the primary radiation and large in comparison with the range of the secondary ionizing particles, the dose may be determined from the known relation between primary energy and dose. For gamma rays in the energy ranges ordinarily encountered the secondary radiation is small in range compared with the attenuation length of the primary radiation. However, in the case of pair production by gamma rays and for inelastic collisions of neutrons with nuclei in which gamma rays are "secondary" radiation the dose to a given point is not entirely determined by the primary flux at the point under consideration but depends to a certain extent upon the size and shape of the body being irradiated. That portion of the dose that is delivered to the small mass of tissue and is entirely determined by the primary flux there is referred to as the "first-collision dose."

Let an arbitrary mixture of radiations enter a medium of arbitrary size and composition. Suppose we are interested in calculating the energy dissipated in a small volume of this medium. If we choose to begin our calculations with the spectrum of radiations incident on the medium as a whole, the calculation involved is referred to as a *multiple-collision calculation* and is discussed further in Sec. C. If, however, the spectra incident upon the small volume are known from measurements, say, then the energy absorbed by this volume may be determined by a *first-collision calculation*. Clearly, if the small volume is itself in free space, the two calculations are identical.

The first-collision dose $D_\gamma(E)$ for gamma rays may be calculated as follows:

$$D_\gamma(E) = \sum_i \sigma_i N_i f_c + \sum_i \tau_i N_i f_{pe} + \sum_i K_i N_i f_{pp}$$

where $D_\gamma(E)$ = dose in units of Mev per gram for 1 photon/cm^2,
N_i = number of atoms of type i in 1 gram of the medium,
σ_i = Compton scattering cross section per atom,

τ_i = photoelectric cross section per atom,

K_i = pair-production cross section per atom,

f_c = average energy transferred per electron undergoing Compton scattering,

f_{pp} = average energy transferred to the positive and negative electrons formed by the pair-production process,

f_{pe} = average energy transferred to an electron formed by the photoelectric process.

The energy transfer functions f_{pe} and f_{pp} are, simply,

$f_{pe} = E$, where E is the photon energy in Mev

$f_{pp} = E - 2\,\text{mc}^2 = E - 1.022$, when $E \geq 1.022$ Mev

The function f_c may be conveniently determined from a paper by Davisson and Evans[10] in which they use $_e\sigma$ as the Compton total cross section and $_e\sigma_a$ as the Compton cross section for the energy absorbed by the electrons. In this notation

$$f_c = E \frac{_e\sigma_a}{_e\sigma}$$

Values of $D_\gamma(E)$ for soft tissue are plotted in Fig. 1. On the same graph values of $D_\gamma(E)$ are plotted for carbon.

Neutrons having energy in excess of about 20 Mev are capable of causing "spallation" or disintegration of nuclear matter. Since most of the neutron sources in existence (the fission process, artificial sources, most accelerator reactions, etc.) produce neutrons of lower energy, we confine our attention to them. The principal reaction of neutrons with energies in the range 0.001 to 20 Mev with tissue elements is elastic collision. Although inelastic scattering, $(n, 2n)$, and other reactions may occur in this range, they are not important so far as tissue dose is concerned. Fast recoil nuclei generated by elastic collision of neutrons in tissue lose energy by ionization and excitation of molecules much as in the case of secondary electrons by gamma interaction. In contrast, slowly moving recoils lose most of their energy by atomic collisions. Although little is known about the mechanism of this type of reaction, its contribution to the total damage is thought to be small. Since only S-wave neutron scattering on light nuclei is important in this energy range, the recoil nuclei generated by neutrons of energy E_0 have a uniform distribution (for purpose of present discussion) in energy from zero up to a maximum value of

$$E_{\max} = E_0 \frac{4mM}{(m + M)^2}$$

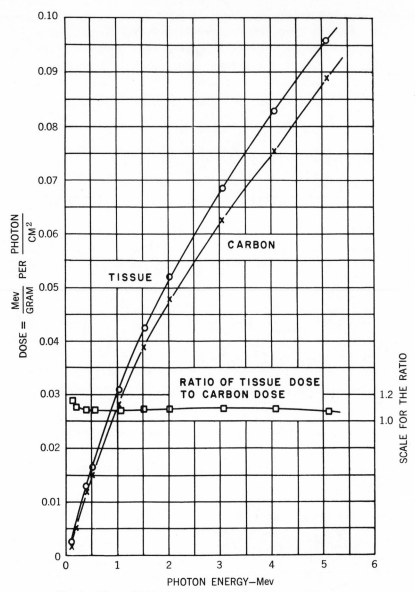

Fig. 1.   First collision dose for photons in tissue and in carbon.

where m and M are the masses of the neutron and recoiling nucleus, respectively. Then the average fractional energy transfer to the recoil f is

$$f = \frac{2mM}{(m + M)^2}$$

Thus f varies from $\frac{1}{2}$ for hydrogen to 0.111 for oxygen.

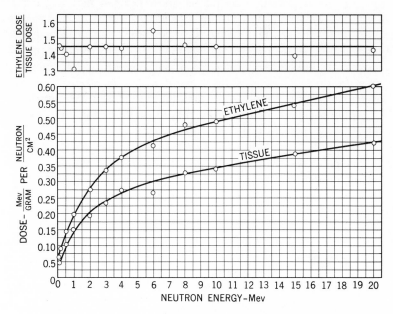

Fig. 2.   First collision dose for neutrons in tissue and in ethylene.

For fast neutrons the first-collision soft-tissue dose due to neutrons of energy E in the range (0.001 to 10 Mev) in which only elastic collisions are important is given by

$$D_n(E) = E \sum_i f_i N_i \sigma_i(E)$$

for unit incident flux. Here f_i is the average fractional part of the neutron energy lost in collisions, σ_i is the elastic cross section, and N_i is the atomic abundance (atoms/gram)— all for the ith kind of nucleus. The summation is carried out over the elements present in soft tissue. For fast neutrons approximately 70 to 90 % of the total dose to soft tissue is absorbed in n–p collisions.

The $D_n(E)$ (Mev/gram) relation for fast neutrons in average soft tissue for (0.1 to 20 Mev) is plotted in Fig. 2. On the same graph the $D_n(E)$ relation is plotted for ethylene. This graph is referred to in a later section.

Thermal neutrons, whether produced in tissue by the slowing down of fast neutrons or by external sources (e.g., the thermal column of a reactor), are considered to be in energetic equilibrium with the molecules of matter in which they are present. They are usually assumed to have a nearly Maxwellian distribution of velocities by virtue of collisions with molecules that have a thermal distribution of energies. Their motion is assumed to be nearly random in direction so that a given neutron may suffer many collisions before being absorbed by a nucleus. In tissue the principal reactions by which thermal neutrons are absorbed and produce damage via the radiation subsequently emitted are the H(n, γ)D reaction, in which the gamma ray has an energy of 2.2 Mev, and the $N^{14}(n, p)C^{14}$ reaction, in which a proton of 0.6 Mev energy is emitted.

In speaking of a first-collision dose in the case of thermal neutrons, we include only the dose delivered by the $N^{14}(n, p)C^{14}$ reaction. For the average tissue composition assumed, one neutron/cm^2 delivers 1.75×10^{-3} Mev/gram. Also when the irradiated mass of tissue is very small only the $N^{14}(n, p)C^{14}$ reaction contributes. The range in tissue of a 0.6 Mev proton is approximately 10^{-3} gram/cm^2; thus a spherical mass with a radius of 10^{-2} cm is more than the size needed to bring the protons into equilibrium. For this amount of tissue we could make a simple first-collision calculation to obtain the total energy absorbed from thermal neutrons, since the contribution to the energy absorbed by the H(n, γ)D reaction is negligible.

As the small mass becomes larger, the importance of the H(n, γ)D reaction increases. For example, Brennan et al.,[11] using the methods of Conger and Giles,[12] have shown that for the idealized mouse (21 cm^3 cylinder whose length is three times its diameter, containing wet tissue having 3% by weight nitrogen and 10% hydrogen) 1 n/cm$^2 = 3.9 \times 10^{-11}$ rad (2.5×10^{-3} Mev/gram). Their calculation is very rough, since the buildup of thermal neutron collision density was neglected, and they tacitly assumed that none of the secondary electrons produced by Compton scattering of the 2.2 Mev gamma rays was able to leave the mouse.

2. Multicollision dose. For purposes of illustration, assume that we wish to measure the dose in a given radiation field. A properly designed dosimeter placed in this field will read the first-collision dose. A man standing at the same point will, in general, receive a different dose at the surface and in the interior of his body because of multiple scattering and absorption of the primary radiations within his body.

To determine this distribution-in-depth for the purpose of radiobiological experimentation, the dose due to each radiation may be measured separately in a mock-up (phantom). Alternatively, the flux and spectrum of each primary radiation may be determined experimentally, and the dose may be calculated by using the first-collision curves given, although this is not usually done because dose measurements are much easier to carry out.

Although the effect of variations in size and shape of the body upon the dose received may be large, certain advantages are attached to the calculation of the effects of multiple scattering for some idealized geometries. Not only do the results enable us to estimate the dose when it cannot be measured, but we may derive an understanding of the general trend of the multiple scattering effect from a study of the results.

Snyder[13] has made depth-dose calculations by assuming a broad plane beam of neutrons incident on the body which is assumed to consist of a semi-infinite slab of soft tissue 30 cm in thickness. The ratio B of the calculated dose at the surface (which coincides approximately with the point of maximum dose in most cases considered) to the first-collision dose existing before the introduction of the man is given in Table 1.

TABLE I. DOSE BUILDUP FACTOR B FOR
FAST NEUTRONS VERSUS ENERGY

Energy (Mev)	B
10	1.52
5	1.68
2.5	1.50
0.5	1.44
0.005	11.27

It is seen that in the range of energies 0.5 to 10 Mev the buildup factor is nearly constant. The reason for the large value of B at 5 kev is that the contribution due to neutrons thermalized in the phantom becomes large, whereas in the Mev region this contribution is negligible. Depth-dose measurements in a large tissue-equivalent phantom using a Po—B source of fast neutrons have been made by Barr and Hurst[14] and substantiate Snyder's calculated value for 2.5 Mev neutrons. Depth-dose measurements with a smaller phantom have also been made.[15]

In the case of gamma rays no systematic theoretical study of buildup and backscattering in phantoms has been made. However, many experimental investigations of depth-dose distribution for x rays have been carried out. Extensive data compiled by Glasser, Quimby, Taylor, and Weatherwax[16] give air, surface, and depth doses for x radiation of various qualities and beam widths. These data show relatively modest surface-dose buildup factors (1.0 to 1.5) for x rays of up to 250 kev energy, using various filters. Data taken by Koch et al.[17] with 5-, 10-, 15-, and 20-Mev gamma rays incident normally on a water phantom show a depth dose that peaks sharply below the surface of the phantom, giving a buildup factor of 3.1 for 20 Mev and 1.3 at 5 Mev at the maximum point, with intermediate values at the other energies.

In problems involving design of shields it is helpful to have values of maximum permissible flux for the different radiations. These values are given in Chapter 7 and are based upon a maximum exposure rate of 60 mrems delivered to soft tissue per eight-hour day.

B. Experimental Determination of the Dose

I. General. A fundamental physical way in which absorbed dose can be measured is by the temperature rise of the irradiated object. Unfortunately, the rise is very small for ordinary irradiations, amounting only to about 2×10^{-6} ° C per rad in soft tissue. However, accurate calorimetric measurements have been carried out in cases in which the radiation intensity is sufficiently high.[18,19,20]

Among the first techniques applied in an attempt to measure dose from x rays and radium were observations of various chemical effects produced by radiations. Ionization techniques superseded these first attempts for practical reasons. Because of the obvious advantages of solid or liquid systems, considerable effort has been devoted to the development of reliable and sensitive methods that exploit chemical effects to measure dose. In practice, it has been found that since about 20 to 35 ev are expended by an ionizing particle for each primary change in a molecule the smallest dose that may be measured with reasonable accuracy without having recourse to chain chemical reactions is a few hundred roentgens. Many workers, notably Taplin and his co-workers,[21] have explored chain reactions in chemical dosimetry. Eventually chemical dosimetry may be employed widely in the measurement of both gamma and neutron doses.

Dosimetry with photographic film is, in principle, another form of chemical dosimetry. Because of the great sensitivity of the results to the developing procedures and because of the existence of complicated blackening laws, as well as the fact that photoelectric absorption in silver and bromine is much greater at critical x-ray wavelengths than in tissue, film must be handled with great circumspection. For x and gamma radiation, however, progress has been made in constructing a film packet that employs special radiators to make the film wavelength independent.[22] Nuclear track film has been used to study the recoils generated in the emulsion by fast neutrons, so that under proper conditions the entire neutron spectrum,[23] and, of course, the dose, may be determined. This procedure suffers from lack of sensitivity and requires a great amount of labor in film reading.

2. Ionization measurements. The Bragg-Gray principle. The use of cavity ionization chambers for the measurement of x and gamma dose was put on a firm basis by the careful work of Gray[24] who also considered the cavity chamber for the measurement of fast neutron dose.[25] He showed that for a cavity chamber the "Bragg-Gray" relation obtains,

$$D = PWJ$$

where D is the dose in the wall in rads, W is the energy in units of 100 ergs required to produce an ion pair in the gas, J is the number of ion pairs formed per gram of the gas, and P is the mass stopping power of the wall material relative to that of the gas for the ionizing particles associated with the incident radiation.[26] A critical review of the "Bragg-Gray" relation for x and gamma rays has been given by Wang.[27] In order for this relation to hold, it is necessary (1) that the dimensions of the cavity be small compared with the range of secondaries in the cavity and (2) that the wall thickness be greater than the range of the most energetic secondaries in the wall and small compared with the attenuation length of the primary radiation in the wall. Other less important conditions may be found in the original literature.[24] If the cavity gas and wall material have the same atomic composition, the first requirement may be relaxed.[28] In this case, neglecting the effects of chemical binding and the state of condensation of matter upon stopping power, $P = \rho$, where ρ is the ratio of the density of the wall material to that of the gas. When wall and cavity are not of the same composition, the relative mass stopping power may be calculated from the conventional stopping-power theory of Bethe as long as the velocity of the ionizing particles is not too low. A recently developed theory by Spencer and Attix[29] shows quantitatively the extent of the error incurred when a small cavity chamber is used with a high-Z wall material.

Some values of W for gases commonly encountered in radiobiological work and in counting applications are given in Chapter 1, Table 1 of this book. It is known that W varies only slightly with the velocity[26] of the ionizing particle and is nearly the same for alpha particles, protons, electrons, etc., as long as the velocity of the particle is greater than that of the valence electrons in the stopping medium. A critical review of the status of W has been given by Bethe and Ashkin,[26] by Marinelli,[30] and by Franzen and Cochran in Chapter 1 of this book.

C. Instruments and Techniques of Dosimetry

I. Direct dose measurements. As pointed out in Sec. A, it is important to measure radiation dose in terms of the energy absorbed by the particular type of matter being irradiated. As advances are made in radiobiology, the need for correlating biological changes with LET will increase. Even at this stage of the science, dosimetry must give the components of a mixture of radiation in which two different types of particles are responsible for the ionization produced and the energy deposited.

Since there is much interest in the problem of studying biological effects of neutrons as compared to gamma rays, much of this section is devoted to the discussion of devices that are helpful in determining the dose components of a mixture of gamma rays and neutrons.

a. Ionization chambers. Because of the empirical fact that W is nearly constant for many types of particles and almost energy-independent, collection of the ionization produced in a gas provides a measure of the energy dissipated. Furthermore, Bragg-Gray designs in which a gas-filled cavity is surrounded by a solid with a similar composition are readily achievable; thus ionization chambers offer a simple means of approximating dose.

For pure gamma rays many satisfactory arrangements have been used, some of which are commercially available. For applications requiring a "precharged" condenser chamber the most convenient is the Victoreen thimble chamber series; whereas, if instantaneous readings of the ionization rate are desired, the carbon-CO_2 [31] ionization chamber is preferable.

In a beam of only fast neutrons an ionization chamber filled with ethylene and surrounded by polyethylene[32] could be used to measure the dose in terms of the energy dissipated per gram of ethylene. This could then be converted to tissue dose by a factor that is essentially energy-independent. (See Fig. 2.) However, neutron beams are always accompanied by gamma radiation, and the foregoing method would indicate both gamma rays and neutrons, a situation that must always be avoided, since predictions of tissue damage or of shielding needed for personnel protection would be in error. The "tissue-equivalent" chamber developed by Rossi and Failla[33] follows the Bragg-Gray design, and care is taken in choosing the gas and walls so that the chamber is nearly tissue-equivalent for fast neutrons, gamma rays, and thermal neutrons. Figure 3 shows a sensitive model of the tissue-equivalent chamber. The ionization produced in the chamber gas is approximately proportional to the energy absorbed by tissue.

b. Proportional counters. Proportional counters may be used to advantage in measuring a fast-neutron dose in the presence of gamma rays.[34] The same approach of achieving a Bragg-Gray cavity may be applied; for example, ethylene gas and polyethylene liners are satisfactory for fast neutrons, since the ratio of energy deposited per gram of ethylene to energy dissipated per gram of tissue is independent of the neutron

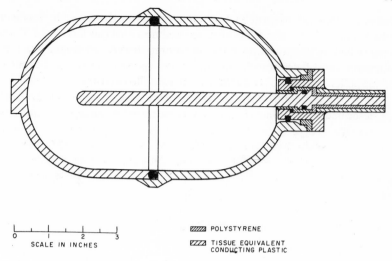

SCALE IN INCHES

▨ POLYSTYRENE

▨ TISSUE EQUIVALENT
CONDUCTING PLASTIC

Fig. 3.   Diagram of the tissue-equivalent ionization chamber.

energy. The essential departure from the ionization-chamber technique is that the ion pairs produced in the gas are determined by a summation of pulse heights rather than an integration of charge or a current measurement. This fact enables us to integrate the pulse due to neutrons while rejecting those due to gamma rays, since the dimensions of the gas cavity and the pressure of gas may be chosen so that the pulse due to electrons (from gamma-ray effects) is smaller than most of the pulses due to recoil protons (from fast-neutron collisions). If the pulse height is proportional to the number of ion pairs, this method of dosimetry is in every way equivalent to the ionization chamber, with the added advantage of being gamma-insensitive.

The equivalence of pulse height and ion pairs depends on two conditions: (1) there must be no electron attachment and (2) the height of the pulse at the output of the linear amplifier must not depend on track orientation. Condition (1) may be fulfilled by excluding from the counter such gases as water vapor and oxygen, which have very large electron attachment cross sections.[35] Very often, liners used in counters and chambers are sources of gas contaminations having large attachment cross sections. These attachment cross sections are often strong functions of the electron agitation energy, which for a given gas depends on the electric field strength. Therefore, in some cases attachment can be minimized by proper selection of the collecting voltage. Condition (2) may be fulfilled by proper selection of the amplifier rise time and decay time.[36] A variation of the angle which recoil protons make with the center wire in a proportional counter causes a variation in the pulse profiles. However, it has been shown[36] that if the rise-time and decay-time constants (assumed to be equal, which is true for many good linear amplifiers)[37] are greater than the collection time of electrons in the counter, the pulse height at the output of the amplifier depends only slightly on the profile rise time.

Many counters that follow these principles have been designed; two[34] are described here. One (Fig. 4) contains an internal alpha source for

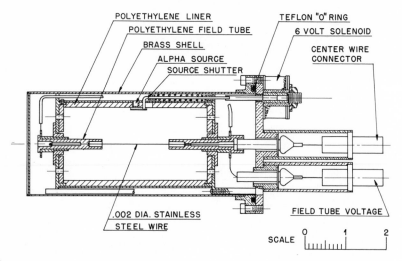

POLYETHYLENE LINER
POLYETHYLENE FIELD TUBE
BRASS SHELL
ALPHA SOURCE
SOURCE SHUTTER

TEFLON "O" RING
6 VOLT SOLENOID
CENTER WIRE CONNECTOR

.002 DIA. STAINLESS STEEL WIRE

FIELD TUBE VOLTAGE

SCALE   0   1   2

Fig. 4.   Diagram of the absolute fast-neutron proportional counter.

calibration. Since the sensitive volume is determined by means of field tubes,[38] the mass of gas is known; hence calibration of the neutron dose may be made without using a known neutron source. The second of these is a simple design that is calibrated either with a known neutron source, using first-collision calculations, or by comparison with the "standard" counter. This instrument was designed primarily for making measurements in tissue-equivalent phantoms and for similar applications. A design that is useful for high-intensity neutron measurements, such as are involved in cyclotron work, is described in Ref. 39. This counter, when used with high-speed electronic equipment is capable of measuring up to 30 rads/min without excessive counting losses, whereas the limits for the "standard" counter and the phantom counter are 0.3 rad/min and 3 rads/min, respectively.

The count rate versus pulse-height curve for Po-Be neutrons for the "standard" counter is shown in Fig. 5. The figure also shows the ease of discriminating against gamma dose rates that are very high compared to the fast-neutron dose rate, for example, the ratio is 100:1 in Fig. 5. Since dose is proportional to the summation of pulse heights, it is also equal to the area under the count rate versus pulse-height curve. The area may be accurately determined with a planimeter, or the summation of pulse heights may be done directly with an electronic pulse integrator.[40] Direct calibration may be made by means of the curve shown for alpha particles.

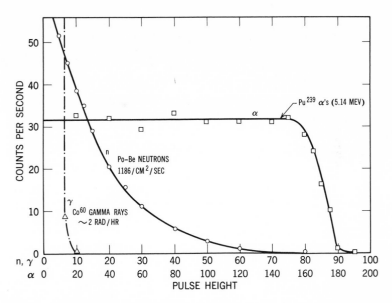

Fig. 5. Counts versus pulse-height curves for gamma rays, fast neutrons, and alpha particles in the absolute counter.

A complete instrument utilizing the standard counter and the pulse integrator has been developed[41] and has been successfully employed in radiation biology and in radiation protection. Consideration of the errors in the fast neutron dose introduced when high intensity gamma-ray fields are "biased out" have been presented.[42,43] Further details have been summarized in National Bureau of Standards Handbook 75.[44]

c. Photographic film. As discussed in Sec. C, bare photographic film is not a true roentgen or gamma-ray dosimeter because the amount of blackening per roentgen depends on photon energy and a thin film would allow secondary electrons to escape. Both objections may be overcome by placing the film in a suitably designed packet such as that developed by Ehrlich.[22] Even with this arrangement, there is quality-dependence in the region of 100 kev which varies with film type as shown in Table 2.

TABLE 2. ENERGY DEPENDENCE FOR EHRLICH-FITCH
FILM DOSIMETER
(Numbers Are Per Cent Deviation from the Correct Dose)

Energy (kev)	DuPont 510	DuPont 605	Eastman 5302	Eastman 5480 (Double Coat)
35	−93	−93	—	—
80	−33	−54	−69	−60
115	+6	−19	−47	−20
150	+24	+7	−25	−15
200	+10	+2	−23	−4
350	+7	0	−11	−2
600	0	0	0	0

The dose ranges* that give an accuracy within approximately ±5%, using the usual photoelectric cell reader, are as shown in Table 3 for various films:

TABLE 3. DOSE RANGES FOR VARIOUS PHOTOGRAPHIC FILMS

Film	Dose Range (rads) Assuming about 1 Mev Photon Energy
DuPont	
Medical x-ray film, extra fast 508	0.05 to 6
Medical x-ray film, par speed 502	0.1 to 10
Industrial x-ray film, very fine grain, 510	1 to 50
Microfilm, positive, 606	15 to 700
Adlux, 1290	15 to 800
Eastman Kodak	
Industrial x-ray film, type K	0.05 to 8
Dental x-ray film, periapical, ultraspeed	0.05 to 25
Spectrographic film, 548–0 (double coated)	1000 to 30,000

The foregoing films may be used in the film dosimeter packet to obtain an accuracy of ±25% (due to energy response only) if the photon energy is greater than 100 kev. Accuracy of the readings over a dose range varies with developing procedures; the foregoing data assume processing in Kodak Liquid X-ray Developer for five minutes at a temperature of 20° C.

2. Spectral measurements, dose, and LET interpretations. The dose at any point in any medium can be calculated through the device of the first-collision curve if the energy spectrum of the radiation actually

---

* Private communication with Margarete Ehrlich, National Bureau of Standards, Washington, D.C.

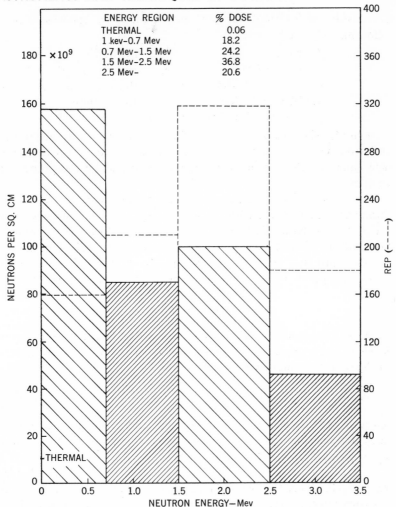

Fig. 6.   Neutron histogram showing a typical spectral measurement.

entering the region can be measured. Then, when the actual measured spectrum is multiplied by the first-collision curve, the dose is obtained. For fast neutrons the use of threshold detectors[45] permits the spectrum to be measured well enough to compute the dose. With the combined use of gold (for thermal neutrons), the $S^{32}(n, p)P^{32}$ reaction, having a threshold at 2.5 Mev, and three fissionable materials (Pu^{239} with B^{10}, Np^{237}, and U^{238}), having effective thresholds at 1 kev, 0.7 Mev, and 1.5 Mev, respectively, spectral information like that shown in Fig. 6 can be obtained.

Conversion to dose in tissue rad units is made by application of the following collision factors:

Thermal	0.028×10^{-9} rad/n/cm^2
1 kev to 0.7 Mev	0.95×10^{-9} rad/n/cm^2
0.7 Mev to 1.5 Mev	2.4×10^{-9} rad/n/cm^2
1.5 Mev to 2.5 Mev	3.0×10^{-9} rad/n/cm^2
greater than 2.5 Mev*	3.7×10^{-9} rad/n/cm^2

Figure 6 is shown as an example and was measured for the ORNL 86-in. cyclotron Be(p, n) reaction. Good agreement was found for the dose as determined by the threshold detector method and by the proportional counter.

One outstanding advantage of the threshold-detector method of dosimetry is that the LET distribution function is easily determined by the use of the calculations of Boag.[46] He has calculated LET distributions for fast neutrons of various energies in water, assuming that all of the absorbed energy is just that of the recoil protons. Based on his formulation, the energy lost per unit distance for protons in water may be written

$$L(E) = \frac{7.93 \ln (31.2E)}{E}$$

where $L(E)$ has units of kev per micron and E is the energy of the proton in Mev. The distribution function $\phi[L(\epsilon)]$, which expresses the distribution of the absorbed energy with L, is given by

$$\phi[L(\epsilon)] = \frac{2\epsilon^2(1 - \epsilon/E_0)}{7.93E_0[\ln (31.2\epsilon) - 1]}$$

where E_0 is the incident neutron energy, and ϵ is the variable energy subject to the condition, $0 \leq \epsilon \leq E_0$. $L(E)$ corresponding to ϵ is obtained by replacing E by ϵ in $L(E)$.

Figure 7 shows the function $\phi[L(\epsilon)]$ for $E_0 = 0.3$, 1.0, 2.0, and 3.0 Mev, respectively. Since the histogram in Fig. 6 contains the first-collision dose for each interval, having average energies 0.3, 1.0, 2.0, and 3.0 Mev, all that is required to get the absorbed energy distribution (as a function of L) for the neutron spectrum is to multiply the curves for the shown values of E_0 by the fractions of dose in the different energy ranges. This gives the broken curve shown in Fig. 7. The mean L may be defined formally as

$$\bar{L} = \frac{\displaystyle\int_0^\infty L\phi(L)\, dL}{\displaystyle\int_0^\infty \phi(L)\, dL}$$

which has a value of 48 kev/μ for the broken curve.

* Assuming a mean neutron energy of 3.0 Mev.

In cases in which the gamma-ray spectrum consists of discrete energies the small single-crystal scintillation spectrometer can be used to determine the spectrum. Gamma-ray tissue dose could then be determined with the first-collision curve (Fig. 1), just as in the case of fast neutrons. However, in the usual dosimetry problem degraded photons due to Compton scattering make the problem of measuring the spectrum very difficult. Two scintillation crystals[47] set for coincidence between the Compton-scattered

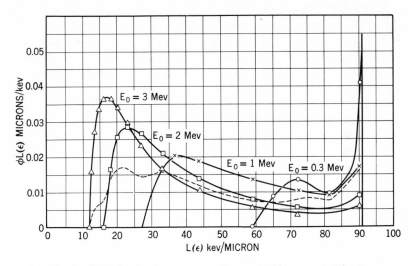

Fig. 7.   LET distribution corresponding to the histogram in Fig. 6.

photon and the scattered electron can be used to determine the spectrum when there is no pair production. When pair production is important, three crystals[48] are used; two of these crystals, when in coincidence, open a gate for the pulses coming from the third. In this manner all lines except those due to pair production are eliminated. Even these methods have serious limitations for dosimetry, since they depend on collimated gamma radiation.

A spherical proportional counter designed to give a direct measure of the LET spectrum engendered by radiation in tissue has been proposed and built by Rossi and Rosenzweig.[7] They have shown that the dose $D(L)$ per unit interval of LET dL is given by

$$D(L) = \frac{1}{2\pi r^2}\left(\frac{L}{h}\right)\left\{-h^3\frac{d}{dh}\left[\frac{Q(h)}{h}\right]\right\}$$

where r is the radius of a spherical tissue equivalent counter and $Q(h)$ is the observed spectrum of pulse heights; h is the pulse height obtained when a particle having a LET L in tissue traverses a major diameter of the counter. A disadvantage of this scheme is the loss of accuracy incurred in the indicated differentiation of the pulse-height spectrum.

3. Determination of the components of a mixture of neutrons and gamma rays. To measure components of a mixture of gamma and neutron radiation ideally, two dosimeters would be used—one completely insensitive to gamma rays, the other completely insensitive to neutrons. Since this ideal cannot be completely realized in practice, other types of measurement are often required.

For fast neutrons, proportional counters (filled with ethylene and lined with polyethylene) may be operated in such a way that only recoil atoms are counted, hence the instrument is insensitive to gamma radiation. It is easy, for example, to measure a neutron dose of 10^{-4} rad/hr in the presence of 2 rads/hr gamma radiation.

Walls and gases of ionization chambers suitable for dosimetry must be of material having low atomic weights. Thus fast neutrons, on colliding with these elements, impart appreciable energy, since the average fraction (f_e) of energy imparted per elastic collision (assuming isotropic scattering in the center of mass system) is $2M/(M + 1)^2$, where M is the atomic mass of the recoil atom. For example, the energy imparted to 1 gram of carbon atoms (D_c) for one incident neutron per square centimeter is

$$D_c = N_c \sigma_c f_c E$$

where N_c, the number of carbon atoms in a gram, is 5.0×10^{22}, σ_c is the scattering cross section for neutrons of energy E, and f_c is the fractional energy imparted per collision. The fraction f_c is equal to 0.142 for carbon. When the quantity D_c is multiplied by the number of neutrons per square centimeter per tissue rad, as determined from Fig. 2, a quantity E_n is obtained which is the amount of energy absorbed by 1 gram of carbon atoms for 1 tissue rad of incident fast neutrons. Let us define the fraction P as

$$P = \frac{E_n}{E_\gamma}$$

where E_γ is the energy absorbed by 1 gram of carbon for 1 rad of gamma radiation. Evaluation of P, based on carbon-neutron cross sections as tabulated, gives the following values of P as a function of neutron energy E (Table 4). A similar calculation gives values for CO_2 which, as seen in Table 4, depend sharply on neutron energy. If the W-values for the recoil atoms and the secondary electrons were assumed to be equal, then the response of a carbon-CO_2 chamber to neutrons would be some value

TABLE 4. VARIATION OF P WITH NEUTRON ENERGY E. P IS THE RATIO OF THE ENERGY ABSORBED IN ONE GRAM OF CARBON (or CO_2) DUE TO ONE RAD OF FAST NEUTRONS TO THE ENERGY ABSORBED IN ONE GRAM OF CARBON (or CO_2) DUE TO ONE RAD OF GAMMA RAYS

E (Mev)	P (%)	
	C	CO_2
0.1	0.11	—
0.2	—	0.08
0.5	0.15	0.11
1.0	0.15	0.12
2.0	0.15	0.09
2.5	—	0.07
3.0	0.15	0.08
3.5	—	0.22
4.0	0.25	0.16
5.0	0.17	0.12
10.0	0.34	0.28
20.0	0.49	—

between C and CO_2. Since the recoil carbon atoms would be largely absorbed in the walls, the response would be very close to the P for CO_2.

Recently it has been shown[49] that special low pressure counters can be used to discriminate against densely ionizing recoil particles when detecting ionization resulting from gamma-ray interactions. The general ideas have been applied in the development of a very convenient gamma-ray dosimeter utilizing a commercially available Geiger-Müller counter,[50] shielded with a filter made of Sn and Pb. The instrument measures the dose in roentgens with nearly uniform response for effective x-ray and gamma energies above 200 kev and up to at least 2.2 Mev. Calculations show that the fast neutron response is less than 0.15%, and experiments indicate that the response to neutrons is less than 0.5%. Its response to thermal neutrons is also quite low; 5×10^9 n/cm² is equivalent to 1 r of gamma radiation.

Unfortunately, not much is known about the response of photographic films to fast neutrons, but for some types of film it is probably less than the response of an ionization chamber in which ionization formed by recoil atoms is collected. There is indication that films similar to DuPont 510 have a low response to neutrons, whereas films such as Eastman 548-0 may have 5% or more fast-neutron response.

The presence of thermal neutrons presents essentially no difficulty in measuring the total dose. In tissuelike media thermal neutrons produce gamma rays by the H(n, γ)D reaction and protons by the $N^{14}(n, p)C^{14}$ reaction. In a biological experiment the gamma rays' contribution would already be measured by whatever dosimeter is being used for gamma rays. In using the gamma-ray dosimeter, however, care must be taken so that it replaces a negligible amount of tissue. Thus the gamma contribution from the H(n, γ)D reaction would not be sensibly altered if the chamber is small compared to the animal. The proton dose could easily be determined by measuring the thermal neutron flux at the point of interest with foils such as gold or indium and converting to energy per gram with the known cross section for the $N^{14}(n, p)C^{14}$ reaction, the known proton energy, and the nitrogen content of the target. In protection work maximum permissible exposures are established in terms of the incident thermal flux, using the calculations of Snyder.[51] In practice, the flux can be measured with BF_3 proportional counters.

NBS-75 summarizes a few of the practical devices that are useful in radiobiology and radiation-protection work. Emphasis has been placed on the devices that help to give the actual tissue dose in rad units in a mixture of gamma rays, fast neutrons, and thermal neutrons. The reader is referred to the references quoted in NBS-75 for further details of the instruments.

REFERENCES

1. See, for example, W. V. Mayneord and W. K. Sinclair, "The Dosimetry of Artificial Isotopes," *Advances in Biological and Medical Physics, IV* (Academic Press, New York, 1952).
   L. D. Marinelli and L. S. Taylor, "The Measurement of Ionizing Radiations for Biological Purposes," in *Radiation Biology*, A. Hollaender, Ed., Vol. I, Part 1 (McGraw-Hill, New York, 1954).
   Glasser, Quimby, Weatherwax, and Taylor, *Physical Foundations of Radiology*, Second Edition, Part B. (Hoeber, New York, 1952).
2. E. H. Quimby, "The History of Dosimetry in Roentgen Therapy," *Am. J. Roentgenol. Radiation Therapy*, **54**, 688 (1945).
3. Handbook 59, *Permissible Dose from External Sources of Ionizing Radiation*," U.S. Department of Commerce, National Bureau of Standards.
4. "Radiological Units—International Commission Recommendations," *Nucleonics*, **8**, (1), 28 (January 1951).
5. Recommendations of the International Commission on Radiological Protection, *Brit. J. Radiol.*, Suppl. No. 6, 91 (1955).
6. R. E. Zirkle, "The Radiological Importance of Linear Energy Transfer," in *Radiation Biology*, A. Hollaender (Ed.), Vol. I, Part 1 (McGraw-Hill, New York, 1954).

7. H. H. Rossi and Walter Rosenzweig, "Measurements of Neutron Dose as a Function of LET," *Radiation Research*, **2**, 417 (1955).

8. J. W. Boag, quoted by U. Fano, "Introductory Remarks on the Dosimetry of Ionizing Radiations," *Radiation Research*, **1**, 3–9 (1954).

9. W. Heitler, *Quantum Theory of Radiation* (Oxford University Press, London, 1944).

10. C. M. Davisson and R. D. Evans, "Gamma-Ray Absorption Coefficients," *Rev. Mod. Phys.*, **24**, No. 2, 79–107 (April 1952).

11. J. T. Brennan, P. S. Harris, R. E. Carter, and W. H. Langham, "The Biological Effectiveness of Thermal Neutrons on Mice—II," *Nucleonics*, **12**, No. 4, 31 (1954).

12. A. D. Conger and N. H. Giles, Jr., "The Cytogenetic Effect of Slow Neutrons," *Genetics*, **35**, 397 (1950).

13. W. S. Snyder, "Calculated Depth Dose Curves in Tissue for Broad Beams of Fast Neutrons," *Brit. J. Radiol.*, **XXVIII**, No. 331, 342–350 (1955).

14. T. A. Barr and G. S. Hurst, "Fast Neutron Dose in a Large Tissue-Equivalent Phantom," *Nucleonics*, **12**, No. 8, 33–35 (August 1954).

15. W. A. Mills and G. S. Hurst, "Fast Neutron Dosimetry in a Small Tissue-Equivalent Phantom," *Nucleonics*, **12**, No. 4, 17–19 (April 1954).

16. Glasser, Quimby, Taylor, and Weatherwax, "Physical Foundations of Radiology," Second Edition, Part B. (Hoeber, New York, 1952).

17. H. W. Koch, D. W. Kerst, and P. Morrison, "Experimental Depth Dose for 5-, 10-, 15-, and 20-Million Volt X-Rays," *Radiology*, **40**, 120–127 (1943).

18. W. T. Ham and E. D. Trout, "Million-Volt Beryllium-Window X-Ray Experiment for Biophysical and Biochemical Research," *Radiology*, **55**, 257–270 (1950).

19. J. S. Laughlin, J. W. Beattie, W. T. Henderson, and R. A. Harvey, "Calorimetric Evaluation of the Roentgen for 400 KV and 22.5 Mev Roentgen Rays," *Am. J. Roentgenol. Radium Therapy*, **70**, 294–312 (1953).

20. J. S. Laughlin and J. W. Beattie, "Calorimetric Determination of Energy Flux of 22.5 Mev X Rays," *Rev. Sci. Instr.*, **22**, 572–574 (1951).

21. G. V. Taplin in *Radiation Dosimetry*, by Hine and Brownell (Academic Press, New York, 1955).

22. Margarete Ehrlich and S. H. Fitch, "Photographic X- and Gamma-Ray Dosimetry, *Nucleonics*, **9**, No. 3, 5–17 (1951).

23. B. G. Whitmore and W. B. Baker, "The Energy Spectrum of Neutrons from Po-Be Source," *Phys. Rev.*, **78**, 799–801 (1950).

24. L. H. Gray, "An Ionization Method for the Absolute Measurement of X-Ray Energy," *Proc. Roy. Soc. (London)*, **A-156**, 578 (1936).

25. L. H. Gray, "The Ionization Method of Measuring Neutron Energy," *Proc. Cambridge Phil. Soc.*, **40**, 72–102 (1944).

26. H. A. Bethe and J. Ashkin, "Passage of Radiations through Matter," in *Experimental Nuclear Physics*, Emilio Segre, Ed., Vol. I, Part II, 166 (Wiley, New York, 1953).

27. T. J. Wang, "Cavity Ionization Chamber for Measurement of Absorbed X-Radiation Energy," *Nucleonics*, **7**, No. 2, 55–71 (1950).

28. U. Fano, "Note on the Bragg-Gray Principle for Measuring Energy Dissipation," *Radiation Research*, **1**, No. 3, 237–240 (1954).

29. L. V. Spencer and F. H. Attix, "The Theory of Cavity Ionization," *Radiation Research*, **3**, No. 3, 239–254 (1955).

30. L. D. Marinelli, "Radiation Dosimetry and Protection," *Ann. Rev. Nuclear Sci.*, Vol. III (Annual Reviews, Stanford, California, 1953).

31. L. H. Ballweg and J. L. Meem, "A Standard Gamma-Ray Ionization Chamber for Shielding Measurements," *Oak Ridge National Laboratory Report 1028* (July 9, 1951).

32. J. Dainty, "Report on Fast Neutron Dosimetry," *CRM 482* (1950).

33. H. H. Rossi and G. Failla, "Neutrons: Dosimetry," Otto Glasser, Ed., *Med. Phys.*, Vol. II, 603–607 (Yearbook Pub., 1950); "Tissue-Equivalent Ionization Chamber," *Nucleonics*, **14**, No. 2, 32 (1956).

34. G. S. Hurst, "An Absolute Tissue Dosimeter for Fast Neutrons," *Brit. J. Radiol.*, **XXVII**, No. 318, 353–357 (June 1954).

35. R. H. Healey and J. W. Reed, "The Behaviour of Slow Electrons in Gases," Amalgamated Wireless (Australasia) Limited, 101 (1941).

36. G. S. Hurst and R. H. Ritchie, "On Energy Resolution with Proportional Counters," *Rev. Sci. Instr.*, **24**, No. 8, 664–668 (August 1953).

37. W. H. Jordan and P. R. Bell, "A General Purpose Linear Amplifier," *Rev Sci. Instr.*, **18**, No. 10, 703–705 (1947).

38. A. L. Cockroft and S. C. Curran, "The Elimination of the End Effects in Counters," *Rev. Sci. Instr.*, **22**, No. 1, 37–42 (1951).

39. G. S. Hurst, W. A. Mills, F. P. Conte, and A. C. Upton, "Principles and Techniques of Mixed Radiation Dosimetry Applications to Acute Lethality Studies of Mice with the Cyclotron," *Radiation Research*, **4**, 49 (1956).

40. F. M. Glass and G. S. Hurst, "A Method of Pulse Integration Using the Binary Scaling Unit," *Rev. Sci. Instr.*, **23**, 67 (1952).

41. E. B. Wagner and G. S. Hurst, "Advances in the Standard Proportional Counter Method of Fast Neutron Dosimetry," *Rev. Sci. Instr.*, **29**, 153 (1958).

42. E. B. Wagner and G. S. Hurst, "Gamma Response and Energy Losses in the Absolute Fast Neutron Dosimeter," *Health Physics*, **2**, 57 (1959).

43. R. H. Ritchie, "Calculations of Energy Loss Under the Bias in Fast Neutron Dosimetry," *Health Physics*, **2**, 73 (1958).

44. National Bureau of Standards Handbook 75, "Measurement of Absorbed Dose of Neutrons, and of Mixtures of Neutrons and Gamma Rays," U.S. Dept. of Commerce (February 3, 1961).

45. G. S. Hurst, J. A. Harter, P. N. Hensley, W. A. Mills, M. Slater, and P. W. Reinhardt, "Techniques of Measuring Neutron Spectra with Threshold Detectors—Tissue Dose Determination," *Rev. Sci. Instr.*, **27**, 153 (1956).

46. J. W. Boag, "The Distribution of Linear Energy Transfer or 'Ion Density' for Fast Neutrons in Water," *Radiation Research*, **1**, No. 4, 323–341 (1954).

47. R. Hofstadter and J. A. McIntyre, "Measurement of Gamma-Ray Energies with Two Crystals in Coincidence," *Phys. Rev.*, **78**, 619–620 (1950).

48. R. Hofstadter and J. A. McIntyre, "Gamma-Ray Measurements with NaI (Tl) Crystals," *Phys. Rev.*, **79**, 389–391 (1950).

49. J. A. Auxier, G. S. Hurst, and R. E. Zedler, "A Single Ion Detector for Measurement of γ-Ray Ionization in Cavities," *Health Physics*, **1**, 21 (1958).

50. E. B. Wagner and G. S. Hurst, "A Geiger-Mueller γ-Ray Dosimeter with Low Neutron Sensitivity," *Health Physics*, **5**, 20 (1961).

51. W. S. Snyder, "Calculations for Maximum Permissible Exposure to Thermal Neutrons," *Nucleonics*, **6**, No. 2, 46–50 (February 1950).

7 TECHNIQUES OF PERSONNEL MONITORING AND RADIATION SURVEYING

KARL Z. MORGAN
Oak Ridge National Laboratory
Oak Ridge, Tennessee

A. Working with Radioactive Materials
B. Maximum Permisssible Levels of Radiation Exposure
C. Instruments Required by a Small Laboratory and Their Use
D. The Health Physicist
E. Special Monitoring Problems
F. Disposal of Radioactive Waste
G. Emergency Precautions

We sometimes consider all ionizing radiation as if it were harmful. In one sense of the word this may be true, since ionizing radiation, even in very low doses, seems to cause a shortening of the expected life span of animals to the extent of about 10^{-4} life spans per roentgen of total body exposure.[1] Also, the genetic mutation rate increases with ionizing radiation exposure; and there is apparently no threshold level of radiation below which there is no genetic effect. However, such an observation may or may not be exactly correct because life on this planet has always been subjected to a certain amount of radiation exposure, and, if not because of it, certainly in spite of it, mutational evolution has continued to take place.

All life on our planet is subjected to radiation exposure from cosmic rays and from radioactive elements in the earth's crust. The intensity of this ionizing radiation, as far as can be determined, has remained almost constant for millions of years. Cosmic radiation increases with geomagnetic latitude and with elevation.[2] In going from 0 to 50° geomagnetic latitude, it increases about 14% at sea level and 22% at 2000 m elevation. At 50° geomagnetic latitude the intensity increases by a factor of 1.7 in going from sea level to 2000 m. Some of the radioactive materials, such as potassium-40, carbon-14, uranium, thorium, and actinium and their radioactive daughter products, are present in varying amounts in the foods we eat and are contained inside the human body. The radium in drinking water may vary by several orders of magnitude. For example, Hursh[3] found the radium in tap water from Joliet, Illinois, to be over 700 times that in tap water from Los Angeles. A large fraction of the background exposure we receive is the result of radiation from the radium-bearing shale and granite used in building our homes. Hultqvist[4] has shown that this absorbed dose may range from 0.01 to 0.05 mrad/hr. Thus our bodies are exposed to various amounts of ionizing radiation, depending upon where we live on the earth with respect to background radiation and upon the concentration of natural radioisotopes inside our bodies. The sum of the absorbed dose to man from background ionizing radiation varies from about 0.01 to 0.1 mrad/hr,* and no evidence is available to indicate that radiation in this range of exposure is either harmful or beneficial to him.

A great deal was learned about the useful and the harmful characteristics of ionizing radiation during the first ten years after the discovery of x rays. E. H. Grubbé[5] of Chicago was probably the first person to receive and observe tissue damage from ionizing radiation. Although Roentgen wrote the first announcement of his discovery of x rays to the Physical Institute of the University of Würtzburg, Germany, on November 8, 1895, it was not until January 4, 1896, that the public press heralded his discovery to the world. Grubbé, who was using a Crookes tube to study the fluorescence of materials, developed a dermatitis on the back of his left hand so acute that he sought medical aid on January 27, 1896. On January 29, 1896, Grubbé treated a patient for carcinoma of the breast with his Crookes tube; he used lead to shield the rest of the body. In April 1896 William Webster[5] of England repeatedly exposed the elbow joint of a patient to x rays for the purpose of diagnosis and found that the rheumatic pains were relieved. In November 1896 Leopold Freund[6] of Vienna treated a large hairy nevus on the back of a patient with x rays. N. S. Scott[7] of Cleveland reported in the spring of 1897 on more than sixty cases of tissue damage caused by x rays. In 1903 N. Senn[8] reported the treatment and cure of a young lady with splenomedullary leukemia. In 1904 J. Bergonié and L. Tribondeau[9] formulated their law that "immature cells and cells in an active state of division are more sensitive to radiation than are cells which have already acquired their adult morphologic and physiological characteristics." In the same year G. Perthes[10] concluded that nuclei in active mitosis are hypersensitive to ionizing radiation. Therefore, from this examination of scattered bits of the early history of ionizing radiation it appears that during the ten years following the discovery of x rays man became acquainted with radiation. In so doing many persons were injured, many of the beneficial uses of x rays were discovered, the principal types

* One rad is defined as that amount of ionizing radiation that is absorbed in any medium (in soft tissue, in this case) to the extent of 100 ergs/gram (1 mrad $= 10^{-3}$ rad). The forerunner of the rad was the rep, which corresponded to an absorption of 93 ergs of ionizing radiation per gram of soft tissue.

of radiation damage were observed, and various methods of radiation protection were instigated.

In spite of man's early understanding of radiation damage and how to prevent such damage, he was rather slow to profit by his experience. During World War I, when there was an increase in the use of x-ray equipment and when the radium dial industry became a flourishing business, many persons were subjected to prolonged external exposure to ionizing radiation and to the ingestion and inhalation of radium. This led to much suffering and a number of deaths. Sidney Russ[11] was one of the first persons to make a comprehensive series of studies for radiation protection. If his suggestions for protective devices to the British Roentgen Society in 1915 had been followed, it is likely that much suffering and loss of life could have been avoided.

Many new problems of radiation protection were introduced between 1930 and 1940 as a result of the development and construction of various types of high-voltage equipment and ion accelerators. A few accidents occurred because of negligence and carelessness, and many persons accumulated unnecessary radiation exposure. Fortunately, however, some consideration was given to problems of radiation protection; consequently, very few serious overexposures resulted.

The first uranium chain-reacting pile was set in operation at the University of Chicago Metallurgical Laboratory on December 2, 1942, and the first production pile began operating at Oak Ridge, Tennessee, on November 4, 1943. These developments marked the beginning of a new era of radiation-protection problems, since even at this time it was recognized that a large pile would produce gamma radiation equivalent to that from hundreds of tons of radium.* In addition, it would be an intense source of neutrons. All this was considered at a time when there was available to man in the entire world only slightly more than two pounds of radium and when, in the careless and improper use of this small amount, many persons had been injured and killed. It is fortunate that a great amount of attention was given to this problem of radiation protection from the very beginning of the atomic energy projects.

The science of radiation protection was first called "health physics" at the University of Chicago in the summer of 1942 and since then has expanded manyfold so that in 1961 there were more than two thousand health physicists in the United States and many abroad. They are to be found on all the Atomic Energy Commission projects and in other laboratories in

---

* There are about 3×10^{10} fissions/sec-watt and 13 Mev gamma energy/fission. The total gamma energy emission per alpha disintegration of Ra is 1.8 Mev. Therefore, a pile operating with a power of 10^8 watts would produce a gamma radiation equivalent to that from 660 tons of radium.

which there is work with radioactive materials. The problems of radiation protection have extended considerably beyond the Atomic Energy Commission projects because of the increased number of high-voltage machines and accelerators and because of the number of shipments of radioactive material from Oak Ridge, Chalk River, Harwell, etc. During 1959 there were 12,900 shipments of radionuclides from Oak Ridge, and throughout 1959 there had been a total of 131,600 shipments of radioactive material from Oak Ridge to hospitals, universities, and industrial laboratories.[12]

Health physicists devote full time to problems of radiation protection. Some of their principal assignments have been as follows:

(a) Aid in the selection of suitable locations for buildings in which radioactive materials are to be produced or used.

(b) Aid in the design of laboratories, hoods, remote-control equipment, radiation shields, etc.

(c) Provide personnel monitoring meters for radiation dosimetry to all persons subject to radiation exposure and read these meters frequently to determine the accumulated dose; make thyroid counts, breath measurements, and urine and feces analyses, check body with body scanners and total body counters, and conduct other tests to aid in estimating how much (if any) radioactive material is fixed in the body; maintain accurate records of the accumulated dose received by each worker for his protection and for the protection of the employer.

(d) Make frequent surveys of all accessible reactor areas, radioactive sources, x-ray equipment, high-voltage accelerators, chemistry and physics laboratories, metallurgical shops, and other working areas in which radiation exposure is possible.

(e) Keep supervisors and research directors informed of all radiation exposure hazards, of permissible working time in a given area, and of radiation protection measures (e.g., protective clothing, shields, remote-control equipment) that are desirable and aid supervision in the solution of new radiation problems as they develop.

(f) Make frequent surveys of all radioactive waste (liquid, solid, and gas) discharged beyond the area of immediate control and maintain accurate records of the level of this radioactivity.

(g) Aid in all emergency operations, such as criticality accidents, traffic accidents involving shipments of radioactive materials, fires, floods, explosions, etc., to minimize any associated radiation hazards.

(h) Furnish and maintain in proper calibration all health-physics survey and monitoring instruments that are used as an aid in the protection of personnel from radiation damage.

(i) Conduct research on radiation protection problems:

(1) Pursue disposal studies of gaseous, liquid, and solid radioactive wastes from laboratories and production plants.
(2) Develop new and better radiation detection instruments.
(3) Study the fundamental behavior of radiation in matter.
(4) Determine and establish the maximum permissible levels of radiation exposure for both external and internal exposure and set the maximum permissible concentrations of radioactive contamination inside and outside our bodies, in the food and water we consume, and in the air we breathe.

(j) Conduct educational programs on the safe handling of radioactive materials; train health physicists to help meet the demand for more senior men in this new profession; point out the responsibilities of various groups, such as medical men, industrial hygienists, public-health officials, sanitary engineers, safety engineers, and insurance underwriters, so that they can aid in furnishing necessary radiation protection and will know when they should seek the assistance of a health physicist.

(k) Assist in radiation protection problems related to national defense.

It will be noted that all of these health-physics problems have their applications in industries, universities, and hospitals as well as in the Atomic Energy Commission projects. The small organization obviously would not be in a position to carry on much health-physics research; nevertheless, there would be many radiation problems peculiar to its own operations which would require some special study and developmental research in determining the best methods of radiation protection. Many of the new and/or smaller operations do not have ideal facilities for working with radioactive materials; they should give special thought to items (a) and (b) (listed above). Since these users of radionuclides usually are supplied only millicurie amounts, their radiation protection problems will always be many orders of magnitude smaller than those faced by the large Atomic-Energy-Commission-supported projects. Nevertheless, they must consider the same precautionary measures in their laboratories and must maintain the general area about their laboratories in an almost virgin condition insofar as radioactive contamination is concerned. This is necessary not only because of the possible health hazards involved but also because quantities of radioactive contamination, which may be insignificant from the standpoint of health hazards, can be sufficient to interfere seriously with the construction of ion chambers, Geiger counters, etc., in a university research shop or physics laboratory or they might conceivably cause some difficulties in a nearby operation making or using very sensitive photographic films. In any case, small quantities of radioactive contamination that spread beyond the controlled area can lead to serious public relations problems unless adequate monitoring procedures are carried out. Another special problem of all users of radionuclides is that of radioactive waste disposal. Special precautionary measures must be taken in order to ensure that no liquid, solid, or gaseous waste causes damage to persons or other operations in the vicinity. For these reasons the Atomic Energy Commission makes a study of the qualifications of applicants before supplying radioactive materials.

Although the applied and research sections of the Health Physics Division at Oak Ridge National Laboratory employ more than 150 persons, some of the industries, universities, and hospitals that use radioisotopes may get along very nicely with only one health physicist. If only two or three men in an institution are using radionuclides, perhaps one of this small group can acquire the necessary knowledge and proficiency to handle the health-physics problems. Most laboratories are using millionths or billionths of the radioactive materials handled constantly by the projects supported by the Atomic Energy Commission. Nevertheless, in spite of the less difficult radiation-protection problems, it is just as essential that these small users of radionuclides try to maintain the same high standards of radiation protection. They must carry on their work in specially designed laboratories; they must be provided with appropriate ventilating equipment, hoods, shielding material, remote-control equipment, and radiation-detection devices. Most of all, they must have men with adequate training and experience who have the proper understanding regarding the necessity of keeping all radiation exposures to man at a minimum and who are constantly vigilant to prevent radiation damage to themselves and others working near them.

A. Working with Radioactive Materials

It is impossible to state what percentage of a radioactive sample will escape into the working area of a given type of laboratory. This value certainly depends upon the kind and duration of experiments, the experience of the operators and the techniques they use, and upon the physical and chemical properties and quantities of radioactive material involved. H. A. Levy[13] was one of the first to provide a chart showing the approximate amounts of radioactivity encountered in various problems. His chart, with the addition of a millimicrocurie range and with a few other minor changes, is given in Fig. 1. As a result, we have four rather arbitrarily chosen levels of radioactive intensity: (1) millimicrocurie level, from background up to about 10^{-3} μc; (2) microcurie level, from 10^{-3} μc to 0.5 mc; (3) millicurie level, from 0.5 mc to 0.5 curie; and (4) multicurie level for all activities greater than 0.5 curies.

1. Millimicrocurie level. There are no radiation hazards involving the health of persons working with radionuclides in this range of activity. The principal problems in this work are to maintain low background counting apparatus and to prevent radioactive contamination from getting into the laboratory and interfering with the experiments by contamination of equipment and/or cross contamination with other radionuclides. The counting chambers must be constructed of special materials that have low natural backgrounds, and unusual precautions must be taken to eliminate spurious counts from electrical pulses originating from external electrical surges. All the chemical reagents, glassware, sample holders, and equipment must be carefully chosen to maintain known low background counts. It may be necessary to require persons entering the area to wear special protective clothing to prevent bringing contamination into the laboratory.

2. Microcurie level. Chemical operations and equipment used with beta- and gamma-emitting radionuclides in this range are not very different from those used in most ordinary chemical operations. At this level of activity, sources should not be handled directly with the hands; sources emitting gamma and hard beta radiations should be manipulated with tongs or other remote handling devices, but alpha and soft beta sources can be handled safely with gloves. The principal hazard in the case of alpha and soft beta sources does not come from external penetrating radiation but from radioactive material that may get into the body by ingestion, inhalation, through open wounds, or directly through the skin. Care must be taken not to work with radionuclides at these higher levels if there are open cuts on the hands, and considerable caution must be exercised to prevent cuts and puncture wounds with contaminated objects. Glassblowing should not be done with contaminated equipment in such a way that contaminated air is breathed; pipetting by mouth must be prohibited. Radionuclides which emit only alpha and soft beta radiation do not cause body damage when kept outside the body. The protective layer of skin about the body, called the epidermal layer, ranges in thickness from 0.07 to 0.12 mm on most parts of the body to 0.8 mm on the palms of the hands and 1.4 mm on the soles of the feet. Therefore, beta emitters with energy less than 70 kev and alpha emitters with energy less than 7 Mev do not present an external hazard because radiation from such sources has a range less than 0.07 mm of skin. However, these sources—especially alpha sources—are hazardous when fixed inside the body because they dissipate their energy over a short range in tissue, with consequent large energy absorption per gram of tissue.

Work with beta and gamma emitters at this level of activity may be done over blotting paper in trays placed in ordinary chemical hoods, provided the rate of air flow and baffle and/or jet arrangement are such as to prevent

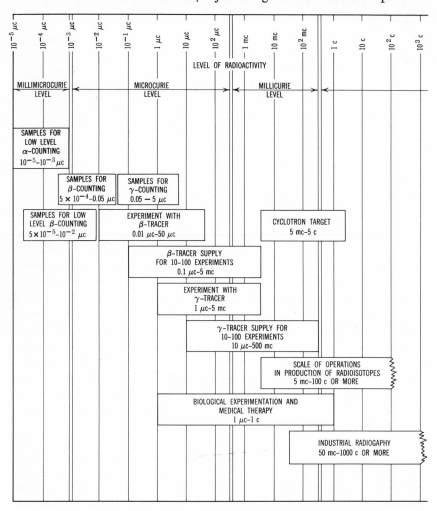

Fig. 1.   Approximate amounts of radioactive material encountered

backflow of contaminated air into the working area. Very little, if any, shielding is required at this level of activity; usually only improvised types of shielding, such as transparent plastics and glass placed about the radioactive material, are used. The exposed surfaces inside the hood should be covered with a material that is easily decontaminated or with a peelable plastic. Ordinary drains may be used for the slightly hazardous and moderately dangerous radionuclides at this level of activity, provided not more than 0.5 mc are disposed of in each section of a sewer system daily and provided sufficient water (not less than 50 gal/0.5 mc) is used for dilution. Similar levels of these same radionuclides, when contained in animal carcasses, may be disposed of daily in an incinerator, provided the stack is high enough or far enough removed that it does not contaminate laboratories or other populated areas and the concentration of the radionuclides in the surrounding air does not exceed the maximum values permitted in the neighborhood of the plant (one tenth of the values permitted for occupational exposure).

Most of the samples prepared for counting are within this microcurie range, and such laboratory facilities are frequently associated as a part of operations in which high levels of activity are involved. Obviously, in such cases every precaution must be taken to prevent the spread of contamination from adjacent high-level areas to laboratories and counting rooms

10^4 c 10^5 c 10^6 c 10^7 c 10^8 c 10^9 c

MULTICURIE LEVEL.

RADIOACTIVE WASTES IN EQUILIBRIUM FROM A 450– MEGAWATT ATOMIC POWER PLANT
6×10^8 c

in various operations.

where work is done with samples of low-level activity. If counting rooms are located 100 yd or more from the areas using high levels of radionuclides that are hard gamma emitters, local lead or iron shields about the counters are usually sufficient; otherwise, the counting-room walls should be constructed of 1 to 2 ft of concrete or equivalent material. Frequently the walls of a

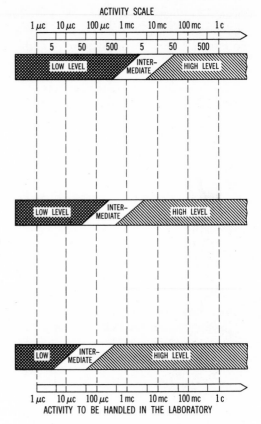

I. *Slight Hazard*
*Na^{24}, K^{42}, Cu^{64}, *Mn^{52},
*As^{76}, As^{77}, Kr^{85}, *Hg^{197}

II. *Moderately Dangerous*
H^3, C^{14}, *Na^{22}, P^{32}, S^{35},
Cl^{36}, *Mn^{54}, *Fe^{59}, *Co^{60},
Sr^{89}, *Cb^{95}, *Ru^{103}, Ru^{106},
Te^{127}, Te^{129}, I^{131}, *Cs^{137},
*Ba^{140}, *La^{140}, Ce^{141},
Pr^{143}, *Nd^{147}, *Au^{198},
*Au^{199}, $Hg^{203,205}$

III. *Very Dangerous*
Ca^{45}, Fe^{55}, Sr^{90}, Y^{91},
*Zr^{95}, Ce^{144}, Pm^{147},
Bi^{210}

Fig. 2.   Selected radionuclides grouped according to relative radiotoxicity, with the amounts considered as low, intermediate, or high level in laboratory practice.

Notes: 1. Effective radiotoxicity is obtained from a weighting of the following factors:
  (a) Half-life,
  (b) Energy and character of radiations,
  (c) Degree of selective localization in the body,
  (d) Rates of elimination,
  (e) Quantities involved and modes of handling in typical experiments.

2. The slant boundaries between levels indicate borderline zones and emphasize that there is no sharp transition between the levels and the associated protection techniques.

3. The principal gamma emitters are indicated by an asterisk (e.g., *Na^{24}). This system does not apply to the hazards of external irradiation.

counting room must be lined with a conducting wire screen, enclosing the counting room as a Faraday cage, in order to minimize electronic disturbances; and for the proper operation of some instruments that are microphonic, the surface of the walls should be soundproofed for best results. The counting room should be air conditioned at about 60% relative humidity, and the temperature should be maintained constant.

All persons working at these levels of radioactivity and higher should be provided with personnel monitoring meters and with equipment to measure the contamination on their hands and clothing. Also, routine analyses should be made of the urine and/or feces to determine the internal dose hazard. Such analyses are essential if one is working with the more dangerous radionuclides and during periods following accidents such as spills or contaminated wounds. Survey equipment with which to check the safe working time and to determine the level of contamination of equipment and of floors, benches, walls, etc., in the working area should be furnished. Air monitoring apparatus should be available to check the concentration of air activity at frequent intervals.

Some radioactive materials, such as Ac^{227}, At^{211}, Pb^{210}, Cm^{242}, Pu^{239}, Po^{210}, Ra^{226}, Sr^{90}, Sr^{89}, and Ce^{144}, are more hazardous than others because of high initial body retention and because of long biological half-life.* The Subcommittee on Safe Handling of Radioisotopes[14] of the National Committee on Radiation Protection has given a tentative grouping of some of the elements as very dangerous, moderately dangerous, or slightly hazardous; the levels of high, low, and intermediate activity for each group are given in Fig. 2. Here it is noted that "high level" occurs at much lower values for the very dangerous radionuclides. Likewise, it should be pointed out that the "high level" should occur at much lower values for dry operations than for wet operations.

The relative hazard from a radionuclide varies inversely with the concentration in air or water required to deliver a permissible dose rate to a portion of the body, and it varies directly with the specific activity of the radioactive material. K. Z. Morgan, W. S. Snyder, and M. R. Ford[15] have made analyses on this basis of the more common radionuclides of interest and listed them in order of decreasing hazard in Table 1. It is pointed out by this analysis that perhaps the probable hazard from getting insoluble radioactive material into a wound is much greater than from ingestion or inhalation of radioactive material, that the inhalation hazard is much greater than the ingestion hazard, and that in case of inhalation of insoluble radioactive material the hazard is either to the lung or a portion of the gastrointestinal tract. In the case of inhalation or wound contamination

* The biological half-life of a radionuclide in a body organ is the time required for half the material to be eliminated from that organ by normal biological processes.

TABLE I. SUMMARY OF THE TWENTY MORE
DANGEROUS RADIONUCLIDES LISTED IN ORDER
OF DECREASING HAZARD

Inhalation		Injection		Inhalation		
Soluble Radioactive Material				Insoluble Radioactive Material		
The Indicated Organ as the Critical Body Organ				Wound Site the Critical Tissue	Lung the Critical Body Organ	GI Tract the Critical Body Organ
Ac^{227} + drs	B	Ac^{227} + drs	B	Ac^{227} + drs	Ac^{227} + drs	Ra^{223} + drs
At^{211} + drs	T	At^{211} + drs	T	Cm^{242}	Pb^{210} + drs	Ra^{224} + drs
Pb^{210} + drs	B	Cm^{242}	B	Pb^{210} + drs	Po^{210}	Th^{228} + drs
Cm^{242}	B	Pb^{210} + drs	B	Po^{210}	Ra^{226} + drs	Th^{227} + drs
Po^{210}	S	Po^{210}	S	At^{211} + drs	Am^{241}	Cm^{242}
I^{131}	T	I^{131}	T	Am^{241}	At^{211} + drs	Po^{210}
Am^{241}	B	Th^{234} + Pa^{234}	B	Ra^{226} + drs	Ba^{140} + La^{140}	Pb^{212} + drs
Ra^{226} + drs	B	Ce^{144} + Pr^{144}	B	Ru^{106} + Rh^{106}	Ag^{105}	Am^{241}
Pu^{239}	B	Ba^{140} + La^{140}	B	Ce^{144} + Pr^{144}	Ru^{106} + Rh^{106}	Ra^{226} + drs
Sr^{90} + Y^{90}	B	Am^{241}	B	Sr^{90} + Y^{90}	Co^{60}	Ac^{227} + drs
Th^{234} + Pa^{234}	B	Sr^{90} + Y^{90}	B	Th^{234} + Pa^{234}	V^{48}	At^{211} + drs
Ba^{140} + La^{140}	B	Ir^{192}	S	Ba^{140} + La^{140}	Ce^{144} + Pr^{144}	Ru^{106} + Rh^{106}
Ce^{144} + Pr^{144}	B	Y^{91}	B	Te^{129}	Te^{129}	Ce^{144} + Pr^{144}
Sr^{89}	B	Ru^{106} + Rh^{106}	K	P^{32}	Sc^{46}	Th^{234} + Pa^{234}
Fe^{59}	Bl	Tm^{170}	B	Sr^{89}	W^{181}	Y^{90}
Y^{91}	B	Sr^{89}	B	Rb^{86}	Sr^{90} + Y^{90}	As^{76}
Te^{129}	K	Te^{129}	K	Y^{91}	Ir^{192}	Bi^{210} + Po^{210}
Tm^{170}	B	Au^{198}	K	Tm^{170}	Zr^{95} + Nb^{95}	Te^{129}
Ru^{106} + Rh^{106}	K	Pu^{239}	B	Ag^{111}	Tc^{96}	Ra^{228} + drs
Au^{198}	K	Fe^{59}	Bl	Te^{127}	Th^{234} + Pa^{234}	La^{140}

Parent radionuclides with radioactive half-lives less than one half hour have been excluded in this comparison.

B—Bone, T—Thyroid, S—Spleen, Bl—Blood, K—Kidneys, drs—radioactive daughter products.

with a soluble radioactive material, the bone, liver, kidney, or some other body organ is the critical organ, as indicated in Table 1.

3. Millicurie level. Special techniques and equipment in addition to the foregoing must be used in handling "intermediate levels" of these materials. They should be worked with over blotting paper and in trays in especially designed hoods and/or dust boxes. The air flow of the hood at maximum opening should not be less than 100 ft/min, or, if it is designed to operate at slower rates of air flow, air jets, baffles, and other arrangements should guarantee that no contaminated air will escape from the hood under various operating conditions. The dust box and/or hood intake and exhaust should be provided with roughing and absolute filters and in some cases one or more additional air cleaning devices; for example, washer, precipitator, or impinger. These should be arranged to permit easy access for cleaning and repair. Special off-gas lines can be connected to the air

cleaning system of the dust boxes and of other small enclosures located inside the hoods. These off-gas lines need handle only small volumes of air which can be cleaned economically by additional filtration before the air is discharged into dispersing stacks. The use of filtered off-gas and vacuum lines simplifies the contamination control and supplements the secondary containment protection provided by the filters in the hood intake and exhaust lines, where much larger volumes of air must be handled. The exposed inner surfaces of the hood and dust box should be made of stainless steel or other material that can be decontaminated readily. Protective clothing,* the ultimate disposal of which can be carefully controlled, should be worn. No food should be brought into these laboratories, and no smoking should be permitted. The hands and face must be washed carefully when leaving the laboratory. Radioactive wastes must not be placed in the regular drains until dilutions equal to or greater than those recommended by the National Committee on Radiation Protection are obtained,[16] and, in general, special provisions must be made for these wastes. This subject is discussed later. Dust should be kept from the laboratories because radionuclides are easily absorbed on dust and transported to the lungs on the submicron dust particles. Areas of the building in which the "very dangerous" materials are used in intermediate or high-level quantities should be separated from the rest of the building.

In addition to the requirements previously mentioned, the principal new requirement at this level is that of adequate general shielding for work with gamma-emitting radionuclides. Close shielding about the individual gamma source of radiation is usually not adequate at this level of radiation, and general hood shielding, consisting of a lead base and a lead wall a few inches thick up to head height, is provided. Some of this lead wall should be easily removable to facilitate setting up apparatus for new experiments. The various operations are carried on by the use of tongs and other mechanical devices with which one reaches over or through the shield. Manipulation devices operated electrically or by air pressure have many advantages over manually operated devices, especially when conducting experiments in a dust box that is located in a hood. Mirrors and thick windows make it possible to see what goes on behind the shields. Hold-up tanks, underground storage vaults, or properly located and designed open waste-disposal pits should be provided for the storage of large amounts of radioactive material if they exceed the limits set by the National

---

* It should be pointed out that protective clothing is provided to protect the skin and/or personal clothing from transferable radioactive contamination. It provides some personnel protection from beta radiation but essentially no protection from x, gamma, or neutron radiation.

Committee on Radiation Protection for discharge into the public streams or sewers.

In working with radioactive material at the millicurie level, it is extremely important that fume hoods, glove boxes, sealed boxes, "hot" cells, etc., be designed and constructed with careful planning and detailed consideration of the radionuclide work that is to be carried out. Pilot runs should be conducted with nonradioactive materials to check each step before the final operation. Potential hazards from fires, explosions, and pressure surges should be carefully evaluated and eliminated when possible. The transfer operations, the sampling procedures, the changing of gloves on the boxes, the decontamination of surfaces, the operation of mechanical devices, the transfer of waste solutions and other materials, the dissipation of heat when the furnaces are operating at full capacity, the fogging of windows—all these and many other details—must be examined during "cold" runs before the introduction of radioactive material into the facilities. The fans and air ejectors, scrubbers, filters (both pre- and absolute filters), charcoal traps, electrical equipment, lighting, mirrors, shielding, remote-control equipment, etc., must be checked out in operating conditions as nearly perfect as possible. The use of pressure suits if required, the procedures to follow in the event of various types of accidents, the program for personnel monitoring, and the urine, fecal, and total body radio-analyses should be provided before the "hot" work begins rather than after the first accident has occurred. Each experiment must be planned in advance to provide a maximum of isolation of the radioactive material and for dependence first on primary containment and second on the secondary and tertiary containment systems. Last, but not least in importance, is a well-planned and continuing health-physics training program for all persons associated with work in which radiation exposure is possible. For more detailed information the reader is referred to the many excellent publications that describe equipment and procedures for "hot" operations.[17]

In addition to the instruments prescribed for the lower levels, monitoring and recording instruments should be installed to maintain a written record of the general radiation level and air activity in the working areas and to sound an alarm signal when permissible levels are exceeded. Protective clothing should be worn for all work at the millicurie level of radioactive material (this requirement does not apply to properly sealed sources). A special decontamination laundry should be provided to remove the radioactive contamination, or a laboratory technician should use a domestic-type washer in one corner of the laboratory to remove the radioactive contamination from the protective clothing before sending it to a public laundry.

4. Multicurie level. All operations at these levels are done in thick-walled cells and are controlled completely by remote equipment. The cell walls may be many feet thick, and the cells are well ventilated by air that is carefully filtered as it enters the cell and before it is discharged up tall stacks. The liquid waste is carried into undergound storage tanks or into properly located and designed open pits. Further details covering these high levels of radioactivity need not be considered here because they concern only a few laboratories and large production operations.

Thousands of persons have been working on the various United States Atomic Energy Commission projects, many of them for ten to fifteen years, yet no one working on any of the projects (with the exception of Los Alamos Laboratory and the Weapons Test Operations in the South Pacific) has received radiation damage that definitely can be identified in the frequent physical examinations by the medical departments as permanent radiation damage. However, there have been serious radiation accidents at Y-12 and the Oak Ridge National Laboratory, Oak Ridge, at Argonne National Laboratory, Chicago, at the Windscale Production Plant, Seascale, England, and at Atomic Energy of Canada, Chalk River, Canada, but in most cases there were no detectable injuries and, so far as can be determined at the present time, all persons involved in these accidents who received radiation injury have recovered or are recovering satisfactorily from any acute radiation damage. There have been only four fatal radiation accidents*—three at Los Alamos and the other near Belgrade. During the early period of the nuclear energy operations, the maximum permissible dose rate for occupational exposure to beta and gamma radiations was 100 mrep/day, and in 1950 it was reduced to 300 mrep/wk. In 1958 the maximum permissible RBE dose rate for occupational exposure to the total body, gonads, or lenses of the eyes was set at 3 rem/13 wk (see Sec. B-1 for definition of rem, rep, and rad) or an average of 5 rem/yr. The health physicist, however, has considered these levels as upper limits of exposure and has striven to maintain all unnecessary radiation exposure to a minimum so that even in the early period the average exposure was considerably less than the present permissible level of 5 rem/yr. For example, Table 2 indicates the annual exposures at Hanford Works[18] and at Oak Ridge National Laboratory. Hanford Works is one of the largest reactor production centers, and Oak Ridge National Laboratory is one of the largest atomic energy research laboratories. Also, the lost-time accident rates are given for the two operations, and for comparison the lost-time accident rates are given for the chemical industry. Similar good records have been maintained at other Atomic Energy

* Three persons were killed in the SL–1 reactor accident at the National Reactor Testing Station, Idaho Falls, Idaho, on January 3, 1961. Presumably they would have been killed by radiation exposure had they not been killed first by the blast.

TABLE 2. RADIATION EXPOSURE AND ACCIDENT FREQUENCY RATES AT HANFORD AND AT OAK RIDGE NATIONAL LABORATORY. A COMPARISON WITH THE ACCIDENT FREQUENCY RATE OF THE CHEMICAL INDUSTRY

	Hanford[18]		Oak Ridge National Lab.		Chemical Industry
Year	Average Annual Exposure (rem)	Accident Frequency* Rate	Average Annual Exposure (rem)	Accident Frequency* Rate	Accident Frequency* Rate
1944		2.71			
1945	0.9	0.90		1.86	10.08
1946	0.6	1.09		1.49	10.09
1947	0.4	0.99	0.1	1.74	8.86
1948	0.3	1.11	0.2	2.42	7.51
1949	0.2	0.84	0.2	1.54	5.72
1950	0.1	2.90	0.2	1.56	5.82
1951	0.1	2.76	0.3	2.09	5.48
1952	0.2	2.97	0.4	1.39	5.10
1953	0.2	3.15	0.3	1.20	4.53
1954	0.2	2.12	0.3	0.79	4.12
1955	0.2	0.79	0.3	0.59	3.77
1956	0.2	0.76	0.3	0.55	3.38
1957	0.2	0.45	0.4	0.70	3.55
1958	0.3	0.32	0.5	1.00	3.56
1959	0.3	0.52	0.4	1.44	3.32
1960	0.3	0.19	0.2	0.78	3.71

* Frequency is the number of injuries per million man-hours worked.

Commission operations. From this comparison it may be concluded that the nuclear energy industry has been one of the safest of American industries; it can continue to maintain this enviable position if proper health-physics precautions and radiation-protection measures are continued.

B. Maximum Permissible Levels of Radiation Exposure

I. External exposure. In July 1921 the British X-Ray and Radium Protection Committee presented its first radiation protection measures; in September 1922 the American Roentgen Ray Society published its first measures for radiation protection. The Second International Congress of Radiology, meeting in Stockholm in July 1928, made proposals for radiation protection and was responsible for the formation of the International Committee on X-ray and Radium Protection[19] which had its second meeting in Paris in 1931. In 1934 in Zurich, and again in 1937[20] in Chicago, this Committee recommended a tolerance dose of 0.2 r/day or 1.0 r/wk. The United States Advisory Committee on X-Ray and Radium Protection endorsed this value in its first report in 1931,[21,22] but in its revised report in 1936 it recommended 0.1 r/day.

When the atomic energy programs for the production of plutonium were organized at the University of Chicago in 1942, it was decided by the representatives of the newly formed medical and health-physics groups to adopt 0.1 r/day as the maximum permissible exposure to x and gamma radiation for personnel associated with atomic energy projects. It was known at that time that fast neutrons were more damaging than x and gamma rays in terms of ergs of ionizing radiation absorbed per gram of tissue, and alpha-emitting radionuclides when deposited inside the body were considered even more damaging, presumably because of their higher specific ionization or linear energy transfer. It was supposed that beta rays were about as damaging as x and gamma rays and that thermal neutrons produced a biological damage intermediate between that of x rays and fast neutrons. On the basis of available information, most of the early atomic energy projects adopted maximum permissible levels of exposure, as indicated in Table 3.

Since, by definition, the roentgen unit is applicable only to x and gamma radiation, it was necessary to adopt some unit that could be applied to any type of ionizing radiation. The roentgen equivalent physical, rep, was originally defined as that amount of ionizing radiation that may be absorbed to the extent of 83 ergs/gram of soft tissue. The magnitude of this unit was increased later from 83 ergs to 93 ergs/gram—the value used in Table 3. In 1953 the magnitude of this unit was increased again, this time to 100 ergs/gram of any medium, and the name of the unit was changed to the rad. The roentgen equivalent man, rem, was defined originally as that amount of ionizing radiation that produces damage in man equal to or considered equivalent to the damage resulting from one roentgen of x radiation from a machine operating at 200 to 250 kv. A more recent relation—and the one used in Table 4—is given by the equation

$$\text{number of rem} = \text{RBE} \times \text{number of rad in soft tissue} \tag{1}$$

in which the relative biological effectiveness, RBE, is given by the equation

$$\text{RBE} = \left\{ \begin{array}{l} \text{rad in tissue from x or} \\ \text{gamma radiation from a} \\ \text{standard source which} \\ \text{produces a specified bio-} \\ \text{logical effect} \end{array} \right\} \div \left\{ \begin{array}{l} \text{rad in same tissue from any} \\ \text{source of ionizing radiation} \\ \text{required to produce the} \\ \text{same biological effect} \end{array} \right\} \tag{2}$$

TABLE 3. LEVELS OF MAXIMUM PERMISSIBLE OCCUPATIONAL
EXPOSURE USED BY THE UNITED STATES ATOMIC
ENERGY PROJECTS UNTIL 1950

Type of Radiation	mr/ day	mrep/ day	mrem/ day	Approximate Flux for a 24-hr Exposure
X or gamma rays	100	100	100	2300 photons of 1 Mev/cm² sec
Beta rays		100	100	35 electrons of 1 Mev/cm² sec
Thermal neutrons		50	100	1500 neutrons of 0.025 ev/cm² sec
Fast neutrons		20	100	65 neutrons of 2 Mev/cm² sec
Alpha rays		10	100	0.007 alphas of 5 Mev/cm² sec

Note: The flux value for electrons reduces to about 23 beta particles/cm² sec, with the normal energy distribution ranging from zero to a maximum energy of 1 Mev, because the specific ionization of electrons increases as the energy decreases. The specific ionization in air of electrons has approximate values of 64, 1.1×10^3, and 10^4 ion pairs/ cm path for electron energies of 1 Mev, 10 kev, and 100 ev, respectively. The corresponding values for beta rays are 97 and 2.1×10^3 ion pairs/cm path in air for maximum energies of 1 Mev and 10 kev, respectively. The specific ionization for 5-Mev alpha particles in air is taken as 2.9×10^4. The flux values in Table 3 assume the rep to correspond to 93 ergs/gram tissue and that W, the energy required to produce an ion pair,[23] is 34 electron volts in the case of x and gamma rays, electrons, and beta particles and 35 electron volts in the case of protons and alpha particles. Many of the earlier flux tables used $W = 32.5$ electron volts/ion pair and defined the rep in terms of an energy absorption of 83 ergs/gram tissue. The relative mass stopping power of tissue with respect to air is taken as 1.14 for electrons and beta particles and 1.21 for alpha particles. The RBE for alpha radiation was taken as 20 from 1948 to 1953; before and after this period it was assumed to be equal to 10. Since the common work period was 8 hr/day, the flux values for the usual occupational exposure were three times these values.

According to the official definition[24] of RBE, the standard source of comparison is an x or gamma source having a linear energy transfer, LET, in water of 3 kev/μ delivered at a rate of about 10 rad/min. For practical purposes the gamma radiation from a properly calibrated Co^{60} source may be used satisfactorily as the standard source of comparison.

Recent biological experiments have indicated that the exposure levels set in Table 3 are probably satisfactory for the occasional radiation exposure, but they do not provide a sufficient safety factor for persons who will be working regularly with radioactive materials. As a result, the National (U.S.) Committee on Radiation Protection, NCRP,[25] and the International Commission on Radiological Protection, ICRP,[26] have recommended new values of maximum permissible exposure, which are given in Table 4 together with the corresponding values of flux. These newly recommended occupational exposure rates, shown for the various body organs in column 3 of Table 5, may be averaged over a year, or they may be increased without limit, provided the integrated RBE dose in any

TABLE 4. MAXIMUM PERMISSIBLE FLUX FOR
OCCUPATIONAL EXPOSURE TO VARIOUS
TYPES OF IONIZING RADIATIONS*

Type of Radiation	RBE	Average Exposure Rate† (mrad/wk)	Approximate Flux to Give a Maximum Permissible Exposure in an 8-hr Day‡
X and gamma rays	1	100	$\dfrac{1400}{E}$ photons/cm²/sec in free air at 0° C (error $< 13\%$ for $E = 0.07$ to 2 Mev)
Beta rays and electrons	1	100	$\dfrac{4.3 \times 10^7}{(RBE)P}$ electrons or beta rays/cm²/sec incident on tissue ($\simeq 23$ electrons or 15 β/cm²/sec of 1 Mev energy)
Thermal neutrons	2.5	40	700 thermal neutrons/cm²/sec incident on tissue
Fast neutrons	10	10	19 neutrons of 2-Mev energy/cm²/sec incident on tissue
Alpha particles	10	10	$\dfrac{4.3 \times 10^7}{(RBE)P}$ alpha particles/cm²/sec incident on tissue ($\simeq 0.005$ alpha of 5 Mev/cm²/sec)
Protons	10	10	$\dfrac{4.3 \times 10^7}{(RBE)P}$ protons/cm²/sec incident on tissue ($\simeq 0.06$ protons of 5 Mev/cm²/sec)
Heavy ions	20	5	$\dfrac{4.3 \times 10^7}{(RBE)P}$ heavy ions/cm²/sec ($\simeq 0.0002$ oxygen ions of 5 Mev/cm²/sec)

* Values of flux corresponding to dose values as recommended in 1959 by the National Committee on Radiation Protection and by the International Commission on Radiological Protection.

† Average occupational exposure rate permissible to blood-forming organs (essentially total body exposure), gonads, and eyes of persons of age 18 or over. These values may be averaged over a year, provided the RBE dose in any thirteen weeks does not exceed 3 rem (rem = RBE × rad). All values in columns 3 and 4 may be increased by a factor of 6 if the exposure is primarily to the skin, thyroid, or bone. They may be increased by a factor of 3 if the exposure is limited to organs other than blood-forming organs, gonads, or eyes.

‡ Maximum permissible exposure rate based on a 20-mrem RBE dose delivered to tissue in an 8-hr day (= 2.5/RBE mrad/hr) and assuming $W = 35$ for alpha and 34 for beta and secondary electrons. The rad in soft tissue is considered to correspond to an energy absorption of 100 ergs/gram. The P is the stopping power in units of electron volts/g/cm² of soft tissue.

TABLE 5. PRESENTLY RECOMMENDED PERMISSIBLE DOSE[a] TO BODY ORGANS OF OCCUPATIONAL WORKERS EXPOSED TO IONIZING RADIATION

Body Organ	Maximum RBE Dose[b] in Any Thirteen Weeks (rem/13 wk)	Average RBE Dose[c] in One Year (rem/yr)	Accumulated RBE Dose to Age $N \geq 18$ Yrs (rem)
Blood forming organs	3 ICRP[k] NCRP[h,i] FRC[q]	5 ICRP[k] NCRP[h,i]	$5(N-18)$ ICRP[k] NCRP[h,i] FRC[q]
Total body	3 ICRP[l] NCRP[i,m] FRC[q]	5 ICRP[l] NCRP[i,m]	$5(N-18)$ ICRP[l] NCRP[i,m] FRC[q]
Head and trunk	3 NCRP[i] FRC[q]	5 NCRP[i]	$5(N-18)$ NCRP[i] FRC[q]
Gonads	3 ICRP[k,l] NCRP[h,i,m] FRC[q]	5 ICRP[k,l] NCRP[h,i,m]	$5(N-18)$ ICRP[k,l] NCRP[h,i,m] FRC[q]
Lenses of eyes	3 ICRP[k,j,d] NCRP[h,i,m] FRC[q]	5 ICRP[k,j,d] NCRP[h,i,m]	$5(N-18)$ ICRP[k,j,d] NCRP[h,i,m] FRC[q]
Skin	8 ICRP[k,l] / 10 NCRP[i,m,p] FRC[q]	30 ICRP[k,l] / 30 NCRP[i,m,f,p] FRC[q]	$30(N-18)$ ICRP[k,l,e] / $30(N-18)$ NCRP[m,f,e,p] FRC[e]
Thyroid	8 ICRP[k,l] NCRP[m] / 10 FRC[q]	30 ICRP[k,l] NCRP[i,m] FRC[q]	$30(N-18)$ NCRP[e] ICRP[e] FRC[e]
Feet, ankles, hands and forearms	20 ICRP[k] / 25 NCRP[i,m] FRC[q]	75 ICRP[k] NCRP[i,m,n] FRC[q]	$75(N-18)$ NCRP[e] ICRP[e] FRC[e]
Bone	$30/n$[g] ICRP[e] NCRP[e]	$30/n$[g] ICRP[l] NCRP[m]	$30/n(N-18)$[g] NCRP[e] ICRP[e]
Other single organs	4 ICRP[k,l]; 5 FRC[q]	15 ICRP[k,l] NCRP[e,l,m,n] FRC[q]	$15(N-18)$ NCRP[e], ICRP[e] FRC[e]

(a) Values of National Committee on Radiation Protection (NCRP), International Commission on Radiological Protection (ICRP), and Federal Radiation Council (FRC) given are in addition to doses from medical and from background exposure.

(b) These values may be used for the accumulated short term exposures in any thirteen-week interval.[j]

(c) These values may be used for a planned emergency exposure.[j]

(d) ICRP does not restrict beta exposures of lenses of eyes to this limit.[j]

(e) Implied but not stated explicitly.[k,l,i,m,q]

(f) Interpreted by author (K. Z. Morgan) to apply only when dose is limited to skin, e.g., it applies to low-energy beta radiation external to body or originating in skin.

(g) This n is referred to as the "relative damage factor." It is one for radium isotopes and for gamma radiation; otherwise it is set equal to five for all radionuclides in bone.[l]

(h) Maximum Permissible Radiation Exposure to Man, an addendum to the NBS Handbook 59, January 8, 1957.

(i) Maximum Permissible Radiation Exposures to Man, an addendum to the NBS Handbook 59, April 15, 1958.

(j) Report on Decisions at the July 1959 Meeting in Munich of the International Commission on Radiological Protection (ICRP), *Am. J. Roentgenol. Radium Therapy Nuclear Med.*, **83**, No. 2, pp. 372–375, February 1960; *Health Physics*, **2**, No. 3, pp. 317, February 1960.

(k) Recommendations of the International Commission on Radiological Protection, ICRP Publication 1, Pergamon Press, September 9, 1958.

(l) Permissible Dose for Internal Radiation—1958 Revision, ICRP Publication 2, Published by Pergamon Press, April, 1960.

(m) Maximum Permissible Body Burdens and Maximum Permissible Concentrations of Radionuclides in Air and Water for Occupational Exposure, NCRP-NBS Handbook 69, June 5, 1959.

(n) Maximum Permissible Amounts of Radioisotopes in the Human Body and Maximum Permissible Concentrations in Air and Water, NCRP-NBS Handbook 52, March 20, 1953.

(p) National Committee on Radiation Protection and Measurements (NCRP), *Radiology*, **75**, No. 1: 122, July 1960.

(q) Federal Radiation Council, Report No. 1 (May 13, 1960); Federal Register, p. 4402, May 18, 1960.

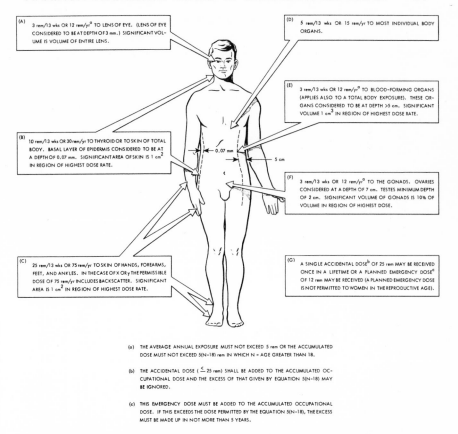

(A) 3 rem/13 wks OR 12 rem/yr^a TO LENS OF EYE. (LENS OF EYE CONSIDERED TO BE AT DEPTH OF 3 mm.) SIGNIFICANT VOLUME IS VOLUME OF ENTIRE LENS.

(D) 5 rem/13 wks OR 15 rem/yr TO MOST INDIVIDUAL BODY ORGANS.

(E) 3 rem/13 wks OR 12 rem/yr^a TO BLOOD-FORMING ORGANS (APPLIES ALSO TO A TOTAL BODY EXPOSURE). THESE ORGANS CONSIDERED TO BE AT DEPTH >5 cm. SIGNIFICANT VOLUME 1 cm^3 IN REGION OF HIGHEST DOSE RATE.

(B) 10 rem/13 wks OR 30 rem/yr TO THYROID OR TO SKIN OF TOTAL BODY. BASAL LAYER OF EPIDERMIS CONSIDERED TO BE AT A DEPTH OF 0.07 mm. SIGNIFICANT AREA OF SKIN IS 1 cm^2 IN REGION OF HIGHEST DOSE RATE.

(F) 3 rem/13 wks OR 12 rem/yr^a TO THE GONADS. OVARIES CONSIDERED AT A DEPTH OF 7 cm. TESTES MINIMUM DEPTH OF 2 cm. SIGNIFICANT VOLUME OF GONADS IS 10% OF VOLUME IN REGION OF HIGHEST DOSE.

(C) 25 rem/13 wks OR 75 rem/yr TO SKIN OF HANDS, FOREARMS, FEET, AND ANKLES. IN THE CASE OF X OR y THE PERMISSIBLE DOSE OF 75 rem/yr INCLUDES BACKSCATTER. SIGNIFICANT AREA IS 1 cm^2 IN REGION OF HIGHEST DOSE RATE.

(G) A SINGLE ACCIDENTAL DOSE^b OF 25 rem MAY BE RECEIVED ONCE IN A LIFETIME OR A PLANNED EMERGENCY DOSE^c OF 12 rem MAY BE RECEIVED (A PLANNED EMERGENCY DOSE IS NOT PERMITTED TO WOMEN IN THE REPRODUCTIVE AGE).

(a) THE AVERAGE ANNUAL EXPOSURE MUST NOT EXCEED 5 rem OR THE ACCUMULATED DOSE MUST NOT EXCEED 5(N-18) rem IN WHICH N = AGE GREATER THAN 18.

(b) THE ACCIDENTAL DOSE ($\leq$ 25 rem) SHALL BE ADDED TO THE ACCUMULATED OCCUPATIONAL DOSE AND THE EXCESS OF THAT GIVEN BY EQUATION 5(N-18) MAY BE IGNORED.

(c) THIS EMERGENCY DOSE MUST BE ADDED TO THE ACCUMULATED OCCUPATIONAL DOSE. IF THIS EXCEEDS THE DOSE PERMITTED BY THE EQUATION 5(N-18), THE EXCESS MUST BE MADE UP IN NOT MORE THAN 5 YEARS.

Fig. 3.   Maximum permissible occupational exposure to ionizing radiations (most recent). 1960 values recommended for use in the United States; see Table 5.

thirteen-week interval does not exceed the limits indicated in column 2 of Table 5 or the age prorated limits indicated in column 4. These permissible exposure limits are shown schematically in Fig. 3. Some types of radiation damage are known to increase with dose rate, and consequently, when possible, the thirteen-week permissible RBE dose should be spread out or prorated on a weekly basis rather than received at very high dose rates (e.g., avoid when possible an exposure of 3 rem/hr or 3 rem/day).

In the equations in Table 4 P is the stopping power in units of electron volts per gram per square centimeter of tissue. It may be obtained directly from Fig. 4[29],[30],[31] or calculated by means of the equation

$$P = \frac{S_a W P_t}{\rho_a} \cong 2.7 \times 10^4 S_a P_t \text{ ev/gram/cm}^2 \qquad (3)$$

in which S_a is the specific ionization of the ionizing particle in air, W is the energy required to produce a pair of ions, P_t is the mass stopping power of tissue relative to air, and ρ_a is the density of air for which S_a is given.

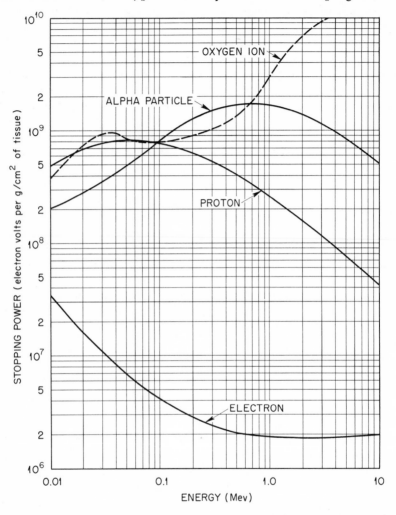

Fig. 4.   Stopping power as a function of energy.

Prior to 1957 it was permissible to double the exposure rate after age 45. (See first edition of Handbook 59.[25]) This provision was impractical and has been omitted in the revised edition of Handbook 59. Also, this revised edition limits the RBE dose to the blood-forming organs (total body), gonads, or lenses of the eyes to $5(N - 18)$ rem, in which N is the age (greater than 18) of the occupational worker. It is to be noted that according to the revised edition of Handbook 59 the maximum permissible RBE dose to the age of 70 resulting from occupational exposure is 260 rem to the blood-forming organs (total body), gonads, or lenses of the eyes, 1600 rem to the skin and thyroid, 3900 rem to the feet, ankles, hands, or forearms, and 780 rem to other organs of the body. It is very unlikely that many employees will accumulate exposures of this magnitude, and it should be emphasized that such accumulated exposures would be harmful and undesirable. The health physicist has always applied his own safety factor of about 10, and it is the opinion of the writer that only in exceptional cases should the accumulated lifetime RBE dose be permitted to exceed one tenth the accumulated values given here. This limitation becomes especially important when many persons are involved in radiation exposure because of accumulated damage such as the shortening of life span, the increase in genetic mutations, and possible increase in leukemic incidence. Animal experiments indicate that 100 rad of total body radiation would probably shorten the average life span[1] of man 1 to 5% and double or triple the spontaneous mutation rate.[32]

The NCRP[25] (1954) and ICRP[26] (1958) regulations permit also an accidental total body RBE dose of 25 rem once in a lifetime of the occupational worker. If this RBE dose exceeds that permitted by the equation $5(N - 18)$, the excess may be ignored, although it is best to add the entire accidental exposure to the accumulated RBE dose and reduce the RBE dose rate in subsequent years until the limit of $5(N - 18)$ is complied with. The duration of this accidental exposure may be over a period up to one month and is assumed to have no effect on a person's radiation tolerance status. However, since this emergency exposure is to occur only once in a lifetime, it may be necessary to modify one's employment in order to eliminate the possibility of a recurrence of such an exposure.

Planned emergency total body RBE doses of 12 rem are permitted by the NCRP and ICRP to occupational workers (provided they are not women in the reproductive age). If this RBE dose exceeds that permitted by the equation $5(N - 18)$, the excess shall be made up by lowering the subsequent exposure rate so that within a period not exceeding five years the accumulated RBE dose will conform to the limit set by this equation. The ICRP in its 1959 recommendations[26] extended the definition of a planned emergency such that the permitted dose to any body organ would be the annual limit summarized in column 3 of Table 5.

Exposures higher than those discussed here can be expected in criticality accidents,[33] reactor accidents, or atomic warfare. It is recognized that in these cases the risks of radiation damage to the rescue teams and others in the contaminated area would be higher and probably should be set at about the same level as other associated risks. No official maximum permissible exposure levels have been established for such cases. but typical instruction to rescue teams might be as follows:

(a) Do not hesitate to take 25 rem in a single exposure.

(b) In case of an exposure required to save life or essential for national defense, do not hesitate to take 100 rem in a single day, 150 rem in a single week, or 300 rem in a single month.

(c) Do not take any unnecessary high exposure and, as far as practical, limit high exposure to persons who do not intend to beget children. High exposure to pregnant women should be avoided.

The Chalk River Conference (September 1949) agreed on the statement, "In the light of present knowledge, no manifest permanent injury is to be expected from a single exposure of persons to 25 r or less, with the possible exception of pregnant women." It is generally believed that detectable damage would result to some persons receiving 50 to 100 rem total body exposure in a single day but that such persons are not likely to be incapacitated by this exposure and in most cases drowsiness and nausea are the worst effects likely to be experienced. This is a small price to be paid by rescue workers and those performing functions essential to national defense.

Experiments of E. Lorenz[34] have shown that one of the symptoms of chronic exposure of mice is an increase in the ovarian tumor incidence when they are subjected to single exposures of 50 r. Carcinogenic effects of radiation on man are generally thought to be much less severe, but it is possible that similar or comparable damage might result many years after large single or chronic exposure. In addition, exposure of this order of magnitude might lead to detectable blood changes and possibly to a temporary reduction in fertility. The Russells[35] have shown that doses of radiation as low as 50 r to the mouse fetus are capable of producing miscarriage, deformities, and other defects. Spermatogonia, the fertilized ovum, and the fetus during the early stages of development are especially sensitive to radiation damage. In order to avoid radiation damage during the critical early stages of pregnancy, the Russells[35] have suggested that large exposures to the abdominal regions of women be limited when possible to the relatively safe interval of two weeks following the beginning of the menstrual period. Probably 50% of the persons receiving 400 rem of total body exposure in a single day would be expected to die within one to three weeks if no medical care were provided. There is some reason to believe that bed rest, medical treatment for infection, the administration of bone marrow, and special chemical medication might increase the mid-lethal dose level. Therefore, it is urgent that early and accurate dose estimates should be made in the case of suspected overexposure and that all persons receiving a single exposure in excess of 25 rem should be placed under the care of a properly informed physician. Every precaution should be taken to minimize any unnecessary radiation exposure, and, if it is necessary to accumulate a large dose of ionizing radiation, the dose should be spread over an exposure period as long as possible. Experience to date on the atomic energy projects has indicated that only a small fraction of the workers in the nuclear energy field should find it necessary to accumulate more than 50 rem total body exposure in a lifetime, and only a few of these people may be expected to accumulate as much as 260 rem (i.e., an occupational worker receiving the average permissible RBE dose of 5 rem/yr from age 18 to 70 would accumulate 260 rem).

As previously indicated, exposure rates of 75 rem/yr are permitted if the radiation is confined to the hands, forearms, feet, and ankles. Exposure to the rest of the body, and in particular to the blood-forming organs, eyes, and gonads, is limited to much lower rates. The hands, forearms, feet, and ankles are believed to be less radiosensitive than most body organs, and in some cases radiation damage to these appendages is more amenable to effective medical treatment. It is on this basis that the larger exposure rates are permitted. Also, it has been observed that certain types of radiation damage such as leukemia (and perhaps life shortening) seem to be more nearly proportional to the gram-rad dose or the total ergs of energy delivered to the entire body than they are to the rad dose (i.e., ergs per gram) to a limited portion of the body. This accounts in part for the low average permissible RBE dose of 5 rem/yr to the blood-forming organs or total body. Obviously this low RBE dose rate is applied to the gonads and to the lenses of the eyes to provide protection from genetic damage and from cataracts, respectively.

There are some types of work (e.g., conducting an experiment that is behind a shield in a chemical hood) in which the exposure to the hands and forearms may be many times the average exposure to the rest of the body. This is especially true when work is done with radioactive material that emits beta radiation. In such cases it is required that meters be worn on the fingers or hands and that this exposure be monitored separately from the total body exposure. For most types of work with radioactive material, however, it is not practical to monitor the exposure to the body appendages separately, and the personnel monitoring meters, such as film badges or pocket condenser chambers, are usually worn on the chest. Numerous surveys have been made at the various Atomic Energy Commission Laboratories which indicate that chambers so worn generally measure a good average body exposure and that meters worn simultaneously on other parts of the body seldom give readings that deviate from the average by more than $\pm 50\%$. In considering a large exposure to radiation that may be confined to a limited portion of the body, it must be kept in mind that the eyes, gonads, and blood-forming organs are especially radiosensitive and should not be permitted exposures in excess of those indicated in Table 5.

2. Internal exposure. The maximum permissible RBE dose limits discussed in the preceding section and summarized in Table 5 apply equally well to internal and external exposure or combinations of the two. Usually the problems of external exposure are relatively more straightforward than those of internal exposure, and often it is difficult to set maximum permissible body burdens of the radionuclides that will give reasonable assurance that the dose rates listed in Table 5 will not be exceeded. It is progressively more difficult to set a satisfactory maximum permissible concentration (MPC) for a radionuclide that is taken into the body by way of air, food, or water. Some of the common uncertainties are the chemical and physical form and isotopic dilution of the radionuclide, the method of entry into the body, the temporary retention in the GI tract or in the respiratory tract, the fraction deposited in the various body organs and the distribution within these organs, the biological half-life or pattern of elimination from the organs, and the relative damage sustained by the various body organs. In many cases one is not certain initially of the identity of the radionuclides responsible for the gross activity in the air we breathe and the water we drink. In most cases of occupational exposure it is desirable to have available values of maximum permissible body burden and corresponding MPC values based on man's experience following many years of intake of these radioactive materials into the body by ingestion and inhalation, through cuts in the skin, or directly through the pores of the skin. Unfortunately, most of this information is unavailable or, in some cases, can be obtained only for short periods of animal exposure.

In 1941 the National Bureau of Standards issued a handbook on the "Safe Handling of Radioactive Luminous Compounds,"[36] which set 0.1 μg of radium deposited in the body as the tolerance limit for industrial workmen. The committee preparing this handbook recommended also that a worker change his occupation immediately if the concentration of radon in his expired air should exceed 1 $\mu\mu c$/liter (10^{-9} μc/cc.) In 1943 the British X-Ray and Radium Protection Committee recommended an upper permissible limit of 10 $\mu\mu c$ of Rn^{222}/liter (10^{-8} μc/cc) of expired air. The United States and British permissible limits of radon exposure were assumed to correspond to 10^{-8} and 10^{-7} μc of Rn^{222}/cc of inhaled air, respectively. The standard method of determining the radium content in the body is to take a measurement of the gamma radiation with a total body counter or to take breath samples and send them to the Bureau of Standards or some other properly equipped laboratory for radon analysis. It is assumed in the latest revisions (1959) of the NCRP[37] and ICRP[38] handbooks that about 70% of the radon produced by radium deposited in the bone is eliminated by way of the expired air, and thus only 30% of the daughter products contribute to the absorbed dose to the bone. In 1953 the tripartite conference on permissible dose meeting at Harriman, New York, agreed to set the permissible concentration of Rn^{222} for occupational exposure at 10^{-7} $\mu c/cc$ of air. It was stated that this value applied when radon is in equilibrium with its daughter products. This value was later defined by the ICRP in April 1956 to apply to a 40-hr/wk exposure so that the maximum permissible concentration (MPC) for continuous exposure was changed to 3×10^{-8} $\mu c/cc$ of air. In 1959 the ICRP again lowered the MPC for continuous occupational exposure, this time to 10^{-8} $\mu c/cc$. It is to be noted[26,38,39] that essentially all of the hazard from airborne radon stems from the inhalation of the daughter products of radon. In particular, most of the radiation damage is thought to be related to the dose delivered by the free (unattached) ions of Po^{218} (RaA). The present ICRP and NCRP continuous occupational exposure MPC value for Rn^{222} of 10^{-8} $\mu c/cc$ is based on the assumption that Po^{218} as free ions constitutes 10% of the equilibrium value. Thus the MPC for continuous occupational exposure is $10^{-6}/(1 + 1000f)$ μc of Rn^{222}/cc in which f is the fraction of equilibrium of Po^{218} in the inhaled air. It follows then that the MPC for 168 hr/wk occupational exposure to Rn^{222} is 10^{-7}, 10^{-8}, and 10^{-9} μc of Rn^{222}/cc for 1, 10, and 100% equilibrium of Po^{218}, respectively. The MPC for exposure 40 hr/wk is three times the foregoing values.

In 1953 the Subcommittee on Internal Dose of the National Committee on Radiation Protection, NCRP, prepared a handbook[37] giving the maximum permissible body burden (q) and maximum permissible concentration (MPC) in air and water of some 70 radionuclides. In the preparation of this handbook, it was possible in a few cases in which the chemical behavior of the element is similar to that of radium to make use of the twenty-five years of experience man had had with radium and to choose values based on those given in Handbook 27,[36] but in most cases the new data were based on limited information from animal experiments that had been in progress for only a relatively short time. In 1955 the International Commission on Radiological Protection (ICRP) published its first handbook[26] giving q and MPC values for 86 radionuclides. The reader is referred to these handbooks for a detailed review of the assumptions made and equations used in arriving at the values of q and MPC.

In 1959 revised handbooks on Internal Dose were published both by NCRP[37] and ICRP.[38] These two handbooks give identical MPC values for 240 radionuclides. The ICRP handbook contains much more detail with reference to the various assumptions and calculations used in arriving at the final MPC values.

The values of maximum permissible body burden, q (with the exception of bone-seeking radionuclides), were obtained for all radionuclides listed in the 1959 revisions of the NCRP and ICRP handbooks by calculating the number of microcuries in the critical organ, qf_2, that would result in the RBE dose rates listed for occupational exposure in Table 5. In this case f_2 is the fraction in the critical organ of that in the total body. The occupational exposure values for q for bone-seeking radionuclides were based on an amount estimated to deliver the same RBE dose rate to the bone that would be delivered by 0.1 μg of Ra^{226} (i.e., the bone-seeking radionuclide would deliver a maximum RBE dose rate of about 30 rem/yr or effective RBE dose rate of about 6 rem/yr). The maximum permissible concentrations (MPC) for occupational exposure correspond to the concentrations in water (or food) and air, respectively, that are expected to result in a total body burden, q, after a person has been exposed continuously to the contaminated water or air for a time, t, assumed to be fifty years. In most cases a condition of equilibrium is reached in a period of continuous exposure that is much shorter than fifty years, and during equilibrium the rate of elimination is equal to the rate of deposition in the critical organ. If the continuous air or water exposure is at a constant level of contamination equal to the occupational MPC values, the RBE dose rate in the critical body organ will become constant during equilibrium at the values listed in column 3 of Table 5. The critical organ is that body organ receiving the radionuclide that results in the greatest damage to the body. In most cases it is that body organ that receives the limiting RBE dose rate (listed in Table 5) from the lowest total body burden, q. The maximum permissible concentrations (MPC) for all critical body organs, with the exception of the gastrointestinal (GI) tract, are given by the equation

$$\text{MPC} = \frac{aqf_2}{Tf(1 - e^{-0.693t/T})} \tag{4}$$

in which MPC = μc/cc of air or water that will result in a total body burden q if the contaminated air or water is used exclusively for a time t

q = μc in total body required to deliver to the critical body organ RBE dose rates listed in Table 5. In the case of bone-seeking radionuclides, q is taken as the microcuries in the bone that are considered to deliver the same RBE dose rate as 0.1 μg Ra^{226}. This corresponds to a maximum RBE dose rate of about 30 rem/yr or effective RBE dose rate of 6 rem/yr

f_2 = fraction of the radionuclide in the critical organ of that in the total body

f = fraction of the radionuclide taken into the body that arrives in the critical organ (in the NCRP and ICRP handbooks $f = f_w$ for ingestion and $f = f_a$ for inhalation)

t = period of time over which the exposure is considered to continue. It is taken as fifty years in the calculation of values of MPC for occupational exposure

T = effective half-life of the radionuclide in the critical organ

$$T = \frac{T_b T_r}{T_b + T_r} \tag{5}$$

T_r = radioactive half-life of the radionuclide

T_b = biological half-life of the radionuclide in the critical body organ

a = constant. If T is given in days, $a = 10^{-7}$ and 9.2×10^{-4} for air and water, respectively, for an occupational exposure of 8 hr/day, 5 days/wk, and 50 wk/yr.

The maximum permissible body burden (except in the case of bone-seeking radionuclides) is given by the equation

$$q = \frac{5.3 \times 10^{-5} mR}{f_2 \Sigma E \, (\text{RBE})n} \tag{6}$$

in which m = mass of critical organ in grams

R = annual RBE dose listed in column 3 of Table 5

E = effective energy of the radiation in Mev per disintegration

RBE = relative biological effectiveness of the radiation as given in Table 4

n = relative damage factor. This is set equal to 5 for the particulate component of radiation (α, β^-, β^+, e$^-$) from all radionuclides for which bone is the critical body organ, with the exception of radium where it is set equal to 1. This factor, n, is set equal to 1 for x and gamma radiation and for all tissue other than bone.

When bone is the critical body organ, q is based on a comparison with Ra^{226}. In this case

$$q = \frac{11}{f_2 \, \Sigma \, E \, (RBE)n} . \tag{7}$$

When the gastrointestinal (GI) tract is the critical body tissue, the lower large intestine usually receives the largest RBE dose. In this case, the value of MPC is given by the equation

$$(MPC)^{GI} = \frac{b}{\Sigma \, E \, (RBE)n \, (e^{-0.12/T} e^{-0.26/T_r})} \tag{8}$$

in which $b = 4.4 \times 10^{-4}$ for ingestion and $b = 4.9 \times 10^{-8}/f$ for inhalation during occupational exposure of 8 hr/day, 5 days/wk, and 50 wk/yr. T_r and T are the radioactive half-life and the effective half-life, respectively, in days. The fraction f, which is inhaled and swallowed, is taken as 0.625 for insoluble material and 0.5 for soluble material. The constant a in (4) or b in (8) should be reduced by a factor of 3 for continuous occupational exposure (168 hr/wk), and there should be further reductions in arriving at suitable values for nonoccupational exposure. For detailed calculations or for special cases not covered by the foregoing equations (e.g., the inhalation of radioactive materials with radioactive daughter products, multiple exposure to several radionuclides, and exposure to other portions of the GI tract) the reader is referred to the revised editions of the NCRP and the ICRP publications.[37,38] In all cases the combined occupational exposures from both external and internal sources of ionizing radiation must not exceed the limits specified in Table 5.

Although the basic principles applied in the 1959 revisions of the internal dose handbooks of the ICRP[38] and the NCRP[37] are essentially the same as those used in the first editions of these handbooks, a number of changes[40] may be summarized:

(a) MPC and q values were given for 70 radionuclides in the 1953 NCRP handbook and for 86 radionuclides in the 1955 ICRP handbook. The 1959 revisions of both handbooks contain MPC and q values for about 240 radionuclides.

(b) The revised (1959) handbooks contain MPC values for each radionuclide based on the GI tract and on the total body as well as values based on other critical body organs. MPC values based on the GI tract were given in the first edition of the ICRP handbook but not in the first edition of the NCRP handbook. MPC values based on the total body were given for only a few of the radionuclides in the old editions of these handbooks.

(c) MPC values are given for both soluble and insoluble forms of the radionuclides in the revised ICRP and NCRP handbooks. Values for insoluble compounds were given in only a few cases in the earlier publications.

(d) In the old editions of the NCRP and ICRP handbooks it was assumed that 55% of the daughter products of Ra^{226} is retained in the body leading to a value of $\Sigma\, E\, (RBE)n$ of 162 and a dose rate to the bone of 0.8 rem/wk. In the revised editions of these handbooks (1959) use is made of recent experimental data to indicate that 30% of the daughter products is retained. This leads to a value of $\Sigma\, E\, (RBE)n$ of 110 [see (7)] and corresponds to a maximum RBE dose rate to the bone of about 30 rem/yr.

(e) In the old editions of the NCRP and ICRP handbooks there were four radionuclides that did not reach equilibrium in the exposure period. In the revised editions about 20 radionuclides do not reach equilibrium. There are three reasons for this change, which may be listed in order of decreasing importance: (1) many additional radionuclides were considered, (2) recent data resulted in an increase in the biological half-life of some of the radionuclides, and (3) the occupational exposure period was decreased from seventy to fifty years.

(f) Equation 7 was applied in most cases in the old editions of the NCRP and ICRP handbooks only when the bone-seeking radionuclide was an alpha emitter. In the revised editions it is applied in the case of all bone-seeking radionuclides, with the exception of those that emit only x and gamma radiation.

(g) In the old editions of the NCRP and ICRP handbooks all MPC values were obtained by assuming $Q = Q_0 e^{-0.693 t_1/T}$, in which $Q_0 = \mu c$ present at time $t = 0$, $Q = \mu c$ present at time $t = t_1$, and $T = $ effective half-life $= T_r T_b/(T_r + T_b)$, where T_r and T_b are the radioactive and biological half-lives, respectively. In the revised editions the foregoing relations were used to obtain the values of MPC. However, when the required data were available, an alternate relation was considered, namely, $Q = A Q_0 t^{-n}$ in which A and n are constants. Sufficient data were available at the time to apply this power function only in the case of isotopes of Sr, U, Pu, and Ra.

(h) In the revised editions of NCRP and ICRP handbooks the average maximum permissible RBE dose rate is changed from 0.3 rem/wk to the annual limits listed in Table 5. No biological data are available for specific radionuclides for the application of the new lower limit of 5 rem/yr to the gonads or the lenses of the eyes as the critical body organs, but the total body is the critical body organ (i.e., the limiting RBE dose rate is 5 rem/yr) in the case of about 15% of the radionuclides.

(i) In the old editions of the NCRP and ICRP handbooks the dose rate of 0.6 rem/wk was permitted only for I^{131}. In the revised editions this dose rate of 0.6 rem/wk (or its equivalent of 30 rem/yr) is permitted for all radionuclides for which the skin or the thyroid is the critical tissue, viz., it is applied in the case of 10 radionuclides.

(j) The average RBE dose rates are given in terms of rem per year instead of rem per week. The maximum rates are given in terms of rem per thirteen weeks. (See Table 5.)

Usually when a person has been exposed to the various radionuclides it is difficult to make an accurate estimate of the total body burden, and considerable precautions should be taken to maintain the air and water concentration of a radionuclide (or equivalent for a mixture of radionuclides) at or below the values listed in the handbooks. All surface contamination of the working area, of the clothing and of the body should be kept at a minimum. In a few cases, such as with radium, the body burden can be checked by measurements of the contamination of the exhaled air, but most often urine or fecal analysis and total body counting give the best indication. Urinalysis is the most common method of routinely checking the body burden of a radionuclide, but many laboratories are installing total body counting equipment to augment the urinalysis program. Frequent checks, appropriate to the radionuclide involved, should be made to determine the body burden of radionuclides for all persons working with radioactive material or otherwise exposed to them. If a person has built up a maximum permissible body burden (q) of a radionuclide, the total amount eliminated by the urine in time $t_2 - t_1$ is given by the equation

$$U = \frac{q f_2 T F}{T_b} \left(e^{-0.693 t_1/T} - e^{-0.693 t_2/T} \right) \tag{9}$$

in which U = total microcuries voided in time $t_2 - t_1$ via the urine and

$$F = \frac{\text{fraction voided via urine of total eliminated}}{\text{fraction eliminated from critical organ of total eliminated}}.$$

It is assumed that the person is removed from further intake of the radioactive material at time $t = 0$ and that all excretions are collected for the time interval $t_2 - t_1$. Frequently F is unknown, and as a result Ff_2 is set equal to 1, letting T and T_b apply to the effective and biological half-lives, respectively, of the entire body, rather than to the critical body organ, and U to total excretion, that is, by the urine and feces.

In the case of a single intake of a radionuclide—as occasionally happens with accidents caused by a leaking chemical hood or a spill of radioactive material—the RBE dose received by the critical body organ is given by the equation

$$D = \frac{74 f I_0 T \Sigma E (RBE) n}{m} \left(1 - e^{-0.693 t/T} \right) \tag{10}$$

in which D is the RBE dose in rem delivered to the critical organ in time t days when I_0 μc are taken into the body and the fraction, f, is deposited in the critical body organ of mass m grams. An effort should be made to limit the body intake (I_0) of a radionuclide in a single event to a value such that the dose D does not exceed the thirteen-week limit given in Table 5. Values of I_0 are given for a number of different radionuclides by Morgan et al.[15,41]

The total fecal excretion of a radionuclide for a few days (not less than 31 hr) following a single intake of I_0 μc is given approximately by the equation

$$U = f I_0 e^{-0.693t/T_r} \qquad (11)$$

in which $U = \mu$c of radionuclide measured in the feces at time t, following the intake of I_0 μc. In this case $f = (1 - f_1)$ for ingestion, $f = 0.62(1 - f_1)$ for inhalation, and f_1 is the fraction passing from the GI tract into the blood.

3. Maximum permissible exposure to various population groups. As already pointed out, radiation exposure to man—no matter how low—is believed to produce some irreparable damage, and on this basis all unnecessary exposure must be avoided. It follows, therefore, that occupational exposure to ionizing radiation must be considered as one of the many industrial hazards, but, as indicated in Table 2, this radiation hazard in the United States atomic energy industry is much less than many of the more conventional hazards that are familiar to the chemical and engineering industries. Because man has not developed a sixth sense that responds to ionizing radiation and in view of the fact that many types of radiation damage are cumulative—appearing much later in life following early exposure—it is very important that adequate instruments be provided to furnish early warning of all high exposures and to integrate all day-to-day absorbed doses of each type of ionizing radiation received. Complete records must be maintained on the current and cumulative occupational exposure of all persons who enter the plant area where they may be subject to exposure. Since the cumulative exposure a man has received may influence not only his health but the type of work in which he may be employed, it is essential that a complete exposure record be maintained and made available to all employees for whom exposure is possible. The 1958 report of the ICRP[26] states, "When the previous occupational exposure history of an individual is not definitely known, it shall be assumed that he has already received the full quota permitted by the formula $5(N - 18)$." Thus an employer who fails to provide an adequate health-physics program and maintain complete exposure records is not properly discharging his responsibilities and may become liable for consequent damage to his employees or visitors to his plant.

All the foregoing discussions have dealt with occupational exposure. Much of this applies to exposure to other groups, but it should be emphasized that nonoccupational exposure levels must be considerably lower than the maximum permissible occupational exposure levels previously

TABLE 6.   PERMISSIBLE GENETIC EXPOSURE TO THE
POPULATION-AT-LARGE* AS SUGGESTED BY THE ICRP
(RBE dose in rem to the gonads to age 30)

4.5 medical

4.5 background

		2.0 general to population-at-large	1.5 internal (waste disposal)
			0.5 external
5.0 other			
—	3.0		1.0 occupational
14 total			0.5 special groups $(B_a, B_b,$ and $B_c)$†
			1.5 reserve

* These values for genetic exposure are given by the ICRP[26] to serve as a guide and not as final recommendations. No similar apportionment of the somatic exposure has been suggested by the ICRP for the population-at-large. In this case consideration should be given to the shortening of the life span (which may decrease linearly with the dose), increased incidence of leukemia, and other biological changes which may or may not represent radiation damage. For the present, values given in Table 6 should serve as a guide, and in providing genetic protection it is anticipated that in most practical cases there will be adequate protection provided also against somatic damage.

† See text.

discussed and summarized in Table 5. This added restriction results from the fact that each industry has occupational hazards peculiar to its own operations (e.g., silicosis for the miner, lead poisoning for the painter, traffic accidents for the taxi driver, burns for the housewife, and radiation exposure for the atomic energy worker). The ICRP (1959)[26] report divides the persons subject to exposure to ionizing radiation into three main groups: (A) occupational, (B) special groups, and (C) the population at-large. The special groups are subdivided into three subgroups: (B_a) adults working in the vicinity of the controlled area, (B_b) adults who enter the controlled area occasionally, and (B_c) persons living in the neighborhood of the controlled area. A controlled area is defined by the NCRP[25] as "an area in which the occupational exposure of personnel to radiation or to radioactive material is under the supervision of an individual in charge of radiation protection." This person is normally a health physicist. The ICRP (1959)[26] report limits the yearly RBE dose to groups B_a and B_b to a maximum of 3 rem for the skin and thyroid and a maximum of 1.5 rem for the blood-forming organs, the total body, the lenses of the eyes, or the gonads. This report limits the yearly RBE dose to group B_c to a maximum of 0.5 rem for the blood-forming organs, the total body, the lenses of the eyes, or the gonads. In general, this implies dose rates ranging from 3/10 to 1/10 those given for occupational exposure.

Exposures to the population-at-large must be lower than occupational exposure by almost two orders of magnitude in order to provide sufficient genetic protection. Reports of the National Academy of Sciences[42] and of the United Nations Scientific Committee[43] indicate that genetic exposure to the gonads should not exceed 10 rem from man-made sources of ionizing radiation. There is considerable variation in human exposure in various parts of the world, especially in exposure to medical sources and background radiation. Because of this variation and because of the uncertainties in the future developments in the atomic energy industry, it is difficult at this time to give a satisfactory apportionment of the genetic dose. With this in mind, the ICRP (1959)[26] has given the data summarized in Table 6 to serve as a guide.

C. Instruments Required by a Small Laboratory and Their Use

I. Personnel monitoring instruments. Everyone working with radioisotopes, nuclear reactors, high-voltage accelerators, or other sources of exposure to ionizing radiation should carry on his person adequate monitoring instruments to determine the rad dose received from each type of radiation, that is, fast neutrons, thermal neutrons, gamma rays, or beta rays. The three principal meters generally used for this purpose are pocket condenser chambers (referred to as pocket chambers), film meters, and pocket electroscopes (dosimeters). Some of the pocket chambers used during the early years (1942–1945) of the atomic energy projects did not give very satisfactory results because they discharged when dropped and because dust and moisture would get across the insulators and cause leakage. In order to minimize the difficulty due to faulty readings, each person exposed to gamma and/or beta radiation wore a film meter and two pocket chambers; the lower of the two pocket-chamber readings was always considered to be the valid one, since errors tended to give exposure readings that were too high. Occasionally, both readings would be off-scale; these were found to be "false" readings, except in the few cases in which the film meter verified an authentic exposure. At that time there was about one "false" pair of readings per 1000 pairs of pocket chambers worn at Oak Ridge National Laboratory. Today, improved pocket chambers[44] are in use, and these instruments give less than one "false" pair of readings per 50,000 pairs of pocket chambers worn. Satisfactory monitoring could be done with the use of only one pocket chamber per person. The principal improvements in this chamber over earlier designs are a more rigid aluminum electrode which prevents jarring against the chamber wall, a graphite coating inside the chamber that does not flake off, and a pressure-fit meter cap that does not come off easily in use and that has no aluminum threads to grind off and short-circuit the insulators. These pocket chambers are read with a projection minometer over a useful range of 5 to 300 mr; they are charged with the same instrument. Some mechanical reader-recorder-charger combinations have been developed, but in 1960 they were not in common use. These pocket chambers are rather energy independent down to x-ray tube potentials of 200 kv.[45,46]

A completely enclosed pocket chamber was developed at Argonne National Laboratory by J. E. Rose. It is charged through a metal charging button that is molded into a flexible plastic in one end of the meter. In some models the charge is applied through a magnetically operated switch. These sealed-in pocket meters give good results and are superior for use in a dusty or humid atmosphere. A number of instrument companies currently are manufacturing types of pocket chambers and electrometers which give very reliable field service. The dosimeters have a built-in fiber electroscope that can be read by looking through one end while pointing the other end to the light. Some of the dosimeters contain a charging mechanism, but most of them in present use must be charged by the use of a separate instrument. Dosimeters are often worn in addition to pocket chambers and film badges during especially "hot" operations and are valued by the technical personnel because they provide a means of keeping a running account of their accumulated dose. Some of the dosimeters can be read with the same accuracy as pocket chambers (± 2 mr) and some are very rugged so that they furnish reliable service for many years. However, they are much more expensive (by a factor of 5 to 10) than pocket chambers.

The film meter is the most reliable and the principal meter in use (1960) for personnel monitoring. This meter is particularly valuable in providing a permanent legal record of the absorbed dose received by each person. Photographic emulsions, covering a useful range of 30 mr to more than 5000 r, are available. The film meter must contain two or more filters[47] to aid in interpreting the absorbed dose and resolving the difficulty due to the fact that unshielded sensitive x-ray films are about twenty times more sensitive to x rays between 50 and 100 kev than to x or gamma rays above 200 kev.[48] Film meters yield reliable absorbed dose measurements that are independent of the dose rate; their operation is not affected by the usual temperatures, humidity, precipitation, sunlight, mechanical shock, etc., and they provide a relatively permanent record. With presently used emulsions the fading is very slight, and any fading errors are automatically corrected by a corresponding fading of the control films.

In order to understand better the meter requirement of a personnel monitoring service, the film badge in use (1960) at Oak Ridge National Laboratory is described here in some detail and Fig. 5 indicates the major features of its construction. The system used requires that everyone entering the controlled area must wear a film badge (called a badge meter at ORNL because it contains metering devices other than film and it is worn also as a security badge). The picture on the badge meter (or other identification on the front of the meter in case of a visitor) serves as a pass authorizing the wearer to enter the laboratory area; thus, for the most part, the badge meters are worn at all times by all persons while they are in the controlled area. Also there is no problem of persons wearing the wrong badge because of a reluctance to display someone else's picture. The badge meters of employees are collected and reissued every thirteen weeks. Each employee is assigned two badges—one red, the other black—and on a meter exchange date each employee turns in one badge and picks up the other, which is the color in use for the next thirteen-week period. In the earlier years of operation at ORNL the badge meters were exchanged on a weekly basis and later after a two-week interval. This had the advantage of a more frequent check on the exposure of each employee but the disadvantages of greater inconvenience, higher cost, and reduced accuracy in maintaining records of the accumulated absorbed dose. The inaccuracy results from the fact that when the blackening of the developed film is measured by a laboratory technician using a photometer to compare the blackening with that of a series of control films there is an error of about ± 30 mr for each reading; that is, the accuracy of the system is such that when each film is read no distinction is made between one film reading zero and another reading 30 mr. Thus, with the present system, a person receiving a weekly absorbed dose of 60 mr would have a measured dose of $13 \times 60 = 780 \pm 30$ mrad (actually the error would be less in this case because upon observing this high absorbed dose value a more careful reading would be made), whereas with the earlier system in which the films were read on a weekly basis the recorded dose would have been $13 \times (60 \pm 30) = 780 \pm 390$.

Since the badge meters are processed at ORNL on a quarterly basis, it is necessary to augment them with pocket chambers and/or dosimeters which are read on a daily basis (or oftener). These auxiliary meters are worn only by those who work in areas in which they are *likely* to be exposed. This group numbers only 500, and the remaining 3500 employees (those who

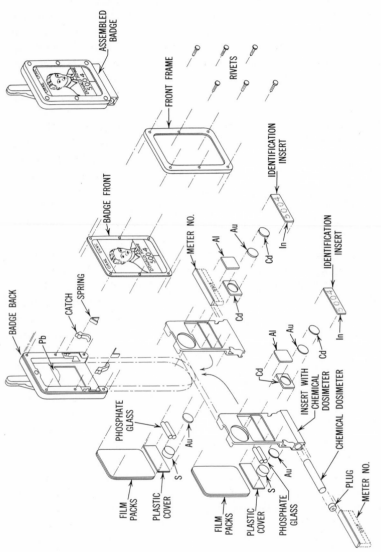

Fig. 5.   Health physics multipurpose badge meter.

are unlikely to be exposed) wear only the badge meters. If a person's pocket meter or dosimeter reads more than 100 mrad in a single day or if there is any other reason to suspect that a person has received more than 100 mrad in a single day, his badge meter is processed immediately.

The present ORNL badge meter has been designed[47] to accomplish four objectives: (1) routine radiation dosimetry, (2) high-level gamma and neutron dosimetry, (3) a means of quickly identifying the persons receiving high absorbed doses in case of accidental exposure, and (4) security identification. The combination with security serves the extremely useful function of guaranteeing that the meter is worn at all times by all persons in the controlled area.

Routine beta-gamma dosimetry is furnished everyone at ORNL by dental films contained in a badge that has four filter combinations in the front and two filters in the rear. The four front-filter combinations are (1) 0.020 in. plastic, 0.015 in. cadmium, 0.005 in. gold, 0.015 in. cadmium, and 0.012 inches plastic, in that order from the front surface of the badge; (2) 0.020 in. plastic, 0.040 in. aluminum, and 0.012 in. plastic; (3) 0.020 in. plastic; and (4) 0.082 in. plastic. This arrangement of filter combinations was carefully selected by experiment in order to provide an accurate and simple method of determining various absorbed doses of beta, gamma, and x radiation and to provide an estimate of the energy distribution of the radiation. The two rear filters are (1) 0.062 in. plastic and 0.010 in. lead, and (2) 0.062 in. plastic. These filters were selected so that exposures to the rear of the badge may be differentiated from those to the front and proper allowance made in determining the dose. Routine neutron dosimetry is accomplished by applying a technique developed by Cheka[49] and using a nuclear track (NTA) emulsion film in conjunction with the front filters of the badge. The film complement presently in use in the badge includes two film packets that have combined ranges of 0.030 to 1000 rads for hard gamma radiation and 0.015 to 10 rads for fast and/or thermal neutron radiation. The gamma radiation range can be extended to 5000 rads by the employment of special film processing techniques.

The high-level (>10 rads) neutron feature consists of three items incorporated into the present ORNL badge structure. These are (1) a sulfur rod, $\frac{1}{8}$ in. in diameter by $1\frac{1}{4}$ in. long (mass 0.5 gram), (2) a gold foil 0.005 in. thick by 7/16 in. in diameter inserted in the cavity with the sulfur rod, and (3) an identical gold foil that is a component of the cadmium-gold filter previously described. These items are activated when exposed to neutrons, and counting techniques permit determination of the thermal neutron exposure from the two gold foils and high-energy (>2.5 Mev) neutron exposure from the sulfur. Exposure to neutrons of intermediate energy is determined by comparing these film-badge exposures with exposure to nearby Hurst threshold detectors,[50] which are distributed in strategic locations throughout the laboratory. Silver phosphate glass rods have been incorporated in this badge as an adjunct to the high-level gamma-ray monitoring.

The fourth objective of the ORNL badge meter (i.e., to provide a means of quickly identifying persons receiving high absorbed doses in case of accidental exposure) is accomplished for neutron exposure by foil activation. The badge contains an indium foil ($1\frac{1}{4} \times \frac{1}{4} \times 0.010$ in.) in addition to the gold foils, both of which serve this purpose. If a person wearing this badge should be subjected to a high neutron exposure, the thermal neutrons would be captured directly in these foils and/or some of the fast neutrons would be thermalized and captured, thereby causing the indium and gold foils to become intense gamma sources that can be detected at a distance of several feet with any of the common types of survey meters. For example, experience during the Y-12 criticality accident[51] on June 16, 1958, indicated that the exposure of a person to an absorbed dose of 200 rads of fast neutrons would activate the indium foil in the ORNL badge so that it would give a reading on a gamma-ray survey meter of about 1 mrad/hr at a distance of 1 ft 1 hr after the exposure. It is possible that the induced activity of the indium foil in some badges might be overlooked during the excitement following a large-scale accident so that by the next day the activity of the indium (with a 54-min half-life) would be negligible and undetectable. However, in this case the activity of the gold foils in the badge (with a half-life of 2.7 days) would remain high enough for several days following such exposure to give an easily detectable reading with a survey meter held against the badge. A bottom slot in the ORNL badge meter contains a provision for a chemical dosimeter to provide a means for quickly sorting out the individuals who may be exposed to high doses of gamma radiation if unaccompanied by neutron exposure. This consists of a small glass tube containing tetrachloroethylene and a dye which undergoes a visible change in color when exposed to x or γ radiation that delivers an absorbed dose greater than about 10 rads.

The ORNL badge meter is fastened to the clothing of the wearer with an alligator clip. The badge is made of plastic and contains a picture of the wearer on the face. Its over-all dimensions are approximately $2\frac{1}{2} \times 1\frac{3}{4} \times 5/16$ in. and the total cost (including the phosphate glass and chemical dosimeter) is about $4.00 per badge.

After the badge meter is worn for thirteen weeks (or sooner if radiation exposure is suspected), the film is removed and put through the developing process under controlled conditions. The humidity and temperature of the developing room and the temperature of the tank solutions are kept constant. A set of calibration films, which has been exposed to known doses from a radium source, is processed with each batch of film to correct the slight variations in the film-developing process and variations of film sensitivity from batch to batch. After the films have been dried, the blackening is determined with a suitable densitometer. Portions of the developed film that were behind the various filter combinations and the open window are read for blackening, and the doses from gamma and beta radiation are determined by comparing the film blackening with that of the calibrated films.

Following exposure of the ORNL badge to neutrons and after development of the NTA film, the portion of this film that was behind the cadmium shield of the badge will have recoil proton tracks that were produced in it by fast neutrons; the portion of the film that was behind the open window of the film badge will have proton tracks that were produced in it by thermal neutrons, as a result of the capture reaction N^{14} $(n, p)C^{14}$, as well as the fast proton recoil tracts. The number of proton tracks per field of vision is determined with the aid of a dark field microscope. The number of proton tracks per unit area of the film is proportional to the RBE dose of neutrons as a result of appropriate filter combinations[49] in the badge. However, the number of tracks corresponding to the maximum permissible RBE dose varies considerably with the batch of film used, so that calibrations must be made for each new batch. For example, a typical batch of film recently developed gave 0.21 track per field of vision (2×10^{-4} cm^2) for an exposure to 4.8×10^7 thermal neutrons/cm^2 (100 mrem) and 0.22 track per field of vision for an exposure to 1.4×10^6 fast neutrons/cm^2 (100 mrem) from a Po-Be source. Of course, neutron monitoring films are not required of persons working only with x- or gamma-ray sources, but they should be worn always by those near high-voltage accelerators, nuclear reactors, potentially critical assemblies, or other producers of neutrons such as Ra-Be or Po-Be sources.

Film monitoring is especially adaptable to radionuclide users in the many small laboratories, but the cost of calibration and proper facilities for developing and reading the films is often prohibitive. As a result, small laboratories frequently find it desirable and economical to obtain film monitoring services from outside agencies.[52]

Several other types of meters have been developed for monitoring ionizing radiation (1960), but none meets all the requirements of a personnel monitoring meter. Undoubtedly the present instrument development programs will lead to many improvements.

In summary, it may be stated that all institutions using radioactivity should provide appropriate badge meters to all who enter the controlled area, and pocket chambers, pocket dosimeters, or the equivalent should be furnished to each person working with or exposed to ionizing radiation.

The principal function of this type of meter is to indicate the day-to-day exposure a person receives. Should a high reading be recorded, it would serve as an indication that greater precautions must be taken and that the film from the badge meter is to be processed immediately to obtain quantitative confirmation of the exposure. Film readings provide a double check on the exposures and furnish a convenient means of quantitative integration of small daily exposures over periods of several weeks or months, exposures that would be difficult to observe with pocket chambers and fiber electroscopes because of their leakage rate of a few mrad per day. Also, films are capable of indicating the dose from beta rays, and x and gamma rays of various energies, and the films, together with the sulfur, gold, indium, phosphate glass, chemical dosimeter, etc., can serve as convenient crash badges to furnish initial warning of large exposures and to aid in estimating the dose and distribution of energy of the neutron and gamma radiation. The open-window and plastic filter readings on the film meters described give an indication of the beta absorbed dose delivered to a depth of 130 mg/cm^2 of tissue. Since the total paper and/or plastic covering the insensitive film in the open window section of the badge meter contains 80 mg/cm^2, this meter furnishes information on dose from beta radiation only if the energy is greater than 0.5 Mev. This same energy restriction to beta dosimetry applies also to most pocket chambers and pocket dosimeters that have wall thicknesses ranging from about 150 to 300 mg/cm^2. Special thin-walled pocket chambers and film rings are available, and they should be worn by persons subjected to exposure to beta radiation.

Hand and foot counters are very convenient and valuable instruments for monitoring large numbers of people for radioactive contamination. A person using one of these instruments steps upon a platform and places his hands in two small pockets of the machine. For most of the instruments, the weight of the hands on microswitches starts the apparatus operating. If the instrument is to monitor beta and/or gamma contamination, the output of G-M counters located below the feet and on each side of the hands is fed into scaling circuits; these, in turn, operate mechanical registers. This apparatus cuts off automatically after a predetermined time—usually 15 to 30 sec—and resets when the operator steps off the platform. These instruments require frequent calibration and are expensive. The institution with few people or scattered groups working with radioactivity can manage very satisfactorily with only a G-M or scintillation-counter probe connected to a scaling circuit or rate meter. This probe is used to check hands, shoes, clothing, hair, chest, and thyroid and thus to some extent obviates the necessity of expensive equipment for each of these separate tests. If alpha contamination is present, suitable alpha monitoring equipment must be made available. This frequently consists of a proportional counter with a thin window or a scintillation-counter probe feeding the pulses produced by the alpha particles into a scaling circuit or rate-meter to indicate the level of contamination; sometimes the individual pulses are applied to a loud speaker, so that by listening to the popping sound one can tell which surfaces are contaminated and can more quickly monitor and decontaminate a large area. In some cases the alpha monitor is similar to the hand and foot counter previously described, except that the G-M counter is replaced by a proportional or scintillation counter.

2. Portable survey instruments. There is no sharp distinction between a survey instrument and a personnel-monitoring instrument. In general, however, a survey meter is one that is used to measure the absorbed dose rate of the various types of ionizing radiation of air, water, and surface contamination in an area that may be occupied. The personnel-monitoring instrument, on the other hand, is used to measure the absorbed dose received by the individual. In most cases this instrument is worn as a badge or pocket meter, but it may also be a large meter such as the hand and foot counter used to measure body and clothing contamination. Obviously, on some occasions a personnel-monitoring meter may serve as a useful survey meter or vice-versa.

All laboratories, large or small, need two types of portable survey instruments: (1) a very sensitive instrument to detect the presence of radiation and to use in making qualitative measurements and (2) a very reliable instrument that is relatively energy-independent, that maintains its calibration almost indefinitely, and can be used for semiquantitative measurements of absorbed dose rate. These instruments are essential for laboratory survey work, and in the small laboratories they may also be used as a substitute for the hand and foot counter.

The instrument of the first type presently available and most commonly used for beta and gamma survey measurement is the portable G-M counter, many types[44] of which are available commercially. The portable proportional counter called "poppy" is typical of this class of instrument as adapted for alpha survey measurement. This instrument can also be used to make qualitative measurements for low-energy beta contamination, such as C^{14} and S^{35}, if it is furnished with a very thin window probe and supplied with a cylinder of argon having 3 % mixture of CO_2, that produces a slow flow of gas into the probe. Scintillation counters offer many advantages of G-M and proportional counters, and there is an indication that they are replacing these instruments for much of this kind of service.

The fiber electroscopes, such as the Lauritsen or the Landsverk-Wollan,[44] are among the most valuable types of instruments for quantitative absorbed dose measurements for both the small university and the large laboratory. They can be furnished with a series of windows to make them useful for alpha, beta, and gamma measurements. There is also available commercially a number of very good electronic rate meters which are similar in circuitry and reliability to some of the earlier meters, such as "cutie pie," "juno," and "zeuto."[44] One of the best and most widely used fast neutron instruments available is "rudolph," a specially designed proportional counter developed by G. S. Hurst et al.[53] This instrument consists of a proportional counter biased to cut out pulses from x and gamma radiation. The counter is so designed that the count rate is proportional to the first collision absorbed dose rate in soft tissue. This instrument has a directional response which, although helpful in locating the source of neutron radiation, is undesirable for some applications. A less portable, nondirectional model[54] is in common use in research programs. This instrument has a proportional counter with a tissue equivalent wall and gas such that it operates in accordance with the Bragg-Gray principle. The energy of the pulses is integrated by feeding the output of the counter into an ordinary binary scaling circuit in such a way that the instrument reads the absorbed dose directly, independent of the energy of the neutrons, and the reading is not influenced by the presence of x and gamma radiation. A built-in alpha source is contained in the instrument and provides an absolute calibration. Thermal neutron flux can be measured by the use of fiber electroscopes provided with a boron-coated chamber wall or with a BF_3 counter and rate meter.

3. Characteristics of a good instrument. In selecting a commercial radiation detection instrument for the laboratory, one should, when possible, choose one with the following characteristics:

(a) It should give the desired accuracy in the measurement of roentgens or rads.

(b) It should maintain its calibration for a long period of time.

(c) The ionization chamber of the meter should have an appropriate geometrical design, and the applied voltage should be high enough to secure saturation of all parts of the chamber at the maximum dose rates for which it is to be used, so that the ions can be collected without any great loss to recombination.

(d) The meter should operate satisfactorily under all expected weather conditions; that is, humidity, temperature, dust, wind, and sunlight, and it should withstand a reasonable amount of rough treatment.

(e) It should be easy to read, preferably directly in the radiation units commonly used.

(f) It should not be excessively geotropic in its behavior, and the maximum parallax error should be small.

(g) It should be lightweight and easy to carry.

(h) If it ceases to operate in a high field of radiation, it should give some indication (other than the fact that the meter reads zero) that it is inoperative; that is, it should "fail safe."

(i) The battery should last a long time in continuous use and should be easily replaceable in the field.

(j) It should not be susceptible to contamination, and/or it should be readily decontaminated.

(k) It should have a range of sensitivities suitable to its application.

(l) It should be constructed of conventional parts that can be purchased without special selection, and the circuit should be conveniently arranged so that it can be repaired easily.

(m) It should not have excessive zero drift and should have a convenient arrangement for zero adjustment in the presence of radiation.

(n) It should have a sensitivity adjustment, but this adjustment should be so enclosed that it cannot be handled except while the instrument is undergoing calibration checks.

(o) The ionization chamber or detector should be as small as possible and of suitable shape and wall thickness to make the desired measurements.

(p) The meter should respond essentially to one type of ionizing radiation at a time or should differentiate sharply between various types of ionizing radiation; for example, a fast neutron meter should measure the fast neutron absorbed dose in the presence of gamma radiation, and an alpha meter should measure the alpha absorbed dose—or disintegrations per second per 100 cm^2—in the presence of beta and gamma radiation. Some ionizing radiation measurements depend upon the difference in ionization in two chambers (e.g., the early Chang and Eng fast neutron survey meter, which measured the difference in ionization in two chambers, one containing ethylene, the other argon), and in such cases small differences in two measured quantities can lead to excessively large errors.

(q) The instrument should not lose an excessive amount of information because of electrical leakage of the ion chamber or because of fading of tracks in the photographic emulsion.

(r) The meter should be relatively energy-independent. All health-physics instruments—film meters, pocket chambers, fiber electroscopes, Geiger counters, scintillation counters, proportional counters, electronic rate meters, etc.—are energy-dependent to some extent over certain energy ranges and as a result do not give a true indication of the absorbed dose in rads for all energies of radiation. Ideally, for the measurement of the absorbed dose an ionization chamber containing tissue walls enclosing a small cavity filled with tissue gas would be preferred. In general, such a chamber is impractical—the gas mixture would be explosive, insensitive, and unstable, and so compromises have been made in chamber design. Actually, such a chamber designed to give a true indication of the absorbed dose in rads would be completely unsatisfactory unless additional provisions were made to indicate the distribution of the absorbed dose between the various types of ionizing radiation. Therefore, the method of measurement must indicate the absorbed dose in rads resulting from each type of ionizing radiation present. Most of the instruments described here give satisfactory results for x- and gamma-radiation measurements in the range of 150 kev to 5 Mev, but the readings may be off by an order of magnitude if certain of them are used to measure the x- or gamma-ray absorbed dose when the energy of the radiation is less than 50 kev. F. H. Day[55] has given calibration correction curves for a number of these instruments over a wide range of x- and gamma-ray energy, and these corrections should be applied for accurate dosimetry. Similar corrections must be made to alpha- and beta-ray measurements, and care must be taken to calibrate all radiation monitoring and survey meters with the types of radiation and in the energy range with which they are to be used. Obviously, all desirable characteristics cannot be built into a single instrument, but the foregoing list may serve as a guide in selecting one of the several types of instruments for a given survey job.

4. Minimum instrument requirements of a small laboratory.[14,56] Most institutions that are beginning the use of radioactivity are interested to know just what new instruments are necessary for radiation protection. Perhaps the instrument requirements of a small laboratory might be summarized as follows:

(a) One pocket condenser chamber, pocket fiber electroscope, or equivalent (such as a chemical dosimeter if and when a satisfactory one is available) for each person exposed to gamma or hard beta radiation.

(b) One film badge containing appropriate filters for each person potentially exposed to x or gamma radiation. This badge should be supplied with film that covers the proper beta and gamma exposure range, and neutron monitoring films should be included if neutron exposures are possible. If high neutron exposures are possible the badge meter should be provided with indium and gold foils and sulfur. Film rings should be furnished when the exposures are primarily to the hands.

(c) Two area survey meters should be provided each laboratory room in which beta and/or gamma activity is used. One of these may be a semi-portable scaler with a thin-walled G-M counter (or scintillation counter) having a sliding window to aid in distinguishing between beta and gamma surface contamination; the other should be a small portable survey meter. This meter may be one of several types: (1) G-M counter, (2) scintillation counter, (3) electroscope, or (4) electronic rate meter. An alternate general rule is to provide a portable survey meter for every two persons working with sources of beta and gamma radiation. Usually it is best to make several different types of meters for measuring beta and gamma radiation available to a laboratory group because each type usually offers advantages for certain kinds of radiation measurement.

(d) At least one instrument should be available for checking air contamination at frequent intervals. This instrument may be a precipitator or air filter collector. Additional instruments of this kind should be provided for every ten rooms in which air contamination is possible.

(e) If work is being done with alpha radiation, fast or thermal neutrons, or with other types of ionizing radiation, two suitable instruments should be provided in every laboratory room for the measurement of the dose delivered by each type of radiation that may be present.

(f) The following auxiliary equipment should be provided for each institution using radioactivity:

(1) G-M and proportional counters with appropriate attachments and scalers to check the alpha, beta, and gamma absorbed dose from the precipitator foils, air filters, smear samples obtained by rubbing filter paper over contaminated surfaces, and other samples such as those obtained by evaporating water or by chemical separation of radionuclides from the urine.

(2) Minometer to read and charge pocket condenser chambers and/or a charging box for the pocket fiber electroscopes. A suitable densitometer to measure the film blackening if the institution does its own film monitoring.

(3) Microscope for counting the proton tracks in the neutron monitoring (NTA) film if neutron exposures are possible.

(4) Calibration sources, such as U for beta calibration, Po for alpha calibration, Po-Be or Pu-Be for neutron calibration, and Ra or Co^{60} for gamma calibration. The use of Ra, Pu, and Po sources that can lead to a contamination problem should be avoided.

(5) File cases in which to keep the radiation exposure records of all persons working in an area where radiation exposure is possible. These records—including both zero and positive readings—are necessary for medical and legal protection of the parties involved.

(6) Sufficient remote-control equipment, such as tongs, stirring rod

holders, bottle-cap removers, pipette wipers, stopcock turners, and pipetting equipment.

(7) A complete change of protective clothing for each person working with radionuclides to prevent the contamination of his own personal clothing and to prevent the spread of contamination beyond the laboratory. Various types of radiation warning signs should be available for posting as required.

(8) If millicurie levels of the moderately dangerous (Fig. 2) or microcurie levels of the very dangerous radionuclides are worked with in the laboratory, a household washing machine and dryer should be provided to remove most of the contamination before sending protective clothing to the public laundry.

(9) Filter paper for smear or swipe tests conducted in estimating the loose surface contamination in the laboratories and neighboring areas.

(10) Counter room in which dust, water, urine, and smear samples can be counted.

(11) Dark room with developing tanks and temperature and humidity control.

5. Calibration of instruments. All institutions using radiation detection instruments must have proper facilities for their routine calibration and adjustment. In the calibration of radiation detection instruments, care must be exercised to take many factors into account, some of which are listed here:

(a) Minimize the radiation exposure of the calibration technicians. In general, it is not wise to employ women in the child-bearing age on those jobs that are certain to result in some radiation exposure.

(b) Design and operate the calibration equipment so as not to contaminate the laboratory. Some recommended precautions are the following:

(1) Use Co^{60} instead of Ra^{226} as a gamma-ray calibration source. Do not use sources that are assembled in such a manner that they are likely to build up an internal gas pressure.

(2) Enclose all calibration sources in an outer, shockproof jacket.

(3) Do not use an air-pressure device for bringing a calibration source into place; instead maneuver it into position with a vacuum or pulley system and place shock-reducing bumpers where the source is brought suddenly to rest. If the source is manipulated by a vacuum system, place filters in the vacuum exhaust and in the atmospheric pressure vents.

(4) Check sources at frequent intervals for leaks. If a vacuum

system is used, the filters should be checked frequently for radio-active contamination. Often a G-M tube is placed near these filters, connected to a continuously recording indicator of background radiation and arranged to sound an alarm if there is an increase above normal background fluctuations. Sources that are kept in lead pots or lead safes can be checked for leaks by the very simple procedure of keeping a wad of cotton about the source when it is in storage and checking the cotton occasionally for contamination. This cotton picks up radon daughter products in the case of a radium leak and recoil particles or surface contamination in the case of Po^{210}, Co^{60}, and other commonly used sources in which flaws may develop in the outer protective jacket.

(5) Place instruction cards in a conspicuous place in the calibration room, source storage facility, and with each source holder, indicating steps to be taken if there should be leakage of the source or if the sources should be involved in a fire. These instructions should recommend that persons remove their contaminated clothing in or near the contaminated area; they should advise the wearing of masks, the shutting off of building fans, the spreading of blotting paper on floors, the temporary sealing up of contaminated rooms, and the use of specified fire extinguishing equipment.

(c) Correct calibration readings for

(1) inverse square law variation with distance from a point source;
(2) the fact that source and chamber are not points in space, and, if distances between source and chamber are small, the electrical and geometrical centers of the chamber cannot be considered to coincide;
(3) air absorption and variation in room pressure, temperature, and humidity if high precision is required;
(4) absorption in source and source holder;
(5) the scattering of the source and its holder, air, walls of the room, the meter itself, and the observer;
(6) radioactive decay of source.

D. The Health Physicist

Regardless of the number of people working with radioactivity, it is essential that all such persons understand how to work safely with radioactive material and remain ever vigilant in efforts to prevent overexposure of themselves or others to ionizing radiation. In an organization in which only three or four persons are working with radioactive material, it may not be necessary to employ a full-time health physicist. However, even here one person must be designated as being primarily responsible for radiation protection. In most cases, in the larger organizations, in which a dozen or more persons are working with radioactivity, high voltage accelerators, nuclear reactors, etc., the full-time services of a health physicist are required, and a health physics surveyor or technician should be added for every twenty persons working regularly in the radiation area.

Perhaps one of the most essential parts of a successful radiation protection program is that of securing a competent health physicist. There has never been a sufficient number of adequately trained health physicists, but the AEC is remedying this situation somewhat by supporting graduate training programs at the masters degree level in health physics (radiological physics). The universities and laboratories at which fellowships are held are

Vanderbilt University and Oak Ridge National Laboratory
University of Rochester and Brookhaven National Laboratory
University of Washington and Hanford Atomic Products Operation
University of Kansas and National Reactor Testing Station
University of California and Lawrence Radiation Laboratory
University of Michigan and Argonne National Laboratory
Harvard University and Brookhaven National Laboratory

In addition, the AEC-supported laboratories are training a number of persons in health physics for their own operations and for special assignments; for example, a limited number of university and industrial employees may make arrangements for study and training in health physics for a few months to a year in one or more of the AEC-supported laboratories. By these programs, altogether, about eighty health physicists are trained and made available each year for employment. Universities that have an expanding program of work with ionizing radiation have found it satisfactory to begin their health-physics program with the employment of one or more recently graduated health physicists on a part-time basis. Such persons work part time as health physicists in charge of the radiation protection program, and the rest of the time take graduate courses. This arrangement has the advantage of economy to the university and has offered the opportunity to a number of health physicisits to obtain a Ph.D. degree. The person in charge of health physics should report directly to the president of the university or to the director of graduate research because the responsibilities of radiation protection cut across all departmental boundaries and even extend beyond the campus. Many organizations have formed local radiation-protection advisory committees which serve as guides to their health-physics programs and as a source of information and advice to others who should be concerned with problems of radiation protection. Often the most difficult task of the health physicist is to re-orient some of the older research personnel in the university and convince them that it is necessary to take added precautions with the x-ray machine, cyclotron, and Van de Graaff as well as with the newer nuclear reactor or isotope program.

Without an adequate health-physics program, there may well be cases of radiation damage to employees and costly projects of building decontamination; even worse, the organization may find it difficult to be certain or to prove in court that it is not responsible for radiation damage in the environment. Such developments could lead to poor public relations and legal complications as well as to injury and various forms of radiation damage. An adequately trained health physicist will organize the radiation-protection program if he has the proper cooperation and support of top management. He will employ assistance as needed and relieve others of many of the day-to-day problems, such as absorbed dose calculations, instrument calibration, area surveys, and waste disposal. The health-physics group in a university or other laboratory will have many responsibilities such as the following:

(a) Buildings and hoods must be appropriately designed and properly located for work with radioactivity.

(b) The proper techniques must be used for safe handling of radioactive materials.

(c) Persons working with radioactive material must have adequate training and understanding of the radiation protection rules and of the maximum permissible levels of radiation exposure, and they must know how to use and interpret properly the readings of the radiation protection meters.

(d) The surface contamination and air activity in the laboratory and in the area surrounding the laboratory must remain at an acceptable level; the waste solids must be properly buried or incinerated, and waste water must not exceed permissible levels of radioactive contamination. High-level radioactive wastes must be properly packaged and turned over to qualified and authorized agencies for disposal.

(e) All the radiation protection instruments that are needed must be available in proper operating condition and maintained in proper calibration.

(f) Complete and up-to-date records must be kept on all personnel exposures and on levels of air and water activity in the area about the plant. The health physicist in charge must take prompt and firm measures when necessary to keep the levels of exposure within acceptable limits. He must see that all shipments of radioactive material (or the returned shipping containers) conform to the regulations of the appropriate federal agencies.[57] He must be ever alert for new problems of radiation protection as they develop or preferably before they develop.

(g) Continuously recording instruments, shields, decontamination facilities, etc., must be provided when needed.

E. Special Monitoring Problems

Many new monitoring problems are introduced when an organization begins the use of radioactive materials for the first time. These problems increase as more and more employees make use of radioactivity in their work. In spite of all precautions in the use of the best equipment and techniques and regardless of the good radiation exposure records of an organization, one would frequently like to know how much radioactive material, if any, has gone astray and become deposited inside the bodies of persons doing this work. Also, regardless of the precautions, accidents will eventually occur wherever reliance must be placed on the human element (i.e., there is a spill of radioactive material; someone is careless and smokes a cigarette with contaminated hands; a piece of glass, contaminated with radioactive material, is stuck in someone's finger).

1. Body fluid, air, and water sampling. Perhaps the best methods of estimating the quantity of radioactivity in the body consist of total body counting and of radiochemical analysis of the urine, feces, sputum, blood, or tissue of the person involved. In the case of radium or $C^{14}O_2$, one of the best tests is to examine the exhaled air. In the case of a puncture wound that is suspected of being contaminated, it is desirable to collect any blood or tissue available from the wound and to analyze it for the suspected radionuclides. Sometimes a G-M or scintillation counter[44] probe can be placed into or near the wound to aid in obtaining an estimate of the extent of tissue contamination. Scintillation counters have been used very successfully with proper gamma-ray energy discrimination in locating small quantities of Pu^{239} in wounds. In spite of its great difficulty, ordinarily the most satisfactory test for estimating the quantity of radioactive materials that has become fixed in the body is to examine the day's urine excretion. Although gross count determinations are made sometimes on an evaporated urine sample to serve as a qualitative indication of the radionuclides present, a chemical separation is necessary before counting the sample if quantitative data are desired. Usually the amount of inert material involved is so large—leading to considerable self-absorption of the radiation—and the natural background due to K^{40} in the urine is so high that it becomes necessary to perform a careful chemical separation by using radioactive tracer techniques if quantitative urinalyses are required, even though the person may have been exposed to only one radionuclide.

In collecting the urine samples, special precautions must be taken; for example, they are taken just after the person has had a bath and over the weekend in order to reduce the probability of contaminating the sample during collection and to eliminate some of the error due to differences in the composition of urine voided at various times during the day. Specially designed low-background counters are required to count the samples, since the permissible amount of radioactivity fixed in the body is small and the fraction excreted daily is often exceedingly small. It is beyond the scope of this text to describe these methods of radiochemical separation and analysis, but information can be obtained on specific radionuclides from published reports[58] and by writing to the laboratories that are using various methods.

Problems of water, mud, and filter-paper analysis are similar to those of urinalysis. Once dust or vapor samples are collected from the air on precipitator foils or on filter paper, the remaining problem is usually one of taking these samples to a counter room and checking the gross beta and gamma activity with a G-M counter or the alpha activity with a proportional or scintillation counter. If the sample is a gamma emitter, it can be identified and the activity measured without any chemical preparation by using the techniques of scintillation spectrometry. If a chemical analysis for radionuclide identification is desired, the same chemical techniques previously referred to must be used to reduce the self-absorption losses. After the samples are prepared and counted, the identity of the activity can be double checked by running time-decay curves and making absorption curves with various filter thicknesses. Alpha samples collected with a precipitator can be checked and immediately identified according to the energy of the alpha radiation by means of a range analyzer, provided that a negligible amount of dust or other extraneous material is collected and that the samples are collected on metal foils so that there is no appreciable self-absorption of the radiation.

One method of estimating the body burden of radionuclides[59] is by the use of total (or partial) body counters. Many types of this equipment are in use and may consist of large banks of ion chambers, Geiger counters, or scintillation counters. These instruments may be placed about the body or the person may lie on a couch and be rolled into a large chamber that is surrounded by instruments in fixed positions. Anticoincidence counters may be used to subtract certain components of the background radiation and in some cases very elaborate low-background shielding may be provided to minimize the background. Some systems use a liquid scintillator that provides a large geometry at a relatively low cost and reduces the counting time required for each total body measurement. Scintillating counters—either solid or liquid—provide energy resolution and make it possible to eliminate much of the background and to identify the radionuclides in the body by a study of the energy spectrum of the x and gamma radiation. In this respect the solid counter is far superior to the liquid counter in that it permits better energy resolution. Some of the systems consist of collimated counters that move back and forth above the body, scanning it in a televisionlike grid. The output of the scanning produces a photograph or drawing depicting the pattern of distribution of the radionuclide in the body. Much of the equipment described is presently in the early stages of development and is too expensive for many of the small organizations using radioactivity. However, arrangements can be made by these smaller groups to send some of their employees who are thought to have high body burdens of radionuclides to laboratories that have total (or partial) body counters so that they may receive an internal dose analysis. In the present state of development, total and partial body counters are extremely useful in estimating the body burdens of radionuclides that emit x or gamma radiation or high-energy beta radiation. (In the case of beta rays the instruments outside the body detect the bremsstrahlung.) In most cases this equipment is not sufficient as the sole means of making internal-dose estimates but serves as a useful augmentation to the body-fluid analysis program previously described.

2. The particle problem. A survey should be made of some of the precipitator foils and paper filters that have been used for air sampling to see if there is a problem of particulate activity. This can be done by placing some of the foils and filters in contact with sensitive x-ray film and leaving them for a few days for radioautographs. If there are large black spots on the developed photographic film, particles of high specific radioactivity are escaping into the area of the air samplers. Therefore, additional filters, precipitators, air washers, or other types of air cleaners are needed in the hoods, fan houses, incinerators, etc., or some operation with radioactivity has not been carried out properly under an appropriate hood and/or glove box. The maximum permissible number of radioactive specks of dust of a particular radionuclide with a given specific activity is not known, and until adequate biological data on this subject become available as a result of experiments with animals extending over a period of many years the safest policy is to prevent radioactive dust from getting into the air where it can be breathed.

Radioactive material deposited in the lungs as small, insoluble specks of high specific radioactivity is usually considered to present a greater hazard than this same amount of material uniformly deposited in the lung in insignificant concentration at any one point. Perhaps the hazard is greater for specks of radioactive material than for the case in which the material is in a soluble form and is transferred from the lungs or other point of lodgment in the body to the critical organ where in general it is more uniformly distributed. Experiments of Lisco et al.,[60] in which implants of 1 μc amounts of Pu^{239} were made into the muscles of animals, indicated an unusually high incidence of malignant tumors at the sites of the implants, many more, for example, than would have been found had the Pu^{239} been deposited in the bone following ingestion or intravenous injection. However, the magnitude of the hazard from particles of high specific radioactivity is very uncertain, since experiments by Brues[61] and Cember[62] have furnished evidence that appears to be contrary to that cited, viz, that most of the biological damage to an animal from ionizing radiation is probably more closely related to the total energy or gram-rad dose absorbed by a large fraction of a given body organ than to the rad absorbed dose to small portions of the body organs in the immediate neighborhood of the radioactive particles.

If the radioactive material is contained in a small insoluble particle that is lodged in the lower respiratory system, the average absorbed dose in rads in a sphere of tissue of radius X cm surrounding the particle is given by the equation

$$D_{av} = \frac{18QET_r}{X^3}(1 - e^{-\mu X})(1 - e^{-0.693t/T_r}) \tag{12}$$

in which Q is the number of microcuries contained initially in the particle, t is the time in days the particle remains fixed in the tissue, T_r is the radioactive half-life in days, E is the effective energy in Mev per disintegration, and μ is the coefficient of absorption of the radiation in tissue. If the radius X of the sphere in which the absorbed dose is calculated becomes greater than the range of the alpha or beta radiation from the particle or if essentially all the gamma energy from the particle is absorbed in the sphere of radius X and if there is negligible radioactive decay of the particle in time t (days), the average tissue absorbed dose is given by the equation

$$D_{av} = \frac{12QEt}{X^3}. \tag{13}$$

Thus, if the particle that is lodged in tissue has a high specific activity (μc/gram) and negligible self-absorption, the dose rate (which varies as $1/X^3$) is very large in close to the particle. As previously indicated, it remains for future experiments and observations on man to ascertain completely the seriousness of this type of exposure.

Some experiments are in progress in an effort to determine the hazards— if any—associated with these particles, but it may require many years to get all the necessary information; for example, it is thought to require ten to twenty years for certain types of malignancies to develop in man. One is concerned primarily with particles of 0.1 to 1 μ in diameter which find their way to the bronchioli and alveoli because the larger particles are likely to be trapped in the upper respiratory tract where they are brought up by ciliary action and swallowed, whereas smaller particles usually contain an insignificant quantity of radioactivity.

Another way to minimize the hazard resulting from radioactive particles is to use filters in air intake ducts of the building to reduce the amount of fine dust entering the laboratories where it can serve as a submicron carrier for radioactivity. The utmost precautions should be taken when chipping out contaminated concrete, when removing old hoods and contaminated air ducts from a building, or when repairing and, especially, welding contaminated waste lines. Workmen engaged in such operations should wear self-contained air-supply masks (such as Chemox) to reduce the chances of inhaling radioactive dust.

3. Hand decontamination. One of the most important special monitoring problems in any laboratory is that of hand decontamination. Usually, a good scrub with soap and water is all that is necessary, but sometimes this is not sufficient to remove enough of the contamination. There are several general procedures[63] that can be followed in such cases, but one that has been used frequently at Oak Ridge National Laboratory is given to illustrate a satisfactory method. Frequently, a procedure specific to a particular radioelement is more satisfactory. Also, a few special precautions to be taken and a list of contents of a suitable hand decontamination kit are given. These kits should be kept available in a convenient location in every laboratory where work with radioactivity is carried on.

a. General procedure for personnel decontamination at Oak Ridge National Laboratory. Ordinarily, the same procedures used for personal cleanliness will suffice to remove radioactive contaminants from the skin, but the specific method will depend upon the form (grease, oil, etc.) of the deposited contamination. Soap and water (sequestering agents and detergents) normally remove more than 99% of the contaminants. If it is necessary to remove the remainder, chemicals can be used on the outer layers of skin upon which the contamination has been deposited. Because of the risk of injury to the skin surfaces, these chemicals (citric acid, potassium permanganate, sodium bisulfite, etc.) should be applied with caution, preferably under medical supervision. Types of lanolin-based creams are used to offset local irritations of skin surfaces after decontamination.

(1) To prevent the spread of radioactive contamination, all personnel should be monitored upon leaving a contaminated area. This will ensure recognition of any unusual case of contamination that may require special handling so that correct procedures can be followed to alleviate the situation. If persons are found to have radioactive contamination on their clothing or bodies, the following steps are taken:

(a) Remove any clothing or equipment found to be contaminated before determining levels of skin contamination.

(b) Decontaminate any areas of the body found to be significantly higher than surrounding areas. This spot cleaning is necessary to prevent the spread of contamination to clean areas of the body that might occur in showering.

(c) If the contamination is general over the body surfaces, a very thorough shower is necessary. Special attention is to be paid to such areas as the hair, the hands, and the fingernails. After showering and monitoring, the residual contamination can be removed by spot cleaning.

(d) Avoid the prolonged use of any one method of decontamination. The effect from repeated ineffective decontamination methods may irritate the skin and thus hamper the success of more suitable decontamination procedures. No one chemical treatment is known to be specific for all of the elements with which one may become contaminated.

(e) Avoid the use of organic solvents. Organic solvents may increase the probability of the radioactive materials penetrating through the pores of the skin. Oxalic acid is a poisonous compound, not to be used under any circumstances.

b. Specific procedure for hand decontamination. (1) Wash the skin thoroughly with lava soap and water, paying special attention to areas between the fingers and around the fingernails. Repeat the procedure if monitoring indicates contamination remaining on the skin in amounts above tolerance.

(2) Apply a sequestrant-detergent liquid mixture (a 5% water solution of a mixture of 30% Tide, 65% Calgon, and 5% Carbose). Repeat the procedure if results prove encouraging.

(3) Apply a sequestrant-detergent cream (a 4% Carbose, 3% Versene, 8% Tide, and 85% water mixture). Rub thoroughly into the skin for

approximately one minute. Repeat the treatment as long as the results show that the contaminant is being removed.

(4) Moisten the contaminated skin area with the sequestrant-detergent liquid. Apply a liberal quantity of Boraxo crystals and rub briskly.

The following chemical decontamination procedures are to be used with discretion and/or under medical supervision, depending upon the condition of the skin at this stage of the decontamination process.

(1) Moisten the skin area with water. Apply citric acid crystals, rub, and follow with a water rinse.

(2) Apply a thin layer of $KMnO_4$ crystals on the skin. Rub into the skin thoroughly and rinse with water. Shake citric acid crystals over the $KMnO_4$ area and rub. If the hands become warm, rinse immediately in water and follow by a soap and water rinse. Remove the $KMnO_4$ stain with $NaHSO_3$.

(3) If all of the foregoing decontamination methods fail to bring the contamination within permissible levels, provide rubber gloves dusted with diatomaceous earth. The continuous wearing of rubber gloves causes sloughing off of the outer layer of skin, hence removal of the contamination and absorption of the diatomaceous earth. Accompany the employee to the Health Division and give the full case history.

(4) When it is necessary to release persons before contamination has been sufficiently eliminated, they should report to Health Physics for daily routine checks until contamination is reduced to permissible levels.

c. Contents of a kit for hand decontamination

(1) 2 bars of lava soap
(2) Sequestrant-detergent liquid
(3) Sequestrant-detergent cream
(4) Six surgical scrub brushes
(5) Boraxo
(6) Citric acid
(7) $KMnO_4$
(8) $NaHSO_3$
(9) Hand lotion
(10) Two pairs of rubber gloves
(11) Kleenex
(12) Paper towels

4. Clothing decontamination. When clothes become contaminated with the more dangerous radioactive materials, as listed in Fig. 2, or if large quantities are involved, the clothing should not be sent to a public laundry unless or until most of the radioactive contamination has been removed. If only small washes are involved, a domestic washer is sufficient for the job.

Best results are obtained at Oak Ridge National Laboratory decontamination laundry by the procedures shown in Table 7 as follows:

TABLE 7. DECONTAMINATION LAUNDRY PROCEDURES AT OAK RIDGE NATIONAL LABORATORY

A. Procedure for cotton garments (shirt, pants, coveralls, laboratory coats, etc.)

Step Number →	1	2	3	4	5
Temperature of water (°F)	120	160 to 180*	160 to 180*	160 to 180*	120
Time of wash (min)	4	8	8	8	8
Treatment	saturation rinse 1 lb Turco 1/2 lb soap	3 lb Turco 4324 wash	rinse	rinse	rinse

* For synthetic garments the temperature of the wash is reduced to 120–140°.

B. Procedure for gloves, shoe covers, plastic, etc.

Step Number →	1	2	3	4	5
Temperature of water	Cold	Cold	Cold	Cold	Cold
Time of wash (min)	4	4	8	8	4
Treatment	3 lb soda ash 1 lb soap 2 lb Versene	rinse	3 lb soda ash 1 lb soap 2 lb Versene	rinse	rinse

F. Disposal of Radioactive Waste

1. Disposal by concentration or dispersion. Radioactive waste disposal has frequently been a difficult problem for the small laboratory or hospital. It is also a problem of greatest importance to the Atomic Energy Commission projects, which have much larger quantities of radioactive waste, but these projects have large land areas under government control, and disposal is a simpler matter. The smaller institutions as well as the large AEC contractors are confronted with the disposal of the three types of radioactive waste—liquid, solid, and gas. For short-lived radionuclides of the less hazardous groups, listed in Fig. 2, the disposal problems are greatly simplified in that a delay of a few weeks in the release of the waste may reduce the hazard to negligible proportions. However, the disposal of the very dangerous group of radionuclides, such as Ac^{227}, Pb^{210}, Sr^{90}, Pu^{239}, Ra^{226}, and Ce^{144}, presents many unsolved problems. There are two opposing philosophies of waste disposal—maximum dilution and maximum concentration—and each has its advantages and useful application. The strongest argument for maximum dilution is that the material is diluted to so low a concentration and dispersed over so great a volume of material (earth, water, and/or air) that presumably it warrants no further consideration. Perhaps the greatest weakness in this argument is that even though the concentration of the radioactive material when leaving the controlled area may be well below any maximum permissible concentrations recommended by the National Committee on Radiation Protection and the International Commission on Radiological Protection there are many processes of selective concentration—biological, chemical, and physical—that tend sometimes to reconcentrate this waste by factors of 10^4 to 10^6. For example, the concentration of a radionuclide in air and water leaving a laboratory may be a factor of 100 below the acceptable maximum permissible concentration for occupational exposure, but by a chain of events the radioactive contaminant finds its way into rivers, where it may be concentrated in succession on particles, in plankton and algae, in fish or vegetation of an irrigation project, and finally may appear in food for man in concentrations above the maximum permissible value. Fortunately, in many cases the reverse is true; that is, much of the radioactive material is isolated in the mud on the river bottom; it is taken up by nonedible plant and animal life, or it is removed by the water-process treatment plant so that the level of contamination at the source of drinking water or in edible fish is much less than at the point of discharge into the river. Nevertheless, the buildup of contamination on the river bottoms, in the sludge from the water-purification systems which is used for fertilizer, or in the flood planes of the rivers may result in long-range effects on man that should be of considerable concern. The effects of radiation on ecology over a long period of time may be just as important as the direct effects on man. For example, in the corn field there is a very delicate balance between the corn plant, fish worms, arthropods, fungi, bacteria, etc., and high concentration of radionuclides in certain components of the food web may adversely affect the soil in such a way as to reduce the corn yield. Long-range fundamental studies in ecology as affected by increase in the background radiation exposure are now getting underway and should eventually yield interesting results.

2. Waste-disposal recommendations for specific radionuclides. There are no specific recommendations for the disposal of any of the radioactive nuclides except P^{32}, I^{131}, and C^{14}. The reader is referred to the publications of the National Committee on Radiation Protection[16] for detailed information regarding these three nuclides and to other references[63] for general information on the control and removal of radioactive contamination from the laboratory. The data given in the handbooks of the NCRP[37] and the ICRP[38] should serve as a guide to the maximum permissible concentrations in incinerator gases, hood exhaust air, process water, and sewage.

3. General values of maximum permissible concentration of radioactive waste. It sometimes happens that when a preliminary check is made of the air and water contamination discharged from a laboratory the gross radioactive contamination collected on filter paper or in an evaporated water sample is measured without waiting for the time-consuming and expensive chemical operations necessary for the identification of the individual radioactive contaminants. For this case the National Committee on Radiation Protection (NCRP)[37] and the International Commission on Radiological Protection (ICRP),[38] have agreed on general values as given in Table 8 for water and in Table 9 for air.

Usually the maximum permissible concentrations for unidentified radionuclides (MPCU) are more conservative (lower) than those given for specific radionuclides in the NCRP and the ICRP handbooks. The values given in Tables 8 and 9 are satisfactory for indefinite periods of occupational exposure (168 hr/wk) but they must be reduced by a factor of $\frac{1}{10}$ for application to populations living in the neighborhood of the plant (or in the vicinity of the controlled area). The International Commission on Radiological Protection[38] has recommended that for exposure of the population at large the permissible limits be set at $\frac{1}{100}$ the permissible limit for continuous occupational exposure (168 hr/wk) in the case of whole body or gonad exposure and that for exposure of individual organs other than the gonads the permissible limit be set at $\frac{1}{30}$ of the corresponding limit for continuous occupational exposure. Since a mixture of radionuclides whose precise composition is only imperfectly known may well produce whole body or gonad exposure, the values in Tables 8 and 9 should be reduced by a factor of $\frac{1}{100}$ for application to the population at large in order to comply with the recommendations of the ICRP.

4. Various methods of radioactive waste disposal. The university or hospital should take great care not to contaminate the water or air of the occupational workers in concentrations greater than indicated by Tables 8 and 9. If the radionuclides are identified, the MPC values for specific radionuclides should not be exceeded. Even greater care should be exercised to maintain the lower values specified for the population living outside the controlled area. Also, special precautions should be taken to

TABLE 8. MAXIMUM PERMISSIBLE CONCENTRATION
OF UNIDENTIFIED RADIONUCLIDES (MPCU-VALUES)
IN WATER

Values that are applicable for occupational exposure (168 hr/wk)
to any radionuclide or mixture of radionuclides

Limitations	$\mu c/cc$ of water†
If Sr^{90}, I^{126}, I^{129}, I^{131}, Pb^{210}, Po^{210}, At^{211}, Ra^{223}, Ra^{224}, Ra^{226}, Ra^{228}, Ac^{227}, Pa^{231}, Th^{230}, Th^{232}, and Th-nat are not present,* the continuous exposure level $(MPC)_w$ is not less than	3×10^{-5}
If Sr^{90}, I^{129}, Pb^{210}, Po^{210}, Ra^{223}, Ra^{226}, Ra^{228}, Pa^{231}, and Th-nat are not present,* the continuous exposure level $(MPC)_w$ is not less than	2×10^{-5}
If Sr^{90}, I^{129}, Pb^{210}, Ra^{226}, and Ra^{228} are not present,* the continuous exposure level $(MPC)_w$ is not less than	7×10^{-6}
If Ra^{226} and Ra^{228} are not present,* the continuous exposure level $(MPC)_w$ is not less than	10^{-6}
In all cases the continuous occupational level, $(MPC)_w$ is not less than	10^{-7}

* In this case "not present" implies that the concentration of the radionuclide in water is small compared with the MPC-value for occupational exposure.

† Use one tenth of these values for interim application in the neighborhood of an atomic energy plant.

prevent radioactive particulates from being discharged into the air. This usually means that filters or some other air-washing devices should be installed in the laboratory vacuum system and in the hoods and incinerators operated in the microcurie level; they are necessary also for operation in the millicurie level and above. When experiments are conducted in the millicurie level—or above—it is recommended that the equipment be enclosed in a glove box located inside the hood. This not only helps to confine the radioactive contamination but makes it possible to filter the small volume of air discharged from the glove box into the vacuum line or hood exhaust and to reduce the hood flow, consequently minimizing the problems associated with the maintenance of proper room temperature. Many methods of concentrating radioactive waste, such as combustion, evaporation, ion exchange, chemical precipitation, flocculation, filtration, and biological retention, have been used. No one method is suitable for all installations, and the reader is referred for detailed information to some of the publications[14,16,26,64] listed in the references. The solid materials

TABLE 9. MAXIMUM PERMISSIBLE CONCENTRATION
OF UNIDENTIFIED RADIONUCLIDES (MPCU-VALUES)
IN AIR

Values that are applicable for occupational exposure (168 hr/wk)
to any radionuclide or mixture of radionuclides

Limitations	$\mu c/cc$ of air†
If there are no α-emitters and if β-emitters Sr^{90}, I^{129}, Pb^{210}, Ac^{227}, Ra^{228}, Pa^{230}, Pu^{241}, and Bk^{249} are not present,* the continuous exposure level $(MPC)_a$ is not less than	10^{-9}
If there are no α-emitters and if β-emitters Pb^{210}, Ac^{227}, Ra^{228}, and Pu^{241} are not present,* the continuous exposure level $(MPC)_a$ is not less than	10^{-10}
If there are no α-emitters and if β-emitter Ac^{227} is not present,* the continuous exposure level $(MPC)_a$ is not less than	10^{-11}
If Ac^{227}, Th^{230}, Pa^{231}, Th^{232}, Th-nat, Pu^{238}, Pu^{239}, Pu^{240}, Pu^{242}, and Cf^{249} are not present,* the continuous exposure level $(MPC)_a$ is not less than	10^{-12}
If Pa^{231}, Th-nat, Pu^{239}, Pu^{240}, Pu^{242}, and Cf^{249} are not present,* the continuous exposure level $(MPC)_a$ is not less than	7×10^{-13}
In all cases the continuous occupational level $(MPC)_a$ is not less than	4×10^{-13}

* In this case "not present" implies the concentration of the radionuclide in air is small compared with the MPC value for occupational exposure.

† Use one tenth of these values for interim application in the neighborhood of an atomic energy plant.

that cannot be burned and the ashes from the incinerator that contain large concentrations of radioactive contamination should be buried in properly established "hot" burial grounds or incorporated into concrete blocks for burial at sea[65] or for disposal in specially designated desert areas. Probably one of the safest methods of waste disposal is by isotopic dilution. This is practical and is sometimes used for common radioactive materials, such as phosphorus, iodine, and carbon, but cannot be used for the scarce elements. In any case, care must be taken when relying on this method of waste disposal to make certain that the element used for dilution is in the same chemical and physical form as the radioelement. It should also be kept in mind that in some cases an increase in the ionic concentration actually increases the body intake; for example, in some experiments with Sr^{90} Romney and others[66] found that an increase in the stable strontium in the soil resulted in an increased uptake of Sr^{90} by the plants.

5. The open-pit method of disposal of radioactive waste. One of the most satisfactory methods of low-level waste disposal is by means of properly located open earth pits. For proper functioning such pits should meet the following requirements:

(a) They should be located in an area that can be controlled permanently—controlled by government agencies, and fenced off and covered over to keep out men and animals while disposal is in progress. When radioactive waste disposal is discontinued, the pits probably could be covered with fresh dirt and converted to restricted use (e.g., Federal or municipal cemeteries).

(b) They should be located on a hillside above flood level and not more than a few hundred yards from a large body of water. There must be no wells or surface springs in the neighborhood to which the contaminated water can drain. No food crops are to be planted near the pits so that their root systems can reach the contaminated soil.

(c) They should be located in a large formation of clay or shale, preferably in soils that are not strongly acid or basic.

(d) They should be ditched (and in some areas covered) to minimize entry of rainwater.

(e) They should not be dug down to water table.

(f) Test wells should be dug in the area below the pit to make certain that there are no limestone strata to divert the contaminated water to wells or springs and to give assurance that all seepage water will move toward the large body of water nearby which can be monitored.

Experience has indicated that most of the radioactive material in such pits is held firmly by the soil between the pits and the nearby body of water. At Oak Ridge National Laboratory ruthenium is the only fission product that migrates in measurable quantities from pits to the test wells. Fortunately, Ru^{106}, when dissolved in water, is one of the less hazardous radioactive materials. Any slow migration can be monitored by measuring the activity of water samples from the test wells or from the large body of water that drains the pit area. The Ru^{106} serves as a tracer to make sure that the test wells are dug in the proper places. This method of disposal has many advantages over underground storage tanks in that floods, earthquakes, or explosions cannot cause failure of these pits because the radioactive material that is disposed of in them is very rapidly fixed on the soil. Also, the construction and upkeep costs of an open pit are negligible compared to the costs of construction and maintenance of an underground tank. The pit is a cheap permanent disposal system, whereas the underground tank is only an expensive temporary expedient. This text is not concerned with the important problem of radioactive waste disposal from the large nuclear power plant. No completely satisfactory method for such facilities has yet been postulated or developed (1960). Among the more promising methods that have been studied are (1) use of sintering pits in which the energy contained in the radionuclides discharged into the earthen pits would furnish sufficient heat to boil the mixture to dryness, melt the soil and fluxing agents placed in the pit, and, upon cooling, form a hard insoluble clinker, (2) disposal at sea, (3) disposal in abandoned salt mines, (4) disposal in deep wells (e.g., abandoned oil wells), and (5) mixing the radioactive waste with mud and/or cement and pumping it into deep underground fractured formations.

G. Emergency Precautions

1. Wounds contaminated with radioactive material. One of the most frequent emergency situations occurring among persons working with radioactivity is the result of cuts and puncture wounds from objects contaminated with radioactive material. Experiments[60] on animals have indicated that some of the radionuclides must be removed from the wound in a matter of minutes or a large fraction of the contaminant will be fixed in the body—both fixed near the wound site and translocated to other parts of the body. This is of serious consequence when we consider that the maximum permissible amount of some radioactive materials in the body is less than a microcurie (or perhaps a few micromicrograms) so that it is possible to fix dangerous amounts of a radionuclide in the body by way of a wound. The first recommended procedure in dealing with these wounds is to avoid any operations in which contaminated wounds are likely to result; the procedures for dealing with a wound that is suspected of being contaminated with radioactive material are considerably different at the various laboratories. The recommended procedures at Oak Ridge National Laboratory are as follows:

PROCEDURE IN DEALING WITH WOUNDS IN WHICH THERE IS A BREAK IN THE CONTINUITY OF THE SKIN THAT MAY RESULT IN CONTAMINATION WITH A RADIOACTIVE MATERIAL. (a) Place the wound under copiously running water immediately (i.e., within fifteen seconds) following the accident. Spread edges of the wound apart with the hands (if possible) to permit complete flushing action. While the wound is being flushed with water, rub it gently with a wet cotton gauze pad using liquid soap if necessary to remove dirt and grease from the wound; follow by b1, or b2, and c.

(b) (1) *If the wound is contaminated with the "very hazardous" materials* (see Fig. 2 and Table 1), if it is located on the body where a tourniquet can be applied, and if medical aid is close at hand, *apply a tourniquet and rush the person to medical aid.* It is desirable that the tourniquet be applied in such a manner that it will stop venous flow but not restrict arterial flow. If it is uncertain how this may be done or if it would cause delay, apply a complete tourniquet and rush the person to medical aid. Proceed with part c.

(2) *If medical aid is not available in fifteen minutes*, or if the wound is contaminated with the "moderately dangerous" or "slightly hazardous" radionuclides, apply the tourniquet if possible to stop only the venous flow (otherwise omit the tourniquet entirely) and continue washing for at least five minutes. If the wound is on the finger, a milking action can be used effectively to increase the bleeding and to retard the backward venous flow of blood. Save the object causing the wound and some blood (if possible) for examination to estimate the extent of the hazard. Proceed with part c.

(c) Report to Medical Division as soon as possible after five or ten minutes of washing. Here the wound will be tested with probe counters; if there is residual radioactive contamination, the physician will débride the wound and forward the excised tissue to the health-physics laboratory for radiochemical analysis.

2. Spills of radioactive materials. Another emergency problem results in the case of spills of radioactive material. These must be handled very carefully and promptly or large areas may be contaminated and considerable property[67] damage as well as personnel injury may result. Emergency instructions should be posted with radium sources, in nuclear reactor buildings and in chemical laboratories where work is conducted with radioactive material at the millicurie and multicurie levels. These instructions should indicate clearly each step to be followed in case of a spill; for example, who is responsible in case of emergency, where to cut off room ventilation fans, where to remove contaminated clothing, doors and windows to be closed, how to summon assistance, and where to obtain masks. At Oak Ridge National Laboratory the procedure used by the person responsible for the clean-up of a spill—usually the person responsible for the spill—is as follows.

PROCEDURE IN CASE OF SPILLS OF RADIOACTIVE MATERIAL: (a) Try to estimate the hazard caused by the spill and evacuate persons from the area by the best prearranged route to a check station. (CHECK ALL PERSONNEL FOR POSSIBLE CONTAMINATED WOUNDS.) Require those remaining in the area (including yourself) to wear appropriate masks if the hazard warrants it.

(b) Prevent spread of activity by

(1) cutting off room ventilation fans;
(2) applying absorbers, such as paper, sand, corn meal, to the contaminated area;
(3) roping off or barricading the contaminated area and placarding with signs bearing the conventional radiation danger symbol and pertinent hazard information;
(4) closing windows and doors and sealing them off with masking tape.

(c) Sound alarm and summon help as needed.

(d) Permit only authorized newcomers to enter the contaminated zone and then only after proper clothing and mask protection have been supplied.

(e) Permit no one to leave the contaminated zone except by way of the check station and require detention there until properly checked for loose contamination that could be spread to other areas. The person in charge of the check station must require persons with contamination on clothing and/or bodies to remove clothing and take a shower—using hand decontamination procedure on contaminated areas of body if necessary. He must take up and replace all personnel monitoring meters, pocket chambers, film meters, etc., and issue uncontaminated clothing, give instructions regarding the collection of urine and fecal samples, and have persons report to the Medical Division. Exceptions should be made to escape excessive irradiation.

(f) Consider protection for those performing clean-up work:

(1) provide proper masks or pressure suits if air activity is involved;
(2) provide expendable protective clothing;
(3) erect shielding or limit working time, if necessary, to prevent overexposure to those doing the clean-up work;
(4) have all persons directly engaged in the clean-up operations go to the check station for body decontamination after each operation or before receiving excessive exposure—preferably not more than 3 rem total body exposure or 25 rem exposure to hands, forearms, and feet;

(5) use suitable instruments to monitor and estimate the exposure of each person engaged in the clean-up operation. A meter such as the thin-walled cutie pie or Zeus is a useful survey instrument, and pocket electrometers are valuable for high-level exposure work.

(g) In cleaning up the spill, do not spread contamination. Clean off all surfaces with damp rags. It may be necessary to tear out woodwork and plaster, or to sand wooden floors. Painted surfaces and concrete can be sand-blasted or surface-burned. Vacuum cleaners can be used frequently during the various operations. Some surfaces can be hosed with water or steamed, and various cleaning solutions can be used with proper caution.

(h) If material involved in the spill is short-lived, it may be advisable to seal off the affected area and leave until activity decays through several half-lives.

(i) Either dispose of or decontaminate materials involved in the spill and clean-up of the radioactive material.

(j) Keep proper records on all spills and how decontamination was effected so that a history of successful decontamination procedures may be referred to when future spills occur. This should aid also in determining methods of preventing recurrence of spills.

(k) Refer to literature[68] for a discussion of decontamination procedures applied to specific cases.

(l) Many spills of radioactive material can be avoided or the consequences minimized by the proper design of laboratories and equipment.[69] The best treatment of spills is to avoid having them by providing adequate equipment and conducting training programs.

3. Fires, earthquakes, explosions, and other happenings resulting in a widespread radioactive hazard. In case of fires, earthquakes, explosions, etc., the fire department should be called immediately, but this means that some working arrangement between the fire department and the person (or persons) responsible for radiation protection should be agreed upon and practiced beforehand. The fire fighters should know in which building work is done with radioactivity in quantities greater than the microcurie level. If possible, some easily recognizable and mutually agreed upon marker should be placed on the entrance doors of all rooms in which millicurie levels of radioactive material or greater levels are to be found. This marker should indicate the types of radionuclides in use in each laboratory and the amount present. It should state whether or not masks (e.g., all-service or self-contained air supply masks) must be worn when entering this immediate area during a fire or following an explosion. As soon as possible after the alarm, the person in charge of radiation protection should be summoned to the stricken area. He and his alternate should leave their telephone numbers with the local fire chief and should place them on the door markers of rooms in which millicurie quantities of radioactive material are handled.

REFERENCES

1. H. A. Blair, "A Formulation of the Injury, Life Span, Dose Relations for Ionizing Radiation," Part I, *Report UR-206* (1952); Part II, *Report UR-207* (1952); H. A. Blair, "Recovery from Radiation Injury in Mice and Its Effects on LD-50 for Deviations of Exposure Up to Several Weeks," *Report UR-312* (1954); H. A. Blair, "Shortening of Life Span by Ingested Radium, Polonium and Plutonium," *Report UR-274* (1953); R. D. Boche, "Observations on Populations of Animals Exposed to Chronic Roentgen Radiation," *Report MDDC-204* (1947); H. Jones, "Aging Effects of Radiation," Paper presented at Health Physics Society Meeting, June 26, 1956 at University of Michigan, Ann Arbor, Michigan; H. P. Yockey, "A Study of Aging, Thermal Killing, and Radiation Damage by Information Theory," *Symposium on Information Theory in Biology* (Pergamon Press, New York, 1958); H. P. Yockey, "Radiation Aging and Its Relation to the Principles of Health Physics," *Health Physics*, 1, No. 4, 417 (1959); H. P. Yockey, "Use of Information Theory in Aging and Radiation Damage," published (1960) in *Proc. Conference on Aging, Gatlinburg, Tennessee*, May 1–7, 1957 by the American Inst. of Biological Sciences, symposium No. 6, pp. 338–347; H. P. Yockey an J. S. Mendell, "Some Problems in the Treatment of Aging and Radiation Damage by Information Theory," presented at Burlington Conference, Burlington, Vermont (August 1958).
2. E. O. Wollan, "Cosmic Rays," *Medical Physics*, 1, p. 282 (Year Book Publishers, Chicago, Otto Glasser, Ed.).
3. John B. Hursh, "Radium Content of Public Water Supplies," *J. Am. Water Works Assoc.*, 46, 43–54 (1954).
4. Bengt Hultqvist, *Studies on Naturally Occurring Ionizing Radiations*, Stockholm: Almqvist and Wiksells Boktryckeri AB (1956).
5. Emil H. Grubbé, "Priority in the Therapeutic Use of X-Rays," *Radiology*, 21, 156–162 (1933).
6. Leopold Freund, *Elements of General Radiotherapy for Practitioners* (Rebman Company, New York, 1904).
7. N. Stone Scott, "X-Ray Injuries," *Amer. X-Ray J.*, 1, 57–60 (1897).
8. Nicholas Senn, "Case of Splenomedullary Leukemia Successfully Treated by the Use of the Roentgen Ray," *Med. Rec.*, 64, 281–282 (August 22, 1903).
9. J. Bergonié and L. Tribondeau, "Médecine—interpretation de quelques resultats de la radiothérapie et essai de fixation d'une technique rationnelle," *Compt. rend.*, 143, 983–985 (1906).
10. G. Von Perthes, "Versuche über den Einfluss der Röntgenstrahlen und Radium-strahlen auf die Zellteilung," *Deut. med. Wochschr.*, 30, 632–634, 668–670 (1904).
11. S. Russ, "Hard and Soft X-Rays," *Arch. Roentg. Ray*, 19, 323–325 (1914–15); S. T. Cantril and H. M. Parker, "The Tolerance Dose," *Report MDDC-1100*

(1945); Robert Stone (Ed.), *Industrial Medicine on the Plutonium Project*, Natl. Nuclear Energy Ser., Vol. IV-20, Chapter 2: "Biological Basis for Maximum Permissible Exposures," S. T. Cantril, 36–74 (1951).

12. Radioisotope and Stable Isotope Reports, Accounting Section, published monthly at Oak Ridge Gaseous Diffusion Plant, Oak Ridge, Tennessee.

13. H. A. Levy, "Some Aspects of the Design of Radiochemical Laboratories," *Chem. Eng. News*, **24**, 3168–3172 (December 10, 1946).

14. Publication of the National Committee on Radiation Protection, *U.S. Bureau of Standards Handbook* 42, "Safe Handling of Radioactive Isotopes," Superintendent of Documents, U.S. Government Printing Office, Washington 25, D.C.

15. K. Z. Morgan, W. S. Snyder, and M. R. Ford, "Maximum Permissible Concentration of Radioisotopes in Air and Water for Short Period Exposure," *Proc. Intern. Conf. Peaceful Uses Atomic Energy*, **13**, *Paper 139*, United Nations, New York (August 1955).

16. Publication of the National Committee on Radiation Protection, *U.S. Bureau of Standards Handbook 49*, "Recommendations for Waste Disposal of Phosphorus-32 and Iodine-131 for Medical Users"; *U.S. Bureau of Standards Handbook 53*, "Recommendations for the Disposal of Carbon-14 Wastes"; *U.S. Bureau of Standards Handbook 58*, "Radioactive-Waste Disposal in the Ocean"; Superintendent of Documents, U.S. Government Printing Office, Washington 25, D.C.

17. L. G. Stang, Jr., "Requirements for Handling a Gamma Emitter in the 1-mc to 1-c Range," *AECU 1185* (June 26, 1951); A series of papers on "Hot Labs—A Special Report," by a number of authors, *Nucleonics*, **12**, No. 11, 35–100 (November 1954); Proceedings of a symposium on "Glove Boxes and Shielded Cells for Handling Radioactive Materials," Academic Press, N.Y. (1958).

18. H. M. Parker, "Radiation Exposure Experience in a Major Atomic Energy Facility," *Peaceful Uses of Atomic Energy*, Vol. 13, 266, United Nations, New York (1956); R. L. Junkins, Personal Communication, Hanford Laboratories Operation, Richland, Washington (December 1958).

19. L. S. Taylor, "The International Commission on Radiological Protection," *Health Physics*, **1**, No. 2 (Pergamon Press, London, 1958).

20. G. W. C. Kaye, as secretary, and L. S. Taylor, as U.S. Representative, *Radiology*, **23**, 682 (1934); *Radiology*, **30**, 511 (1938).

21. L. S. Taylor et al., *National Bureau of Standards Handbook No. 15* (1931); *Handbook No. 20* (1936).

22. L. S. Taylor, "Brief History of the National Committee on Radiation Protection and Measurements (NCRP) Covering the Period 1929–1946," *Health Physics*, **1**, No. 1 (June 1958).

23. W. P. Jesse, "Measurements of W for Alpha and Beta Radiation," Paper presented at the Radiation Research Meeting (May 17, 1955).

24. *U.S. Bureau of Standards Handbook 62*, "Report of the International Commission on Radiological Units and Measurements (ICRU)" (April 1956), Superintendent of Documents, U.S. Government Printing Office, Washington 25, D.C.

25. Publication of the National Committee on Radiation Protection, *U.S. National Bureau of Standards Handbook 59*, "Permissible Dose from External Sources of Ionizing Radiation" (September 24, 1954). See also the April 15, 1958, addendum of *NCRP Handbook 59*, Superintendent of Documents, U.S. Government Printing Office, Washington 25, D.C.

26. Publication of the International Commission on Radiological Protection, "Recommendations of the International Commission on Radiological Protection,"

Supplement No. 6, *Brit. J. Radiol.* (1955). (See also reference 38, the 1959 revision of the *ICRP Handbook* published by Pergamon Press, London.)

27. W. S. Snyder, "Calculations for Maximum Permissible Exposure to Thermal Neutrons," *Nucleonics*, **6**, No. 2 (February 1950).

28. W. S. Snyder and J. Neufeld, "Calculated Depth Dose Curves in Tissue for Broad Beams of Fast Neutrons," *Brit. J. Radiol.*, **28**, No. 331 (July 1955). Depth dose curves in which RBE has the same functional relationship to specific ionization, as given in *U.S. Bureau of Standards Handbook 59*, are given in *U.S. Bureau of Standards Handbook 63*, 40–64.

29. W. S. Snyder and J. Neufeld, "On the Passage of Heavy Particles Through Tissue," *Radiation Research*, **6**, No. 1, 67–78 (January 1957).

30. W. Bothe, *Handbuch der Physik*, **22.2**, 56, Edward Brothers, Ann Arbor, Michigan (1943).

31. R. M. Sternheimer (quoted by L. D. Marinelli in Annual Review of *Nuclear Sci.*, **3**, 259).

32. H. H. Plough, "Radiation Tolerances and Genetic Effects," *Nucleonics*, **10**, No. 8, 16–20 (August 1952).

33. J. R. Dietrich, "Experimental Investigation of the Self Limitation of Power During Reactivity Transients in a Sub-Cooled Water-Moderated Reactor," Borax-1 Experiments, *ANL-5323* (1954); J. G. Hoffman, "Radiation Doses in the Pajarito Accident of May 21, 1946," *LA-687* (1948); R. W. Paine, Jr., R. S. Dike, J. D. Orndoff, and D. P. Wood, "A Study of an Accidental Radiation Burst," *LA-1289* (May 20, 1951); "Accidental Radiation Excursion at the Y-12 Plant, June 16, 1958," *Y-1234*, Union Carbide Nuclear Company (September 12, 1958).

34. Egon Lorenz, "Biologic Effects of Long-Continued Whole Body Irradiation with Gamma Rays on Mice, Guinea Pigs, and Rabbits," Part VI, unclassified project report *MDDC-656*.

35. L. B. Russell and W. L. Russell, "Radiation Hazards to the Embryo and Fetus," *Radiology*, **58**, 3, 369–376 (March 1952).

36. L. F. Curtiss, "Safe Handling of Radioactive Luminous Compounds," *National Bureau of Standards Handbook 27* (1941), Superintendent of Documents, U.S. Government Printing Office, Washington 25, D.C.

37. Publication of the National Committee on Radiation Protection, *National Bureau of Standards Handbook 52*, "Maximum Permissible Amounts of Radioisotopes in the Human Body and Maximum Permissible Concentrations in Air and Water" (1953). See also the 1959 revision of the *NCRP Handbook 52* for sale as *Handbook 69* (June 5, 1959), Superintendent of Documents, U.S. Government Printing Office, Washington 25, D.C.

38. Recommendations of the International Commission on Radiological Protection, *ICRP, Publication 2*, "Report of Committee II on Permissible Dose for Internal Radiation," Pergamon Press, London, England (1959); *Health Physics*, **3**, 1–380 (June 1960) includes the "Bibliography for Biological Data," in addition to the *ICRP Publication 2*.

39. K. Z. Morgan, "Maximum Permissible Concentration of Radon in the Air," unpublished memo (October 27, 1954).

40. K. Z. Morgan, "Maximum Permissible Internal Dose of Radionuclides—Recent Changes in These Values," *Nuclear Sci. Eng.*, **1**, No. 6, 477–500 (December 1956); K. Z. Morgan, "Recent Changes in Maximum Permissible Exposure Values," *A.M.A. Ind. Health*, **16**, 357–362 (November 1957); K. Z. Morgan, "Current

Status of the Internal Dose Problem," *Health Physics*, **1**, No. 2, 125–134 (September 1958).

41. K. Z. Morgan and M. R. Ford, "Developments in Internal Dose Determinations," *Nucleonics*, **12**, No. 6, 32–39 (June 1954); K. Z. Morgan, "Internal Dose from Short-Lived Radionuclides," *Symposium on the Shorter-Term Biological Hazards of a Fallout Field*, G. M. Dunning, Ed. (December 12–14, 1956), Superintendent of Documents, U.S. Government Printing Office, Washington 25, D.C.

42. "The Biological Effects of Atomic Radiation," *Nat. Acad. Sci., Nat. Research Council*, Washington, D.C. (1956).

43. "Report of the United Nations Scientific Committee on the Effects of Atomic Radiation," General Assembly, Official Records: 13th Session Supplement, No. 17(A/3838), New York (1958).

44. D. M. Davis, E. D. Gupton, and J. C. Hart, "Survey Monitoring Instrument Manual," *ORNL 332*, 1st revision (1954).

45. L. J. Deal, J. H. Roberson, F. H. Day, "Roentgen Ray Calibration of Photographic Films Exposure Meters," *Am. J. Roentg. Radium Therapy*, **59**, No 5. p. 731 (1948).

46. G. J. Hine and G. L. Brownell, *Radiation Dosimetry* (Academic Press, New York, 1956).

47. D. M. Davis, J. C. Hart, and K. Z. Morgan, "Personnel Meters," Prepared for Radiation Emergencies Steering Committee Summary Report, *KL-258*, CF No. 58-12-39, Oak Ridge National Laboratory (1958).

48. E. Tochlin, R. H. Davis, and J. Clifford, "A Calibrated X-Ray Film Badge Dosimeter," Naval Radiological Defense Laboratory, *ADP-78* (1949); R. B. Wilsey, "The Use of Photographic Film for Monitoring Stray X-Rays and Gamma Rays," *Radiology*, **56**, No. 2 (1951); Robley D. Evans, *Nat. Research Council Publ. 205* (Preliminary Report No. 11), p. 17 (1951).

49. J. S. Cheka, "Recent Developments in Film Monitoring of Fast Neutrons," *Nucleonics*, **12**, No. 6, 40–43 (1954); J. S. Cheka, "Nuclear Emulsion Instability," *Nucleonics*, **12**, No. 10, 58 (1954).

50. G. S. Hurst, J. A. Harter, P. N. Hensley, W. A. Mills, M. Slater, and P. W. Reinhardt, "Techniques of Measuring Neutron Spectra with Threshold Detectors—Tissue Dose Determination," *Rev. Sci. Instr.*, **27**, No. 3, 153–156 (March 1956).

51. "Accidental Radiation Excursion at the Y-12 Plant" (June 16, 1958), *Y-1234*, U.S. Department of Commerce, Washington 25, D.C; Dixon Callihan and Joseph T. Thomas, "Accidental Radiation Excursion at the Oak Ridge Y-12 Plant—I. Description and Physics of the Accident," *Health Physics* **1**, 363–372 (March 1959); J. D. McLendon, "Accidental Radiation Excursion at the Oak Ridge Y-12 Plant—II. Health Physics Aspects of the Accident," *Health Physics*, **2**, 21–29 (July 1959); G. S. Hurst, R. H. Ritchie, and L. C. Emerson, "Accidental Radiation Excursion at the Oak Ridge Y-12 Plant—III. Determination of Radiation Doses," *Health Physics*, **2**, 121–133 (October 1959); G. A. Andrews, B. W. Sitterson, A. L. Kretchmar, and M. Brucer, "Accidental Radiation Excursion at the Oak Ridge Y-12 Plant—IV. Preliminary Report on Clinical and Laboratory Effects in the Irradiated Employees," *Health Physics*, **2**, 134–138 (October 1959).

52. *Nucleonics* (*Buyer's Guide Issue*), **17**, No. 11, 301 (November 1959) gives the following: Film badge and/or ring meter service can be obtained by writing to the following places: Ansco Division, General Aniline and Film Corp., 175 Clinton Street, Binghamton, New York; Atomic Accessories, Inc., 811 W. Merrick Road, Valley Stream, New York; Atomic Film Badge Corp., 811 W. Merrick Road, Valley Stream, New York; Baldwin Industrial Controls, Dartford, Kent, England;

Controls for Radiation, Inc., 130 Aiewife Brook Parkway, Cambridge 40, Massachusetts; Curtiss-Wright Corporation, Wood-Ridge, New Jersey; Eastman Kodak Company, 343 State Street, Rochester 4, New York; Health Physics Services, Inc., 1111 Low Street, Baltimore 2, Maryland; Isotopes Specialties Company, Division of Nuclear Corporation of America, 170 West Providencia, Burbank, California; Laundauer, Jr. and Co., R. S., 3920 216th Street, Matteson, Illinois; Meillon Inc., George T., 132 Nassau Street, New York 38, New York; Nuclear-Chicago Corp., 345 E. Howard Avenue, Des Plaines, Illinois; Nuclear Service Laboratory, P.O. Box 1885, Knoxville 1, Tennessee; Nucleonic Corporation of America, 196 Degraw Street, Brooklyn 31, New York; Patterson Moos Division, Universal Winding Company, 90–28 Van Wyck Expressway, Jamaica 18, New York; Radiation Detection Company, 4047–49 Transport Street, Palo Alto, California; St. John X-Ray Laboratory, Califon, New Jersey; Samples Machine Co., A. M., 2908 Tazewell Pike, Knoxville 18, Tennessee; Technical Associates, 140 West Providencia Avenue, Burbank California; Tracerlab, Inc., 1601 Trapelo Road, Waltham 54, Mass.; U.S. Nuclear Corporation, 801 North Lake Street, P.O. Box 208, Burbank, California; Universal Transistor Products Corporation, 36 Sylvester Street, Westbury, New York; Volk Radiochemical Company, 5412 North Clark Street, Chicago 40, Illinois; X-Ray Monitoring Corporation, 43 West 61st Street, New York 23, New York.

53. G. S. Hurst, R. H. Ritchie, and H. N. Wilson, "A Count-Rate Method of Measuring Fast Neutron Tissue Dose," *Rev. Sci. Instr.*, **22**, No. 12, 981 (December 1951).

54. G. S. Hurst, "An Absolute Tissue Dosimeter for Fast Neutrons," *Brit. J. Radiol.*, **27**, No. 318, 353–357 (June 1954).

55. F. H. Day, "X-Ray Calibration of Radiation Survey Meters, Pocket Chambers, and Dosimeters," *Ra-Det*, **3**, No. 4 (April 1950).

56. Many useful suggestions of radiation instrument requirements of a laboratory are given in the *National Bureau of Standards Handbooks* published by the National Committee on Radiation Protection. They may be procured from the Superintendent of Documents, U.S. Government Printing Office, Washington 25, D.C. Of particular interest are *Handbook 51*, "Radiological Monitoring Methods and Instruments"; *Handbook 55*, "Protection Against Betatron-Synchrotron Radiations Up to 100 Million Electron Volts"; and *Handbook 57*, "Photographic Dosimetry of X and Gamma Rays."

57. *C. A. B. No. 16—Official Air Transport Restricted Articles Tariff No. 6-B*, "Transportation of Restricted Articles by Air," Emery F. Johnson, Agent, National Airport, Washington, D.C. (March 1957); H. A. Campbell, *Tariff No. 10*, "ICC Regulations for Transportation of Explosives and Other Dangerous Articles by Land and Water by Rail Freight Service and by Motor Vehicle (highway) and Water Including Specifications for Shipping Containers," Bureau of Explosives, Office of Chief Inspector, 30 Vesey St., New York 7, New York; Robley D. Evans, "Physical, Biological, and Administrative Problems Associated with the Transportation of Radioactive Substances," *Nuclear Sci. Ser., Preliminary Report No. 11, Publ. 205, Nat. Acad. Sci.* (1951); *Explosives or Other Dangerous Articles on Board Vessels—Regulations Prescribed by the Commandant of the Coast Guard*, Chapter I, Part 146, 391 (July 1, 1954), Superintendent of Documents, U.S. Government Printing Office, Washington 25, D.C.; *Handbook of Federal Regulations applying to "Transportation of Radioactive Materials,"* Superintendent of Documents, U.S. Government Printing Office, Washington, D.C. (1955); *Postal Manual, U.S.*

Post Office Department, Chapters 1 and 2, 125.2 (October 8, 1958), Superintendent of Documents, U.S. Government Printing Office, Washington 25, D.C.; Regulations of U.S. Coast Guard, given in *Federal Register*, 21, No. 183 (September 1956), 7108, Superintendent of Documents, U.S. Government Printing Office, Washington 25, D.C.

58. Evan E. Campbell, B. M. Head, and Morris F. Milligan, "An Extraction Method for the Determination of Uranium Alpha Activity in Urine," *LA-1920* (June 1955); F. C. Cowan and Jerome Weiss, "Analysis of Urine for Gross Radioactivity," *BNL-1000* (October 1951); L. B. Farabee, "Procedure for the Determination of Plutonium in Human Urine," *Mon H-218* (April 1947); L. B. Farabee, "Procedure for the Radiochemical Analysis of Strontium and Barium in Human Urine," *A.M.A. Arch. Ind. Health* (March 1958). *ORNL-1932*; J. Fresco, E. Hardy, and G. Welford, "Radiochemical Determination of Strontium-89 and Strontium-90," *NYO-4617*; J. B. Hursh, "The Measurement of Breath Radon by Charcoal Absorption," *UR-258*, *Nucleonics*, 12, No. 1, 62 (1954); M. E. Koshland, L. M. Brown, and M. J. Cook, "Procedure for the Determination of Plutonium in Urine," *Mon-N-92*, declassified (January 1956); E. A. Martell, "Absolute Assay of Strontium-90 in Biological Materials, Soils, Waters and Air Filters," *AECU-3262*; C. A. Mawson and I. Fisher, "The Estimation of Radioactive Strontium and Other Fission Products in Urine and Water," *CRM-455*; J. McClellan and M. F. Milligan, "Determination of Tritium in Urine and Water," *LA-1645*; M. F. Milligan et al., "Analytical Procedures of the Industrial Hygiene Group," *LA-1858*, second edition; W. P. Norris and J. J. Liebner, "Determination of Radon in Expired Air," *ANL-4531*; M. C. Robbins, B. C. Eutsler, and Morris F. Milligan, "The Determination of Polonium in Urine," *LA-1904* (April 1955); J. Rundo, "The Analysis of Biological Samples for Polonium," *AERE-HP/R-627* (December 1950); L. C. Sahwendiman, J. W. Healy, and D. L. Reid, "The Application of Nuclear Track Emulsions to the Analysis of Urine for Very Low Level Plutonium," *AW-22680*; S. Marshall Sanders, Jr., "Determination of Plutonium in Urine," *DP-146* (March 1956); Jack Schubert, L. S. Myers, Jr., and Jean A. Jackson, "The Analytical Procedures of the Bioassay Group at the Argonne National Laboratory," *ANL-4509*, declassified (June 1955); Paul C. Tompkins, L. B. Farabee, and J. X. Khym, "Procedure for the Radiochemical Analysis of Barium, Strontium and Rare Earth in Human Urine," *ORNL-368, AECD-2692* (September 1949); M. M. Trojanowski and R. L. Bouton, "A Method for the Detection of Enriched Uranium in Human Urine," *KAPL-667* (December 1951); T. C. Whitson and T. Kwasnoski, "An Electrodeposition Method for the Determination of Uranium in Urine," *K-1101* (June 1954); A. L. Boni, "Urinalysis Method for Enriched Uranium," *Health Physics*, 2, 288–290 (February 1960); A. L. Boni, "Rapid Determination of Mixed Beta-Gamma Radionuclides in Urine," *Health Physics*, 2, 186–188 (October 1959); Sarah C. Leidt and S. Marshall Sanders, Jr., "A New Procedure for Plutonium Urinalysis," *AECU-4414* (July 1959); George W. Rouster, Jr., "Electrodeposition of Uranium from Urine," *Health Physics*, 2, 291–294 (February 1960).

59. Ernest C. Anderson, "The Los Alamos Human Counter," *Brit. J. Radiol.*, Supplement No. 7, 27–32 (1957); P. R. J. Burch, "Body Gamma-Ray Monitoring: Some Basic Considerations," *Brit. J. Radiol.*, Supplement No. 7, 20–26 (1957); L. D. Marinelli, "The Use of NaI-Tl Crystal Spectrometers in the Study of Gamma-Ray Activity in Vivo: A Summary of Developments at the Argonne National Laboratory," *Brit. J. Radiol.*, Supplement No. 7, 38–43 (1957); R. B. Owen,

"Measurement of Whole Body Radioactivity with NaI-Tl Scintillation Counters," *Brit. J. Radiol.*, Supplement No. 7, 33–37 (1957); J. Rundo, "The Use of the Copenhagen Ionization Chamber Apparatus in the Study of Thorium Dioxide Poisoning," *Brit. J. Radiol.*, Supplement No. 7, 13–19 (1957); Rolf M. Sievert and Bengt Hultqvist, "Some Swedish Investigations of the Radioactivity of the Human Body," *Brit. J. Radiol.*, Supplement No. 7, 1–12 (1957).

60. Hermann Lisco, Miriam P. Finkel, and Austin M. Brues, "Carcinogenic Properties of Radioactive Fission Products and of Plutonium," *Radiology*, **49**, 361–363 (1947).

61. A. M. Brues, unpublished experiments in which placques of radionuclides were found to be more damaging when spread evenly rather than unevenly over the irradiating surface. Argonne National Laboratory (1953).

62. H. Cember, J. A. Watson, and T. B. Grucci, "Pulmonary Radiation Effects as a Function of Absorbed Energy," *Am. Ind. Hyg.*, **17**, No. 4 (1956); H. Cember, J. A. Watson, and A. A. Spitzer, "Bronchogenic Carcinoma from Radioactive Cerium Fluoride," *A.M.A. Arch. Ind. Health*, **19**, No. 1 (1959).

63. *National Bureau of Standards Handbook 48*, "Control and Removal of Radioactive Contamination in Laboratories," Superintendent of Documents, U.S. Government Printing Office, Washington 25, D.C.; "Rules Concerning Radioactive Substances and Associated Hazards," Oak Ridge National Laboratory (1946), 29, for a discussion of use of TiO_2 method of hand decontamination: Frances Sachs, *Report Y-914*, "Skin Decontamination" (A Literature Search), *Report Y-850*, "Skin Decontamination" (A Literature Search), *Report Y-B4-4*, "Skin Decontamination" (A Literature Search), *Report Y-B4-10*, "Skin Decontamination" (A Literature Search).

64. American Water Works Association, Report of Committee E5.12 (formerly Task Group E5W-12), "Progress in Radioactivity Instrumentation and Testing," *J. Am. Water Works Assoc.*, **46**, 641–642 (July 1954); S. I. Auerbach and D. A. Crossley, Jr., "Strontium-90 and Cesium-137 Uptake by Vegetation Under Natural Conditions, *Proc. Intern. Conf. Peaceful Uses Atomic Energy*, Geneva, Switzerland (August 1958), United Nations, New York; N. R. Beers, "Stack Meteorology and Atmospheric Disposal of Radioactive Waste," *Nucleonics*, **4**, No. 4, 28–38 (April 1949); Melvin W. Carter, "Removal of Radioactive Iodine (I^{131}) by Use of Laboratory Trickling Filter," *Sewage and Ind. Wastes*, **25**, 5, 560–565 (May 1953); K. E. Cowser and F. L. Parker, "Soil Disposal of Radioactive Wastes at ORNL: Criteria and Techniques of Site Selection and Monitoring," *Health Physics* **1**, No. 2, 152–163 (1958); K. E. Cowser and R. J. Morton, "Treatment Plant for Removal of Radioactive Contaminants from Process Waste Water, Part II: Evaluation of Performance," presented at meeting of American Society of Civil Engineers (October 17, 1958), published in the Proceedings of this meeting in the Journal of Sanitary Engineering Division (May 1959) by Amer. Society of Civil Engineers, 2500 S. State Street, Ann Arbor, Michigan; K. E. Cowser, Roy J. Morton, and E. J. Witkowski, "The Treatment of Large-Volume, Low-Level Waste by the Lime-Soda Softening Process," *Proc. Intern. Conf. Peaceful Uses Atomic Energy*, Geneva, Switzerland (August 1958), United Nations, New York; F. L. Culler, Jr., "Notes on Fission Product Wastes from Proposed Power Reactors," Oak Ridge National Laboratory, *ORNL CF 55-4-25* (April 15, 1955); W. de Laguna, K. E. Cowser, and F. L. Parker, "Disposal of High Level Radioactive Liquid Wastes in Terrestrial Pits—A Sequel," *Proc. Intern. Conf. Peaceful Uses Atomic Energy*, Geneva, Switzerland (August 1958), United Nations, New York; Richard Dennis, Leslie Silverman, C. E. Billings, D. M. Anderson, W. R. Samples,

H. M. Donaldson, Jr., and Philip Drinker, "Air Cleaning Studies," progress report for July 1, 1954, to June 30, 1955, General Electric Company, Hanford Atomic Products Operation, Richland, Washington, *NYO-4611* (October 1956); "Final Report on the Decontamination of Radioactive Waters," ORNL-2557, Oak Ridge National Laboratory and U.S. Public Health Service, Office of Tech. Services, U.S. Dept. of Commerce, Washington 25, D.C. (1959); J. M. Garner, Jr., and Ford Kalil, "System Continuously Records Water Level and Contamination," *Nucleonics*, 14, No. 7, 56–60 (1956); Lee Gemmell, "Efficiency of Filter Beds for Treating Radioactive Waste," *Nucleonics*, 10, No. 10, 40–42 (October 1952); E. Glueckauf, "Long-Term Aspect of Fission Product Disposal," *Proc. Intern. Conf. Peaceful Uses Atomic Energy*, Geneva, Switzerland (August 1955), 9, *Reactor Technology and Chemical Processing*, 3–8, United Nations, New York (1956); Arthur E. Gorman, "Waste Disposal as Related to Site Selection," *J. Sanitary Eng. Div., Proc. Am. Soc. Civil Eng.*, 82, *Paper No. 1000*, 1–8 (June 1956); B. Kahn and A. Goldin, "Radiochemical Procedures for the Identification of the More Hazardous Nuclides," *J. Am. Water Works Assoc.*, 49, No. 6 (June 1957); B. Kahn, E. R. Eastwood, and W. J. Lacy, "Use of Ion Exchange Resins to Concentrate Radionuclides for Subsequent Analysis," *ORNL-2321* (May 1957); B. Kahn, "Procedures for the Analysis of Some Radionuclides Absorbed on Soil," *ORNL-1951* (September 28, 1955); Kellex Corporation Progress Reports, "Development of Laboratory Disposal Unit," *AEC Doc. Nos. KLX-1330, 1340, 1345, 1352, and 1354* (1952); W. C. King, "Monitoring the Liquid Wastes Discharged from the Idaho Chemical Processing Plant," Phillips Petroleum Company, 29, *IDO-14378*, Atomic Energy Division, Idaho Falls, Idaho (June 12, 1956); Simon Kinsman, *Radiological Health Handbook*, 358, Robert A. Taft Sanitary Engineering Center, Cincinnati, Ohio, *PB-121784* (January 1957); F. W. Kittrell, "Radioactive Waste Disposal to Public Sewers," *Sewage and Ind. Wastes*, 24, 8, 985–993 (August 1952); J. B. Lackey, "The Suspended Microbiota of the Clinch River and Adjacent Waters, in Relation to Radioactivity in the Summer of 1956," Oak Ridge National Laboratory, Oak Ridge, Tennessee, *ORNL-2410*, 36 (November 13, 1957); W. J. Lacy and Bernd Kahn, "Survey Meters and Electroscopes for Monitoring Radioactivity in Water," *J. Am. Water Works Assoc.*, 46, No. 1, 55–64 (January 1954); W. J. Lacy, "Clay Decontamination of Radioactivity Polluted Water," *Indus. Eng. Chem.*, 46, 1061–1065 (May 1954); W. J. Lacy, "Radioactive Waste Disposal Report on Seepage Pit Liquid Waste-Shale Column Experiment," Oak Ridge National Laboratory, Oak Ridge, Tennessee, *ORNL-2415*, 22 (Nov. 12, 1957); J. R. LaPointe and Robert D. Brown, "Control of Radioactive Material at the Pressurized Water Reactor," Westinghouse Electric Corporation, Bettis Plant, Pittsburgh, Pa., *WAPD-T-436*, 24 (1957); R. A. Lauderdale and A. H. Emmons, "Decontamination of Small Volumes of Radioactive Water," *Nucleonics*, 8, No. 5, 21–26 (May 1951); R. A. Lauderdale, Jr., "Studies on the Removal of Radioisotopes from Liquid Wastes by Coagulation," Oak Ridge National Laboratory, Oak Ridge, Tennessee, *ORNL-932*, 30 (October 23, 1956); Joseph A. Lieberman and Arthur E. Gorman, "Treatment and Disposal of Atomic Energy Industry Wastes," *Proc. Am. Soc. Civil Engrs.*, 80, Separate No. 422 (March 1954); H. N. Lowe, W. J. Lacy, B. F. Surkiewicz, and R. F. Jaeger, "Destruction of Microorganisms in Water, Sewage, and Sewage Sludge by Ionizing Radiation," *J. Am. Water Works Assoc.*, 38, No. 11, 1363–1372 (November 1956); R. F. McCauley, R. A. Lauderdale, and Rolf Eliassen, "A Study of the Lime-Soda Softening Process as a Method for Decontaminating Radioactive Waters," Mass. Inst. Technol.,

Cambridge, Mass., Sedgwick Laboratories of Sanitary Science, *NYO-4439*, 94 (September 1, 1953); *Meteorology and Atomic Energy*, U.S. Department of Commerce, Weather Bureau, Washington, D.C., *AECU-3066*, 182 (July 1955); R. J. Morton and C. P. Straub, "Removal of Radionuclides from Water by Water Treatment Processes," *J. Am. Water Works Assoc.*, **48**, No. 5, 545–558 (May 1956); R. J. Morton and E. G. Struxness, "Ground Disposal of Radioactive Wastes," *Am. J. Public Health*, **46**, No. 2, 156–163 (February 1956); J. F. Newell and C. W. Christenson, "Radioactive Waste Disposal," *Sewage and Ind. Wastes*, **23**, 7, 861–868 (July 1951); J. F. Newell and C. W. Christenson, "The Latest to be Learned from Los Alamos. What Treatment for Radioactive Wastes?" *Eng. News-Record*, **147**, 37–38 (November 8, 1951); I. L. Ophel and C. D. Fraser, "The Chalk River Liquid Disposal Area, 1956," *Report CRHP-709*, Atomic Energy of Canada, Ltd., Chalk River Project, Chalk River, Ontario (June 1957); F. L. Parker, "Tracers in Hydrological Studies," paper presented at the 38th Annual Meeting of the American Geophysical Union, Washington, D.C. (April 29–30, 1957); Oliver R. Placak and R. J. Morton, "Research on the Disposal of Radioactive Wastes," *J. Am. Water Works Assoc.*, **42**, No. 2, 135–142 (February 1950); Clinton C. Powell and Howard L. Andrews, "Radioactive Waste Disposal," *Public Health Repts. (U.S.)*, **67**, 12, 1214–1215 (December 1952); "Precautionary Measures Against Radiological Health Hazards," *AMC Manual No. 160-2*, a publication of Wright-Patterson Air Force Base, revised December 15, 1952; "Progress in Radioactivity Instrumentation and Testing," Report of AWWA Committee E5.12 (formerly Task Force Group E5W-12), *J. Am. Water Works Assoc.*, **46**, 641–642 (July 1954); *idem. Instrumentation for Radioactive Pollution Studies*, *J. Water Works Assoc.*, **48**, 397–416 (April 1956); "Report of Working Meeting on Fixation of Radioactivity in Stable, Solid Media at the Johns Hopkins University," *TID-7550* (June 19–21, 1957); W. A. Rodger and Philip Fineman, "Radioactive Waste Disposal," *Chem. Eng.*, **58**, 146–150 (1951); W. A. Rodger and Philip Fineman, "A Complete Waste Disposal System for a Radiochemical Laboratory," *Nucleonics*, **9**, No. 6, 51–61 (December 1951); C. C. Ruchhoft and L. R. Setter, "Application of Biological Methods in the Treatment of Radioactive Wastes," *Sewage and Ind. Wastes*, **25**, 1, 48–60 (January 1953); C. C. Ruchhoft and S. Feitelberg, "Concentration of Radioiodine in Sewage and Sludge from Hospital Wastes," *Nucleonics*, **9**, No. 6, 29–34 (December 1951); "Sanitary Engineering Aspects of the Atomic Energy Industry," a Seminar Sponsored by the AEC and the U.S. Public Health Service, held at the Robert A. Taft Engineering Center, Cincinnati, Ohio (December 6–9, 1955), *TID-7517*, Pt. 1a, Pt. 1b (October 1956); Sanitary Engineering Conference, Baltimore, Maryland, April 15–16, 1954, U.S. AEC Division of Reactor Development, Washington, D.C., *WASH-275* (August 1955); R. L. Shannon, "Radioactive Waste Disposal," a bibliography, *AEC Doc. No. TID-375* (August 1950); C. P. Straub and Richard B. Hahn, "Determination of Radioactive Strontium and Barium in Water," *J. Am. Water Works Assoc.*, **47**, No. 4, 335–340 (April 1955); C. P. Straub, "Effects of Radioactive Materials on Environmental Health," *Public Health Repts. (U.S.)*, **67**, 3, 298–305 (March 1952); C. P. Straub, Roy J. Morton, and Oliver R. Placak, "Studies on the Removal of Radioactive Contaminants from Water," *J. Am. Water Works Assoc.*, **43**, 10, 792–793 (October 1951); C. P. Straub and E. G. Struxness, "The Impact of Radioactive Waste Disposal on Chemical Processing," *ORNL CF 55-8-97* (Aug. 15, 1955); C. P. Straub, "Limitations of Water Treatment Methods for Removing Radioactive Contaminants," *Public Health Repts. (U.S.)*, **70** (9),

897–904 (1955); C. P. Straub, The Column 'Nuclear Notes' in Civil Engineering: XII "Statistics of Nuclear Measurements," **25** (7), 90 (1955), paper prepared by B. Kahn; XIII "Preparation of Samples for Assay," **25** (8), 82 (1955), paper prepared by B. Kahn; XIV "Identification of Radioisotopes by Relative Counting Techniques," **29** (9) 86 (1955), paper prepared by M. I. Goldman; C. P. Straub, W. J. Lacy, and R. J. Morton, "Methods of Decontamination of Low Level Radioactive Liquid Wastes," *Proc. Intern. Conf. Peaceful Uses Atomic Energy,* Geneva, Switzerland, August 1955, **9,** 24–27, United Nations, New York (1956); E. G. Struxness and J. O. Blomeke, "Multipurpose Processing and Ultimate Disposal of Radioactive Wastes," *Proc. Intern. Conf. Peaceful Uses Atomic Energy,* Geneva, Switzerland (August 1958), United Nations, New York; E. G. Struxness, R. J. Morton, and C. P. Straub, "Disposal of High Level Radioactive Liquid Wastes in Terrestrial Pits," unpublished paper (1955); E. G. Struxness, R. J. Morton et al., "Waste Disposal Research and Engineering, Health Physics Division, Annual Progress Report," *ORNL-2590,* 1–99 (October 1958); "Symposium on Liquid Industrial Wastes," (a) J. H. Hayner, "Atomic Energy Industry," *Ind. Eng. Chem.,* **44,** 472–476 (1952); (b) C. C. Ruchhoft, A. E. Gorman, and C. W. Christenson, "Wastes Containing Radioactive Isotopes," *Ind. Eng. Chem.,* **44,** 545–549 (1952); "Symposium on Radioactive Wastes," *Ind. Eng. Chem.,* **43,** 7, 1499–1544 (July 1951): (a) Frank N. Browder, "Liquid Waste Disposal at Oak Ridge National Laboratory," 1502; (b) C. W. Christenson, M. B. Ettinger, Gorden G. Robeck, E. R. Hermann, K. C. Kohr, and J. F. Newell, 1509; (c) James H. Jensen, "National Committee on Radiation Protection," 1500; (d) R. A. Lauderdale, "Treatment of Radioactive Water by Phosphate Precipitation," 1538; (e) S. K. Love, "Natural Radioactivity in Water," 1541; (f) G. E. McCullough, "Concentration of Radioactive Liquid Waste by Evaporation," 1505; (g) John F. Newell, C. W. Christenson, E. R. Mathews, C. C. Ruchhoft, H. L. Krieger, and D. W. Moeller, 1516; (h) C. C. Ruchhoft, Francis I. Norris, and Lloyd R. Setter, "Activated Sludge from Foods for Treatment of Radioactive Waste," 1520; J. G. Terrill and M. D. Hollis, "Sanitary Engineering and Reactor Waste Disposal," *J. Sanitary Eng. Div.,* American Society of Civil Engineers, **83,** SA5, 1407 (1957); "The Biological Effects of Atomic Radiation," Summary reports from a study by the National Academy of Sciences, released June 13, 1956, *Nat. Acad. Sci., Nat. Research Council,* Washington, D.C. (1956); "The Disposal of Radioactive Wastes on Land," *Report of the Committee on Waste Disposal, NAS-NRC,* Washington, D.C., Publ. 519 (September 1955); "The Nature of Radioactive Fallout and Its Effect on Man," record of hearings before the Special Subcommittee on Radiation of the Joint Committee on Atomic Energy, Congress of the United States, May 27 to June 7, 1957, Superintendent of Documents, U.S. Government Printing Office, Washington, D.C.; E. C. Tsivoglou, E. D. Harward, and W. M. Ingram, "Stream Surveys for Radioactive Waste Control," *J. Am. Water Works Assoc.,* **49,** 750 (1957); Hugh E. Voress, Theodore F. Davis, and Thomas N. Hubbard, Jr., "Radioactive Waste Processing and Disposal—A Bibliography of Selected Report Literature," *U.S. Atomic Energy Comm., Technical Information Service, TID-3311* (June 1958); E. G. Struxness, "Fixation and Ultimate Disposal," *Industrial Radioactive Waste Disposal,* **3,** 1852–1855 (1959). Published hearings before the special Subcommittee on Radiation of the Joint Committee on Atomic Energy, Congress of the United States (January 28–30, February 2–3, 1959); F. L. Parker (Ed.), W. J. Boegly, Jr., R. L. Bradshaw, J. Crowell, E. R. Eastwood, F. M. Empson, B. Gunter, L. Hemphill, O. H. Myers, and E. G. Struxness, "Status

Report on Waste Disposal in Natural Salt Formations: II," *ORNL-2700* (April 9, 1959); Y. Feige, F. L. Parker, and E. G. Struxness, "Analysis of Waste Disposal Practice and Control at ORNL," *ORNL CF-60-8-72* (October 4, 1960); F. L. Parker, W. J. Boegly, R. L. Bradshaw, F. M. Empson, L. Hemphill, E. G. Struxness, and T. Tamura, "Disposal of Radioactive Wastes in Natural Salt," *Proc. Intern. Sci. Conf. Disposal Radioactive Wastes*, Monaco, November 16–21, 1959, **2** (1960); E. G. Struxness, K. E. Cowser, W. de Laguna, D. G. Jacobs, R. J. Morton, and T. Tamura, "Waste Disposal Research and Development in the U.S.A.," *Proc. Intern. Sci. Conf. Disposal Radioactive Wastes*, November 16–21, 1959, Monaco, **1, 2** (1960).

65. H. J. Dunster, "The Disposal of Radioactive Waste to the Sea During 1956 by the United Kingdom Atomic Energy Authority," United Kingdom Atomic Energy Industrial Group H.Q., Risley, Lancs, England, IGS-R/R-2, 4 (January 1958); A. Joseph, "United States' Sea Disposal Operations. A Summary to December" (1956), *U.S. Atomic Energy Comm. Rept., WASH-734* (1957); Publication of the National Committee on Radiation Protection, *National Bureau of Standards Handbook 58*, "Radioactive Waste Disposal in the Ocean," Superintendent of Documents, U.S. Government Printing Office, Washington 25, D.C.; C. E. Renn, "Disposal of Radioactive Wastes at Sea," *Proc. Intern. Conf. Peaceful Uses Atomic Energy, Geneva, Switzerland*, **9**, 718 (1956); "Status Report on Handling and Disposal of Radioactive Wastes in the AEC Program," *U.S. Atomic Energy Comm. Rept., WASH-742*, Division of Reactor Development, Washington, D.C. (August 1957).

66. E. M. Romney, G. V. Alexander, G. M. Le Roy, W. A. Rhoads, J. W. Neel, and K. H. Larson, "Effects of Calcium and Strontium on Plant Uptake of Sr^{90} and Stable Strontium from Nutrient Solutions and Soils," unclassified report *UCLA-374* (July 15, 1956).

67. Robert G. Gallaghar, Mitchell R. Zavon, and Henry N. Doyle, "Radioactive Contamination in a Radium Therapy Clinic," *Public Health Repts. (U.S.)*, **70**, No. 7, 617–624 (July 1955); Paul B. Klevin, William B. Harris, and Hanson I. Blatz, "Decontamination of Buildings Used for Processing Alpha Emitters," unclassified report *NYO-4600* (April 1954).

68. "Decontamination, a Literature Search," Report *Y-964*, by R. L. Curtis (May 19, 1953); "Routine Decontamination Procedures and Formulas for Plutonium Contamination," Report *LA-1530*, by E. J. Cox and R. F. Baker (January 1, 1953).

69. "Laboratory Design for Handling Radioactive Material," BRAB (Building Research Advisory Board) *Conference Report No. 3* (November 27–28, 1951). Classified report *ANL-4670*, "Hot Laboratories and Equipment," Papers presented at AEC Division of Reactor Development Information Meeting (May 16–18, 1951). Classified report *ORNL CF 52-10-230*, "Second Information Meeting Hot Laboratories and Equipment," held in Oak Ridge at Oak Ridge National Laboratory (October 7–9, 1952). Report *BNL-302*, "Hot Laboratory Information Meeting," Brookhaven National Laboratory (May 26–28, 1954). Report *TID-5280* and Supplement, "Hot Laboratories Information Meeting," held in Washington, D.C. (September 29–30, 1955). *Proceedings of Hot Laboratories and Equipment*, meeting held in Philadelphia, Pennsylvania (1957). *Hot Laboratories and Equipment*, meeting held at International Amphitheater in Chicago, Illinois on March 19–21, 1958. *Hot Laboratories and Equipment*, conference held in Cleveland, Ohio (1959).

AUTHOR INDEX

Abers, E. L., 359
Abraham, M., 52
Accardo, C. A., 358
Ackerman, N., 357
Adams, N. I., 303, 304
Ageno, M., 358
Agnew, H. M., 63, 64
Alexander, G. V., 469
Allen, J. S., 56, 60
Allison, B., 165
Ames, O., 165
Anderson, D. M., 465
Anderson, E. C., 355, 464
Andrews, G. A., 462
Andrews, H. A., 467
Andrews, P. T., 158
Anfinsen, C. B., 357
Anger, H. O., 356, 358
Angus, J., 7, 68, 72, 76
Anker, H. S., 303
Armstrong, W. D., 357
Ashkin, J., 377
Ashley, J. E., 164
Aten, A. H. W., Jr., 357
Attix, F. H., 377
Audric, B. N., 358, 359
Auerbach, S. I., 465
Auxier, J. A., 390
Axel, P., 353

Bagge, E., 77
Bailey, V. A., 25, 26
Bair, J. K., 162
Baker, R. F., 469
Baker, R. G., 318
Baker, W. B., 389
Baker, W. M., 163
Bakker, C. J., 77
Baldinger, E., 41, 44
Balfour, J. G., 356
Ballweg, L. H., 390
Banks, T. E., 357
Barabaschi, S., 304
Barber, W. C., 12
Barnet, H. M., 357
Barnothy, J., 357

Barr, T. A., 375
Barschall, H., 41, 45, 51, 55, 56, 63, 64
Barth, G., 209
Bashkin, S., 98
Basile, L. J., 119
Basson, J. K., 360
Batchelor, R., 81
Battat, M. E., 79
Baumgartner, W., 165
Bayhurst, B. P., 321
Beattie, J. W., 389
Becker, R. L., 150
Beckerley, J. G., 192
Beers, N. R., 465
Beghian, L. E., 60, 96
Belcher, E. H., 358
Beling, J. K., 72
Bell, C. G., 164, 360
Bell, D. A., 304
Bell, P. R., 135, 136, 142, 342, 345, 351, 352
Bell, R. E., 359
Bennett, W. R., 125, 126
Beranek, L. L., 305
Bergkvist, K. E., 360
Bergonié, J., 392
Bernstein, W., 162
Berstein, I. A., 359
Berthelot, A., 355
Bethe, H. A., 12, 377
Beusch, W., 163
Biber, C., 15
Bichsel, H., 78
Billings, C. E., 465
Bindman, J. C., 359
Biondi, M. A., 19
Birkhoff, R. D., 5, 163
Birks, J. B., 108, 109, 110, 111, 115, 116, 162
Bishop, G. R., 79, 80
Bisi, A., 80, 165
Bistline, J. A., 20, 27, 60
Bjørnholm, S., 360
Black, L. D., 164
Blair, H. A., 459

471

Blatz, H. I., 469
Blau, M., 360
Bloembergen, A., 359
Blomeke, J. O., 468
Blüh, O., 358
Blunck, O., 5
Bly, D. A., 162
Boag, J. W., 384, 389
Boche, R. D., 459
Bode, H. W., 303, 305
Boegly, W. J., 468, 469
Bogart, L., 95
Bohr, N., 8
Boicourt, G. P., 127
Bollinger, L. M., 124, 143, 155
Bonanomi, J., 93, 95, 96
Boni, A. L., 464
Bonner, T. W., 163
Borkowski, C. J., 162, 360
Bortner, T. E., 15, 16, 17, 19, 25, 26, 27, 28
Bothe, W., 50, 461
Bouton, R. L., 464
Bowen, E. J., 109, 111, 150
Bowen, T., 162
Bowles, B. J., 357
Boxall, R. H., 356
Brabant, J. M., 183
Bradbury, N. E., 18, 19, 28
Bradley, E. F., 81
Bradshaw, R. L., 468, 469
Breitenberger, E., 144
Brennan, J. T., 374
Bridge, H. S., 32
Bridgman, P. W., 85
Bright, W. C., 64
Brinkman, H. C., 77
Broda, E., 357
Brolley, J. E., 127
Brooks, F., 342
Brooks, F. D., 110, 162, 165
Browder, F. A., 468
Brown, D. E., 302
Brown, F., 76
Brown, F. H., 164
Brown, L. M., 464
Brown, R. D., 466
Brown, S. C., 358, 359
Brownell, G. L., 356, 358, 360, 389, 462

Brubaker, W. M., 304
Brucer, M., 462
Brucker, G. J., 163
Brues, A. M., 445
Buck, W. L., 107, 110, 112, 113, 123
Buckley, H. E., 161
Buneman, O., 51, 52, 53, 54
Burch, D. S., 19
Burch, P. R. J., 464
Burhop, E. H. S., 21, 80
Burtt, B. P., 356
Button, J., 151

Caldecourt, V. J., 303
Callihan, D., 462
Campbell, E. E., 464
Campbell, H. A., 463
Campbell, N. R., 239
Campion, P. J., 360
Cantril, S. T., 459, 460
Carlson, R. R., 162
Carswell, D. J., 360
Carter, M. W., 465
Carter, R. E., 389
Cassidy, J., 359
Cathey, L., 136
Cavallo, L., 357
Cember, H., 445
Cerenkov, P. A., 166
Chalmers, J. A., 355
Chamberlain, O., 179, 181
Chanin, L. M., 19
Chase, R. L., 304
Cheka, J. S., 163, 429
Chiang, R. S., 333
Chiozzoto, M., 358
Chleck, D. J., 120
Christenson, C. W., 467, 468
Christian, D., 356
Chu, K. Y., 358
Clark, D. D., 6, 7
Clark, G. W., 162
Clark, R. A., 357
Cleland, M. R., 162
Clifford, J., 462
Cobble, J. W., 360
Cochran, L. W., 14, 377
Cockcroft, A. L., 7, 8, 47, 68, 72, 76, 390
Colby, L. J., Jr., 360

Colli, L., 79
Collie, C. H., 45, 55, 80, 356
Comar, C. L., 357
Conger, A. D., 374
Conte, F. P., 390
Conway, D. C., 360
Cook, G. B., 333, 356
Cook, M. J., 464
Coon, J. H., 41, 80
Coryell, C. D., 356, 357, 358
Cottini, C., 304, 305
Cowan, C. L., 162, 163, 164
Cowan, F. C., 464
Cowing, R. F., 356
Cowser, K. E., 465, 469
Cox, E. J., 469
Craggs, J. D., 18
Cranshaw, T. E., 51, 52, 53, 54
Craven, J. H., 357
Crawford, J. A., 45, 359
Creutz, E., 164
Croall, I. F., 357
Crompton, R. W., 26, 27
Crossley, D. A., Jr., 465
Crouthamel, C. E., 162, 359, 360
Crowell, J., 468
Culler, F. L., Jr., 465
Cuninghame, J. G., 357
Cunningham, B. B., 359
Curran, S. C., 7, 8, 10, 15, 46, 47, 68, 69, 70, 72, 74, 76, 77, 107, 390
Curtis, H. L., 222, 223, 224, 227
Curtis, M. L., 360
Curtis, R. L., 469
Curtiss, L. F., 461
Czyzak, S. J., 162

Dainty, J., 390
Davidson, J. D., 360
Davis, D. M., 462
Davis, R. C., 142, 151, 153, 342, 345, 351, 352
Davis, R. H., 163, 462
Davis, T. F., 468
Davis, W. J., 358, 359, 389
Davisson, C. M., 359, 371
Dawson, J. K., 50, 81
Day, F. H., 436, 462
Deal, L. J., 462
DeAmisis, E., 356

De Benedetti, S., 77
DeCroës, M., 360
de Laguna, W., 465, 469
den Hartog, H., 303
Dennis, R., 465
der Mateosian, E., 359
Deutsch, M., 356, 358
Dicke, R. H., 193
Dietrich, J. R., 461
Dike, R. S., 461
Doehring, A., 19
Dohne, C. F., 124
Donaldson, H. M., Jr., 466
Douglas, R. A., 162
Doyle, H. N., 469
Dreven, R. W. P., 76
Drinker, P., 466
Duffenback, O. S., 356
Duncan, J. F., 333, 356
Dunning, G. M., 462
Dunning, W. W., 356
Dunster, H. J., 469
Dunworth, J. V., 358
du Toit, S., 79

Eastwood, E. R., 466, 468
Eby, F., 99, 100, 165
Eggler, C., 129, 359
Ehrlich, Margarete, 381, 382
Eidinoff, M. L., 358
Einbinder, H., 165
Eisberg, R. M., 6, 7
Eklund, S., 356
Elder, F. R., 80
Eliassen, R., 466
Elioff, T., 162
Ellett, W. H., 360
Elliot, J. O., 110
Elliott, N., 356
Elmore, W. C., 304
Emerson, L. C., 462
Emmons, A. H., 466
Empson, F. M., 468, 469
Engelkemeir, A. G., 358
Engelkemeir, D. W., 97, 305, 356, 357, 358, 359
English, W. N., 20, 25, 26, 27, 59
Engstrom, R. W., 137
Enz, H., 162
Erskine, G. A., 16

Estabrook, G. M., 165
Estes, H. D., 333
Ettinger, M. B., 468
Eutsler, B. C., 464
Evans, R. D., 359, 360, 371, 462, 463

Facchini, U., 20, 51
Failla, G., 78, 357, 378
Fairstein, E., 304, 305
Fano, U., 7, 8, 69, 70, 288, 389
Farabee, L. B., 464
Farmer, E. C., 163, 359
Feige, Y., 469
Feigelson, P., 360
Feitelberg, S., 467
Field, R. F., 222, 224, 227
Filosofo, I., 183
Fineman, P., 467
Finkel, Miriam P., 465
Finney, G. D., 360
Fisher, I., 464
Fitch, S. H., 389
Fitch, V., 174, 186
Fleishman, H., 165
Flügge, S., 164
Flynn, K. F., 359, 360
Fontana, B. J., 358
Ford, M. R., 401, 462
Forro, M., 358
Forstat, H., 78
Fowler, I. I., 61
Francis, J. E., 163
Francis, V. J., 302
Franck, J., 109
Frank, I., 192
Franzen, W., 40, 41, 44, 45, 60, 61, 163, 377
Fraser, C. D., 467
Fraser, J. S., 149
Freedman, M. S., 358, 359
Fresco, J., 464
Freund, L., 392
Fried, S., 311
Friedman, A. J., 333
Frisch, D., 173, 178, 179
Frisch, O. R., 70
Fulbright, H. W., 53, 63, 77
Fulmer, C. B., 163
Funt, B. L., 164, 165, 358
Furst, M., 110, 121, 358

Gabbard, F., 163
Gadsen, C. P., 305
Gale, H. J., 356
Gallaghar, R. G., 469
Gardiner, E. W., 8
Garlick, G. F. J., 92
Garner, J. M., Jr., 466
Gatti, E., 51, 304, 305
Geballe, R., 18, 19
Gemmell, Lee, 466
Getting, I. A., 176, 186, 192
Ghiorso, A., 359
Gianelli, G., 305
Gibbs, D. S., 57
Gibson, G. E., 8
Giles, N. H., Jr., 374
Gillespie, A. B., 44, 45, 304, 305
Gillette, R. H., 87
Gilmartin, T. H., 303
Ginther, J., 165
Ginzton, E. L., 304
Glass, F. M., 63, 303, 390
Glasser, Otto, 375, 388, 390
Gleason, G. I., 356
Glendenin, L. E., 356, 359, 360
Glenn, W. E., Jr., 247
Glover, A. M., 162
Glueckauf, E., 466
Goldin, A., 466
Goldman, M. I., 468
Goodman, C., 163, 360
Gora, E. K., 357
Gorman, A. E., 466, 468
Gould, R. G., 357, 359
Govaerts, J., 357
Graf, W. L., 357
Grashem, W. E., 360
Graves, E. R., 64
Gray, J. A., 355
Gray, L. H., 8, 12, 377
Greene, L. C., 88
Grenchik, R., 303, 357
Grimeland, B., 360
Gross, W., 78
Grubbé, E. H., 392
Grucci, T. B., 465
Grummitt, W. E., 355
Gueben, G., 357
Gunnink, R., 360
Gunter, B., 468

Gupton, E. D., 462
Gurney, R. W., 8, 12, 15
Gursky, J. M., 125, 131

Haasbroek, F. J., 360
Haenny, C., 357
Hafstad, L. R., 202, 206, 208
Hahn, B., 163
Hahn, R. B., 467
Haissinsky, M., 357
Halban, H. H., 45, 55, 59, 60
Hall, G. R., 360
Hall, T., 77
Hall, T. A., 39, 45, 61
Halpern, J., 40, 165
Ham, W. T., 389
Hammel, J. E., 164
Handley, T. H., 360
Hanna, G. C., 7, 8, 25, 26, 27, 45, 51,
    63, 70, 71, 72, 76
Hanson, H. G., 104
Hardy, E., 464
Hardy, J. E., 163
Harrington, R. E., 57
Harris, C. C., 142
Harris, P. S., 389
Harris, W. B., 469
Harrison, F. B., 150, 162, 358
Harrison, M. A., 18, 19
Hart, J. C., 462
Harter, J. A., 390, 462
Harvey, J. A., 51, 52, 53, 54
Harvey, R. A., 389
Harward, E. D., 468
Hawkins, R. C., 358
Hayes, F. N., 122, 123, 355, 358, 359,
    360
Hayner, J. H., 468
Hazen, W. E., 32
Head, B. M., 464
Healey, R. H., 18, 19, 26, 30, 390
Healy, J. W., 356, 464
Heath, R. L., 152, 154, 359, 360
Hedgram, A., 79
Heiberg, E., 192
Heitler, W., 389
Helf, S., 358
Hemphill, L., 468, 469
Henderson, W. T., 389
Hendricks, R. H., 357

Henriques, F. C., 357
Hensley, P. N., 390, 462
Hermann, E. R., 468
Herreng, P., 19
Herwig, L. O., 55
Hess, W. N., 173
Hewitt, M. A., 356
Hickey, F. C., 357
Hiebert, R. D., 359
Higinbotham, W. A., 304
Hine, G. J., 389, 462
Hinrichs, H., 116
Hoagland, E. J., 358
Hoffman, J. G., 461
Hofstadter, R., 163, 165, 183, 184, 359,
    390
Hollander, J. M., 345
Hollis, M. D., 468
Hoover, J. I., 124
Hornyak, W. F., 158, 159
Horrocks, D. L., 360
Houtermans, F. G., 357
Hubbard, T. N., Jr., 468
Hubbell, J. H., 163
Hubble, H. H., Jr., 163
Huber, P., 15, 41
Huddleston, C. M., 129, 359
Hughes, V., 162
Hultqvist, B., 392, 465
Hume, D. N., 333
Hunter, R. F., 358
Hurley, P. M., 360
Hursh, J. B., 391, 464
Hurst, G. S., 15, 16, 17, 19, 25, 26, 27,
    28, 375, 390, 430, 434
Hurst, R., 360
Huston, J., 357
Hutchens, T. T., 359
Huxley, L. H. G., 28

Igo, G. J., 6, 7
Ingram, W. M., 468
Insch, G. M., 72, 77
Irvine, J. W., Jr., 107, 109, 110, 118
Ishawari, R., 78

Jack, W., 164
Jackson, Jean A., 464
Jacobs, D. G., 469
Jacobs, J. A., 162

Jaeger, J. C., 304
Jaeger, R. F., 466
Jaffe, G., 22
Jaffe, I., 358
Jaffey, A. H., 356, 359, 362
Jannay, C. D., 358
Jastrow, R., 342
Jelley, J. V., 167, 176, 177, 186, 189
Jensen, J. H., 468
Jentschke, W., 45, 99, 100
Jesse, W. P., 11, 13, 14, 15, 16, 358, 460
Johnson, C. E., 359
Johnson, C. H., 148
Johnson, E. F., 463
Johnson, J. B., 304
Johnson, P. D., 163
Johnsrud, A. E., 164
Johnston, F., 356
Johnston, L. W., 114
Johnston, R. W., 258
Jones, H., 459
Jones, J. W., 359
Jones, M. D., 163
Jordan, W. H., 304, 390
Jorgenson, T., 64
Joseph, A., 469
Junkins, R. L., 460
Justus, K. M., 356

Kageyama, S., 7
Kahn, B., 359, 360, 466, 468
Kalil, F., 466
Kalkstein, M. I., 345, 355
Kallman, H., 110, 121, 124, 358
Kallman, M., 358
Kalmon, B., 356
Kandiah, K., 302, 304
Kanner, M., 41
Kantz, A., 184
Kaplan, S., 192
Katz, J. J., 356, 359
Katz, L., 318
Kaye, G. W. C., 460
Keeley, T. C., 302
Keepin, G. R., 164
Keevil, N. B., 360
Kegel, G. H. R., 162
Kelley, G. G., 144, 162, 248, 359
Kelvin, P. B., 469

Kephart, J. F., 164
Kern, B. D., 148, 149, 160
Kerr, V. N., 163
Kerst, D. W., 389
Ketelle, B. H., 358
Khym, J. X., 464
Kimura, K., 78
Kimura, S., 78
King, R. W., 80
King, W. C., 466
Kinsey, B. B., 181, 182, 189
Kinsman, S., 466
Kirkbride, J., 124
Kirkpatrick, C. B., 19
Kirkwood, D. H. W., 8, 70, 71, 72
Kirshner, J. M., 79
Kittel, C., 163
Kittrell, F. W., 466
Klema, E. D., 56, 58, 60
Knipp, J. K., 9, 14
Knoepfel, H., 95, 163
Koch, H. W., 304, 375
Koch, L., 125
Kohman, T. P., 365
Kohr, K. C., 468
Koontz, P. G., 39, 45, 61, 164
Koshland, M. E., 464
Koski, W. S., 358
Kovarik, A. F., 309, 314
Kramers, H. A., 77
Kreger, W. E., 148, 149, 160
Krenz, E. H., 110
Kretchmar, A. L., 462
Krieger, H. L., 468
Kruger, P. G., 165
Kruse, H. W., 162
Kwasnoski, T., 464
Kyropoulos, S. Z., 85

Lackey, J. B., 466
Lacy, W. J., 466, 468
Landau, L. D., 5
Landsverk, O. G., 433
Langevin-Joliot, H., 77
Langevin, M., 76
Langevin, P., 22
Langford-Smith, F., 305
Langham, W. H., 358, 389
Lapointe, J. R., 466
Larson, F. C., 360

Larson, K. H., 469
Lassen, N. O., 78
Lauderdale, R. A., 466, 468
Laughlin, J. S., 389
Lauritsen, C. C., 433
Lazar, N. H., 154, 162, 342, 345, 351, 352
Leachman, R. B., 14, 77
Leboeuf, M. B., 359
Lee, D. D., 357
Lee, W., 360
Leidt, Sarah C., 464
Leipuner, L., 81
Leisengang, S., 5
Lerch, P., 320
Le Roy, G. M., 469
Lesueur, R., 125
Levy, H. A., 396
Lewis, G. M., 359
Lewis, I. A. D., 304
Libby, W. F., 324, 355, 358, 360
Lieberman, J. A., 466
Liebner, J. J., 464
Liebson, S. H., 110, 162
Lindemann, A. F., 200, 201
Lindemann, F. A., 200, 201
Lindemann, W. W., 305
Ling, R. C., 9, 14
Lisco, H., 445
Livingston, R., 109
Lockhart, H. S., 358
Loeb, L. B., 24
Loepfe, E., 163, 164
Long, J. V. F., 358, 359
Lorenz, E., 414
Love, S. K., 468
Love, T. A., 165
Lowe, H. N., 466
Lowry, R. A., 14
Lyon, W. S., 359, 360

Macdonald, P. A., 303
Macklin, R. L., 362
Macnee, A. B., 305
Madsen, B. S., 14
Maeder, D., 163, 258
Magnusson, L. B., 305
Maienschein, F. C., 162, 164
Malmberg, P. R., 165
Malvicini, A., 20

Mandleberg, C. J., 50
Manley, J. H., 63, 64
Mann, W. B., 357, 358, 359
Manning, J. J., 139
Manning, W. W., 359
Manov, G. G., 311
Marinelli, L. D., 377, 388, 461, 464
Markus, J., 304
Marshall, J., 167, 173, 175, 176, 177, 178, 186, 188, 189, 191, 192
Martell, E. A., 464
Martin, D. S., Jr., 356
Masket, A. V. H., 362
Massey, H. S. W., 21
Mather, R. L., 166
Matheson, R. M., 305
Mathews, E. R., 468
Mawson, C. A., 464
Maxwell, J. C., 52
May, J., 359
Mayneord, W. V., 388
McCauley, R. F., 466
McClelland, J., 355, 464
McCullough, G. E., 468
McCutchen, C. W., 19
McGuire, A. D., 162
McIntyre, J. A., 163, 359, 390
McLendon, J. D., 462
McMahon, J. P., 360
Mealey, J., 358
Meem, J. L., 390
Melton, C. E., 16
Mendell, J. S., 459
Merritt, W. F., 357
Metcalf, G. E., 303
Meyer, A., 164
Meyer-Schütsmeister, L., 357
Michel, W. S., 358
Mikiewicz, E., 162
Miller, D. E., 359
Miller, G. H., 14, 55
Miller, J. M., 290
Miller, W. W., 358
Milligan, M. F., 464
Millman, J., 305
Mills, W. A., 389, 390, 462
Milsted, J., 50, 357, 360
Milton, J. C. D., 55, 149
Mitchell, A. C. G., 360

Miyake, K., 78
Moe, H. J., 17
Moeller, D. W., 468
Moljk, A., 76
Montague, J. H., 77
Moody, N. F., 213
Moore, H. B., 163
Morgan, K. Z., 401, 423, 461
Morrison, P., 389
Morton, R. J., 465, 467, 468, 469
Motley, R., 193
Mott, W. E., 139
Moyal, J. E., 5
Moyer, B. J., 183, 358
Muehlhause, C. O., 124
Muirhead, E. G., 165
Mulholland, G. I., 355
Müller, A., 15
Muller, F. A., 303
Muller, R. H., 356
Murray, R. B., 139, 163, 164
Myers, L. S., Jr., 464
Myers, O. H., 468

Neel, J. W., 469
Neher, H. V., 302
Nehls, J. W., 360
Nergaard, L. S., 305
Nervik, W. E., 357
Neufeld, J., 461
Newell, J. F., 467, 468
Newton, A. S., 58, 59, 358
Newton, J. O., 50, 70, 72
Nicholson, K. P., 164
Nielsen, C. E., 303
Nielsen, J. M., 360
Nielsen, O. B., 360
Nielsen, R. A., 25, 26, 28
Nishimura, K., 7
Nobles, R., 173
Nobles, R. A., 125, 126, 129, 130
Nogami, H. H., 360
Norris, F. I., 468
Norris, T. H., 357
Norris, W. P., 464
North, D. O., 305
Northrop, J. A., 125, 126, 127, 129,
  130, 131, 132
Norton, F. J., 303

Novey, T. B., 356
Nyquist, H., 305

O'Donnell, T. J., 302
Ophel, I. L., 467
Ophel, T. R., 164
Oppenheimer, J. R., 77
Orndoff, J. D., 461
Ott, D. G., 120, 163
Overman, R. T., 359
Owen, G., 165
Owen, R. B., 464

Page, L., 303, 304
Paine, R. W., Jr., 461
Palevsky, H., 221, 358
Palmer, H. L., 162
Pappas, A. C., 314
Parker, F. L., 465, 467, 468, 469
Parker, H. M., 459, 460
Parker, W., 327
Parkinson, G. B., 358
Parsons, J. H., 359
Pate, B. D., 326, 327
Pecjak, F. A., 165
Peelle, R. W., 163, 165
Pelchowitch, I., 303
Penick, D. B., 209
Perey, M., 357
Perkins, R. W., 360
Peterson, P., 35, 37
Placak, O. R., 467
Plough, H. H., 461
Pontecorvo, B., 7, 8, 70, 71, 72, 76
Povelites, J. G., 327
Powell, C. C., 467
Praglin, J., 303
Prescott, J. R., 303
Prestwood, R. J., 321
Price, W. J., 164
Pringle, R. W., 120, 165
Proctor, W., 41
Pullman, B., 357
Putman, J. L., 355, 356

Querzoli, R., 358
Quimby, Edith H., 375, 388

Raben, M. D., 359
Raboy, S., 360

Randall, J. T., 164
Rasmussen, J. O., 360
Ravilious, C. F., 162
Reed, J. W., 18, 26, 30, 390
Reid, A. F., 357
Reid, D. L., 464
Reiffel, L., 163
Reines, F., 162, 163, 164
Reinhardt, P. W., 390, 464
Remley, M. E., 165
Renard, G. A., 77
Renn, C. E., 469
Reynolds, D. C., 163
Reynolds, G. T., 358
Rhoads, W. A., 469
Rhodes, J., 41
Ribe, F. L., 77, 160
Ritchie, R. H., 390, 462, 463
Ritsma, R. J., 221
Robbins, M. C., 464
Robeck, G., 468
Roberson, J., 462
Roberts, J. D., 358
Rodger, W. A., 467
Rogers, B. S., 163, 358
Romney, E. M., 454
Ronzio, A. R., 164
Rose, B., 50, 70, 72
Rose, J. E., 426
Rosen, F. D., 358
Rosenzweig, W., 385
Rossel, J., 93, 95, 96, 162, 163
Rossi, B., 5, 6, 23, 26, 27, 32, 41, 42, 60
Rossi, H. H., 378, 385
Rothwell, P., 5, 7, 50, 72, 74, 75
Rouster, G. W., Jr., 464
Rozzi, G., 305
Rubinson, W., 356
Ruchhoft, C. C., 467, 468
Rudd, J. B., 26
Rundo, J., 464
Russ, S., 393
Russell, L. B., 414
Russell, W. L., 414

Sachs, Frances, 465
Sadauskis, J., 11, 14, 15, 16
Sahwendiman, L. C., 464
Salmon, L., 359
Salvani, G., 358

Samples, W. R., 465
Sanders, S. M., Jr., 464
Sands, M., 304
Sangster, R. C., 107, 109, 110, 118
Saunders, B. G., 163
Saunders, P. C., 163
Saunderson, J. L., 356
Sayres, A., 126, 127, 128, 129, 130, 132
Schaetti, N., 165
Scharenberg, R. P., 162
Schenck, J., 101, 156
Scherb, F., 162
Scherbatskoy, S. A., 303
Schmidt, C. T., 164
Schmidt, H. W., 355
Schmitt, H. W., 14, 164, 362
Schonland, B. F. J., 355
Schorr, M. G., 358
Schottky, W., 305
Schroeder, F., 359
Schubert, J., 357, 464
Schuh, R. L., 359
Schumann, R. W., 360
Schwebel, A., 328
Schweber, S. S., 77
Schweitzer, G. K., 357, 360
Schwendiman, L. C., 356
Scofield, N. E., 163
Scott, N. S., 392
Seaborg, G. T., 356, 359
Segre, E., 77, 162, 179, 193
Seliger, H. H., 121, 317, 328, 358, 359
Senn, N., 392
Setter, L. R., 467, 468
Sevier, K. J., 360
Shaler, W. J., 165
Shannon, R. L., 467
Shapiro, E., 356
Sharpe, J., 165, 359
Shaw, P. F. D., 356
Sheline, R. K., 360
Sherr, R., 35, 37, 163
Shroeder, F., 345
Siegbahn, K., 79, 360
Sievert, R. M., 465
Silverman, L., 465
Sinason, H., 360
Sinclair, W. K., 388
Sitterson, B. W., 462

Sizeland, M. L., 357
Skinker, M. F., 26
Skyrme, T. H. R., 50
Slater, M., 390, 462
Slätis, H., 327
Smaller, B., 359
Smith, A., 359
Smith, C. C., 358
Smith, D. B., 357
Smith, F. W., 162
Smith, W. B., 162
Snelling, G. F., 164
Snyder, H. S., 67
Snyder, W. S., 375, 388, 390, 401, 461
Sobering, S., 164
Solomon, A. K., 333, 356, 357
Sommer, A. H., 139
Spencer, L. V., 377
Spitzer, A. A., 465
Stafford, G. H., 59, 359
Stang, L. G., Jr., 460
Staub, H., 26, 27
Stearns, M., 81
Stearns, M. B., 81
Stebler, E., 78
Stein, B. R., 357, 360
Steinberg, E. P., 359, 360
Steiner, H. M., 162
Stephens, W. E., 40, 41
Sternheimer, R. M., 461
Stetter, G., 8, 13, 45
Stetter, W., 50
Stevenson, P. C., 357
Stewart, E. C., 164
Steyn, J., 334, 358, 360
Stockbarger, D. C., 85
Stockendal, R., 360
Stoll, P., 163, 164
Stone, R., 459
Stone, W. G., 14, 25, 26, 27, 28
Stoppani, A. D. M., 357
Storey, R. S., 101
Stoudenheimer, R. G., 162
Straub, C. P., 467, 468
Strickler, T. D., 17
Strong, J., 302
Struxness, E. G., 467, 468, 469
Studier, M. H., 360
Surkiewicz, B. F., 466
Sugarman, N., 356, 357, 358

Sugihara, T. T., 360
Sun, K. H., 165
Suttle, A. D., 324
Sutton, D. J., 26, 27
Sutton, R. B., 139
Svec, H. J., 57
Swank, R. K., 107, 110, 112, 113, 122, 123, 303, 358, 359
Swartz, C. E., 183
Swartz, C. D., 157, 158
Swift, G., 303
Symon, K. R., 5

Tabern, D. L., 356
Tamm, I., 192
Tamura, T., 469
Taplin, G. V., 376
Taub, H., 305
Taylor, C. J., 113, 114
Taylor, J. D., 356
Taylor, L. S., 375, 388, 460
Terentiuk, F., 358
Terrill, J. G., 468
Thomas, G. E., Jr., 124, 143, 155
Thomas, J. T., 462
Thomas, L. H., 77
Thompson, B. J., 303
Thompson, J. S., 357
Thomson, J. J., 22
Thorburn, R. C., 356
Thornburn, R., 78
Thorndike, E. H., 165
Tizard, H. T., 28
Tobias, C. A., 356
Tochlin, E., 462
Toffolo, D. S., 79
Tompkins, P. C., 464
Torney, F. L., 358
Townsend, J. S., 25, 26, 28
Tozer, B. A., 18
Trail, C. C., 148, 360
Tribondeau, L., 392
Trojanowski, M. M., 464
Trout, E. D., 389
Tsivoglou, E. C., 468
Tunnicliffe, P. R., 13, 50, 61
Tyndall, A. M., 24

Upton, A. C., 390
Utterback, N. H., 55

Valentine, J. M., 10, 11, 15
Valley, G. E., Jr., 303, 304, 305
van der Ziel, A., 305
Van Heerden, P. J., 303
Van Rennes, A. B., 304
Van Sciver, W. J., 90, 95, 103, 104
van Zelst, J. J. Z., 303
Villaire, A. E., 127
Vincent, D. H., 357
Vogdes, F. B., 80
von Laue, M., 52
von Perthes, G., 392
Voress, H. E., 468

Wagner, E. B., 390
Wagner, P. B., 356
Waldman, B., 64
Wallace, R., 183
Wallman, H., 303, 304, 305
Walton, G. N., 318, 320, 333
Wang, T. J., 377
Ward, A., 13, 50
Ward, A. G., 78, 80
Watson, J. A., 465
Watts, H. V., 163
Weatherwax, J. L., 375, 388
Webster, W., 392
Weigl, J. W., 357
Weingart, R., 162
Weiss, J., 464
Welford, G., 464
Wells, F. H., 304
West, D., 50, 70, 72, 73, 74, 75, 77
Whetstone, A., 142, 144, 146, 147
White, C. G., 358
Whitmore, B. G., 389
Whitney, I. B., 357
Whitson, T. C., 464
Wick, A. N., 357
Wiedenbeck, M. L., 358
Wiegand, C., 162, 179, 181
Wilkins, M. H. F., 164
Wilkinson, D. H., 22, 24, 305

Willard, J. E., 333, 356
Williams, E. J., 15, 16
Williams, F. E., 92, 163
Williams, R. W., 32
Willis, H. H., 357
Wilsey, R. B., 462
Wilson, H. N., 463
Wilson, H. W., 76
Wilson, R. S., 45, 47, 55, 59, 61, 63
Wilson, W., 355
Wingate, C., 78
Witkowski, E. J., 465
Wold, 303
Wolfgang, R. L., 360
Wolicki, E. A., 342
Wollan, E. O., 433
Wood, D. P., 461
Wouters, L. F., 107, 127, 150
Wright, G. T., 115, 116, 144
Wright, P. W., 360
Wu, C. S., 126, 127, 128, 129, 130, 132
Wynn-Williams, C. E., 303

Yaffe, L., 76, 326, 327
Yamagata, T., 183
Yamashita, S., 78
Yankwich, P. E., 357
Yockey, H. P., 459
Ypsilantis, T., 162, 193
Yuasa, K., 78

Zaazou, A. A., 79
Zappa, L., 70, 144
Zavon, M. R., 469
Zedler, R. E., 390
Zeluff, V., 304
Zerby, C. D., 145
Ziegler, C. A., 120, 121, 358
Zipprich, B., 302
Zirkle, R. E., 388
Zobel, W., 165
Zumwalt, L. R., 313, 314, 317

SUBJECT INDEX

Aberrations, in Cerenkov counters, 187
Accidents, radiation, 405
Activation, alkali halide crystals, 86, 90, 91
Activator concentration, in scintillators, 99 ff
Afterglow, 92
Agitation velocity, electron, 18, 24
Air, electron drift velocity in, 28–29
Air flow in hoods; air filters, 402, 403, 439, 452
Alpha counting, 335–339
   beta pulse pile-up, 338
   effects of scattering and absorption, 336, 337
   geometry factor, 336
   relative and absolute, 339
   resolution losses, 339
   use of standards, 339
αNPO (2-(1-naphthyl)-5-phenyloxazole), 121, 127
Amplification factor, 204, 279, 282
Amplifiers, pulse, 234 ff
   effect of response upon pulse shape, 43–45
   linearity, 237, 294 ff
   time constants, 44, 238, 379
Angular distribution of neutron recoils, 41–43
Anthracene, 107, 108, 109, 110, 111, 113, 114, 115, 116, 121
   as fast-neutron counter, 157
   gamma-ray discrimination, 160
   scintillation characteristics, 117
Anticoincidence discrimination, in proportional counters, 50–51
   in scintillation counters, 151–153, 355
Anticoincidence shielding, 308, 443
Argon, as gas scintillator, 125, 127, 130
   electron mobility, 25
   mixtures with other gases in ionization chambers, 16
   purification, 56–58, 126
   use in ionization chambers, 13
   use in proportional counters, 73–76
Attachment, electron, 17–20, 379

Background, ionizing radiation, 391, 392
Background counting rate, 307–308
   in coincidence counting, 331
   in scintillation counting, 333
Backscattering, 45, 56, 375
   in alpha counting, 336
   in beta counting, 315, 323, 324
Badge meter, 427 ff
BBO(2,5-di-(4-biphenyl)-oxazole), 123
Beta counters, 323–329
   end-window, 308, 310
   Geiger-Müller and proportional, 308
   screen-wall, 324–325
   2π, 323
   4π, 325–328
Beta-particle counting, 308 ff
   absolute, 320
   absorption and scattering, 309
      by air and counter window, 313
      by housing of counter, 317
      by sample covering, 314
   counting yield, 309
   detection probability, 310
   effect of backscattering, 315, 324
   effect of forescattering, 314
   effects of self-absorption and self-scattering, 317, 322
   external gas, 329
   geometrical factor, 311, 362
   internal gas, 328
   liquid sample, 333
   relative, 307, 323
   scintillation, 333
   2π, 323
   4π, 325, 334
Biological half-life, 419
Blocking, 259
Body burden of radionuclides, maximum permissible, 417–420
Bootstrap circuit, 213, 297
Boron trifluoride, electron attachment, 60
   electron drift velocity, 27
   proportional counter, 388
   purification, 60–61

Bragg-Gray cavity; ionization chamber, 28, 378
Bragg-Gray principle, 377, 434
Bridgman method, crystal growth, 85 ff
Buildup factor, 375

Cable, noise, 213
  delay line, 251
  shielding, 264
Cadmium sulfide, 87
Cadmium tungstate, 87
  scintillation characteristics, 106
Calcium tungstate, 87
Calcium turnings, use in purifiers, 56–57
Calibration, of gamma counters, 340
  of gamma-ray scintillation counters, 350, 353
  of proportional counters, 72
  of radiation instruments, 437
Calorimetric measurements of radiation, 376
Campbell's theorem of the mean, 239
  of the mean square, 198, 239, 244
Capture, electron, by atoms and molecules, 18–21, see Attachment
Carbon-CO_2 ionization chamber, 378
Carbon dioxide, electron drift velocity, 26–27
  purification, 60
  recombination, 23
Cascode circuit, 290
Cathode follower, 212, 213, 290
Cathode-interface formation, 289
Cerenkov angle, 167–168
Cerenkov counters, focusing, 175 ff, 186
  nonfocusing, 171 ff
Cerenkov radiation, characteristics, 167
  efficiency and resolution of counting methods, 184
Cesium fluoride, 93
  scintillation characteristics, 105
Cesium iodide, pure, 83, 93
  scintillation characteristics, 102
  temperature dependence of luminescence, 95
Cesium iodide, thallium activated, 93, 95
  response to charged particles, 98
  scintillation characteristics, 102

Cesium iodide, thallium activated, scintillation efficiency, 99
  temperature dependence of luminescence, 95
  use for charged-particle detection, 146–147, 150
Chain reactions, in chemical dosimetry, 376
Chamber, ionization, see Ionization chambers
Chamberlain-Wiegand counter, 179
Chang and Eng, 435
Charged particles, discrimination of, in scintillators, 129, 150
  ionization by, 7 ff
  maximum permissible flux for occupational exposure, 409
  response of scintillators to, 97 ff, 113 ff, 116, 121, 129, 145 ff
Circuits, input, for pulse amplifiers, 290
Clamp circuit, 260, 261
Clipping, 241 ff
  delay-line, 249
  double, 244, 245, 246, 258, 259, 261
  RC, 242
Clothing, protective, 403, 404
  decontamination of, 448
Coincidence counting, dead-time losses in, 332
  radioactive assay by, 329–333
  with complex decay schemes, 332
  with internal conversion of gamma ray, 331
Collection time, electrons in ionization chamber, 30, 32, 33, 380
Compton scattering, 73, 74, 369, 385
  contribution in scintillation spectra, 154, 353
  cross sections for, 371
  in proportional counter, 73
  use in scintillation spectrometer, 153
Concentration, maximum permissible (MPC) of radionuclides in body, 416–418, 420, 451
  of radionuclides in air, 453
  of radionuclides in water, 452
Conversion efficiency, of photocathode, 133, 139, 184
Conversion factor, neutron dose to rad units, 384

Conversion factors in amplifier theory,
average to rms, 291–292
cycles to radians, 266
equivalent noise charge to equivalent
electrons, 288
mean-squared noise voltage to mean-
squared noise charge, 265
rms deviation to fractional width at
half maximum, 237, 238
rms deviation to "resolution," 237,
238
transconductance to equivalent noise
resistance, 271
Correction factors, escape peak, 353
in alpha counting, 336
in beta counting, 307, 313–322
in coincidence counting, 332
in internal gas counting, 328
in 2π counting, 323
in 4π counting, 326
Cosmic rays, detection by scintillation
counters, 150
dosage variation, 391
in background counting rates, 307–
308
Counters, Cerenkov, 170 ff
Chamberlain-Weigand, 179
Fitch, 174
focusing, 175, 186
Frisch, 178
Getting-Jelley, 176
Kinsey, 181
Marshall, 177
nonfocusing, 171
total photon absorption, 182
end-window, 308, 309
Geiger-Müller, 308, 387, 433
hand-and-foot, 432
proportional, 64 ff, see also Proportional counters
scintillation, 82 ff, 432, 433, 435–437,
442
"standard," for fast-neutron dosimetry, 380, 381
total body, 443–444
2π, 323
4π, 325, 334
Counting rooms, 399–401
Counting yield, 309
Critical body organ, 418, 420, 421

Crossover point, see Floating-grid potential
Cross section, Compton, 371
differential, for neutron scattering, 43
electron capture, 9, 18, 19; see also
Attachment
electron loss, 9
Current measurement, in ionization
chambers, IR drop, 195, 196
loss-of-charge (or rate-of-drift),
195, 197, 219
statistical fluctuations (noise), 197,
202, 213, 220
Current pulse, ionization chamber, 17,
36
scintillation counter, 93, 94, 132
Cyclopropane, electron drift velocity,
27–28
purification, 60
Cylindrical boundary, ionization
chamber, 50

Damage factor, relative, for radiations
in the body, 419
Dead-time loss, 364
Decay time, amplifier pulse, see Fall
time
in scintillators, 84, 93, 95, 96, 100,
101 ff, 110, 111, 113, 117, 118,
122, 129
Decontamination, clothing, 404, 448,
449
hand, 446, 447, 448
kit, 448
laundry, 404
laundry procedures, 447–449
Delay cables, 251
Depth dose, calculations and measurements, 375
Detector characteristics; counter, chamber, and scintillation compared,
235
Deuterium, purification of, 58–60
used in high pressure chamber, 55
Differentiating network, 241
Diffusion of electrons, 29–30
in grid ionization chambers, 55
Discriminator, differential, 237, 300
pulse height selector, 76, 236, 292

Disintegration rates, absolute, 309
  in α counting, 339
  in β counting, 320, 321
  in γ counting, 345
Dispersion, optical, in Cerenkov counters, 189
Disposal of radioactive waste, 449 ff
Dissociation, molecular, 4
Distribution, angular, for neutron recoils, 41
  isotropic, pulse spectrum, in ionization chamber, 36–39
Dose, buildup factor, 375
  first collision, 370 ff
  gram-rad, 415
  maximum permissible to body organs, 410
  multicollision, 374
  variation with energy of gamma rays and neutrons, 369
Dose measurements, direct, 377 ff
  fast neutron, by threshold detectors, 383
Dose ranges, photographic film, 382
Dosimetry, chemical, 376, 430
  gamma rays and neutrons, 376 ff, 386, 425 ff
  techniques and instruments, 377 ff
  thermal neutrons, 388
Double clipping, see Clipping
DPO (2,5-diphenyloxazole), 121, 123
Dri-film, 227, 229
Drift velocity, electron, 20, 24–29
  ion, 23–24
Dust, radioactive, 403, 444
Duty cycle, in pulse amplifier, 244, 261

Ecology and waste disposal, 450
Ehrlich-Fitch film dosimeter, 382
Electric field, about grid wire, 52
  in parallel-plate, cylindrical and spherical chambers, 32
  penetration through grid, 53
  spatial limitation by guard electrodes, 46
  work done by, in ionization chamber, 31
  in proportional counter, 64
Electrometer circuits, Barth-Penick, 209

Electrometer circuits, drift, 200, 202, 205, 206, 207, 212, 217, 218
  feedback, 210 ff, 213, 219, 230, 231
  Hafstad, 206
  Moody, 213, 214
  noise, 202, 212, 213, 220, 221
  response time, 197, 212
  vibrating-capacitor (or dynamic condenser), 214, 220
  Wynn-Williams or balanced-bridge, 208
Electrometers, 194 ff
  Hoffman, 200
  Lindemann, 200 ff
  quartz-fiber, 199, 200
  vacuum tube, 202 ff
  vibrating-capacitor, 214
Electron attachment (capture), 18–21, 379
Electron collection, 17–18, 30
  time, 32, 33
Electron diffusion, 29, 55
Electronegative gases, 18–21, 379
Electron motion, in ionization chamber, 24, 30
Electron multiplication, in photomultiplier, 184
Electron temperature, 24
Electroscope, fiber, 433, 435, 437, 458
Emergency, permissible exposure, 413, 414
  precautions, 455–459
Emission spectrum, Cerenkov radiation, 167
  effect of wavelength shifter, 127
  noble gases, 125
  optical, of inorganic scintillators, 102 ff
  organic scintillators, 108, 117 ff
  plastic scintillators, 118
  solvents and solutes, 109 ff
Energy bands, inorganic crystals, 88 ff
Energy imparted by fast neutrons to absorbing medium, 386
Energy levels, organic crystals, 108
Energy loss, of ionizing particle, 4 ff
  of gamma rays and neutrons, 369
  particle, effect upon Cerenkov process, 191

Energy loss distribution, along path of ionizing particle, 5–7
in thin absorbers, 5
Energy per ion pair (W), 8–17, 411
Energy transfer, inorganic scintillators, 99
linear (LET), 369
organic liquids, 119, 333
organic scintillators, 109, 110
plastic scintillators, 110, 113
Epidermal skin thickness, 397
Equivalent circuit of amplifier, 267
Equivalent noise charge, 265
Escape peak, in proportional counters, 74–75
in scintillators, 351, 353
Ethylene, electron drift velocity in, 27, 28
purification, 60
Exciton, 89 ff
Exciton migration, 109
Excretion of radioactive material, 422, 423
Exposure, internal radiation, 416–423
due to Rn^{222} and Ra^{226}, 416–418
measurement, 443, 444
of critical body organs, 418, 420, 421
relation with effective and biological half-lives, 419
relation with maximum permissible body burden, 417–420
relation with maximum permissible concentration (MPC) of radionuclides in body, 416–418, 420, 451
relative damage factor, 419
Exposure, radiation, external and general, 406 ff
emergency, 411, 413, 414
historical, 392, 393, 406–407
internal, see Exposure, internal radiation
occupational and nonoccupational, 424
of special groups, 423 ff
permissible particle fluxes, 408, 409
permissible values, early, 405–408
present, 409–415

Exposure, radiation, records at Hanford and Oak Ridge, 406
to population-at-large, 423–425
Exposure groups, 424
occupational, 408 ff
population-at-large, 424, 425
special, 424

Fall time, amplifier, 238, 379–380
control by clipping, 241 ff
Fano factor, 69–70, 287
Fast-neutron recoils, in ionization chamber, 41
Fast-neutron spectrometry, with scintillators, 147, 157 ff
Fatigue of photomultiplier dynodes, 136
Field tubes, 47, 380; see also Guard electrode
Film, photographic, dose ranges, for various kinds, 382
energy dependence for Ehrlich-Fitch dosimeter, 382
nuclear track, 376, 429
packet, 376
quality dependence, 381
Film meter, badge, 426 ff
ring, 415, 432
Filter, air, 402, 403, 452
First-collision dose, 369, 370, 384
calculation, 370
curve, 372, 382
due to neutrons in soft tissue, 373
due to thermal neutrons, 374
Fission fragments, ionization, 9, 14
range-energy curve from pulse shape, 35, 36
scintillation detection, 149, 150
spectrum in gas scintillator, 128, 129
Fitch counter, 174
Floating-grid potential (or crossover point), 204, 205, 279, 281
Fluctuations, in specific ionization, 5–7, 67–70
in total ionization, 7, 287; see also Noise
Fluorescence, 92, 108, 109
Fluorescence yield in counter gas, 74–75
Fluorochemical FC-75, 171, 173, 179
Fluorothene, use in ionization chambers, 63

Fluxes, maximum permissible, for various particles and radiations, 409
Four-pi counting, 325–328, 334
FP-54, 204, 207
Freon 13, refractive index, 173, 174
Frisch counter, 178

Gamma-ray counting, 340–355
  absolute and relative, 340
  efficiency, 340
  scintillation, 341–355
    Compton distribution, 354, 355
    discrimination against, 160
    intrinsic peak efficiency, 344
    peak-to-total ratio, 151
    pulse-height analysis, 341, 343
    standard sources, 350, 353
    total intrinsic efficiency, 342
Gamma-ray spectrometry, with scintillators, 83, 151 ff, 354
Gas counting, external, 329
  internal, 328
Gases, purification, for ionization chambers, 56
  for scintillation counting, 126
Gases for scintillators, 124 ff
  binary mixtures, 131
  for fission fragment detection, 128
  for neutron detection, 131
  liquified, 132
  purification, 125–127
  wavelength shifters, 127
Gaskets, for ionization chambers, 63
Geiger-Müller counter, 235, 308, 309
  discrimination against fast and thermal neutrons, 387
  gamma-ray efficiency, 340
  use in monitoring instruments, 432, 433, 436, 437, 439
Genetic effects of ionizing radiation, 391, 414
Genetic exposure, permissible, 424, 425
Geometry factor, in alpha counting, 336
  in beta counting, 307, 311
  formula for off-axis point source, disk source, 362–364
Getting counter, 176
Glass, for Cerenkov counters, 182–183
Glass, as insulator, 225, 226

Glass, scintillating, boron or lithium loaded, 156
Glove boxes, 452
Gram-rad dose, 415
Grid current, in electrometer tubes, 202
Grid ionization chambers, 51
Grids, field about wires, 52
  loss of electrons upon, 54
Grid shielding (inefficiency of), 53
Guard electrodes, 46–47, 61, 63, 222
Guard ring, 46, 230, 231

Half-triggering point (HTP), 298, 300
Hands, decontamination of, 446–448
Health physics and the health physicist, 439–442
  duties and objectives, 394, 440, 441
  history, 393
  number required, 440
  training, 440
Helium, as gas scintillator, 125, 129, 130, 131
  as liquid scintillator, 132
  electron mobility, 25–26
  metastable excited state, 16
  purification, 58
  W-value in gas mixtures, 16
High-pressure ionization chambers, 55–56
Hoods, 398, 402, 403, 452
Hornyak button, 158, 159
Hum, 262
Hydrogen, electron drift velocity, 27
  high pressure chamber use, 59
  purification, 58

Index of refraction, glasses of high, 183
  media of low, 171
Inelastic scattering, 371
Inorganic scintillators, 85 ff
  decay of light, 92
  effect of activator concentration, 99
  preparation, 85
  response to charged particles, 97
  scintillation characteristics, 102 ff
  scintillation process, 88
  temperature effects, 93
Instruments, health physics, calibration, 437, 438, 439
  personnel monitoring, 425

Instruments, portable survey, 433
requirements, 434–438
Instruments of dosimetry, 377
Insulating materials, properties, 63,
222–230
Internal exposure, see Exposure, internal radiation
International Commission on Radiation
Protection (ICRP), 388, 408–
410, 413, 417–421, 423–425,
450, 451
International Commission on Radiological Units (ICRU), 367
Ion collection, 17
Ionization chamber, Bragg-Gray, 28,
377, 378
cylindrical, 33, 38, 40, 41, 46, 48, 61
diffusion of electrons, 29
effect of electron capture, 18–21, 30
effect of recombination, 21
electron collection time, 32
electron mobility, 23–28
for dosimetry, 386, 434, 435
grid, 51–55
high-pressure, 55
ion and electron collection, 17
measurement of dc current, 195
parallel-plate, 32, 33, 38, 40, 46, 47,
61
pulse, 3 ff
pulse profiles, 33–39
spherical, 33, 38, 47, 48, 63
techniques of construction, 61
techniques of filling, 56
tissue-equivalent, 378
wall effect, 45
Ionization efficiency, 9
Ionization in gases, by alpha particles,
11–15
by electrons, 9–12
by fission fragments, 14
by protons and deuterons, 13
by recoil atoms, 14
Ionization in tissue, 368, 369
measurement of, 377
Ion pair, energy required to produce
(W), 8 ff, 377, 408, 412
statistics of formation, 5
Ions, creation, 4
drift velocity, 24

Ions, life history, in ionization chamber,
17
mobility, 23–24
negative, 18–21

Krypton, as gas scintillator, 127, 130
use in proportional counters, 73–75
Kyropoulos method, crystal growth,
85 ff

Laplace transformation, use in computing signal-to-noise ratio, 266
Laundry, for decontamination, 404
procedure, 449
LET, see Linear energy transfer
Leukemia, 392, 415
Life span, shortening by radiation, 391,
415
Light pipe, 142
Linear energy transfer (LET), definition, 369
fast-neutron distribution function in
energy, 384
measurement by spherical counter,
385
relation to RBE, 369, 378, 408
Linearity of response, amplifiers, 294 ff
ionization chambers, 8 ff
proportional counters, 64–65, 71 ff
scintillators, 97 ff
Liquids, beta counting, 333
for Cerenkov counters, 171
Liquid scintillators, 119 ff
decay times, 122
light output, 121
loaded, for neutron detection, 123,
155
purification, 119
solvents and solutes, 123
Lithium fluoride, unsuccessful as scintillator, 106
Lithium iodide, europium activated, effect of activator concentration,
101
emission spectrum, 104
for neutron detection and spectrometry, 155, 160
scintillation characteristics, 103
temperature dependence of luminescence, 96

Long-tailed pair (cathode-coupled amplifier), 260
Luminescence, 92
  in organic materials, 108

Marshall counter, 177
Maximum permissible body burden of radionuclides, 416–420
Maximum permissible concentration of radioactive waste, 451
Maximum permissible concentrations of unidentified radionuclides (MPCU), in air, 453
  in water, 452
Metastable states, in scintillators, 92
Methane, electron drift velocity in, 27, 28
  purification of, 60
Mica, 225, 226
Microphonics, 17
Miller effect, 290
Mobility, 23–29
  of electrons, 24
  of ions, 24
Molecular crystals, scintillation in, 108
Multicollision dose, 374
Multiple collision dose calculation, 370
Multiple coulomb scattering of charged particles, 190

Naphthalene, 109, 110, 111
National Committee on Radiation Protection (NCRP), 403, 408, 410, 413, 417–421, 450, 451
NBS Handbook 59, 388, 412
NBS Handbook 75, 381, 388, 390
Negative ions, see Electron attachment
Neon, electron drift velocity, 26
Neutron recoils, in ionization chamber, 41–43
  in proportional counter, 13
Neutrons, detection and spectrometry, with scintillators, 154 ff
Nitrogen, electron drift velocity, 26
  liquid, as Cerenkov counter, 171, 172
  purification, 60
  removal from argon, 56–58
Noble gases, liquified, as scintillators, 132
  purification, 56, 125

Noble gases, use as scintillators, 124 ff
Noise, in amplifiers, 262 ff
  in electrometer circuits, 220
  grid-current, in receiving tubes, 276
  measurement of, 291
Np-237, as threshold detector, 383

Operating point, electrometer tube, 204
Optical dispersion, in Cerenkov counter, 189
Organic crystals as scintillators, 106 ff
  characteristics of various, 117
  for fast neutron counting, 157
  preparation, 107
  purification, 106–107
  radiation damage, 115
  response to charged particles, 113
  scintillating properties, 110
  scintillation process, 108
Organic liquid scintillators, 119 ff
  decay time of light, 122
  loaded, 123–124, 155
  preparation and purification, 119
  scintillating properties, 121
  useful solvents and solutes, 123
Overshoot, in amplifiers, 243
Oxygen, electron attachment, 18–19
  liquid, as Cerenkov counter, 171, 172
  removal from organic scintillators, 120

Pair spectrometer, crystal, 154, 385
Particle identification, by Cerenkov effect, 166
Particles, radioactive; inhalation as a problem in health physics, 444–446
Partition noise, in amplifiers, 271, 290
PBD (2-phenyl-5-(4-biphenyl)-1,3,4-oxadiazole), 121, 123
Pedestal, of amplifier pulse, 255–258
Personnel monitoring meters, 425–433
  chemical dosimeter, 428, 430, 432
  film meters, 425–431, 435, 436
  film rings, 432, 436
  hand and foot counters, 432
  Hurst threshold detectors, 430
  NTA (neutron monitoring film), 428, 431, 436, 437

Personnel monitoring meters, pocket chambers, 425, 426, 431, 435, 436
  pocket dosimeters, 425, 426, 431, 435, 436, 437
  silver phosphate meters, 428, 430
  when required, 401, 404, 415
  where worn, 415
Perveance, in amplifier tubes, 279
Phosphorescence, 92
Photoelectric effect in counter gas, 72–73
Photomultipliers, 132 ff
  characteristics, 139 ff
  dark current, 133
  dependence of gain on count rate, 135–136
  effect of magnetic field, 137
  electron transit-time spread, 137
  multialkali photocathodes, 139, 141
  photocathode, 133
  photon conversion efficiency, 184–185
  secondary emission, 135
  spectral response function, 133 ff, 185
  temperature-dependent effects, 138–139, 141
Photon emission, in Cerenkov effect, 167–170
Photon spectrometer Cerenkov counters, 182–184
Pile-up, 17, 240
Plastics as insulators, 225, 227
Plastic scintillators, 107 ff
  characteristics, 118
  decay time of luminescence, 110
  effect of composition upon light emission, 111–113
  response to charged particles, 113
Plateau, counter, 236
  in alpha counting, 338
  in beta counting, 310
Polarization (dielectric absorption), 223
Polymerization, organic plastics, 107
Polystyrene, as base for plastic scintillators, 107, 110, 112, 118
  as insulator, 227, 228
Polyvinyltoluene, as base for plastic scintillators, 107, 118
POPOP, 121–124, 127

Porcelain, use in ionization chambers, 61–63
  as insulator, 225, 226
Potassium iodide, thallium activated, 99, 105, 148
  scintillation characteristics, 105
  scintillation efficiency, 99
  use as alpha counter, 148
PPO, see DPO
Proportional counter, 64–77
  applications, 76
  as survey instrument, 433, 434
  calibration, 72
  end-window, 308
  escape peaks, 74–76
  for fast neutrons, 386
  for slow neutrons (BF_3), 388, 434
  in dosimetry, 378–381, 386
  output signal, 235
  proportionality, 71–72
  pulse profile, 65–66
  spherical, 385
  statistics of multiplication, 67–71
Pulse generator, 298, 299
Pulse height selector, see Discriminator
Pulse integrator, 381
Pulse profiles, deduction of ionization and range curves, 35
  effect of amplifier response, 43; see also Pulse shaping
  from electron collection in ionization chambers of different shapes, 33–34
  in proportional counters, 65–66
  interpretation, in ionization chambers, 3
Pulse shaping, 238 ff
  clipping, 241, 249–259
  flattening, 247
  forming, 251
  limiting, 261
Pulse spectrum, in ionization chamber, effect of grid, 51
  effect of walls, 45–51
  from isotropic distribution of point charges, 36
  from neutron recoils, 41
  from source on wall, 39
Purification of gases, argon, 56–58
  boron trifluoride, 60

Purification of gases, carbon dioxide, 60
  helium, 58
  hydrogen and deuterium, 58–59
  methane, 60
  nitrogen, 60
  noble gases, 126
Purification of scintillators, liquid, 119
  organic, 106–107

Quaterphenyl, 126, 127, 128
  scintillation characteristics, 117
Quenching, organic scintillators, 113, 115

r (roentgen unit of radiation), 367
Rad, 367, 392, 407
Radiation, exposure to, *see* Exposure, radiation
Radiation, maximum permissible levels of exposure, external, 406 ff
  emergency, 413–414
  for various body parts, 410 (table), 411, 415
  for various population groups, 423
  for various radiations (table), 409
  genetic, 424
  internal, 416 ff
Radiation damage, organic scintillators, 115
  biological, 368, 392, 393, 414
Radionuclides, hazardous, 402
  handling, at various levels of activity, 396–406
Range-energy curve, deduction, from ionization chamber pulse shape, 35
RBE (relative biological effectiveness), 368, 407, 409, 412, 415, 418, 419, 422, 425
Recoil nuclei, dosage from, 371
  in ionization chamber, 41
Recoil proton ionization chamber, 41, 60
Recoil proton telescope, 147
Recombination, 21–23
  columnar, 22, 23
  dielectronic, 21
  dissociative, 21
  preferential, 22

Recombination, radiative, 21
  three-body, 22
  volume, 22
Reflection, coefficient of, in delay line, 249
Relative damage factor, 419
Relative hazard of radionuclides, 400–402
Rem (roentgen equivalent, man), 368, 407
Rep (roentgen equivalent, physical), 368, 392, 407, 408
Resistivity, surface and volume, of insulators, 226, 227
Resolution, in amplifiers, 237, 287, 288
  in Cerenkov counters, 184
  in scintillation counters, 130, 143 ff
  losses ("dead-time" losses), determination, 364
    in sample counting, 339, 364
  velocity, in Cerenkov counters, 186
Ringing, 213
Rise time, 238, 241

$S^{32}(n,p)P^{32}$ reaction as neutron threshold detector, 383
Sampling, for radioactivity, air, 443
  body fluid, 442, 443
  water and mud, 443
Scintillation counters, assembly, 141 ff
  for personnel monitoring, 432, 433, 435 ff, 442
  large crystals, 142–143
  pulse height, 235
Scintillation counting, *see* Beta-particle counting, Charged particles, Gamma-ray counting, Neutron detection
Scintillation efficiency, for charged particles in inorganic scintillators, 99
  for gaseous scintillators (relative), 127, 128
  for organic crystals and plastics, 113
Scintillation process, gases, 125
  inorganic crystals, 88 ff
  organic crystals, 108 ff
  organic liquids, 121
Scintillators, applications, 145 ff
  characteristics, inorganic, 102

Scintillators, characteristics, organic, 117
  plastic, 118
  solution, 123
  gaseous, 124 ff
  glass, 156
  inorganic, 85 ff
  liquified gases, 132
  loaded liquid, 123
  organic crystals and plastics, 106 ff
  organic liquids, 119
Scintillators, preparation and purification, gases, 125
  inorganic crystals, 85
  organic crystals and plastics, 106
  organic liquids, 119
Screen-wall counter, 324–325
Shield, magnetic, for photomultiplier tubes, 137, 141
Shielding, gamma-ray, 403
  anticoincidence, 308, 443
Shipment of radionuclides, 394, 442
Signal-to-noise, optimization, 275
Sodium iodide, pure, emission spectrum at low temperature, 103, 104
  luminescence at low temperatures, 95, 96
  mechanism of luminescence, 90
  scintillation characteristics, 102
Sodium iodide, thallium activated, effect of thallium concentration, 99–101
  linearity of energy response to gamma rays, 97
  response to charged particles, 97–98, 114
  scintillation characteristics, 102
  thin crystal for charged-particle detection, 146–147
Spectrum, measurement of, in dosimetry, LET, 385
  gamma-ray, 385
  neutron, 382
Spectrum, photon, of Cerenkov radiation, 167
Spectrum, pulse, in ionization chamber, from isotropic distribution, 36 ff
  from wall, 39
Spills, radioactive, 456–458

"Standard" counter, for fast-neutron dosimetry, 380, 381
Steatite, 225
Stilbene, 107, 108, 109, 114, 117, 157, 158, 160
  as fast-neutron detector, 157, 158
  gamma-ray discrimination, 160
Stockbarger method, crystal growth, 85 ff
Stopping power, 377, 408, 409, 411, 412
Summing junction, 212
Survey instruments, 433 ff
Switch, electrometer, 231 ff
  grounding, 233
  rotary, 225, 233

Teflon, use in ionization chambers, 63
Temperature-dependence of scintillation intensity, inorganic crystals, 93 ff
  organic crystals, 110 ff
  organic liquids, 121
Temperature rise, dosimetry by, 376
Terphenyl, p-, 118, 120, 123
Tetraphenylbutadiene, 127
Thermoluminescence, 92
Thimble chamber, 378
Threshold detectors, in fast-neutron dosimetry, 383
Time constant, amplifier, 44, 93, 238, 241, 242 ff, 380
  reduction by feedback compensation, 212, 213
Time constant, fluorescence, 93
  of gaseous scintillators, 129
  of inorganic scintillators, 102
  of liquid scintillators, 122
  of liquified and solidified gases, 132
  of organic crystals, 117
  of plastic scintillators, 118
Tissue-equivalent chamber, 378, 434
Toluene, 119, 122, 123
Total-absorption spectrometer for neutrons, 157
Total body counter, 443, 444
Transition probability, in luminescent materials, 93, 94, 95
Trigger circuit, 235, 298, 300
Tubes, electrometer, 204

Tubes, input, for pulse amplifiers, 279 ff
Two-pi beta counting, 323–325

Undershoot, 243, 244
Unscrambling of scintillation pulse-height spectra, 154, 354
Uranium, for gas purification, 58
U-238, as threshold neutron detector, 383

Velocity, drift, 20, 24–29
resolution, by Cerenkov counter, 186
Voltage pulse, from scintillation counter, 93, 94, 235
from various radiation detectors, 235

Wall effect, in ionization chambers, 45–51

Wall source, 39–41
Waste, radioactive, 395, 399, 403, 449 ff
disposal by open pit, 454
maximum permissible concentration, 451–453
Wavelength shifter, 127, 128
for Cerenkov counter, 173
Wounds, decontamination of, 397, 455
W-values, 8 ff, 377, 408

Xenon, as gas scintillator, 125–130
as liquid and solid scintillator, 132
use in proportional counter, 73–75
Xylene, 121–123, 334

Zinc sulfide, 82, 87, 146
for neutron detection, 155, 159
scintillation characteristics, 105